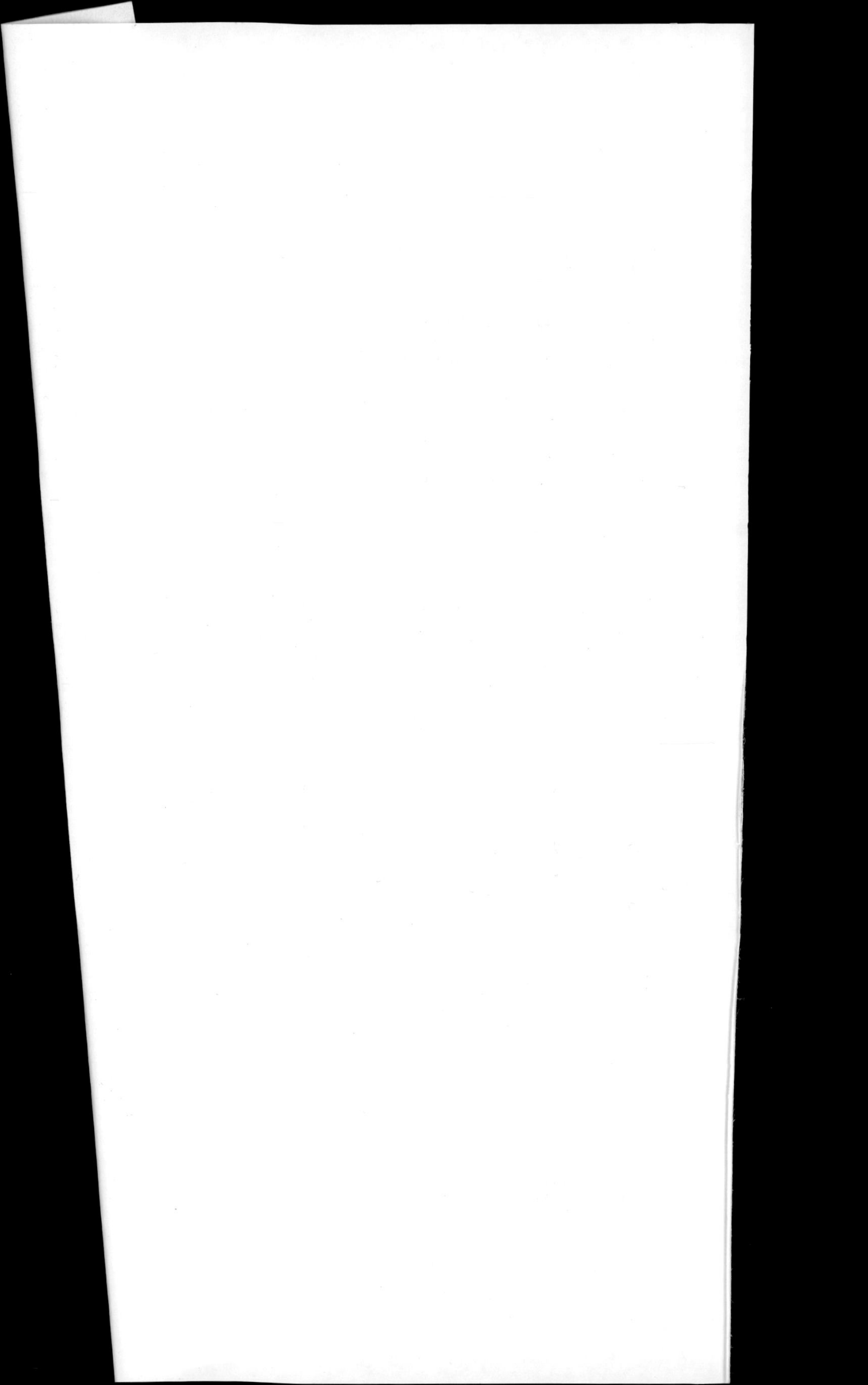

INTRODUCTION TO
STATISTICAL ANALYSIS
AND INFERENCE
for Psychology and Education

INTRODUCTION TO STATISTICAL ANALYSIS AND INFERENCE

for Psychology and Education

SIDNEY J. ARMORE

The George Washington University

JOHN WILEY & SONS, INC. New York · London · Sydney

FIRST CORRECTED PRINTING, AUGUST, 1967

Library of Congress Catalog Card Number: 66-22834
Printed in the United States of America

To JEROME and SUSAN

PREFACE

The material included in this book was intended to be of sufficient scope to provide the reader with a secure foundation in both the methods of descriptive statistics and statistical inference. It seemed that a secure foundation could be achieved only by providing the reader with an enriched treatment of carefully selected statistical theory and methods. This text covers a broad spectrum of theory and methods. A particularly careful and instructive manner of presentation was adopted. The objective was to facilitate the learning process by maximizing the reader's *understanding* of the material presented. Comments from the readers relating to scope of material included and style of presentation would be welcomed.

Clearly, an author is influenced by his background of associations and experience. I would like to give recognition to the pleasant and stimulating associations and work experience I have had in the United States Office of Education and in the Personnel Research Branch of the Department of the Army, United States Department of Defense. As a supervisory statistician in the United States Office of Education, I advised educator-specialists in research and survey problems. As a statistical advisor to research psychologists in the Personnel Research Branch, I had the pleasure of working with a highly competent group of psychologists in the field of psychometrics. This latter experience was particularly valuable because of the stimulating association with research psychologists who were highly competent in the use of statistical methods as well.

The largest share of my debt for the motivation to write this book goes to the students to whom I have had the pleasure and privilege of teaching introductory statistics. I have in mind the students in all of my introductory statistics classes, not only those students with psychology or education as a specialty. Lecture preparation and students' classroom reactions and questions started me thinking about the type of textbook I would like to have for my classes.

Of course, writing a textbook is a major undertaking, requiring a sustained effort over a long period of time. More importantly, this is usually an "extra-curricula" activity, done after the "normal" work is completed. As many authors have recognized, such a project can be undertaken and completed only with the wholehearted support of a devoted wife. I am indebted to my wife, Ethel Armore, for such support. Her gentle spirit, her sympathetic understanding, and her steadfast character made the completion of this book possible. Moreover, she contributed many excellent ideas which served to expedite considerably the production phases of textbook writing. Additionally, my wife spent long hours typing a draft of this manuscript from my rough handwritten notes and proofreading with me. My children, Jerome and Susan, contributed in their way toward the completion of this project.

I wish to thank the authors and publishers for their kind permission to reprint statistical tables as follows: John Neter and William Wasserman, *Fundamental Statistics for Business and Economics*, Second Edition, Allyn and Bacon, Boston, 1961 (Table B.2); John E. Freund and Frank J. Williams, *Modern Business Statistics*, Prentice-Hall, Inc., Englewood Cliffs, N.J., 1958 (Table B.4); H. Sorenson, *Statistics for Students of Psychology and Education*, McGraw-Hill Book Company, New York, 1936 (Table B.5). I am indebted to the Literary Executor of the late Sir Ronald A. Fisher, F.R.S., Cambridge; to Dr. Frank Yates, F.R.S., Rothamsted; and to Messrs. Oliver & Boyd Ltd., Edinburgh, for permission to reprint Table No. III from their book *Statistical Tables for Biological, Agricultural and Medical Research* (Tables B.3 and 9.3.1). Also, I wish to thank the U.S. Interstate Commerce Commission for the use of page 1 of "Table of 105,000 Random Decimal Digits," Statement No. 4914, File No. 261-A-1, May 1949, Washington, D.C. (Table B.1); and the author and the American Statistical Association for permission to use "The Choice of a Class Interval," by H. A. Sturges, *Journal of the American Statistical Association*, Vol. 21, 1926, as the basis for construction of Table 3.2.5.

Sidney J. Armore

The George Washington University
Washington, D.C.
June 1966

NOTE TO THE READER

This textbook has been prepared for the nonmathematical reader who is a beginner in statistics. The introductory level of this text has been achieved by presenting statistical methods and procedures in *careful detail* and explaining to a *very large extent* the "why" of each method in nonmathematical terms. The meaning and application of each statistical method and procedure, *without exception*, are carefully and copiously illustrated by problems worked out and explained *step by step*.

The presentation in this text is subject-matter oriented. The study of statistics is considered to be difficult enough by many readers whose primary interest is in the subject matter itself (psychology and/or education), rather than in statistical methods. When the discussion and explanations of the method of statistics are in his field of interest, such a reader at least feels that he is on familiar ground with respect to the subject matter. This helps make the study of statistics a little easier and, perhaps, reduces the tensions and fear which often beset a nonmathematical reader who enters upon the study of statistics. A text which is subject-matter oriented provides a familiar and, consequently, a friendlier milieu for the reader.

Typically a college course in introductory statistics requires a year's study of elementary algebra as a prerequisite. This presents a problem to many readers who feel that they do not really know much algebra. Some readers whose study of algebra has been fairly recent feel insecure about their achievement. Others may have studied algebra so long ago that whatever had been learned has been forgotten through disuse.

Appendix A has been prepared for such readers. This appendix provides a comprehensive "refresher" on algebraic symbols and elementary algebraic operations to the extent required to handle the material in this text. This appendix is in easy-to-use outline form and should also be helpful to the reader who has never studied algebra.

A knowledge of only the bare essentials of elementary algebra is required to follow the presentation in this text. It is strongly recommended that the reader review Appendix A at an early stage of his study of this text. Of course, this appendix is always available for review and reference purposes as he progresses through the text. The outline form in which this appendix has been prepared permits rapid reference as needed. Students have often approached me after class to confide that they do not remember how to deal with + and − signs. Or, they have completely forgotten how to solve a simple algebraic equation. Or, they have forgotten the meaning of the various mathematical symbols. Or, they just do not remember "how to do logarithms." Reference to the table of contents, for Appendix A will indicate that help is provided for all of these problems.

A specific objective of this text is to reduce to a *minimum* gaps in the presentation of statistical theory. More specifically, it becomes necessary from time to time to state that an adequate explanation of a method or procedure is omitted because it is not appropriate to include such material in an introductory text. However, it will be a surprise to the reader when he discovers how infrequently this is necessary. It is nearly always true that an adequate and satisfying explanation can be presented in nonmathematical terms. The reader will find that, in this text, each and every method and procedure is adequately and clearly explained, generally in nonmathematical terms. *A specific objective of this text is to get the reader to feel that he knows what to do, why it is to be done, and how to go about doing it.*

Each chapter includes a *large number of problems* for practice and review, with answers provided for the even-numbered problems. These problems, generally, appear *throughout a chapter*, after each section, as appropriate. This is a convenience for the reader as well as for the instructor.

Although introductory and written with the nonmathematical reader in mind, this text contains an *enriched treatment of statistical inference.* This provides the reader with a secure foundation for using the statistical methods presented in this text with confidence and thoughtfulness, and for further study of statistical methods.

Mathematical proofs and derivations are occasionally presented. However, these are not generally included in the main text but appear in a separate section on *algebraic notes* at the end of a chapter. These notes may be omitted, with no loss of continuity. However, the reader is encouraged to review these notes, since they are presented in a very elementary, easy-to-follow manner, showing each step with *considerable care and completeness*. These notes will provide considerable enrichment for the serious reader.

This text is especially suitable for the reader who wishes to study statistics on his own. Such a reader may wish to restrict himself, on his first reading, to a basic (minimum content) statistics course. The material to be included in such a first reading is suggested in the *Note to the Instructor*, which follows.

The references in this book have been carefully organized for reader convenience. For example, Section 2.3 refers to Section 3 in Chapter 2. Equations, figures, and tables are numbered consecutively in each section of a chapter. For instance, in Equation 4.3.2, the first number refers to the chapter, the second to the section, and the third indicates the sequence in which it appears.

NOTE TO THE INSTRUCTOR

This text is suitable for a full-year introductory course in statistics. It is also suitable for a half-year introductory course, providing the instructor with considerable choice of material to be covered. This text can be used for a course where descriptive statistics is to be given emphasis, as well as for a course where statistical inference is to be given emphasis. *The text is enriched in both areas of statistical methods*. Owing to the enriched treatment of statistical inference, this text is suitable, as well, for courses in intermediate statistics, and as a companion text in higher-level courses. In full-year introductory courses, as well as in intermediate statistics courses, it is recommended that the entire text be covered. Some instructors in such courses may wish to supplement the material in this text with reading on nonparametric statistics and, perhaps, analysis of variance. However, it is expected that such supplemental reading will not be required by most instructors.

Each instructor, of course, will want to decide for himself the material to be included in a course. However, I would like to present some suggestions, chapter by chapter, as to how this text could be used in various types of *half-year* introductory statistics courses, as well as comment on various special features of each chapter, as appropriate.

Chapters 1 and 2, of course, would be included in all introductory courses. However, in a basic statistics course (organized on a minimum content basis) the summation rules in Chapter 2, Section 2.6 could be omitted.

Chapter 3 presents a *fully developed* model frequency distribution

(Section 3.3) which helps the reader to understand this important descriptive tool of statistics. The concept of a distribution is carefully developed and presented early in the text (Section 3.6). This chapter may be included in its entirety in all introductory statistics courses.

Chapter 4, Sections 4.3 and 4.4, present a variety of special-purpose equations for the arithmetic mean. Section 4.9 contains a *comprehensive, carefully coordinated* discussion and comparison of the properties of the various averages. If it is desired to maximize the time spent on inductive statistics, then consideration should be given to omitting all or part of the following: Section 4.3, *Situation* 8 in Section 4.4, and Section 4.10. However, if it is desired to give more time to descriptive statistics, then all of Sections 4.3 and 4.4 should be included. Similarly, if the mathematical aspects are to be emphasized, then Section 4.10 should be included as well. In a basic statistics course, Sections 4.3, 4.4, 4.6, 4.7, and 4.10 may be completely omitted and Section 4.8 should be covered only for raw (ungrouped) data.

In Chapter 5, special emphasis is given to an explanation of the *meaning* of the standard deviation (Section 5.2), conceptually the most important single measure in all of statistics. A variety of special-purpose equations for the standard deviation are presented in Sections 5.3 and 5.4. If it is desired to emphasize inductive statistics, consideration should be given to omitting all or part of the following: Section 5.3, *Situation G* in Section 5.4, and Section 5.8. On the other hand, if descriptive statistics is to be emphasized, then all of Sections 5.3 and 5.4 should be included. If it is desired to emphasize the mathematical aspects, then Section 5.8 should be included also. In a basic statistics course, Sections 5.3, 5.4, and 5.8 may be omitted.

Chapter 6 provides a *separate* treatment of probability in *carefully organized* detail. This is an important chapter for the reader who wishes to understand the methods of statistical inference. This chapter provides a considerably more enriched treatment of probability than is found in many introductory textbooks on statistics. Nevertheless, the treatment is truly introductory and suitable for the serious reader who is a beginner in statistics. However, some instructors who wish to emphasize statistical inference and, certainly, those who choose to emphasize descriptive statistics will want to consider covering only the first two sections of Chapter 6. It should be noted that Sections 6.3, 6.4, and 6.5 are interdependent and so should be included or excluded as a unit. Of course, Section 6.5 could be omitted even if Sections 6.3 and 6.4 are included. Section 6.6 contains a *specially arranged* introductory presentation of *set notation and operations.* This section may be omitted, if desired, with no loss of continuity. However, if included, it permits the study of probability in terms of sets.

Chapter 7 provides an unusually enriched introduction to random sampling. Section 7.2 carefully defines and illustrates the concept of random sampling *separately* for sampling from a finite population without replacement, sampling from a finite population with replacement, and sampling from an infinite population. The treatment is truly introductory and within the capabilities of the beginner in statistics. In a course where statistical inference is emphasized, all of Chapter 7 may be included. However, in some such courses and especially where descriptive statistics is given emphasis, Section 7.2 may be included only in so far as it relates to random sampling without replacement from a finite population. Where only the first two sections of Chapter 6 are included in a course, then only the first part of Section 7.4, Chapter 7, should be covered.

The concept of a *theoretical sampling model* as a vehicle for identifying the appropriate statistical theory applicable to problems encountered in practice is introduced in Chapter 8. Sections 8.5, 8.6, and 8.7 present *separately and in detail* the binomial population, the sampling distribution of a frequency, the sampling distribution of a proportion, and the normal approximation to the binomial. This is usually not done in introductory statistics texts. This detailed treatment should be of considerable help to the reader in his study of this important area of statistical theory. Section 8.8, which explains and illustrates the way in which theoretical sampling models *are to be used*, should be of particular value to the reader as preparation for the application of inductive statistics in subsequent chapters. All of Chapter 8, except possibly Sections 8.3 and 8.9, may be included in a course which emphasizes statistical inference. On the other hand, where the emphasis is on descriptive statistics and for a basic statistics course, Section 8.3 might be included and Sections 8.5, 8.6, and 8.9 omitted.

In Chapter 9, the statistical theory underlying construction of confidence intervals is developed with *special care*, in a detailed, yet introductory manner. The requirements (assumptions) for the various procedures for constructing confidence intervals are carefully explained, *with appropriate summaries* to assist the reader in their application. Where statistical inference is emphasized, all of Chapter 9 may be included, except possibly Section 9.5. Where the emphasis is on descriptive methods, Sections 9.3, 9.5, and much of Section 9.6 should be omitted. In a basic statistics course, all of Sections 9.3, 9.5, and 9.6 should be omitted.

Chapter 10 presents the statistical theory underlying tests of hypotheses, in a detailed, yet introductory manner. The statistical procedure for conducting a test of hypothesis is analyzed into its basic components. *An organized three-phase procedure is devised which guides the reader in the analysis and statistical formulation of a decision-making problem, construction of a decision model, and evaluation of sample data leading to a decision* (Section 10.7). All introductory statistics courses may include Chapter 10 in its entirety.

Chapters 11, 12, and 14 present a large variety of *decision-making problems involving tests of hypotheses*. For each variety, *without exception*, there is a careful discussion of the sampling model appropriate and a *step-by-step* application to illustrative problems of the three-phase procedure for conducting a test of hypothesis. If Section 9.3 of Chapter 9 was omitted, then Section 11.3 of Chapter 11 should be omitted. In half-year introductory courses, Chapter 12 may well be entirely omitted.

Chapters 13 and 15 present descriptive correlation and regression analysis, and Chapter 14 presents inductive correlation and regression analysis. In Chapter 13, omit Section 13.5 if Sections 4.4 and 4.6 were omitted in Chapter 4 and Section 5.4 was omitted in Chapter 5. In any event, Sections 13.5 and 13.6 may well be omitted from half-year introductory courses in statistics.

Chapter 14 introduces and carefully defines a set of theoretical *normal models* for application to two-variable prediction problems. Procedures for the application of the methods of statistical inference to such problems are *carefully* presented and illustrated. Only Section 14.1 should be included in half-year introductory statistics courses. No part of Sections 14.2, 14.3, and 14.4 should be included.

In Chapter 15, the methods for computing correlation measures and regression equations for *curvilinear relationships* are carefully explained and copiously illustrated in Section 15.1. Curvilinear correlation and regression analysis is not used too frequently in psychology and education and is not usually included in an introductory statistics text. However, it was decided to introduce this material in this text for two reasons. First, it is a relatively easy step ahead after studying simple linear correlation and regression analysis. Consequently, this material can enrich the reader's general grasp of correlation and regression analysis with relatively little effort. Furthermore, the greater one's knowledge, the more stimulation is provided and the greater is the flow of new ideas when engaged in research and intellectual thinking. Section 15.1 would not ordinarily be included in half-year introductory statistics courses. Section 15.2 is likely to be included in all introductory statistics courses.

CONTENTS

PART I ORIENTATION AND BASIC CONCEPTS 1

1 Introduction *3*

1.1 Why Study Statistics? 3
1.2 Is Statistics Difficult? 4
1.3 What is Statistics? 5
1.4 Applicability of Statistical Methods 6

2 Basic Concepts and Operations *8*

2.1 Populations and Samples 8
2.2 Descriptive Statistics 9
2.3 Inductive Statistics 10
2.4 Variables 13
2.5 Symbolic Notation 14
2.6 Rules for Summation 16
2.7 Measurement Scales 24

PART II STATISTICAL DESCRIPTION AND ANALYSIS 31

3 Frequency Distributions *33*

3.1 Introduction 33
3.2 Organization of Raw Data 33
3.3 A Model Frequency Table 40
3.4 Construction of a Frequency Table 52

3.5 Graphic Representation 64
3.6 The Underlying Distribution 73
3.7 Nominal and Ordinal Scale Data 78

4 *Measures of Central Tendency* *83*

4.1 Introduction 83
4.2 Arithmetic Mean: Definition 84
4.3 Arithmetic Mean: Special Situations 86
4.4 Arithmetic Mean: Frequency Distributions 99
4.5 Median: Definition 107
4.6 Median: Frequency Distributions 109
4.7 Percentiles, Quartiles, Deciles 117
4.8 Mode 120
4.9 Properties and Comparisons 125
4.10 Algebraic Notes 131

5 *Measures of Variation* *136*

5.1 Introduction 136
5.2 Standard Deviation: Definition 138
5.3 Standard Deviation: Special Situations 144
5.4 Standard Deviation: Frequency Distributions 157
5.5 Other Measures of Variation 162
5.6 Relative Variation 163
5.7 Standard Scores 165
5.8 Algebraic Notes 171

PART III FOUNDATION FOR STATISTICAL INFERENCE 185

6 *Probability* *187*

6.1 Introduction 187
6.2 Definition 187
6.3 Permutations and Combinations 198
6.4 Combining Probabilities 203
6.5 Probability Distributions 218
*6.6 Sets: Notation and Operations 223

7 *Random Sampling* *231*

7.1 Introduction 231
7.2 Definition 234
7.3 Sample Design and Selection 237
7.4 Sampling Distributions 240

* May be omitted with no loss of continuity.

8 Theoretical Distributions *247*

8.1 Introduction 247
8.2 Normal Distribution 248
8.3 Fitting a Normal Curve 258
8.4 Sampling Distributions of the Mean and the Median 265
8.5 Binomial Population 272
8.6 Binomial Probability Distributions 275
8.7 Normal Approximation to the Binomial 285
8.8 Sampling Models and Statistical Inference 301
8.9 Algebraic Note 303

PART IV APPLICATIONS OF STATISTICAL INFERENCE 305

9 Estimation and Confidence Intervals *307*

9.1 Point and Interval Estimates 307
9.2 Means: Large Samples 309
9.3 Means: Small Samples 316
9.4 Proportions 322
9.5 Finite Populations 326
9.6 Sample Size 329

10 Tests of Hypotheses: An Area of Decision Making *335*

10.1 Introduction 335
10.2 Formulating the Problem 338
10.3 Constructing the Decision Model 343
10.4 Evaluating the Sample Data 350
10.5 Decision Risks 352
10.6 One-Tail vs. Two-Tail Tests 355
10.7 Summary Note 358

11 Statistical Decision Making: Single-Sample Tests *360*

11.1 Proportions 360
11.2 Means: Large Samples 364
11.3 Means: Small Samples 368

12 Statistical Decision Making: Two-Sample Tests *375*

12.1 Introduction 375
12.2 Proportions 377
12.3 Means: Large Samples 383
12.4 Means: Small Samples 387
12.5 Means: Equal Variances 389
12.6 Means: Dependent Samples 392

PART V ASSOCIATION AND PREDICTION 401

13 Measures of Association *403*

13.1 Introduction 403
13.2 Basic Concepts 404
13.3 Regression 411
13.4 Correlation 425
13.5 Frequency Distributions 431
13.6 Computational Notes 437

14 Prediction *445*

14.1 Uses and Abuses 445
14.2 The Normal Model 447
14.3 Interval Estimation 453
14.4 Tests of Hypotheses 459

15 Further Measures of Association *463*

15.1 Curvilinear Relationships 463
15.2 Correlation of Ranks 476

Appendix A Review of Basic Algebra *483*

A.1 Introduction 483
A.2 General Algebraic Symbols 483
A.3 Operations Involving + and − Signs 485
A.4 Operations Involving Parentheses 486
A.5 Operations Involving Fractions 486
A.6 Operations Involving Exponents 487
A.7 Operations Involving Multiplication 487
A.8 How to Compute a Square Root 488
A.9 Operations Involving Square Roots 491
A.10 Operations Involving Equations 491
A.11 Logarithms 494

Appendix B Tables *497*

Table B.1 Table of Random Numbers 498
Table B.2 Table of Areas Under the Normal Curve 500
Table B.3 *t* Distribution: Table of Areas in Both Tails of the Distribution 501
Table B.4 Common Logarithms 502
Table B.5 Table of Squares and Square Roots 504

Answers to Even-Numbered Problems *517*

Index *527*

Part I
Orientation and Basic Concepts

1

INTRODUCTION

1.1 WHY STUDY STATISTICS?

Statistical methods and concepts have much to offer students in psychology and education. It is generally recognized that research workers in these and other fields require the use of statistical methods to plan research projects and evaluate research findings. However, an understanding of statistical theory, methods, and concepts is of substantial importance to others in the fields of psychology and education, as well.

Psychologists and educators not directly involved in research need a good understanding of statistical methods to comprehend much of the material contained in the professional journals. Psychologists and teachers often need to understand and interpret psychological test scores. Standardized achievement tests are administered as a regular procedure in modern school systems. A good knowledge of statistical concepts and basic statistical theory and methods is required for the psychologist and educator who will need to read and understand test manuals and interpret test scores.

It is not difficult to illustrate research problems which might face psychologists and educators. Is a proposed new teaching method superior to a currently used method? What is the best elementary school grade in which to begin the teaching of foreign languages? Which of a large pool of test items are best for prediction of success in clerical work? Is a proposed new method of psychotherapy superior to a currently used method? Do environmental factors play a part in the causation of prenatal pathology of the nervous system? Are IQ scores affected by social-status background? Questions such as these are often the basis for research projects. The first stage in undertaking any research work is to carefully and clearly formulate the research problem, precisely defining the issues involved. Then, decisions must be made concerning the analytical approach to be taken and the methods to be used in evaluating and interpreting the results. Every step of this process either requires or is done substantially better if one has an understanding of statistical methods and concepts. At some early stage of development of many research projects, the use of statistical methods cannot be avoided, if the research is to be carried on efficiently and if maximum benefits are to be obtained.

Admittedly, a course in introductory statistics will not make one into a skilled statistician. However, it should provide a good appreciation of what, in general, statistics can and cannot do. Furthermore, it should help one to become more competent in his own field of psychology or education. A good introductory statistics background will help substantially in understanding articles in the professional journals which often involve statistical concepts and terminology.

Psychologists and educators need not be highly trained statisticians in order to read and understand many of the published professional articles or to use the test manuals and interpret test scores. They need not be skilled statisticians, either, if they aspire toward research work. Where more than elementary statistical methods are involved, one could call for the assistance of a trained statistician. However, knowledge of elementary statistical methods, concepts and terminology is necessary if the psychologist or educator is to obtain maximum advantage when employing the services of a statistical consultant. He will then be able to better formulate his research problem and to communicate with the statistician. He will also be able to more fully profit from the statistical results and will be better able to understand how to interpret the findings within the framework of his research problem. In the simpler situations, he may be able to carry on by himself, assured that he is properly employing the methods of statistical analysis and evaluation.

1.2 IS STATISTICS DIFFICULT?

Students sometimes approach their first course in statistics with overpowering apprehension. The thought of studying in a field of mathematics often results in a mental block, causing problems for the student which are in no way connected with possible subject-matter difficulty. Admittedly, a college course in statistics, even at the introductory level, is a college-level course. However, this is equally true for courses in psychology and education. There is no reason to approach an introductory course in statistics with any greater apprehension than an introductory course in these other areas. A student must set aside any fears he may have if he is to expect any degree of success in learning statistics.

It is a goal of this text to present the elements of statistical methods at a truly introductory level. Only a knowledge of arithmetic and the bare essentials of elementary algebra are required mathematical background. It is realized that some students will have become "rusty" or will have forgotten much of the elementary algebra they once knew. Such students should refer to Appendix A, which presents a review of the notation and operations of elementary algebra. It is a good idea for all students who have been away from algebra for a time to review Appendix A.

The student may have observed that, in some subjects, there is only a loose relationship between the various phases of the subject matter presented during the semester. In the study of statistics, this is quite definitely *not* true. The presentation of statistical concepts and methods in this text follows a carefully structured plan. The basic building blocks are first presented, followed by presentation of additional concepts and methods. There is a development and an interlacing of concepts and methods as the material is presented throughout the text. In statistics, more than in some other fields of learning, one cannot advance through the material presented without first mastering what has come before.

This means that it is *essential* for the student to keep up-to-date. Practice and review problems are presented after each section, as appropriate. The student should test his learning of the subject matter and sharpen his understanding by working out the practice and review problems conscientiously, step by step, as he progresses through the text. There is *absolutely* no substitute for working at practice and review problems. *Statistics cannot be learned by cramming.* However, with conscientious effort and careful practice, no student who is capable of doing college-level work should find the study of introductory statistics beyond his ability.

1.3 WHAT IS STATISTICS?

An important first question for us is: What is *statistics*? More specifically, since this is a text on statistical methods, the question for us is: What do we mean by *statistical methods*? Some, who have never taken a course in statistics nor had any contact with statistical methods in their work, think of statistics as a set of numbers. Baseball scores published in the daily newspapers, stock market quotations, figures on automobile performance characteristics, IQ and other psychological test scores—these are considered to be statistics. As far as statistical methods are concerned, there is considerable vagueness. Sometimes, this is thought to mean computing averages and percentages.

In the popular sense, the term *statistics*, when used in the plural, means a set of numerical data or numerical records. A more technical meaning of this term, when used in the plural, is *statistical methods*. For example, textbooks on statistics are texts on statistical methods. When used in the singular, the term *statistic* is sometimes popularly used to denote a particular entity in a set of numbers or a particular item in a numerical record. For example, you may be warned, "Watch out for automobiles as you cross, or you will become a statistic." This, of course, refers to the possibility of becoming an entry in the traffic mortality records. However, the term *statistic* has an important technical meaning as well. As will be explained later, a *statistic* is a computed measure, such as an average, based on a sample.

Statistical methods comprise a scientific methodology, a branch of applied mathematics. These methods include a wide variety of techniques for collecting, organizing, tabulating, analyzing, interpreting, describing, and presenting numerical data. For example, statistical methods are used when an elementary school teacher computes the class average on a spelling test, when a psychologist interprets a score on a personality inventory, and when a psychometrician selects a sample of students to try out a new test battery.

1.4 APPLICABILITY OF STATISTICAL METHODS

Statistical methods have wide application. For example, statistical methods are used in the fields of psychology, education, sociology, anthropology, engineering, medicine, business, economics, and accounting. There may be specialized methodology developed to handle special problems in a given field; however, the same *basic* methodology is applicable to all fields. A text on statistical methods for students in psychology and education presents all discussions and exercises in terms of the subject matter of interest to these students—psychology and education.

Statistical methods are applicable to numerical data. There is no limit to the kind and quantity of numerical data to which statistical methods can be applied. For example, statistical methods are applicable to data made up of only a handful of items as well as to data made up of a large number, even an infinite number, of items. Suppose data are collected measuring the effect of a new method of psychotherapy tried out on eight subjects.

Statistical methods are available for analysis and evaluation of such data. Suppose a new teaching device is tried out on the freshmen in a large high school. Statistical methods are available to analyze and evaluate the effectiveness of this new device. Suppose the board of education in a large city wishes to determine the best elementary grade in which to introduce the study of a foreign language, taking into consideration the elementary school population to be served in the years ahead. Statistical methods are available to design and evaluate a study directed toward an answer to this problem.

When a problem needs to be solved, a decision needs to be made, or a question needs to be answered, it is not always necessary to employ statistical methods. However, when the need to use statistical methods arises, it is *always* because there is a problem to be solved, a decision to be made, or a question to be answered. For example, the dean in a university decides to collect and evaluate data on student part-time employment in order to provide him with a basis for determining the need to establish a student-loan program. A company psychologist decides to collect and analyze data on employee ages, by occupational categories, to assist him in determining the advisability of establishing a training program. *Generally, a most important part of the application of statistical methods is to carefully and precisely define the problem to be solved, the decision to be made, or the question to be answered.*

2

BASIC CONCEPTS AND OPERATIONS

2.1 POPULATIONS AND SAMPLES

Statistical methods deal with two types of data—*population* data and *sample* data. *The complete set of data relating to an area of interest is called the population.* For example, suppose a high school principal needs to know the age distribution of all the students in his school. Then, the ages of all the students in his school make up a population—a population of ages. If there are 2525 students in the school, this is a population of 2525 ages. Also, we may speak of this as a population of 2525 students, even though our interest is in a particular characteristic of these students (age).

A teacher may be interested in the distribution of grades made by the students in his class in the last quiz. If the class consists of 28 students, the population in this case is the set of 28 quiz grades (or 28 students). If this class is made up of 16 girls and 12 boys and if the teacher's only interest is in reviewing the grade distribution separately for the girls and the boys, then we have two populations to consider, the 16 grades obtained by the girls and the 12 grades obtained by the boys. Perhaps this teacher is interested in the distribution of all the quiz grades as a group, and also the separate grade distributions for girls and boys. In this case, all 28 quiz grades make up a population, while the 16 grades obtained by the girls and the 12 grades obtained by the boys make up *subpopulations.*

The illustrations presented represent *finite populations. These are populations which are in some way limited and contain a determinable number of items.* Finite populations may be small or extremely large. For example, a finite population could consist of eight scores on an aptitude test. Or a psychologist may be interested in making a study of the attitude of United States voters toward a certain issue. In this case, the finite population is composed of all the voters in the nation. On the other hand, a population may be *infinite. An infinite population contains an unlimited or indefinitely large number of items.* For example, an infinite population could consist of all outcomes (heads and tails) of an unlimited number of tosses of a coin. Or, say, an educational research team is making a study of the effect of a new teaching method on achievement in mathematics by high school juniors. The population for this study may be considered infinite since it includes all high school juniors in the country today and for years ahead. Some texts use the term *universe* instead of population. These terms are interchangeable.

If a set of data contains less than the full scope of information in which you are interested, it represents a sample. For example, a psychologist is interested in the reaction to a certain stimulus of all seniors in a given college, but obtains reaction scores on only 145 of the 1630 seniors in the college. The 145 reaction scores represent a sample of the population of 1630 possible reaction scores if all the seniors had been tested. Suppose an elementary school principal wishes to know something about the reading-readiness scores of the 120 newly admitted pupils, and his assistant collects 35 of these scores. Then, these 35 reading-readiness scores represent only part of the totality of scores in which the principal is interested. That is, the 35 scores represent a sample of the population of 120 reading-readiness scores. Hence, *a sample represents a part of the population.*

It should be noted that a collection of data may represent a population from one point of view and a sample from another. For example, consider the IQ scores for the 5500 students enrolled in a university. If you are interested in studying the IQ scores of these 5500 students, then the 5500 scores make up a population. On the other hand, you may be interested in studying the IQ scores of university students in general, but all the information available to you is the collection of 5500 scores from this one university. In such a case, those 5500 scores represent a sample of the IQ scores of all university students.

2.2 DESCRIPTIVE STATISTICS

When statistical methods need to be applied to a set of data which comprise the entire population of interest, the methods required are called *descriptive statistics. Descriptive statistics provide methods to organize, summarize, and describe sets of data which represent populations.* In other words, descriptive statistics are applicable when complete information is available.

For example, a large firm is converting to automation for some phases of production and needs to know something about the mechanical aptitude of the work force. The company psychologist administers a mechanical aptitude test to the employees to determine the general problems relating to employee retraining. After the test scores are obtained for the 250 employees in the work force, it is necessary to organize and summarize these score data and compute certain descriptive measures. For instance, the data might be organized into a table showing how many employees obtained scores which indicate high mechanical aptitude, low mechanical aptitude, and any number of specified intermediate levels of mechanical aptitude. It might be considered useful to compute the average test score obtained by the employees and also some measure of how the 250 test scores vary. Descriptive statistics provide methods to help the psychologist evaluate the mechanical ability of the population of employees as measured by their test scores.

2.3 INDUCTIVE STATISTICS

Usually psychologists and educators deal with sample data rather than population data. This is quite understandable when it is realized that collection of data for an entire population is often expensive and time-consuming and sometimes impossible. Suppose it is desired to determine the proportion of students in American universities whose parents both have college degrees. The population includes all students enrolled in American universities. It would certainly be a time-consuming and expensive project to collect information from the entire population. Suppose it is desired to determine the effectiveness of a new type of reader in increasing the reading skill of elementary school pupils. The population in this case includes all elementary school pupils enrolled today and for some years ahead. Clearly, it would be impossible at present to determine the effectiveness of the new reader for this entire population. In both illustrations, it would be considerably less expensive and less time-consuming to collect the information from a sample than from the entire population. In the latter situation, it would be the only practical thing to do. Later in the text, it will be shown that sample data could provide useful and adequate estimates of population characteristics. Therefore, it is usually unnecessary to collect information for an entire population.

Sample data are collected when it is desired to estimate one or more population characteristics. Use of sample information to estimate population characteristics is a form of *inductive inference*. That is, it involves reasoning from the particular (sample) to the general (population). Statisticians speak of this as generalizing from the sample to the population. For example, in a sample of families from a community, 75% have one or more children enrolled in the public schools. This finding is generalized to the population by estimating that 75% of all the families in the community have one or more children enrolled in the public schools. *When statistical methods are to be applied to sample data in order to make generalizations to the population, the methods used are called inductive statistics.*

In statistics, inductive inference is called *statistical inference*. Risk is always involved when an inference is made. For example, if a new employee is observed coming late to work during his first few days of employment, his supervisor might make the inference that this employee has a habit of tardiness. This might be an incorrect inference. Perhaps his wife is ill and he is obliged to take his children to school until she recovers. Likewise, risk is always involved when a statistical inference is made. Suppose, in a sample of college students, 30% are opposed to a certain candidate for president of the student council and the inference is made that 30% of all the students in the college are opposed to this candidate. It is hardly to be expected that this inference is *exactly* correct. What are the risks involved? That is, is 30% a good estimate or is the true percentage opposed to the candidate far different?

How do we go about determining the risks involved in making a statistical inference? *Inductive statistics, based on the mathematics of probability, provide methods for making statistical inferences about a population based on sample data and for evaluating the risks involved.* Since statistical inferences are determined on a probability basis, they may be called *probability inferences.*

Clearly, then, *all statistical methods are directed toward description of a population. Descriptive methods are used to describe a population based on population data. Inductive methods are used to describe a population based on sample data. The population concept provides the frame of reference for all statistical methods.*

PROBLEMS FOR PRACTICE AND REVIEW

1. Define and illustrate the following:
(a) Population
(b) Subpopulation
(c) Finite population
(d) Infinite population
(e) Sample

2. A population is made up of all the data in an area of interest, such as a population of *ages of college students*. We may refer to this as a population of college students, for convenience of expression. However, this is a population of *ages of college students*. For each illustration below, identify the population and, where applicable, the subpopulations:

(a) The dean of an engineering school has made a review of the quality point indexes for seniors in his school who expect to specialize in civil engineering.

(b) An article in a psychological research journal discusses the reaction times to an electrical stimulus of American males employed in the construction industry.

(c) The business manager in a midwestern university asks his assistant to provide him with data relating to the size of loans requested by students for the next school year. He wishes to study the size of loans separately for undergraduate and graduate students, as well as for all students combined.

(d) A mathematics teacher in a high school is planning a study of year-end grades in algebra obtained by students in the school during the last five school years. The objective is to compare achievement, generally, in this subject between boys and girls.

(e) A psychologist is planning a study of the extent to which adults aged 40 and over are accident-prone. He plans to base his study upon the scores obtained on a well-established psychological test of accident-proneness. He is not interested in all adults aged 40 and over as a group, but only in the following categories of such adults: males with a college education, males without a college education, females with a college education, females without a college education.

(f) An experimental laboratory reports on the effect of a new drug on the reaction time to a stimulus of rats of a specified strain, based upon a study of the reaction times of a sample of 35 rats.

(g) An educational research firm is planning a study of the effectiveness of a new teaching aid for foreign-language instruction in the junior high schools in New York City. The study will involve an evaluation of achievement test scores obtained from a sample of 500 junior high school students after they receive foreign-language instruction using the new teaching aid.

3. Explain briefly and illustrate the difference between descriptive and inductive statistics.

4. Explain how the following relate to each other, as discussed in the text: inductive statistics, inductive inference, statistical inference, risk, probability.

5. In what way does the population concept provide the basis for all statistical methods?

6. For each illustration, indicate whether descriptive or inductive statistics are involved:

(a) A teacher studies the test scores obtained by the students in his three sections on Early European History in order to determine whether he is succeeding in getting these students to think through the basic problems.

(b) The history teacher just mentioned analyzes the test scores in order to determine whether his teaching method generally succeeds in getting students to think through the basic problems.

(c) A psychologist studies the memory retention effect of stress on a sample of eight white rats.

(d) A psychologist studies the ability of a company's employees to learn the new skills required by automation.

(e) The reading progress made by the 50 first graders in an elementary school is used to determine the need for increasing the number of hours for pupil reading practice.

2.4 VARIABLES

The concept *variable*, as you might expect, implies variation. We might say that *a variable is a quantity that varies; or, it is a quantity that takes on different values.* The variable is a basic concept in the development of statistical methods.

A language professor is interested in studying the achievement of a particular student. He examines the grades obtained by this student in the ten short quizzes given since the beginning of the semester. The quiz grade obtained by the student varies from quiz to quiz. In this case, the variable is the student's quiz grade. A psychologist administers a psychological test to a group of subjects. He is interested in studying the variable "test score," which varies from subject to subject. Other variables are height, weight, price, reaction time, and strength. The reader, no doubt, can think of many others.

Variables fall into two categories—*discrete* and *continuous*. Think about variables like number of pupils per class, number of children per family, result of rolling a die or spinning a roulette wheel. These variables can take on only certain values. For example, the number of pupils per class can be only a whole number. It might be 20, 22, 28, etc. It cannot be 22.3 nor 27.58 nor any number containing a fraction. It might even be restricted to numbers not less than, say, 20 nor more than, say, 45. In rolling a die, the variable is the number on the uppermost surface of the cube. This variable can take on only the values: 1,2, 3, 4, 5, or 6. *A variable is discrete if it can take on only specified values.* The number of values possible may in some way be limited. In the case of a die, the limits are 1 and 6. No number less than 1 nor greater than 6 can be obtained when rolling a single die. Furthermore, only the specified values: 1, 2, 3, 4, 5, or 6 are possible. Values in between are impossible. Hence, discrete variables contain gaps. Of course, the limits placed on a discrete variable may be very wide. As an extreme, we might consider a discrete variable which can take on the value of any whole number from zero to infinity. A discrete variable results from counting (e.g., the number of pupils per class). Another name for a discrete variable is a *discontinuous* variable.

Now, consider such variables as time, height, weight, and length. If you think about it, these variables are somehow different from the first set. You will notice that these variables are based on a measuring device (other than counting). For example, the height of a person is determined by, say, a yardstick. Time is determined by a watch. Weight is determined by a scale. Furthermore, these variables do not contain gaps, since *any* value between specified limits is possible. If we have the proper measuring stick, we could determine a person's height to as many decimals as we please. For example, we might measure a person's height only roughly as, say, 62 inches. Or we might measure it as 61.7 inches, or 61.68 inches, or 61.683215 inches. The variable "height" can take on *any* value between specified limits. These are *continuous* variables. The limits placed on a continuous variable may be very restricted or very wide. For example, if we are dealing with the continuous variable "summertime temperature during July in New York City," the limits may possibly be 75° (lower limit) and 101° (upper limit). The possible values of this variable could be any temperature levels between these limits. On the other hand, a continuous variable might be specified which can take on any value from zero to infinity.

It should be noted that any *recorded* variable is discrete. Consider the continuous variable "time." It can be determined to any desired degree of accuracy, assuming a sufficiently calibrated chronometer is available. However, once it is recorded, it becomes discontinuous. For example, suppose a teacher records the time required by each pupil to perform a given task. The teacher must decide whether to record the time required in seconds, tenths of a second, etc. Once the decision is made, all scores will be recorded with the same degree of accuracy. Suppose it is decided to record the time in tenths of a second. The recordings for, say, five pupils might read as follows (in seconds): 5.3, 5.4, 5.5, 5.6, 5.7. There cannot be a recording between, say, 5.4 and 5.5. A continuous variable, even though it is recorded with discontinuities (gaps), is still to be considered as continuous. Actually, a continuous variable is a theoretical concept.

A quantity which can have only a single value is called a constant. For example, suppose a teenager gets five dollars a week allowance from his father, never more nor less. Then, weekly allowance for this teenager is a constant. If a given amount, say, ten, is added to each score in a set, then we may say that the scores are increased by a constant (ten).

2.5 SYMBOLIC NOTATION

Each field of knowledge develops its own language. In the field of statistics, and in all branches of mathematics, the student needs to learn, not only new terminology, but a new way of communicating. That is, he must learn to think and work in the generalized terms of symbolic notation. He must learn to use symbols, such as Latin and Greek letters, to represent variables and operations. Symbolic notation makes possible the power and elegance of mathematics. With a little effort and some patience, any student capable of college-level work should be able to master this. Furthermore, introductory statistics requires the use of relatively simple notation. It is the needless worry concerning the use of symbols that is responsible for much of the panic reaction some students exhibit upon entering into the study of introductory statistics.

Say we measure the height of three men and obtain (in inches): 68, 62, 70. The variable we are concerned with here is height (in inches). Let $X =$ height and let X_1, X_2, and X_3 stand for the height of each of the three men. (The symbol X_1 is read "X sub 1" or, more simply, "X one.") Then: $X_1 = 68$, etc. Notice, we use a letter X as the general symbol for the variable (height) and attach a subscript to this letter (1, 2, or 3) to obtain a specific symbol for each particular height. For example, if we wish to specify the height of the second man, we write X_2. If we wish to refer to *any one* of these heights in general, we write X_i, which stands for the height of the ith man. In this case, i is a variable subscript which can equal 1, 2, or 3. In place of X_i, if we prefer, we could write X_j, where j is the variable subscript, with possible values 1, 2, or 3. Clearly, it does not matter which symbol we use, just as long as we know for what it stands.

There are certain conventions which are generally followed in the use of symbols. Unfortunately, there is not enough standardization in this regard. However, we shall adopt standard usage to the extent that it is available. Usually, the letters X, Y, Z or the lower case letters x, y, z will be used to represent variables. If only one variable is involved, we will use X. If two are involved, we will use X and Y. We will use Z to represent a third variable. However, in an introductory statistics course, you almost never deal with three variables in one problem. The early letters of the alphabet, usually lower case (a, b, c, d), are used to represent constants. The letters k and g, likewise, are often used to denote constants. Sometimes the upper case letters A, B, C, D, K, G are used to represent constants.

Suppose we are writing up a research project involving, say, two test scores for each of 75 subjects. These might be scores on a word recognition test and a vocabulary recall test. The following notation might be used:

X = word recognition test score
X_i = score for the ith subject (any one of the 75 subjects)
X_1 = score for the "first" subject
X_2 = score for the "second" subject
.
.
.
X_{75} = score for the "75th" subject

Y = vocabulary recall test score
Y_i = score for the ith subject (any one of the 75 subjects)
Y_1 = score for the "first" subject
Y_2 = score for the "second" subject
.
.
.
Y_{75} = score for the "75th" subject

We should explain what is meant by the "first" subject, "second" subject, or "75th" subject. In general, what meaning, if any, attaches to the sequence of the subscripts? Actually, the ordering of the subscripts may have a particular significance or none at all. In some situations, it might be useful to give special meaning to the order of the subscripts. For example we could let X_1 = the highest test score, X_2 = the next highest, etc. Such usage of the subscripts is not frequent. Generally, the ordering of the subscripts has no particular significance. That is X_1 stands for a particular score, perhaps the first on some list, etc. It is only necessary that we know which one is X_1, which one is X_2, etc. When dealing with two variables for each subject, the subscripts should be so arranged that, say, scores X_{26} and Y_{26} stand for the X and Y scores, respectively, for the same subject (the 26th subject).

The foregoing discussion was meant to introduce the idea of symbolic notation. Other symbols, representing variables and operations, will be introduced as needed. The reader should exercise extreme caution when referring to other statistics books. Often, the use of symbols is likely to differ from text to text; sometimes only a little, sometimes a lot. Understanding the meaning of each symbol is necessary to correctly follow any text in statistics or any article using symbolic notation. If the reader has not already done so, this is a good time to suggest that he read Appendix A where the symbolic notation and algebraic operations helpful for following the material presented in this text are reviewed. Readers who need to brush up on their elementary algebra and general algebraic notation will find this appendix most helpful.

2.6 RULES FOR SUMMATION

The key to the development and application of statistical procedures is the *summation* operation. The various statistical procedures which we will encounter typically require the addition (summation) of sets of terms. Let X stand for "score on a personality inventory," and X_i then represents a particular score. Let us consider, say, four specific scores: X_1, X_2, X_3, X_4.

We may represent the summation of these four scores by the symbol $\sum_{i=1}^{4} X_i$. The capital Greek letter Σ (sigma) denotes the summation operation. That is, Σ stands for the phrase "the sum of." The full symbol $\sum_{i=1}^{4} X_i$ is read as "the sum of X_i, i varying from 1 through 4." In other words, this symbol specifies the sum of the individual X_i scores obtained as i takes on the values 1, 2, 3, and 4, one at a time. For example, when $i = 1$, X_i becomes X_1, when $i = 2$, X_i becomes X_2, etc. We may show the meaning of this summation symbol algebraically as follows:

$$\sum_{i=1}^{4} X_i = X_1 + X_2 + X_3 + X_4$$

Suppose $X_1 = 20$, $X_2 = 15$, $X_3 = 18$, and $X_4 = 25$. Then, we may write

$$\sum_{i=1}^{4} X_i = 20 + 15 + 18 + 25 = 78$$

or

$$\sum_{i=1}^{4} X_i = 78$$

The letter i is called the *index* of the summation. The range of this index is specified by showing the lower limit ($i = 1$) below the summation sign (Σ) and the upper limit (4) above it. In the illustration the range of the *summation index* is from 1 through 4.

Sometimes we may not wish to add all the scores in a set, but only some of them. We may indicate this symbolically as follows:

$$\sum_{i=1}^{2} X_i = X_1 + X_2$$

$$\sum_{i=2}^{4} X_i = X_2 + X_3 + X_4$$

The summation notation may be used to specify sums of any number of terms. In general, we may speak of N terms. For example, we may speak of summing N X scores. That is, when $N = 4$, we mean 4 scores; when $N = 1000$, we mean 1000 scores, etc. Generally, then, we may specify the summation of N X scores as

$$\sum_{i=1}^{N} X_i = X_1 + X_2 + X_3 + \cdots + X_N \qquad (2.6.1)$$

We read the left-hand side of Equation 2.6.1 as "sum of X_i, i varying from 1 through N." The right-hand side of the equation indicates this specifically by showing that the individual X scores are to be added. The three dots indicate that there are additional X scores between X_3 and X_N which are not shown but which are to be added in with the others to obtain the desired sum.

The summation notation is often simplified. For example, we might write ΣX_i, which is read "sum of X_i." The fact that i takes on certain values is left unspecified when it is clear just which values i is to take on. In the more usual case, we may merely write ΣX, which is read "sum of X." The fact that certain individual X values are to be summed is not stated when it is clear just which X values are meant to be included in the summation. This latter form is used frequently, since it allows the greatest degree of simplification. However, as already noted, these abbreviated forms are to be used only where it is obviously clear just what is to be included in the summation. Fortunately, this is often the case.

In statistics, we often encounter summations of the types illustrated as follows:

$$\sum_{i=1}^{N} X_i Y_i = X_1 Y_1 + X_2 Y_2 + X_3 Y_3 + \cdots + X_N Y_N \tag{2.6.2}$$

$$\sum_{i=1}^{N} kZ_i = kZ_1 + kZ_2 + kZ_3 + \cdots + kZ_N \tag{2.6.3}$$

$$\sum_{i=1}^{N} \frac{Y_i}{aX_i} = \frac{Y_1}{aX_1} + \frac{Y_2}{aX_2} + \frac{Y_3}{aX_3} + \cdots + \frac{Y_N}{aX_N} \tag{2.6.4}$$

$$\sum_{i=1}^{N} (X_i - Y_i + a) = (X_1 - Y_1 + a) + (X_2 - Y_2 + a) + (X_3 - Y_3 + a) + \cdots + (X_N - Y_N + a) \tag{2.6.5}$$

$$\sum_{i=1}^{N} \frac{1}{b}(X_i - aY_i) = \frac{1}{b}(X_1 - aY_1) + \frac{1}{b}(X_2 - aY_2) + \frac{1}{b}(X_3 - aY_3) + \cdots + \frac{1}{b}(X_N - aY_N) \tag{2.6.6}$$

Note that in Equation 2.6.3, k is a constant and so does not need a subscript. Likewise, a and b in Equations 2.6.4 through 2.6.6 are constants.

There are three simple rules of summation which are very helpful and frequently used in the development and application of statistical procedures. Consider the scores obtained by five men in a three-part mechanical ability test as presented in Table 2.6.1. Let us use the following notational scheme for these scores: X = Part 1 score, so that X_i represents the Part 1 score obtained by the ith man (one of the five men). More specifically, $X_1 = 18$, $X_2 = 12$, etc. Similarly, Y = Part 2 score and Z = Part 3 score. The last column in the table shows the total test score $(X_i + Y_i + Z_i)$ for each man. The last row in the table shows the sum of all scores for each part. For example, the sum of all Part 1 scores for the five men (ΣX_i) is 76; the sum of all part 2 scores (ΣY_i) is 66, etc.

Suppose it is desired to obtain the summation of the total score ($X_i + Y_i + Z_i$) for all five men. This may be computed in two ways. For example,

Table 2.6.1 SCORES OBTAINED BY FIVE MEN IN A THREE-PART MECHANICAL ABILITY TEST

Subject	Part 1 Score, X_i	Part 2 Score, Y_i	Part 3 Score, Z_i	Total Score, $X_i + Y_i + Z_i$
A	18	10	4	32
B	12	11	4	27
C	20	15	4	39
D	11	17	4	32
E	15	13	4	32
Total	76	66	20	162

we could add the five total scores as shown in the last column of the table to obtain

$$\sum_{i=1}^{5} (X_i + Y_i + Z_i) = 32 + 27 + 39 + 32 + 32 = 162$$

Or we could add the total for each part as shown in the last row of the table to obtain

$$\sum_{i=1}^{5} X_i + \sum_{i=1}^{5} Y_i + \sum_{i=1}^{5} Z_i = 76 + 66 + 20 = 162$$

Clearly, the summation of the sum ($X_i + Y_i + Z_i$) is equal to the sum of the individual summations (ΣX_i, ΣY_i, ΣZ_i). This leads to our first rule of summation.

Rule 1

$$\sum_{i=1}^{N} (X_i + Y_i - Z_i) = \sum_{i=1}^{N} X_i + \sum_{i=1}^{N} Y_i - \sum_{i=1}^{N} Z_i \qquad (2.6.7)$$

This rule states that the summation of a sum (or difference) of terms is equal to the sum (or difference) of the individual summations of each term. It is a worthwhile exercise for us to prove this rule algebraically. Expand the summation on the left-hand side of Equation 2.6.7 (in the same manner as presented in Equation 2.6.5) to obtain

$$\sum_{i=1}^{N} (X_i + Y_i - Z_i) = (X_1 + Y_1 - Z_1) + (X_2 + Y_2 - Z_2) + (X_3 + Y_3 - Z_3) + \cdots + (X_N + Y_N - Z_N) \quad (2.6.8)$$

Remove the parentheses on the right-hand side of Equation 2.6.8 and collect the X, Y, and Z terms separately to obtain

$$\begin{aligned} \sum_{i=1}^{N} (X_i + Y_i - Z_i) = {} & X_1 + X_2 + X_3 + \cdots + X_N \\ & + Y_1 + Y_2 + Y_3 + \cdots + Y_N \\ & - Z_1 - Z_2 - Z_3 - \cdots - Z_N \end{aligned} \quad (2.6.9)$$

Note that the sequence of subtractions $(-Z_1 - Z_2 - Z_3 - \cdots - Z_N)$ may be expressed as $-(Z_1 + Z_2 + Z_3 + \cdots + Z_N)$. Then, using the summation notation to express the summation (separately) of the X, Y, and Z terms in Equation 2.6.9, we complete the proof of *Rule 1* as follows:

$$\sum_{i=1}^{N} (X_i + Y_i - Z_i) = \sum_{i=1}^{N} X_i + \sum_{i=1}^{N} Y_i - \sum_{i=1}^{N} Z_i$$

Suppose it is desired to double all Part 1 scores and then obtain the total. This may be accomplished in two ways. For example, we could multiply each Part 1 score by 2 and then add them, as follows:

$$\sum_{i=1}^{5} 2X_i = (2)(18) + (2)(12) + (2)(20) + (2)(11) + (2)(15) = 152$$

Or, noting that the scores are being multiplied by a constant (2), we could add the Part 1 scores and *then* multiply the summation by the constant. Using this approach, we obtain

$$\begin{aligned} 2\sum_{i=1}^{5} X_i &= 2(18 + 12 + 20 + 11 + 15) \\ &= 2(76) = 152 \end{aligned}$$

This leads to our second summation rule.

Rule 2

$$\sum_{i=1}^{N} kX_i = k\sum_{i=1}^{N} X_i \quad (2.6.10)$$

This rule states that the summation of a term involving a constant (k) times a variable (X_i) is equal to the constant times the summation of the variable. We can prove this rule by, first, expanding the summation on the left-hand side of Equation 2.6.10 (in the same manner as presented in Equation 2.6.3) to obtain

$$\sum_{i=1}^{N} kX_i = kX_1 + kX_2 + kX_3 + \cdots + kX_N \tag{2.6.11}$$

Factoring out the constant k from the right-hand side of Equation 2.6.11, we obtain

$$\sum_{i=1}^{N} kX_i = k(X_1 + X_2 + X_3 + \cdots + X_N) \tag{2.6.12}$$

Finally, using the summation notation to express the summation of the X terms in Equation 2.6.12, we complete our proof of *Rule 2* as follows:

$$\sum_{i=1}^{N} kX_i = k \sum_{i=1}^{N} X_i$$

Now, let us suppose that it is desired to obtain the sum of the Part 3 scores, which happen to be all the same. This may be obtained in two ways. First, we could just add the five identical scores, to obtain

$$\sum_{i=1}^{N} Z_i = \sum_{i=1}^{5} 4 = 4 + 4 + 4 + 4 + 4 = 20$$

Or, since the Part 3 scores happen to be a constant, we could multiply this constant score (4) by the number of times it appears in the summation (5). Using this approach, we obtain (5)(4) = 20. This leads to the third rule of summation.

Rule 3

$$\sum_{i=1}^{N} k = Nk \tag{2.6.13}$$

This rule states that the summation of a constant is equal to the constant times the number of times it is included in the summation.

PROBLEMS FOR PRACTICE AND REVIEW

1. Define and illustrate: variable, constant.

2. Compare and illustrate: discrete variable, continuous variable.

3. Are recorded variables always discrete? Discuss and illustrate.

4. Indicate whether each of the following items represents a constant, a discrete variable, or a continuous variable:

(a) Height of men aged 16 and over.

(b) Number of pupils per class in a large city.

(c) Speed of running through a maze.
(d) Reaction times for an experimental group.
(e) Reading speed per pupil recorded to the nearest second.
(f) Time spent yesterday (35 minutes) by a given student in preparing an assignment.
(g) Number of childern per family.
(h) Age per student recorded to the nearest half year.
(i) Weight per pupil in an elementary school.
(j) Length (in days) of the month of January.
(k) Scores on an achievement test.
(l) Number of subjects in each of a series of ten experiments who failed to respond correctly.
(m) Time required to run 100 yards by each of six runners, recorded to .001 seconds.

5. Explain the meaning of the following symbols which, let us suppose, were found in a research journal:

(a) X_6 (b) X_i (c) k

(d) $X_7 + X_{10}$ (e) $\sum_{i=2}^{4} X_i$ (f) $\sum_{i=1}^{N} X_i$

(g) $\sum Y$

6. Write in *condensed* summation form:

(a) $Y_1 + Y_2 + Y_3 + Y_4 + Y_5 + Y_6 + Y_7$

(b) $R_1 + R_2 + R_3 + \cdots + R_M$

(c) $(a_3 - X_3) + (a_4 - X_4) + (a_5 - X_5) + (a_6 - X_6)$

(d) $X_1Y_1 + X_2Y_2 + X_3Y_3 + X_4Y_4$

(e) $\dfrac{X_1 + Y_1}{k} + \dfrac{X_2 + Y_2}{k} + \dfrac{X_3 + Y_3}{k} + \dfrac{X_4 + Y_4}{k}$

(f) $(Y_3 - Z_3 - X_3) + (Y_4 - Z_4 - X_4) + (Y_5 - Z_5 - X_5)$

(g) $\frac{1}{2}X_1Y_1 + \frac{1}{2}X_2Y_2 + \frac{1}{2}X_3Y_3 + \cdots + \frac{1}{2}X_NY_N$

(h) $X_4(Y_4 - Z_4) + X_5(Y_5 - Z_5) + \cdots + X_{12}(Y_{12} - Z_{12})$

(i) $[Z_1(4 - Y_1) - X_1] + [Z_2(4 - Y_2) - X_2]$
$\quad + [Z_3(4 - Y_3) - X_3] + \cdots + [Z_{100}(4 - Y_{100}) - X_{100}]$

(j) $a + a + a + a + a + a + a + a$

7. Write in *expanded* summation form:

(a) $\sum_{i=1}^{3} X_i$

(b) $\sum_{i=1}^{N} Y_iZ_i$

(c) $\sum_{i=3}^{6} \dfrac{Z_iT_i}{X_i + Y_i}$

(d) $\sum_{i=1}^{4} \frac{1}{2}(X_i - Y_i + Z_i)$

(e) $\sum_{i=2}^{N}\left(H_i - \frac{X_i + 3}{Y_i - 4}\right)$

(f) $\sum_{i=10}^{14}\left(M_i + \frac{Z_i}{k} - 2X_i\right)$

(g) $\sum_{i=1}^{3} g$

(h) $\sum_{i=76}^{78}(X_i - Y_i + aZ_i - bT_i)$

8. Simplify by using *summation rules* (do not expand):

(a) $\sum_{i=1}^{N}(X_i - Z_i + Y_i)$

(b) $\sum_{i=1}^{N}\frac{a}{2}(X_i - k)$

(c) $\sum_{i=2}^{20}\left(\frac{Z_i}{M_i} + \frac{Y_i}{X_i}\right)$

(d) $\sum_{i=1}^{T}[X_i(Y_i + 4) + k - 3]$

(e) $\sum_{i=1}^{G} k$

(f) $\sum_{i=10}^{30}\frac{X_i Y_i - Z_i}{8}$

(g) $\sum_{i=10}^{20} 10$

9. Given:

$X_1 = 2$	$Y_1 = 0$	$Z_1 = 3$	$k = 100$
$X_2 = -4$	$Y_2 = 4$	$Z_2 = 6$	$g = 2$
$X_3 = 6$	$Y_3 = 2$	$Z_3 = 9$	$a = 4$
$X_4 = 10$	$Y_4 = 8$	$Z_4 = 24$	

Determine the value of each summation:

(a) $\sum_{i=2}^{4}(X_i - Y_i)$

(b) $\sum_{i=1}^{4}(X_i + gZ_i - Y_i)$

(c) $\sum_{i=1}^{3}\left(\frac{Y_i}{g} + \frac{Z_i}{3} + k\right)$

(d) $\sum_{i=2}^{4}(k - X_i Y_i)$

(e) $\sum_{i=1}^{3}\left(\frac{aZ_i - Y_i}{g}\right)^2$

10. Prove the following equalities by use of the *summation rules*, indicating the summation rule (or rules) used in each case:

(a) $\sum_{i=1}^{N}(X_i + Y_i - k) = \sum_{i=1}^{N} X_i + \sum_{i=1}^{N} Y_i - Nk$

(b) $\sum_{i=1}^{M} \frac{aX_i + bY_i^2}{a} = \sum_{i=1}^{M} X_i + \frac{b}{a}\sum_{i=1}^{M} Y_i^2$

(c) $\sum_{i=1}^{100} \frac{X_i^2 Y_i - kX_iZ_i}{kX_iZ_i} = \frac{1}{k}\sum_{i=1}^{100} \frac{X_iY_i}{Z_i} - 100$

(d) $\sum_{i=1}^{10}(X_i + 3)^2 = \sum_{i=1}^{10} X_i^2 + 6\sum_{i=1}^{10} X_i + 90$

(e) $\sum(X_i + Y_i)^2 = \sum X_i^2 + 2\sum X_iY_i + \sum Y_i^2$

(f) $\sum \frac{X^2Y + k^2Z}{akY} = \frac{1}{ak}\left[\sum X^2 + k^2\sum \frac{Z}{Y}\right]$

2.7 MEASUREMENT SCALES

Measurement implies a scale. For example, to measure a man's height we use a scale, such as a yardstick, which tells how much height he has. If we wish to measure his mechanical aptitude, we use a scale, such as an aptitude test score-scale, which tells how much mechanical aptitude he has. Or we might wish to "measure" his occupation and use a predetermined list of occupation catagories as our "scale." Of course, it is recognized that, in this last instance, the use of "measure" and "scale" does not follow the usual ideas relating to these terms. Nevertheless, in classifying a man according to his occupation, we are also applying a measuring scale. However, this measuring scale differs from the first two scales noted and it may not even be apparent that a "scale" is involved. There are fundamental differences in the meaning of *measure* and *scale* among the three illustrations presented. Furthermore, if we rank a group of men according to some characteristic, say skill in hitting a target, we are likewise using a scale of measurement. In this instance, we are using yet a different meaning of *measure* and *scale*.

How do *measure* and *scale* differ in the four illustrations presented? The differences are in degree. We might say that there is *more* measure and *more* scale in one situation than in another. These are sometimes referred to as different *levels of measurement*. Figure 2.7.1 presents the four scales of measurement illustrated previously and the scale properties. The most elementary scale of measurement is a classificatory scale, called a *nominal scale*. This involves setting up categories which are clearly defined and delineated, but in such a way that the only measure of a characteristic available from the measurement scale is *equivalence* (equality). For example, we may classify students according to country of birth, using the nominal scale (categories): United States, England, France, etc. Students who fall into the same category are equivalent (equal) with respect to the characteristic measured (country of birth). There is no other measurement information available from this scale other than equivalence (belonging

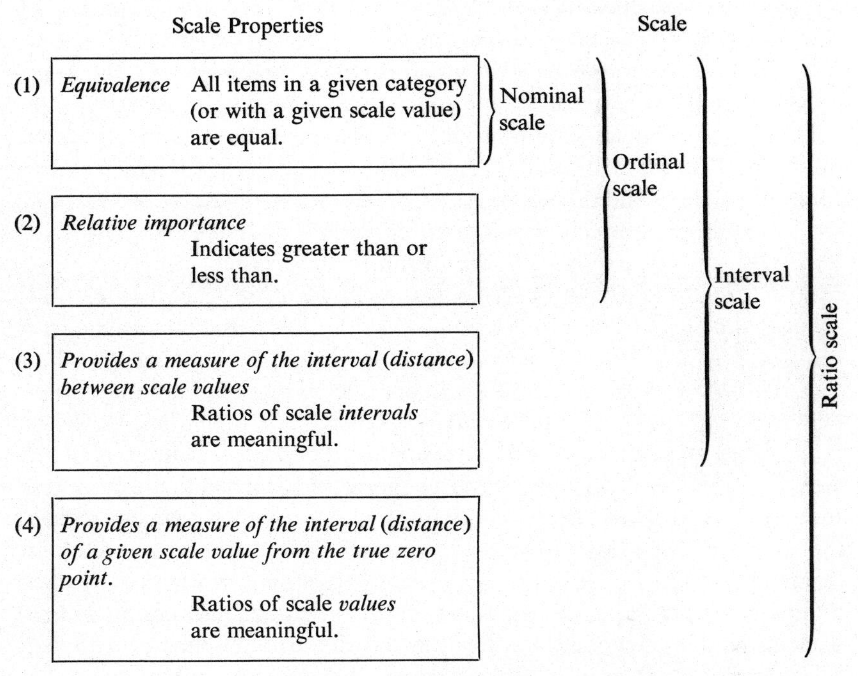

Fig. 2.7.1. Properties of the four scales of measurement.

to the same category). Other nominal scales are sex, occupation, and state of residence.

The scale elements (categories) in a nominal scale may be denoted by numbers, letters, names, or any set of symbols. The only purpose served by the symbols is to uniquely identify the categories making up the scale. As an example, we could set up a nominal scale referring to state of residence as follows: Alabama, California, Arkansas, Kansas, etc. (it is not necessary to list the states in alphabetical sequence). Or we might set up our scale as: A, B, C, D, etc. In this case, we define: $A =$ Alabama, $B =$ California, etc. Or we could use numbers: 1, 2, 3, 4, etc. In this case $1 =$ Alabama, etc. We could use any other symbols, if we wish. The use of number or letter sequences to denote scale elements in a nominal scale in no way implies more than merely category identification.

The next highest scale of measurement is the *ordinal scale*. This is a scale of rank or relative importance. An example is the scale of titles assigned to faculty members in a university: professor, associate professor, assistant professor, instructor. These titles make up an ordinal scale, since they indicate relative importance in faculty status. Such a scale contains two degrees of measurement, as indicated in Figure 2.7.1: *equivalence* and *relative importance* (*greater than or less than*). Faculty members with the same title, say assistant professor, are equivalent (equal) in status. As you proceed from one end of the scale (say, professor) to the other (instructor) there is a constant decline in relative status. Another illustration of an ordinal scale is a scale of responses by individuals to the question: Do you favor candidate A? The response scale might be structured as: favor candidate A very much, favor candidate A, opposed to candidate A, very much opposed to candidate A. We have an ordinal scale when ranks are assigned to a group of individuals. Suppose ranks from 1 (highest) through 20 (lowest) are assigned to a group of 20 trade school students to indicate mechanical ability. The student assigned the rank of 3 is considered to have more mechanical ability than those assigned ranks 4, 5, 6, etc., and he is considered to have less mechanical ability than those assigned the ranks of 1 and 2.

The scale elements in an ordinal scale may be expressed in terms of any set of symbols which provides the property of ranking. For example, if we wish to rank three subjects on running speed, we might set up a scale as follows: fast, faster, fastest. Or we might use: A, B, C where A = fast, etc. Or we might use: 1, 2, 3 where 1 = fast, etc. It should be noted that, while number or letter sequences may be used in the construction of an ordinal scale as well as a nominal scale, the information supplied is different. The use of 1, 2, 3 for a nominal scale provides only the information that there are three categories. In the ordinal scale, this information is provided *plus* the information of relative importance. In the illustration of running speed, 2 identifies a speed category different from 1. Furthermore, 2 indicates more speed than is indicated by 1. However, although ordinal scales indicate greater than and less than, they provide no information on *how much* of a difference exists.

The *interval scale* represents the next highest level of measurement. For example, suppose a spelling test made up of 50 words of equal difficulty (assuming this is possible) is given to a class of students. If each correctly spelled word scores one point, test scores could range from 0 to 50. If this test is considered to be a measure of spelling ability, then the scale of test scores (0, 1, 2, . . . , 50) represents an interval scale. Such a scale has the properties of equivalence and relative importance plus a *unique unit of measurement*. For example, students with the same score are considered to have equal spelling ability. A higher score indicates a higher degree of spelling ability than is indicated by a lower score. The unit of measurement in this scale is one point, representing the score assigned for a word spelled correctly. The unit of measurement is unique since the score value assigned to each and every correctly spelled word is one point and, furthermore, the words are assumed to be of equal difficulty so that one point always measures the same amount of spelling ability.

Owing to the existence of a unique unit of measurement, the interval scale provides a measure of the interval (distance) between scale values. In the spelling test noted, suppose three students obtained scores of 10, 15, and 25, respectively. These scale values (scores) permit us to *measure* the difference (distance) between any pair. For example, we may observe that the second score is 5 points higher than the first, whereas the third score is 10 points higher than the second. *Moreover, with an interval scale, ratios of scale intervals are meaningful.* For example, consider the spelling score intervals (differences) of 5 and 10 just noted. The *interval ratio* $\frac{10}{5} = 2$ indicates that the third score (25) exceeds the second (15) by twice as much as the second exceeds the first (10).

A limitation of an interval scale is the *lack of an absolute zero point.* For example, if a student did not spell any of the test words correctly, his score would be zero. However, this could hardly be taken to mean that he has absolutely zero spelling ability, since there may be some words (no matter how simple) which he could spell. In an interval scale, the zero point is arbitrary. An additional limitation is the fact that, in an interval scale, the ratio between scale *values* is *not* meaningful. For example, if two students have scores of 20 and 40 in the spelling test, respectively, it cannot be concluded that the score of 40 indicates twice as much spelling ability as a score of 20. The scale values in an interval scale can only be expressed numerically.

The highest level of measurement is achieved when we use a *ratio scale.* A *ratio scale* has all the properties of an interval scale plus an *absolute* or *true zero point.* The scales on which we measure time, length, and weight represent ratio scales. If an object is said to weigh 0 pounds, we mean that this object has no weight. If the reaction time to a stimulus is measured as 0 seconds, we mean that it took no time for the reaction to occur; it was an instantaneous response. If we state that an object measures 0 feet in length, we mean that this object has no length at all. These are illustrations of absolute or true zero points.

Owing to the true zero point, a ratio scale provides a measure of the interval (distance) of a given scale value from the true zero level. For example, a height of ten feet means an interval of ten feet from zero height. Because of this important additional property of a ratio scale, the ratio between two scale *values*, as well as the ratio between two scale *intervals*, is meaningful. For example, suppose two objects weigh 100 pounds and 25 pounds, respectively. It may be concluded that the heavier object is four times as heavy as the lighter one. The scale values in a ratio scale can only be expressed numerically.

In the discussion of the interval scale, we used the illustration of a spelling test of 50 words given to a class of students. It was noted that, if this test is considered to be a measure of spelling ability, then the scale of test scores constitutes an interval scale. On the other hand, we might consider these test scores only as a measure of a student's ability to spell the 50 words included in the test. In this instance, the scale of test scores constitutes a ratio scale, since it contains all the properties of the interval scale plus an absolute zero point. That is, a test score of 0 now represents a true measure of zero ability to spell the particular 50 words included in the test.

A knowledge of scales of measurement is important for students in education and psychology who desire to understand the use of even the elementary methods of statistics. This is so because not all statistical computations, nor all arithmetic operations, are permissible for some levels of measurement. For example, in the case of the nominal scale, none of the arithmetic operations is permissible. As an illustration, consider the nominal scale established to classify a group of people as to region of residence in the United States: 1 = northeastern states, 2 = southeastern states, 3 = midwestern states, etc. Since each numerical designation merely constitutes a code, it is not meaningful to add (or subtract) the nominal scale values assigned to any two or more persons in the group.

This is also true for values in an ordinal scale. For example, suppose a group of men are ranked on running speed where the rank of 1 is assigned to the fastest man, 2 to the second fastest man, etc. It is, obviously, not meaningful to add (or subtract) the ranks for any two persons. Similarly, neither multiplication nor division is permissible for values referred to a nominal or ordinal scale. On the other hand, all the arithmetic operations are permissible when dealing with an interval or ratio scale. The permissible statistical operations are also determined by the scale of measurement used. At this point, since no statistical measurements have yet been introduced, it is not possible to present illustrations. However, from time to time throughout this text, appropriate comments concerning scales of measurement will be made.

Scales of measurement often present serious problems in the fields of psychology and education. For example, what is the level of measurement for grades on a final examination in a course in advanced principals of education? Since a final examination can hardly be expected to include all the material covered in a course, a grade of zero cannot be considered to represent zero achievement in the course. Therefore a score of zero is not a true zero point. At best, scores on such an examination may represent an interval scale. Yet, even this is not true, since the unit of measurement is probably not unique in the scoring. That is, the amount of achievement represented by one point is not identically the same throughout the examination.

It will be recalled that in the previously mentioned illustration of the 50-word spelling test, it was specified that the words included in the test were of equal difficulty. This specification was necessary to insure a unique unit of measurement. Similar problems exist in the scoring of psychological tests. It is questionable for most psychological tests whether the scoring scales contain a true zero point or unique units of measurement. However, it is often found useful to assume a level of measurement which is not actually contained in the scale. Such an assumption permits the use of certain statistical methods, not otherwise applicable. However, it is important to know that such an assumption is being made in any given situation.

PROBLEMS FOR PRACTICE AND REVIEW

1. For each scale, define, list the properties, and illustrate: (a) Nominal scale; (b) ordinal scale; (c) interval scale; (d) ratio scale.

2. Identify the scale of measurement involved and defend your answer, stating any assumptions you may make:

(a) List of books identified by subject matter (agriculture, electricity, etc.).

(b) A list of IQ scores, where each score is identified only as: below 81, 81–90, 91–100, 101–115, 116–118, 119 and above.

(c) Reaction times for a group of subjects.

(d) Club members classified according to type of membership (senior, associate, etc.).

(e) Grades on an arithmetic test.

(f) Grades on a typing test for beginners.

(g) Scores on a science aptitude test.

(h) Number of items incorrectly completed in a 100-item completion test.

(i) Number of items attempted in a speed test.

(j) Students identified only as male or female.

3. A teacher of second-year French finds that student A obtained 80 in a midterm examination, B obtained 40, C obtained 10, and D obtained 0 (zero). Would you agree with each of the following statements? Defend your answer.

(a) A knows eight times as much French as C and twice as much as B.

(b) D does not know any French.

(c) It may be stated that A's score exceeds B's score by half as much as it exceeds D's score.

4. Ed, Tom, Harry, and Ned were ranked on proficiency in science, from least proficient (1) to most proficient (4), as follows: (1) Harry, (2) Tom, (3) Ed, (4) Ned. Would you agree with the following statements? Why?

(a) Ed is more proficient in science than Tom but less than Ned.

(b) Ned is twice as proficient in science as Tom and four times as proficient as Harry.

(c) Ed exceeds Tom in proficiency in science by as much as Tom exceeds Harry.

Part II
Statistical Description and Analysis

3

FREQUENCY DISTRIBUTIONS

3.1 INTRODUCTION

Part II presents methods for organization and summarization of statistical data and computation of measurements describing the distribution of the data. Generally speaking, Part II presents the methods of descriptive statistics which are applicable to population data. However, these methods, sometimes with some adjustment, are applicable to sample data as well. Therefore, applications of these methods to sample data will be included as appropriate.

3.2 ORGANIZATION OF RAW DATA

Very frequently, the psychologist or educator finds himself faced with a large mass of *raw* (*unorganized*) *data*. For example, the psychometrician who tries out a newly constructed test on, say, 250 subjects will have to decide what to do with the resulting 250 scores. The elementary school principal who wishes to study the performance of the 130 first-graders who took the reading-readiness test must find some way of organizing and summarizing the 130 reading-readiness test scores. The dean of a large university who collects information on the time spent on part-time employment by a sample of 500 students from the university, in order to determine the need for a student loan program, must somehow organize and summarize this mass of information, if he hopes to learn something

Table 3.2.1 SCORES ON A REASONING ABILITY TEST FOR 224 SUBJECTS

98	103	104	96	108	112	103	104	106	103	106	105	95
105	107	111	111	101	106	117	115	94	110	110	112	103
101	93	105	107	108	107	108	103	108	99	106	106	104
103	108	114	106	104	111	106	122	128	101	105	115	106
97	106	108	91	108	87	111	97	101	108	107	98	101
108	103	95	111	105	115	99	108	110	117	91	108	102
102	114	111	104	101	97	104	107	105	99	102	103	104
106	93	107	97	107	110	115	89	107	115	97	112	97
99	105	104	112	93	107	101	104	117	107	103	106	
107	118	112	95	110	98	108	123	102	104	112	105	
104	104	107	103	110	107	105	95	112	103	104	108	
107	114	93	114	97	107	99	103	106	94	108	106	
97	101	110	118	115	105	108	106	118	106	98	118	
105	114	106	97	122	104	102	114	105	110	106	107	
108	95	117	110	110	101	106	93	122	97	104	99	
98	118	104	106	103	123	96	122	107	111	114	118	
115	106	118	117	122	97	123	104	123	111	106	104	
103	117	106	115	106	123	108	108	103	106	107	123	

Table 3.2.2 SCORES ON A REASONING ABILITY TEST FOR 224 SUBJECTS, RANKED

87	97	99	103	104	105	106	107	108	110	112	115	122
89	97	99	103	104	105	106	107	108	110	112	117	123
91	97	99	103	104	105	106	107	108	110	112	117	123
91	97	99	103	104	105	106	107	108	110	112	117	123
93	97	101	103	104	105	106	107	108	110	114	117	123
93	97	101	103	104	105	106	107	108	110	114	117	123
93	97	101	103	104	105	106	107	108	110	114	117	123
93	97	101	103	104	105	106	107	108	111	114	118	128
93	97	101	103	104	105	106	107	108	111	114	118	
94	97	101	103	104	106	106	107	108	111	114	118	
94	97	101	103	104	106	106	107	108	111	114	118	
95	98	101	103	104	106	106	107	108	111	115	118	
95	98	101	103	104	106	106	107	108	111	115	118	
95	98	102	103	104	106	106	107	108	111	115	118	
95	98	102	103	104	106	106	107	108	111	115	122	
95	98	102	104	105	106	107	108	110	112	115	122	
96	99	102	104	105	106	107	108	110	112	115	122	
96	99	102	104	105	106	107	108	110	112	115	122	

from the data. The methods for organization and summarization of raw data presented in this chapter are applicable equally to population data and sample data.

Table 3.2.1 presents the scores on a reasoning ability test administered to 224 subjects. Clearly, even careful study will yield little understanding of this collection of scores or how these scores are distributed, unless these data are somehow organized. The first thought which may come to one's mind is to put these scores in order, say from lowest to highest. This has been done and is presented in Table 3.2.2. The *ranking*, as observed from this table, does add to the meaningfulness of the set of scores. For example, it is now apparent that the scores range from a low of 87 to a high of 128. It may be observed that most scores occur more than once. For example, two subjects obtained a score of 91, and 5 obtained a score of 93. It can be seen that a large number of subjects obtained scores of 101, 103, 104, etc. However, in general, only limited insight into the data is possible by merely ranking.

Ranking, of course, is a form of *organization* which adds systematic arrangement to the formerly unorganized collection of raw score data. However, what is needed is *summarization*, as well as *organization*, since a large volume of data is too much for the mind to comprehend. Table 3.2.3 presents a possible form of data summarization, including systematic arrangement. The table is arranged in two columns. The first column lists all possible values of the *score variable* (X_i), from the lowest obtained score (87) to the highest (128). Of course, it may be possible on this test for one to obtain a score lower than 87 or higher than 128. However, we need not concern ourselves with these scores, since none of the 224 scores we are studying is outside the range 87–128. The second column shows the *frequency* (f_i) with which each score occurs among the 224 subjects. For example, the score of 87 occurs only once, 93 occurs 5 times, 106 occurs 24 times. It will be observed that some scores between 87 and 128 have zero frequency (do not occur at all among the 224 scores in the collection). This is shown by a dash in the frequency column. Some of the scores with zero frequency are 88, 100, and 124. The summarization of the 224 scores presented in Table 3.2.3 we will call *simple grouping*, because it is the simplest form of score grouping possible and because no information is lost in the summarization process. That is, this table leaves no doubt as to *exactly* which scores are included in the collection.

A simple grouping frequency table, such as Table 3.2.3, exhibits the *frequency distribution* of a collection of raw scores. It will be observed that this summarization permits better understanding of how the scores are distributed. For example, it reveals that the greatest concentration of scores occurs in the range 103–108, each of the scores within this range

Table 3.2.3 SIMPLE GROUPING OF SCORES ON A REASONING ABILITY TEST FOR 224 SUBJECTS

Score, X_i	Frequency, f_i	Score, X_i	Frequency, f_i
87	1	108	18
88	–	109	–
89	1	110	10
90	–	111	8
91	2	112	7
92	–	113	–
93	5	114	7
94	2	115	8
95	5	116	–
96	2	117	6
97	11	118	7
98	5	119	–
99	6	120	–
100	–	121	–
101	9	122	5
102	5	123	6
103	15	124	–
104	18	125	–
105	12	126	–
106	24	127	–
107	18	128	1

having a relatively substantial frequency (ranging from 12–24). Outside of this score range, we note reasonably large frequencies for the scores of 97, 101, and 110. However, outside the score range 103–108, the scores are generally found to occur with low frequencies. It would have been very difficult, if at all possible, to learn about these features of the score distribution by inspection of the ranked listing of the 224 individual scores. Nevertheless, only seldom does simple grouping provide an *adequate* understanding of the score distribution. Nearly always, further summarization is required in order to assist the mind in visualizing the distribution of the data.

Further summarization of the data requires more condensed grouping of the scores. For example, Table 3.2.4 presents four *frequency tables* with varying degrees of summarization of the 224 reasoning ability test scores. Consider part *A*, where the scores are grouped into score *intervals* (score ranges) made up of two consecutive scores each. For example, the first interval, 86–87, is made up of the scores 86 and 87. We note that the

Table 3.2.4 FREQUENCY TABLES OF SCORES ON A REASONING ABILITY TEST FOR 224 SUBJECTS

(*A*)		(*B*)		(*C*)		(*D*)	
Score Interval	Frequency, f_i	Score Interval	Frequency, f_i	Score Interval	Frequency, f_i	Score Interval	Frequency, f_i
86–87	1	87–89	2	85–89	2	85–94	11
88–89	1	90–92	2	90–94	9	95–104	76
90–91	2	93–95	12	95–99	29	105–114	104
92–93	5	96–98	18	100–104	47	115–124	32
94–95	7	99–101	15	105–109	72	125–134	1
96–97	13	102–104	38	110–114	32		
98–99	11	105–107	54	115–119	21		
100–101	9	108–110	28	120–124	11		
102–103	20	111–113	15	125–129	1		
104–105	30	114–116	15				
106–107	42	117–119	13				
108–109	18	120–122	5				
110–111	18	123–125	6				
112–113	7	126–128	1				
114–115	15						
116–117	6						
118–119	7						
120–121	–						
122–123	11						
124–125	–						
126–127	–						
128–129	1						

frequency for this score range is 1. That is, there is only one score which fits into the interval. We know, from the raw data table, that this score is 87. The score interval 94–95 is made up of the scores 94 and 95. The frequency for this interval is 7 and, from the raw data, we know that this includes two scores of 94 and five of 95.

It will be observed that summarization beyond simple grouping is accompanied by some loss of information. That is, *a frequency table, such as in part A, indicates how many scores fit into each score interval but provides no information as to the value of the individual scores in an interval.* However, the gain from adequate summarization *in a well-constructed frequency table* far outweighs any loss of information. The loss is usually minor, but the gain in comprehension of the distribution of raw data is always major. A frequency table, with summarization beyond simple grouping, presents a more compact, more easily visualized representation of the frequency distribution.

In summarizing a set of raw data, an important question is how far to go. Table 3.2.4 contains four different degrees of summarization of the 224 reasoning ability test scores. Part *A* presents a frequency table with 22 *classes* or *class intervals.* Part *B* presents a frequency table containing 14 classes; part *C*, 9 classes; and part *D*, 5 classes. How much condensation of the raw data is desirable? On the one hand, if *too many* classes are used in summarizing the raw data, the resulting frequency table is likely to look too "stretched out." Furthermore, the mind can only inadequately visualize the distribution of score frequencies if too many classes are used for summarization. That is, the distribution of the scores will tend to be less well defined. For example, if there is a tendency for the scores in a collection to bunch up within a particular score range, this tendency may be expected to be less apparent when scores are summarized into too large a number of classes. On the other hand, if *too few* classes are used, there is a likelihood that the data will be overcondensed, resulting in a serious loss of information relating to the distribution of the data.

Examine the four frequency distributions presented in Table 3.2.4. Part *A*, which involves only a moderate amount of summarization, is a considerable improvement over simple grouping. However, it is still quite lengthy and difficult to grasp visually. It is generally agreed that 22 classes, as in part *A*, are too many for adequate visualization of the score distribution. Furthermore, the number of scores in a class tend to rise and fall irregularly in the part *A* distribution instead of exhibiting a more or less smooth pattern. For example, the frequencies in the 88–89 class through the 96–97 class rise continuously from 1 to 13. In the next two classes, the frequencies decline. In the following three classes, the frequencies rise again, and so on.

Part *B* represents a substantial improvement over part *A*. The reduced number of classes (14) permits easier visualization of the distribution of the data. Furthermore, the sequence of class frequencies exhibits a smoother pattern. However, for many purposes, part *C* is more desirable. In this table, the frequency distribution is more clearly defined, since the number of classes is smaller and therefore easier for the eye to grasp. The sequence of class frequencies follows a smooth pattern. Note that class frequencies rise steadily from the lowest class interval to a peak of 72 (for the 105–109 class) and then decline steadily. It will be observed that the general nature of the distribution of the 224 scores is quite similar, as revealed by the various frequency distributions of these scores so far discussed. For example, the simple grouping table indicated a tendency for the scores to be concentrated in the 103–108 range, and to decline in frequency for scores below 103 and above 108. The same general pattern of frequencies is noted in the distributions exhibited in parts *A*, *B*, and *C* in Table 3.2.4. However, the distribution is more clearly defined ("sharper," "more visible") in part *C*.

On the other hand, a frequency distribution such as in part *D* is usually inadequate because the data are too highly condensed. As a result, too much information relating to how the scores are distributed is lost. This table provides only a very rough representation of the score distribution. Yet, there may be purposes for which part D provides an adequate amount and type of distribution information. There is no single answer to the question, "How much summarization of a collection of scores is desirable?" The most important consideration relates to the purposes to be served. For example, if it is desired to make a very detailed analysis of a set of data, the tendency would be to use more classes than would generally be required. On the other hand, if it is desired merely to determine how many scores are equal to or less than, say, 99 and how many are above 99, then only two classes are required (99 or less, over 99).

Although special requirements may have to be taken into consideration, *a typically important reason for construction of a frequency table is to exhibit the distribution of a set of data and, often, to use the table to compute required measures of the distribution.* Even for these purposes, there is no specific answer as to the desirable amount of summarization. Nevertheless, there are certain considerations that need to be taken into account. For example, a decision on the number of classes to use should take into consideration the number of raw scores in the collection to be summarized. Generally, the larger the collection of raw data, the more class intervals ought to be used. On the one extreme, a very small collection of items requires no tabular summarization. For example, if a set of data consists of, say, five scores, there is clearly no need to construct a frequency table to summarize these scores. On the other extreme, it is usually considered inadvisable to use more than 20 classes, no matter how many items are being summarized, since then the summarization is itself too lengthy. If the collection contains under 1000 scores, 10 classes or less are suggested. If 1000 or more scores are to be put into a frequency table, use 11 to 20 classes.

A frequently suggested rule of thumb is to use 15 classes. Table 3.2.5 is presented to suggest, in some detail, the number of class intervals to use when constructing a frequency table. Table 3.2.5 suggests that 9 classes be used for construction of a frequency table for the 224 scores on the reasoning ability test discussed previously. Referring to Table 3.2.4, note that the frequency table in part C contains 9 classes. Actually, this does present an easy-to-visualize summarization of the 224 scores without too much condensation. However, part B presents a frequency table which also has merit.

In this section, we discussed the difficulties of analyzing a large collection of unorganized numerical data, such as test scores, and considered various means of data organization and summarization. Construction of frequency distributions by grouping the raw data into class intervals was presented as an effective method of data organization and summarization.

Table 3.2.5 APPROXIMATE NUMBER OF CLASSES TO USE WHEN CONSTRUCTING A FREQUENCY TABLE[1]

Number of Items of Raw Data	Approximate Number of Classes to Use
15–29	5
30–59	6
60–99	7
100–199	8
200–499	9
500–999	10
1,000–1,999	11
2,000–3,999	12
4,000–7,999	13
8,000–14,999	14
15,000–34,999	15
35,000–69,999	16
70,000–149,999	17
150,000–299,999	18
300,000–499,999	19
500,000 and over	20

[1] Generally based on the results obtained following the procedure in H. A. Sturges' article, "The Choice of a Class Interval," *Journal of the American Statistical Association*, Vol. 21, 1926.

In Section 3.3, a "model" frequency table is used to present and discuss the various features of a frequency table.

3.3 A MODEL FREQUENCY TABLE

Before considering how frequency tables are constructed, it will be helpful to present a model frequency table. Tables 3.3.1 and 3.3.2 present a model based on part *C* of Table 3.2.4. It should be noted that this is a "model" in the sense that it has been constructed along generally accepted lines and, in addition, it contains all the tabular features generally associated with frequency tables. However, it is not a "model" in the sense that it presents the one and only acceptable table for summarizing and presenting the 224 scores on reasoning ability. Actually, a particular frequency distribution is "best" if it has been constructed properly, as discussed in Section 3.4, and if it is adequate for the purposes for which it is to be used. Table 3.3.2 may be considered another version of Table 3.3.1, since it presents *relative frequencies* (*proportions*), whereas Table 3.3.1 presents *frequencies*.

We will first consider Table 3.3.1 in some detail. It will be observed that the first column is headed *Discrete Class Limits* instead of *score interval* as shown in part *C*, Table 3.2.4. Actually, *Discrete Class Limits* is a more descriptive heading since it takes into account the discrete scale in which all variables are recorded (even continuous variables) and it indicates that the column presents the "limits" which specify the range of each class interval. For example, the first set of limits in this column, 85–89, specifies the first class interval by indicating that 85 is the lowest score in this class and 89 is the highest score in this class. In other words, this class interval includes the scores 85, 86, 87, 88, and 89. We call 85 the *lower discrete class limit* and 89 the *upper discrete class limit*.

More generally, we may say that *a class interval includes all permissible values of the variable, from the lower discrete class limit up to and including the upper discrete class limit*. It should be noted that the discrete class limits themselves represent permissible values of the variable. That is,

Table 3.3.1 FREQUENCY DISTRIBUTION OF SCORES ON A REASONING ABILITY TEST FOR 224 SUBJECTS

Discrete Class Limits	Frequency, f_i	Midpoint, X_i	Continuous Class Limits	Less than cum f_i	More than cum f_i
			84.5	0	224
85–89	2	87			
			89.5	2	222
90–94	9	92			
			94.5	11	213
95–99	29	97			
			99.5	40	184
100–104	47	102			
			104.5	87	137
105–109	72	107			
			109.5	159	65
110–114	32	112			
			114.5	191	33
115–119	21	117			
			119.5	212	12
120–124	11	122			
			124.5	223	1
125–129	1	127			
			129.5	224	0

Table 3.3.2 RELATIVE FREQUENCY DISTRIBUTION OF SCORES ON A REASONING ABILITY TEST FOR 224 SUBJECTS

Discrete Class Limits	Relative Frequency, p_i	Continuous Class Limits	Less than cum p_i	More than cum p_i
		84.5	0	1.000
85–89	.009			
		89.5	.009	.991
90–94	.040			
		94.5	.049	.951
95–99	.129			
		99.5	.179	.821
100–104	.210			
		104.5	.388	.612
105–109	.322			
		109.5	.710	.290
110–114	.143			
		114.5	.853	.147
115–119	.094			
		119.5	.946	.054
120–124	.049			
		124.5	.996	.004
125–129	.004			
		129.5	1.000	0

while a set of raw data may not actually contain items equal to one or more of the discrete class limits, these limits always represent possible values of the variable. For example, the discrete limits 85, 90, and 100 do not appear among the 224 scores from which this frequency table was constructed; however, these are possible scores on the reasoning ability test. On the other hand, 90.2 is *not* a permissible score, since fractional scores were not used for this test. Therefore, 90.2 should not be used as a discrete class limit. Other texts on statistical methods use names such as: *class limits*, *end points*, or *class values* in place of *discrete class limits*. However, *discrete class limits* is a more descriptive title.

The length of class interval in a frequency table is equal to the difference between successive lower or successive upper discrete class limits. For example, the difference between the successive lower limits 85 and 90 is five, which is the length of the 85–89 class interval. Likewise, the difference between the successive upper limits 89 and 94 is also five. This is the length of the 90–94 class. The frequency column f_i, as noted previously, shows the number of scores in the collection of 224 scores which fall within the class interval. For example, two scores are in the 85–89 class interval, nine are in the 90–94 class interval, etc. Of course, the frequency table does not tell us the exact value of the scores included in each class interval.

The first two columns presented in Table 3.3.1 contain all of the basic information. The other columns, which present information derived from the first two columns, are useful in analysis of the distribution of the data, or as a means for performing certain computations to measure specific properties of the distribution (discussed in Chapters 4 and 5), or for both purposes. The column headed *Midpoint*, denoted by the variable X_i, presents the middle position of each class interval. *The class midpoint is computed as the average of the discrete class limits for an interval.* For example, the first midpoint, 87, is computed as the sum of the discrete class limits, 85 and 89, divided by two. Clearly, this is the middle position of the class interval, since two score values in this interval (85 and 86) are below 87 and two score values (88 and 89) are above it.

The class midpoint is used in certain computations (discussed in Chapters 4 and 5) to represent the value of each score in a class interval since, as already noted, it is not possible to determine the actual raw score values from a frequency table. For example, we note that there are two scores included in the first class interval, 85–89. However, we do not know the value of these scores from the frequency table itself and it is often useful to assume that they are equal to the class midpoint, 87. This assumption is usually not true. However, in a well-constructed frequency table this generally causes little difficulty since, for the purposes for which it is used, it is only necessary that *on the average* the class midpoint is representative of the items contained in a class interval.

In other words, although usually the items in a class will be either larger or smaller than the class midpoint, it is only necessary that these differences tend to balance out. Of course, it should be recognized that using class midpoints to represent raw score values leads to discrepencies when a frequency table is used for computation of the various descriptive measures of a frequency distribution. However, with a well-constructed frequency table, these discrepencies are usually small and may be ignored. The *class midpoint* is sometimes called the *class mark*.

The column headed *Continuous Class Limits* is needed for the computation of certain descriptive distribution measures based on the frequency table. Discrete class limits contain discontinuities or gaps, which are to be expected in a discrete scale. The gaps referred to are those between the upper discrete limit of one class and the lower discrete limit of the next highest class. For example, consider the discrete class limits shown in Figure 3.3.1. It will be observed that there are gaps between 89 and 90, 94 and 95, etc. Since the scores which were summarized in the frequency table are whole numbers, these gaps present no problem. That is, no reasoning ability test score in the collection of 224 scores has a value which falls within any of these gaps.

However, for certain uses of the frequency table, these gaps have to be eliminated by converting the discrete class limits to continuous class limits. *This is accomplished by "spreading out" each class interval just enough to eliminate the gaps.* For example, the gap between 89 and 90 is divided in half, one-half placed in the 85–89 class and the other half placed in the 90–94 class. More specifically, we compute the continuous class limit

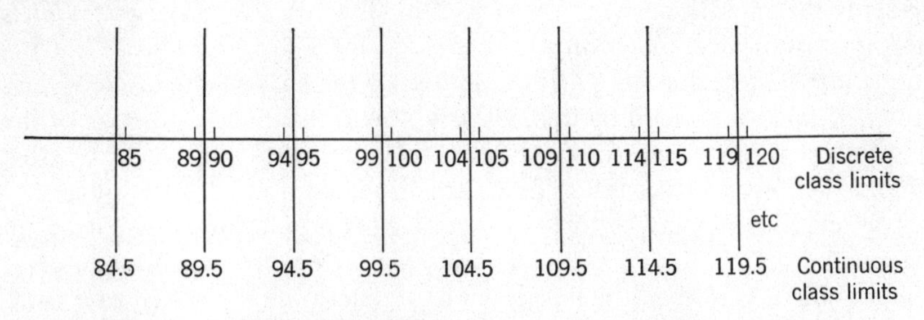

Figure 3.3.1. Relationship between discrete and continuous class limits.

between 89 and 90 by dividing the sum of 89 and 90 by 2. This results in the continuous class limit of 89.5. In the same way, we obtain the next highest continuous class limit, 94.5, by dividing the sum of 94 and 95 by 2.

As a result of this operation, the *two* discrete class limits such as 89 and 90 needed to separate two class intervals are replaced by a *single* continuous class limit located between them (89.5), as indicated in Figure 3.3.1. Observe, in the figure, that the class interval delineated by the discrete limits 90–94, is spread out to range from 89.5–94.5. That is, the lower discrete limit is lowered a half unit, whereas the upper discrete limit is raised a half unit.

In the *continuous class interval* 89.5–94.5, 89.5 is called the *lower continuous class limit* and 94.5 is called the *upper continuous class limit*. However, in the next highest continuous class interval (94.5–99.5), 94.5 is now the *lower* continuous class limit, since it is the common value dividing the two classes. For this reason, it will be observed in Table 3.3.1 that the arrangement of continuous class limits in the column is different from that of discrete class limits. The continuous limits are shown *between* the classes. Furthermore, note that the lowest discrete class limit in the frequency table, 85, is lowered a half unit to 84.5 and the highest discrete class limit in the table, 129, is raised a half unit to 129.5 to obtain the corresponding continuous class limits. In other texts, *continuous class limits* are called by such names as *real limits, class boundaries*, and *exact limits*.

There is a further consideration relating to discrete and continuous class limits which should be noted. Discrete class limits are appropriate when we are dealing with a discrete variable. The reasoning ability test scores represent a discrete variable since they can only be whole numbers. A score between, say, 90 and 91 does not occur. Of course, the scoring procedure could have been established to provide for fractional scores. For example, the scoring procedure could have specified that all scores will be

Table 3.3.3

Discrete Class Limits	Frequency, f_i	Continuous Class Limits
		29.995
30.00–30.29	8	
		30.295
30.30–30.59	11	
		30.595
30.60–30.89	17	
		30.895
30.90–31.19	22	
		31.195
31.20–31.49	35	
		31.495
Etc.		

determined to one decimal place. In such event, scores of 90.1, 90.2, etc., would be permissible values of the score variable. However, this would still be a discrete variable, since a score between, say, 90.1 and 90.2 could not occur. As noted in Chapter 2, any continuous variable becomes discrete when recorded. Suppose we record the time (in seconds) required to run a certain distance for each of a group of runners and set up a frequency table as in Table 3.3.3.

It is clear in Table 3.3.3 that running time was recorded to two decimals, as indicated by the discrete class limits. Therefore, values of the variable (seconds) between, say, 30.64 and 30.65 do not occur. *Continuous class limits imply that we are dealing with a continuous variable*. That is, the variable itself, not merely the class limits, is converted. In the reasoning ability test scores, we are converting the discrete score variable to a continuous score variable, when we convert from discrete to continuous class limits. Figure 3.3.2 presents the discrete score scale, indicating the gaps between the scores. As indicated in the figure, *when converted to continuous scores, each discrete score is replaced by an interval spreading out above and below the score sufficiently to eliminate the gaps.* The implication of the interval is that *any* value of the variable (test score) within the interval becomes a permissible value of the variable. For example, the score 88 is replaced by the interval 87.5–88.5, implying that, if the scoring were sufficiently precise, a discrete score of 88 could actually be any score within the 87.5–88.5 interval.

What is the logical interpretation of this conversion? Consider the

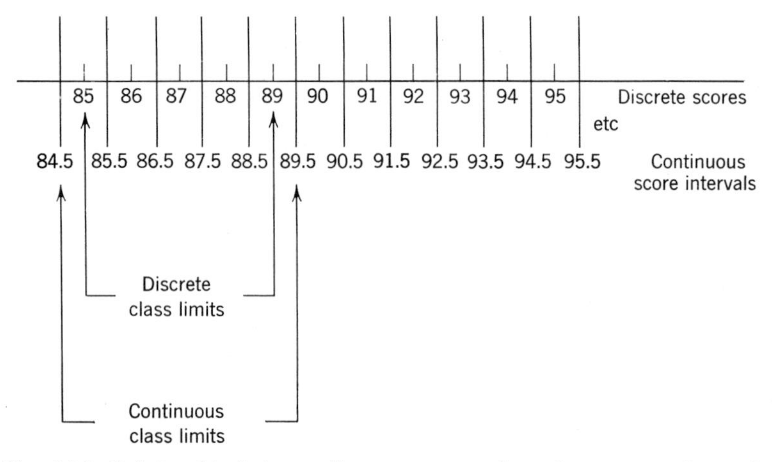

Fig. 3.3.2. Relationship between discrete scores and continuous score intervals.

reasoning ability test score, 106. Although 24 subjects obtained this identical score, as noted in Table 3.2.3, it is highly unlikely that they all have identical reasoning ability. It is to be expected that there is at least some variation in reasoning ability among these 24 subjects, no matter how slight. However, because of the limitation of the scoring procedure, only discrete scores, such as 105, 106, or 107, are possible. Conversion to a continuous score variable attempts to correct for this scoring limitation by specifying that the 24 subjects who obtained a score of 106 are actually in the 105.5–106.5 score interval. In other words, conversion to a continuous scale implies that, if the scoring procedure had established a more precise scoring scale, the 24 subjects would have had scores spreading out over this range. The continuous class limits in a frequency table take this into account by closing the gaps between the discrete class intervals. The relationship between discrete and continuous class limits is indicated by the two pairs of arrows in Figure 3.3.2.

Often, another interpretation of the conversion to a continuous variable is appropriate. Suppose the weights of a group of boys are recorded to the nearest pound as 51, 52, 53, etc. Then, weights such as 51.7 pounds and 52.3 pounds are rounded and recorded as 52 pounds. The recorded variable "weight" in this illustration is, of course, discrete. Consequently, there are gaps between 51 and 52, 52 and 53, etc., since fractional weights are not permissible values of this variable. When converted to a continuous variable, the weight of 52 pounds becomes the continuous interval 51.5 pounds to 52.5 pounds. The interpretation of such intervals is apparent. Clearly, recorded weights of 52 pounds represent actual weights which lie anywhere within the corresponding continuous interval.

Table 3.3.4

Discrete Class Limits	Frequency, f_i	Continuous Class Limits
		−.5
0–14	12	
		14.5
15–29	42	
		29.5
30–44	8	
		44.5
Etc.		

It will be noted from the two illustrations, the reasoning ability test scores and running times, that continuous class limits contain one more decimal place than are used for discrete class limits. Furthermore, length of class interval and class midpoint can be determined from continuous class limits, as well as from discrete class limits. *Length of class interval is equal to the difference between successive continuous class limits. Class midpoint is computed by adding the upper and lower continuous limits for a class and dividing the sum by 2.*

Finally, it should be noted that continuous class limits sometimes take on an unreal character. For example, consider Table 3.3.4, a frequency table of the number of pupils per class. The upper continuous class limit of the 0–14 discrete class is 14.5 pupils per class. This is obviously an unreal limit. Furthermore, the lower continuous class limit of this discrete class is −.5 pupils per class, also an unreal limit. All the continuous class limits in this frequency table are unreal. However, even though unreal, continuous class limits serve a useful purpose in computations of statistical measures based on a frequency table.

The last two columns of Table 3.3.1 represent analytical columns which supply useful information for certain purposes. In addition, they are useful in certain computations of descriptive measures. *Less than cum* f_i stands for *less than cumulative frequency* whereas *More than cum* f_i stands for *more than cumulative frequency*. It will be observed that these cumulative frequencies are listed in the columns to correspond with the continuous class limits. The first entry in the *Less than cum* f_i column is 0 and it appears on the same line with the continuous class limit 84.5. This tells us that no (0) scores *less than* 84.5 are included in the frequency table. Obviously, this is true since the lower limit of the lowest discrete class interval is 85. The next entry is 2 and it appears on the same line with the continuous class limit 89.5. This indicates that two scores are *less than* 89.5. It will be noted that there is only one class interval less than 89.5 (85–89) and the frequency for this class is 2. The third entry in the *Less than cum* f_i column is 11, which indicates that the frequency table contains 11 scores which are *less than* 94.5. This is determined by noting that there are two classes less than 94.5, one (85–89) with a frequency of 2 and the other (90–94) with a frequency of 9. The sum (cumulation) of these frequencies is 11.

It is now clear that *each "less than cum* f_i*" indicates the number of scores which are less than the corresponding class limit. Furthermore, this number is determined as the sum (cumulation) of the frequencies for all class intervals less than the given continuous class limit in value.* As another illustration, the less than cum f_i of 191 in the table indicates that 191 scores are *less than* 114.5 and is determined by cumulating the frequencies for the six classes which are less than 114.5. It will be observed that the less than cum f_i increases as you go from the cumulative frequency associated with the lowest-valued continuous class limit (listed first in the table) to the cumulative frequency associated with the highest-valued continuous class limit (listed last in the table). This is to be expected since, as the continuous class limit increases in value, the number of scores with a lower value, of course, accumulates.

Although the *Less than cum* f_i column starts with 0 at the *top* of the column (where it is associated with the *lowest* continuous class limit), the *More than cum* f_i column starts with 0 at the *bottom* of the column (where it is associated with the *highest* continuous class limit). This indicates that none (0) of the scores included in the table have a value *more than* the highest continuous class limit, 129.5. The second entry from the bottom in the *More than cum* f_i column is 1, indicating that only one score has a value *more than* the associated continuous class limit, 124.5. This is determined by noting that there is only one discrete class (125–129) more than 124.5 in value and the frequency for this class is 1. The third entry from the bottom is 12, indicating that 12 scores *more than* the associated continuous class limit 119.5 are included in the frequency table. This is determined by cumulating the frequencies for the two classes which are *more than* 119.5 in value (120–124, 125–129).

Each "more cum f_i*" indicates the number of scores which are more than the corresponding continuous class limit. This number is determined as the sum (cumulation) of the frequencies for all class intervals more than the given continuous class limit in value.* The more than cum f_i increases as you proceed from the cumulative frequency associated with the highest-valued continuous class limit (listed last in the table) to the cumulative frequency associated with the lowest-valued continuous class limit (listed first in the table).

Note that, for any continuous class limit, the sum of the associated less than cum f_i and more than cum f_i is equal to the total number of scores included in the frequency table, which in this case is 224. For example, for the continuous class limit 109.5, the sum of the less than cum f_i (159) and the more than cum f_i (65) is 224. It will not be difficult for the reader to figure out why this is so.

The cumulative frequency columns are useful in providing certain types of information relating to the scores which are summarized in the frequency table. For example, suppose scores of 99 or less are considered failing, and scores of 100 or more are considered passing. Then, the continuous class limit 99.5 is the dividing point between passing and failing. The associated less than cum f_i tells us that 40 of the 224 scores summarized in the frequency table are failures and the more than cum f_i indicates that 184 are passing scores.

Table 3.3.2 is presented to show various *relative frequency* columns which are often useful. *A relative frequency is a proportion: the proportion of the total frequency (total number of items) included in the table.* The frequencies presented in Table 3.3.1 are *absolute* frequencies, since they present the actual counts in a given category. For example, Table 3.3.1 shows 29 in the Frequency f_i column for the discrete class 95–99. The *Relative Frequency* p_i column in Table 3.3.2 indicates that these 29 scores make up .129 or 12.9% of the 224 scores included in the table. This proportion is determined by dividing 29 by 224. The p_i column in Table 3.3.2 indicates that .210 or 21.0% of the 224 scores are in the 100–104 class interval, and as much as .322 or 32.2% fall in the 105–109 class interval. Clearly, the total of the p_i column should equal 1.000. However, sometimes this total differs slightly from 1.000, owing to rounding of the proportions computed for the individual class frequencies. It is often considered a good idea to adjust as needed to force the column total to equal 1.000. For example, this column first totaled .999. Therefore, the relative frequency computed for the 105–109 class, which was .321, was adjusted to .322, resulting in a total of 1.000 for the column of proportions. Note that the *largest* p_i was selected for adjusting. This is always done, since a small adjustment results in the least distortion when applied to the largest p_i.

In the same way, the last two columns of Table 3.3.2 express the cumulative frequencies shown in Table 3.3.1 as proportions. *Less than cum* p_i is read as *less than cumulative relative frequency*, each entry in this column expressing the *less than cum* f_i as a proportion of the 224 scores included in the table. For example, the cumulative relative frequency .853 in this column indicates the proportion of the 224 scores which are less than 114.5, the corresponding continuous class limit. *More than cum* p_i stands for *more than cumulative relative frequency*, each entry in this column expressing the *more than cum* f_i as a proportion of the total number of scores included in the frequency table. For example, we may observe that .612 of the scores are more than 104.5, the associated continuous class limit. Furthermore, we can tell from the last two columns in Table 3.3.2 that .946 (94.6%) of the scores are less than 119.5, whereas .054 (5.4%) are more than 119.5.

A considerable amount of information relating to the distribution of the 224 reasoning ability test scores has been developed and exhibited by the summarization and analysis contained in the model frequency table (presented in two parts, Tables 3.3.1 and 3.3.2). The first two columns of Table 3.3.1 are always developed when constructing a frequency table. However, in the typical situation, not all the other columns are developed. Only as many of the other columns as are needed in a given situation should be prepared.

When a frequency table is used to compute measures describing the distribution of the data, one of two equivalent assumptions is made, owing to the loss of information relating to the actual scores included. In some instances, it is assumed that all scores in a class interval are equal to the class midpoint. This has already been noted. Other times, it is assumed that the scores in a class are evenly distributed throughout the class interval. This assumption is made when the continuous class limits are used in making computations based on the frequency table. When these assumptions are used for computations discussed in later chapters, it will be indicated in each case which one of the two assumptions is involved.

PROBLEMS FOR PRACTICE AND REVIEW

1. Given the ten scores 26, 23, 25, 23, 25, 25, 26, 27, 25, 26, construct a simple grouping table.

2. List three ways in which the length of class interval may be computed for a frequency distribution.

3. Indicate two ways in which the class midpoint may be determined for a frequency distribution.

4. Given the discrete class limits 105–109, 110–114, 115–119, 120–124, 125–129, 130–134, determine the class midpoints, continuous class limits, and the length of class interval.

5. Given the discrete class limits 44.00–47.99, 48.00–51.99, 52.00–55.99, 56.00–59.99, 60.00–63.99, 64.00–67.99, 68.00–71.99, determine the class midpoints, continuous class limits, and the class interval.

6. Given the discrete classes .005–.009, .010–.014, .015–.019, .020–.024, .025–.029, determine the class midpoints, continuous class limits, and the class interval.

7. Scores on a reading speed test were summarized into a frequency distribution as follows:

Discrete Class Limits	f_i
0–19	1
20–39	2
40–59	5
60–79	8
80–99	11
100–119	27
	54

Determine:
(a) Continuous class limits
(b) Class midpoints (X_i)
(c) More than cum f_i
(d) Less than cum f_i
(e) Relative class frequencies (p_i)
(f) More than cum p_i
(g) Less tham cum p_i
Arrange your work in the same manner as in Tables 3.3.1 and 3.3.2.

8. Scores on an anxiety scale were grouped into the following frequency distribution:

Discrete Class Limits	f_i
24.0–26.9	3
27.0–29.9	17
30.0–32.9	20
33.0–35.9	30
36.0–38.9	15
39.0–41.9	11
42.0–44.9	4
	100

Determine (a) through (g), as in *Problem* 7.

9. Time required (in seconds) to perform a specified task was recorded for 1000 students and organized into a frequency table, as follows:

Time Required, Seconds	Number of Students
45.00–49.99	25
50.00–54.99	25
55.00–59.99	50
60.00–64.99	70
65.00–69.99	95
70.00–74.99	115
75.00–79.99	170
80.00–84.99	250
85.00–89.99	125
90.00–94.99	75
	1000

Determine (a) through (g), as in *Problem* 7.

10. The distribution of reaction times (seconds) for 50 subjects was recorded, as follows:

Discrete Classes	f_i
1.25–1.49	14
1.50–1.74	11
1.75–1.99	4
2.00–2.24	8
2.25–2.49	13
	50

Determine (a) through (g), as in *Problem* 7.

3.4 CONSTRUCTION OF A FREQUENCY TABLE

Construction of a frequency table begins with a clear understanding of the purposes the table is to serve. For example, if a frequency table is to be prepared for the IQ scores of entering freshmen in a university, an important objective being to make a special review of the distribution of scores between 100 and 115, the frequency table should be constructed so as to permit such review. If grades on an achievement test taken by foreign language majors are to be organized into a frequency table, an important objective being to study in detail the grade distribution of the brighter students, the frequency table should be constructed to present an adequate distribution of the higher grades. Generally, important uses of a frequency table are to study the over-all distribution of the raw data and to provide a tabular summary convenient for computation of various descriptive measures. Our discussion of how to construct a frequency table will take only these uses into consideration, ignoring any special requirements.

However, these are usually important uses of a frequency table even when other requirements also need to be taken into account.

As a general rule, there is no need to organize the raw data into a rank order listing, since this type of organization usually provides little gain in understanding the data. Only occasionally will it be worthwhile to organize the raw data into a simple grouping table. There may be instances when so little is known about the data that simple grouping may be considered a desirable first step. A simple procedure is available to accomplish such grouping. First review the raw data to determine the general order of magnitude of the individual items. We will use the unorganized collection of 224 reasoning ability test scores presented in Table 3.2.1 for our illustration. Note that the lowest scores are in the 80's and the highest in the 120's. Using this information, set up a tally table as shown in Table 3.4.1, part *A*. Scores are tallied in the appropriate cells, using vertical tally strokes.

The first score in Table 3.2.1 is 98. This is tallied in the 98 cell, which is in the 90 row and 08 column. The second score is 105, which is tallied in the cell in the 100 row and 05 column. Each fifth stroke is made horizontally to tie each set of five tallies into a bundle. This facilitates counting after all scores are tallied.

It is a simple matter, after all scores are tallied, to determine the score frequencies, as shown in Table 3.4.1, part *B*. For example, we note from part *A* that there is one tally mark for score 87 (80 row, 07 column). Therefore, we enter 1 in part *B*, row 80, column 07. There are five tally marks for score 93 in part *A*; therefore, enter 5 for this score in part *B*. The total of all cell frequencies in part *B*, of course, should equal 224, the total number of items summarized. This can be used as a check that all items were tallied. The only way to check the tallies in the individual cells is to set up a second tally table and repeat the tallying procedure. Construction of a simple grouping table for the 224 scores can be accomplished immediately from part *B*.

Specifically, set up the two column headings (*Score* and *Frequency*) as in Table 3.2.3 and post the frequency of each score directly from part *B*. Remember to list *all* scores from the lowest to the highest, even if the frequency is 0. Omission may lead to an erroneous impression concerning the score distribution, particularly if there are many scores with 0 frequency. Often, the tally table itself may be sufficient, without the need to set up a simple grouping table, especially if it is planned to further summarize the data into a frequency table. Study of the tally table reveals various characteristics of the score distribution, such as the score range and the scores with the highest frequencies. For example, it is clear from the tally table that the scores in the 100 row generally have the highest frequencies.

Table 3.4.1 TALLY TABLE FOR SIMPLE GROUPING: SCORES ON A REASONING ABILITY TEST FOR 224 SUBJECTS

(*A*)

	00	01	02	03	04	05	06	07	08	09
80								/		/
90		//		卌	//	卌	//	/ 卌 卌	卌	卌 /
100		卌 ////	卌	卌 卌 卌	卌 /// 卌 卌	// 卌 卌	卌 卌 //// 卌 卌	卌 /// 卌 卌	卌 /// 卌 卌	
110	卌 卌	卌 ///	卌 //		卌 //	卌 ///		卌 /	卌 //	
120			卌	卌 /					/	

(*B*)

	00	01	02	03	04	05	06	07	08	09
80								1		1
90		2		5	2	5	2	11	5	6
100		9	5	15	18	12	24	18	18	
110	10	8	7		7	8		6	7	
120			5	6					1	

Usually, a collection of raw data is summarized into a frequency table, without intermediate stages of summarization. Let us begin all over again with the raw data presented in Table 3.2.1. The first step in constructing a frequency table is to determine the number of items in the collection. We note that there are 224 reasoning ability test scores to be summarized. Next, decide on the number of classes to use. Referring to Table 3.2.5, we observe that for 224 scores, nine classes are suggested. Reviewing the raw data in Table 3.2.1, we note that the lowest score is 87 and the highest is 128. This indicates that the range of these data is 41 (the difference between

Table 3.4.2 TALLY TABLE: SCORES ON A REASONING ABILITY TEST FOR 224 SUBJECTS

Discrete Class Limits	Tally	Frequency, f_i
85–89	//	2
90–94	~~////~~ ////	9
95–99	~~////~~ ~~////~~ ~~////~~ ~~////~~ ~~////~~ ////	29
100–104	~~////~~ ~~////~~ ~~////~~ ~~////~~ ~~////~~ ~~////~~ ~~////~~ ~~////~~ ~~////~~ //	47
105–109	~~////~~ ~~////~~ ~~////~~ ~~////~~ ~~////~~ ~~////~~ ~~////~~ ~~////~~ ~~////~~ ~~////~~ ~~////~~ ~~////~~ ~~////~~ ~~////~~ //	72
110–114	~~////~~ ~~////~~ ~~////~~ ~~////~~ ~~////~~ ~~////~~ //	32
115–119	~~////~~ ~~////~~ ~~////~~ ~~////~~ /	21
120–124	~~////~~ ~~////~~ /	11
125–129	/	1

128 and 87). Therefore, if we think in terms of summarizing the 224 scores into nine classes, we must divide the full range of the scores (41) into nine equal parts (intervals). Then, $41 \div 9$ or 4.56 is the approximate length of class interval to use. Let us round this to 5, which is a more convenient class length.

We are now ready to determine the discrete classes. This is accomplished by first selecting the *lowest* discrete class limit. Since 87 is the lowest score, it would seem as if this score should be the one selected. However, it is best to select a round number *equal to or lower than* the lowest score and a multiple of the length of class interval, which in our illustration is 5. Therefore, let us select 85. Then, by successively adding the length of class interval to 85, the *lower* discrete class limits are generated (e.g., 85, 90, 95, 100, etc.). Table 3.4.2 shows how a frequency table is constructed. The first column shows the discrete class limits. Note that the lower class limits are as we have just developed them. Then, the first discrete class becomes 85–89; the second, 90–94, etc. Care should be taken to set up sufficient classes so that the item with the highest value in the collection can fit into the highest discrete class. In the illustration, the highest score is 128 and this score fits into the highest class interval, 125–129.

It will be observed that there are exactly nine classes, the suggested number. However, this does not always occur when following the foregoing procedure. There may be some difference between the number of classes actually used and the number suggested by Table 3.2.5. This is due to several considerations. The length of class interval decided upon and the score selected for the lowest discrete class limit are somewhat arbitrary. Furthermore, a sufficient number of classes must be established so that the highest discrete class can accommodate the highest score in the raw data. Choice of a convenient class length and selection of a suitable score for the lowest discrete class limit may lead to a different number of classes than suggested by Table 3.2.5, if the highest class is to accommodate the highest score.

We must now determine the class frequencies. This is easily accomplished by tallying, as shown in Table 3.4.2. Tallies are recorded in a manner similar to that explained for simple grouping. For example, the first score in Table 3.2.1 is 98. This is tallied in the 95–99 class. The second score is 105, which is tallied in the 105–109 class, etc. The last column in Table 3.4.2 summarizes the tallies into frequencies for each class. The resulting class frequencies are, of course, the same as presented in Table 3.3.1. The total of these class frequencies should equal the total number of scores included in the raw data (224). This can be used to check that all items were tallied. If it is desired to verify the accuracy of the tallies in each class, it is necessary to set up a second tally table and repeat the tallying procedure. The two columns *Discrete Class Limits* and *Frequency* provide all the basic data needed when constructing a frequency table. The other columns presented in the model frequency table (Tables 3.3.1 and 3.3.2) may be derived from these two basic columns of information, as needed.

Certain additional considerations need to be taken into account when constructing a frequency table. *Overlapping* discrete class limits must always be avoided. This occurs when the *upper* limit of one discrete class is the same as the *lower* limit of the next highest discrete class. For example, consider the following discrete classes:

27–30
30–33
33–36
36–39
39–42

The upper limit of the class 27–30 is also the lower limit of the next higher discrete class, 30–33. This leaves in doubt where items with the value 30 are to be included. Are they to be included in the lower class or the higher class? The same question arises in connection with the other overlapping discrete class limits, such as 33, 36, etc. This can be avoided by establishing the discrete classes as 27–29, 30–32, 33–35, etc. Lower discrete class limits should be carefully selected since they stand out more than the upper limits. For example, suppose the following discrete classes were set up:

13–16
17–20
21–24
25–28
29–32

It will be observed that it requires close study for the mind to grasp and retain such limits as 13, 17, etc. Note that the lower limits are not multiples of class length. The class length is four and the lower limits 13, 17, 21, etc., are not multiples of four. Usually, more desirable classes would be

12–15
16–19
20–23
24–27
28–31

The frequency tables discussed so far were made up of classes of equal length. This is preferred when constructing a frequency table. Classes of unequal length present a misleading impression of the distribution of a set of data. For example, consider the following frequency table of weights (pounds):

Discrete Class Limits	Frequency
5.0–9.9	4
10.0–14.9	5
15.0–24.9	6
25.0–34.9	7
35.0–49.9	7

The frequency column gives the impression of a generally rising frequency as you move up to higher weight classes. Closer inspection of the table, however, indicates that the first two classes are of length 5 pounds, and the next two classes are of length 10 pounds. The last class, moreover, has a length of 15 pounds. If the frequency table were reconstructed using classes of equal length (say, 10 pounds), the frequency table following on page 58 might result.

Discrete Class Limits	Frequency
5.0–14.9	9
15.0–24.9	6
25.0–34.9	7
35.0–44.9	5
45.0–54.9	2

This certainly gives a different impression of the distribution of the data.

There are times when it is considered more convenient to use classes of unequal length. This may occur where the high (or low) end of the scale of values for the data stretches out with negligible frequencies. Then it may be convenient to summarize the string of values with very low frequencies into one or two classes. For example, let us examine the number of trials required by each of 45 subjects to perform correctly a certain task, as presented in the following frequency table:

Number of Trials Required	Number of Subjects
1–2	5
3–4	11
5–6	14
7–8	8
9–10	1
11–12	–
13–14	2
15–16	2
17–18	–
19–20	–
21–22	1
23–24	–
25–26	1

It may be considered more convenient to regroup the higher-value classes of the table, resulting in the following frequency table:

Number of Trials Required	Number of Subjects
1–2	5
3–4	11
5–6	14
7–8	8
9–16	5
17–26	2

In this reconstructed table, four classes were combined into the single class interval 9–16, and the last five classes were combined into the 17–26 interval. The reconstructed frequency table is certainly neater looking. However, care is required, when studying such a table, to take into account the variation in length of class interval. Note that, in place of the statistical heading *Discrete Class Limits*, we used the subject-matter heading *Number of Trials Required* and, in place of the statistical heading *Frequency*, we used *Number of Subjects*. This is, of course, preferred since it adds concrete meaning to the data presented. We will often use statistical headings in our illustrations, although not exclusively, in order to emphasize the statistical aspects of what we are doing. Generally speaking, other than for learning purposes, subject-matter headings are to be preferred.

Sometimes *open-end* class intervals are used, especially when the raw data contain a few unusually high or unusually low values. The following frequency table of scores on an aptitude test shows an open-end class at each end of the table:

Scores	Frequency
Under 100	7
100–119	11
120–139	24
140–159	36
160–179	19
180–199	8
200 and over	3

The problem with open-end classes is that there is no way of knowing the range of the scores included. For example, the table indicates that there are seven scores below 100 and three in the 200 and over class. How much below 100 is the lowest of the seven scores? How much above 200 is the highest of the three scores? It is a good idea to add a footnote to such a frequency table to give at least the range of scores involved. It is better if the actual scores included are noted in the footnote. If such tables are to be used for purposes for which both limits of a class are required, estimated class limits will have to be substituted for the unspecified limits. For example, such estimates would be required if it were desired to compute the class midpoints or if certain measures relating to the distribution of the data are to be computed.

The foregoing procedure for construction of a frequency table should be applied *thoughtfully*. There is no such thing as a *single* best-constructed frequency table. The uses to which the frequency table will be put must be carefully considered if the best table for a particular purpose is to be obtained. In our work with frequency distributions, we will always assume that we are dealing with classes of equal length and that there are no open-end class intervals.

Let us apply the procedure we have learned to construct a frequency table for the time required by each of 72 white rats to run through a maze. The raw data (in minutes) are presented in Table 3.4.3. The frequency table is to be used to exhibit the distribution of the data and to compute various measures to describe the distribution. Referring to Table 3.2.5, we find that for 72 items, seven classes are suggested. Reviewing the raw data,

Table 3.4.3 TIME (MINUTES) REQUIRED TO RUN THROUGH A MAZE FOR 72 WHITE RATS

4.50	6.68	6.25	.70	3.92	7.32
4.62	.85	4.64	4.30	1.15	6.24
2.10	.52	3.13	3.06	.67	3.47
1.39	2.09	1.68	1.00	2.96	2.27
1.33	.71	3.01	1.01	3.21	1.84
3.65	7.20	1.15	1.10	.55	.80
.73	3.00	.96	1.29	1.61	2.04
1.41	3.85	.82	.54	1.40	3.27
.56	.75	.94	1.26	.55	4.11
4.48	1.88	.95	7.98	3.31	.85
1.61	.70	.81	1.28	1.21	6.11
1.10	1.78	5.17	6.87	1.23	3.25

we find that the least number of minutes required is .52 and the most is 7.98, indicating a range of 7.46 minutes. Dividing the range by the suggested number of classes (seven), we obtain 1.07 minutes as the approximate class length. Rounding this to 1.00 minute, we have a convenient class length to use. Now we determine the discrete class limits by first deciding on the lowest limit. Since the lowest observed value of the variable (minutes) is .52, then .50 is a convenient and acceptable limit with which to start. (Note that .50 is not an integral multiple of the class length 1.00. However, this length is an integral multiple of .50 which also will result in convenient lower discrete class limits.) Then, by successively adding the class length to .50, lower discrete class limits are generated (.50, 1.50, 2.50, etc.). Table 3.4.4 presents these limits in the first column.

The discrete classes are then determined as .50–1.49, 1.50–2.49, etc. Finally, the class frequencies are determined by tallying. The columns on discrete class limits and class frequencies provide the basic data. Any additional columns needed, as already noted, can be derived from this basic information.

Table 3.4.4 TALLY TABLE: TIME (MINUTES) REQUIRED TO RUN THROUGH A MAZE FOR 72 WHITE RATS

Discrete Class Limits	Tally	Frequency
.50–1.49	~~||||~~ ~~||||~~ ~~||||~~ ~~||||~~ ~~||||~~ ~~||||~~ ||||	34
1.50–2.49	~~||||~~ ~~||||~~	10
2.50–3.49	~~||||~~ ~~||||~~	10
3.50–4.49	~~||||~~ |	6
4.50–5.49	||||	4
5.50–6.49	|||	3
6.50–7.49	||||	4
7.50–8.49	|	1

PROBLEMS FOR PRACTICE AND REVIEW

1. Given the scores on research aptitude for 53 subjects, as follows:

152	155	161	161	151	167
174	157	177	166	158	150
151	158	164	164	152	173
155	158	168	164	178	178
160	155	156	156	161	174
163	152	151	166	152	153
152	153	150	160	158	156
166	156	160	155	167	151
168	150	151	157	153	

(a) Organize the data into a simple grouping table.
(b) Summarize the data into a frequency distribution.
(c) Determine the class midpoints and the relative class frequencies (p_i).

2. Given the following scores on a personality inventory for 49 subjects:

15.48	15.73	15.61	16.23	15.27
16.61	15.81	15.48	16.58	16.45
15.60	16.70	15.89	15.99	15.34
15.26	15.91	15.51	16.45	15.54
15.53	16.27	15.34	16.38	15.74
16.24	15.75	16.12	15.31	16.68
15.32	16.42	16.42	16.11	16.73
16.70	16.68	15.27	16.61	16.45
16.61	16.31	16.58	16.61	15.34
16.02	16.69	16.22	16.06	

(a) Organize the data into a frequency distribution.
(b) Determine the continuous class limits, class midpoints, more than cum f_i.

3. The number of errors made by each of 70 subjects in performing a certain task was recorded, as follows:

24	28	22	29	21	30	23
21	26	27	24	25	25	28
30	25	25	18	24	23	28
23	19	23	26	29	31	31
26	29	27	28	31	26	32
33	24	22	25	24	37	24
22	33	28	24	19	38	23
27	24	19	31	26	29	27
34	28	34	27	34	30	28
25	36	30	25	22	24	20

(a) Construct a frequency distribution.
(b) Determine the continuous class limits, class midpoints, and the less than cum f_i.

4. The number of words misspelled by 113 junior high school pupils was recorded, as follows:

72	128	32	125	130	142	105	158	120
123	152	174	121	152	171	160	162	156
135	172	70	158	123	76	152	29	162
160	151	141	113	143	164	153	55	143
104	164	162	46	148	22	87	158	167
163	40	136	132	134	171	132	144	110
171	123	65	156	119	139	143	178	135
117	80	171	128	94	152	164	95	106
144	110	165	110	166	38	170	151	65
83	59	142	152	121	164	83	164	
151	165	171	176	152	155	178	153	
177	178	176	130	178	178	164	170	
119	154	128	138	98	106	148	98	

(a) Organize these data into a frequency distribution.
(b) Determine the continuous class limits and class midpoints.
(c) Determine the more than cum f_i.
(d) Determine the less than cum f_i.

5. The following scores were obtained in a science aptitude test by 183 second-year biology students:

46.7	76.2	40.3	87.1	49.9	79.0	83.1	65.1	86.0	64.9	86.8	37.2
52.3	86.7	86.0	55.6	93.2	93.3	48.3	65.1	87.1	59.7	97.3	72.8
67.5	64.5	45.2	65.0	84.3	39.1	75.3	84.3	45.0	75.3	57.2	100.0
55.9	72.4	38.3	45.3	68.9	54.2	95.7	62.6	63.5	56.9	67.7	106.9
72.9	63.7	67.0	46.0	63.9	52.0	40.0	30.7	67.1	72.8	106.9	46.9
35.9	76.1	50.2	56.2	59.1	34.0	64.6	40.3	72.6	63.5	75.3	63.5
63.3	47.0	62.4	37.0	67.2	44.7	72.5	46.2	64.8	93.3	67.7	32.9
58.7	67.7	58.8	64.7	40.3	67.4	70.0	57.5	49.9	64.6	76.4	
72.1	64.3	65.2	30.7	40.1	83.7	66.9	56.3	59.4	84.2	40.1	
49.9	76.2	62.9	75.0	55.7	56.3	64.9	62.5	67.7	31.2	87.6	
77.2	64.3	40.1	62.6	78.2	49.9	66.7	67.3	62.6	76.4	105.1	
78.1	86.8	54.1	77.2	73.3	70.0	57.4	76.4	86.8	86.8	52.6	
87.4	78.2	83.4	56.3	83.3	70.0	97.0	55.8	52.7	94.8	86.9	
90.1	97.0	90.1	90.0	97.0	83.3	105.6	73.4	87.5	59.7	94.9	
62.9	95.9	46.2	94.7	90.1	106.2	108.6	106.8	73.4	104.7	67.5	
46.1	86.7	107.1	108.2	57.4	97.4	104.3	76.3	86.8	83.2	104.1	

(a) Construct a frequency distribution.
(b) Determine the continuous class limits and class midpoints.
(c) Determine the more than cum f_i and the more than cum p_i.
(d) Determine the less than cum f_i and the less than cum p_i.
(e) Determine the relative class frequencies.

6. The following grades were obtained by 325 graduate students in *Educational Research Methods and Procedures:*

81	88	89	91	86	90	85	95	91	90	90	89	84	95	88	95	90	90	84	88
87	90	85	97	90	97	88	95	91	92	89	91	91	90	89	90	93	83	88	82
85	97	83	91	88	97	91	82	91	92	85	92	88	96	87	90	97	93	85	
86	87	84	86	91	91	88	88	91	91	96	92	92	86	93	86	92	89	92	
81	89	85	90	90	85	94	84	89	96	88	82	86	92	92	92	92	87	89	
84	90	91	87	89	91	85	82	88	92	91	87	93	82	93	83	87	87	89	
84	89	80	97	83	90	85	87	89	92	87	94	86	89	87	91	91	91	91	
80	90	83	92	86	91	86	83	91	83	92	85	89	89	93	85	89	97	85	
87	87	83	87	84	90	82	91	82	88	88	90	88	98	83	91	88	89	92	
80	89	89	89	96	91	90	85	94	85	87	90	82	88	93	84	87	92	92	
84	90	81	90	90	86	90	81	91	88	86	89	92	85	94	88	94	94	82	
97	90	80	88	96	88	91	85	90	83	92	85	94	93	87	88	86	89	95	
80	87	84	92	81	84	91	88	91	97	88	89	95	95	82	93	92	95	89	
87	90	92	94	92	91	90	90	90	94	96	83	96	85	97	93	97	95	89	
84	96	80	87	94	93	94	88	92	86	89	92	86	94	95	86	92	86	93	
81	89	93	93	94	93	89	94	94	83	96	90	96	83	93	93	95	93	95	
80	89	80	92	88	94	94	81	90	96	84	93	93	90	94	93	92	88	93	

(a) Construct a frequency distribution.
(b) Determine the continuous class limits and class midpoints.
(c) Determine the more than cum f_i.
(d) Determine the less than cum f_i.

7. The scores on the opposite page (in minutes) were obtained by 250 subjects in a speed test:

(a) Organize these data into a frequency distribution.
(b) Determine the continuous class limits and class midpoints.
(c) Determine the less than cum f_i and the less than cum p_i.
(d) Determine the more than cum f_i and the more than cum p_i.
(e) Determine the relative class frequencies.

3.5 GRAPHIC REPRESENTATION

Graphic representation of a frequency distribution, as exhibited in a frequency table, assists in defining the shape of the distribution. Figures 3.5.1, 3.5.2, and 3.5.3 present the three types of graphs usually constructed from a frequency table. The particular graphs presented are based on the model frequency distribution in Tables 3.3.1 and 3.3.2. Figure 3.5.1

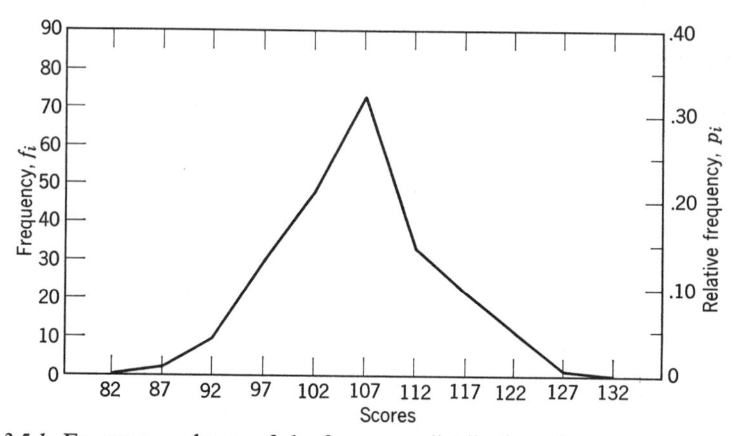

Fig. 3.5.1. Frequency polygon of the frequency distribution of scores on a reasoning ability test for 224 subjects.

presents the *frequency polygon*. The horizontal axis (*abscissa*) contains the score scale, with the class midpoints specifically marked off on it. Observe that the midpoint for a class below the lowest class is also marked off (82), as well as the midpoint for a class above the highest class (132). These are determined, respectively, by deducting the length of class interval (5) from the lowest midpoint (87) and adding this length to the highest midpoint (127). A frequency scale is marked off on the left vertical axis (*ordinate*). The frequency for each class is plotted by placing a dot directly above the class midpoint, at the proper height corresponding to the frequency, and the dots are connected by straight lines. (Sometimes it is desirable to mark off *relative frequencies*, as indicated in the right vertical scale. Then, the

57.23	60.00	61.07	46.18	66.92	53.43	68.07	50.78	74.85	61.38	42.37	56.20	65.68	75.83	63.73	50.79	42.15
70.60	70.71	67.60	70.59	72.93	54.41	63.00	74.90	63.31	75.30	70.77	75.29	75.77	64.67	75.98	53.57	43.21
71.63	71.94	55.99	72.89	61.46	72.93	62.41	67.89	57.37	66.57	42.23	70.97	63.37	75.98	67.78	62.83	75.99
64.07	42.16	69.52	71.65	56.44	74.88	69.46	53.11	73.95	74.96	54.62	75.68	64.58	50.91	65.71	51.93	67.43
57.02	69.74	68.27	57.45	73.97	40.01	72.47	56.10	74.89	46.92	63.24	64.49	74.99	70.41	63.52	61.78	64.92
68.03	72.31	66.42	73.01	57.55	73.97	69.50	68.13	61.23	66.38	48.09	70.98	60.56	70.99	75.96	57.00	57.36
54.60	73.29	52.37	61.29	69.89	60.37	60.08	54.64	67.92	54.79	57.49	63.39	70.46	63.48	75.98	61.19	75.99
71.53	71.93	53.39	68.04	47.91	62.43	68.24	71.77	62.30	64.30	50.00	65.59	43.97	70.48	75.98	50.11	67.52
43.78	68.28	60.42	72.56	64.11	57.32	68.21	66.90	40.05	70.99	57.56	56.13	69.27	74.83	63.92	59.93	65.00
69.63	56.09	73.46	70.56	52.21	68.15	48.04	69.99	53.57	67.58	67.95	54.00	66.59	71.43	71.47	58.09	44.00
69.71	49.99	62.35	43.16	72.00	61.59	67.96	57.15	64.24	62.50	62.99	62.53	71.00	69.37	75.72	62.78	
68.48	71.91	54.01	71.95	65.31	49.21	60.91	68.19	65.99	69.44	52.41	70.31	52.49	74.67	65.99	44.15	
60.73	72.00	67.96	60.12	68.93	70.34	43.57	69.16	54.33	68.39	48.02	69.24	67.01	66.67	75.98	64.81	
72.25	69.00	72.79	72.57	66.79	65.47	69.09	73.64	61.11	65.48	71.79	68.42	73.58	74.99	57.14	67.11	
65.09	70.40	42.11	70.38	71.80	71.86	73.77	57.39	73.97	73.84	66.92	74.62	60.60	74.71	63.98	59.91	

relative frequencies would be plotted above the midpoints, instead of the frequencies.)

It is customary to close the frequency polygon at both ends. This is accomplished at the low end by connecting the dot above the lowest midpoint in the frequency table (87) to the dot (at 0 frequency) for the added lower midpoint (82). At the high end, the dot above the highest midpoint in the frequency table (127) is connected to the dot (at 0 frequency) for the added higher midpoint (132). Plotting the *total class frequency* above the class midpoint means that *construction of the frequency polygon is based on the assumption that all scores included in a class are equal to the class midpoint.* The assistance afforded by this type of graphic presentation to exhibit the shape of the frequency distribution is apparent.

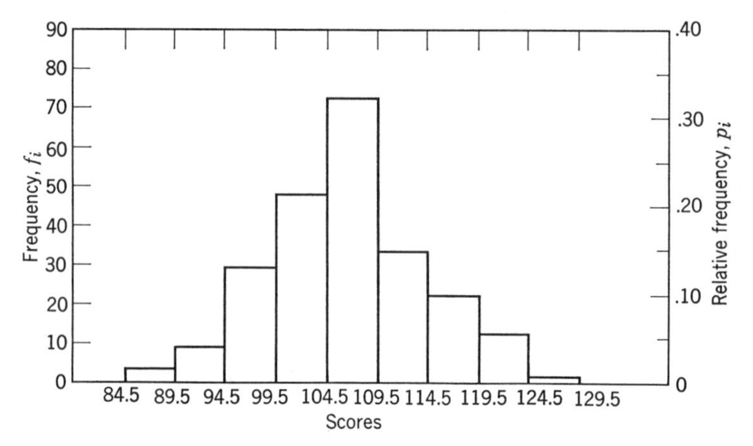

Fig. 3.5.2. Histogram of the frequency distribution of scores on a reasoning ability test for 224 subjects.

Figure 3.5.2 presents a *histogram* of the frequency distribution of reasoning ability test scores. The score scale along the abscissa is marked off to identify the continuous class limits. The ordinate (left scale) presents a scale of class frequencies. The frequency for each class is plotted as a *horizontal line* over the *full* length of the class interval (from lower continuous class limit to upper continuous class limit) at the proper height corresponding to the frequency. The ends of this horizontal line are connected by vertical lines to the corresponding continuous class limits marked off on the abscissa. The histogram has the appearance of a bar chart, with the bars of equal width (equal class intervals) closely positioned. There is no space between bars because *continuous* class limits are used, thereby eliminating gaps between the class intervals. Since the total class frequency is plotted as a horizontal line over the full length of the class interval, *construction of a histogram implies the assumption that the scores included in a class are evenly distributed over the class interval.*

The *area* of each rectangular bar in a histogram represents the class frequency. This is in contrast to the frequency polygon in which the *height* of the dot above the class midpoint represents the class frequency. Of course, with equal class intervals, as in our illustration, the height of the bar also represents the class frequency. However, it is more useful to think in terms of areas. The area of the first bar represents the two scores contained in the 84.5–89.5 continuous class interval. The area of the second bar represents the nine scores contained in the next highest class. We may also think in terms of contiguous areas made up of adjacent bars. For example, the area under the histogram between 84.5 and 104.5 (as defined by the corresponding bars) represents 87 scores. The area under the *entire* histogram (all bars) represents the total number of scores summarized in the frequency table (224).

The right-hand ordinate scale in Figure 3.5.2 indicates the *relative frequency* or proportion of the total frequency included in a class interval. For example, the area of the bar for the 99.5–104.5 class accounts for .210 of the total number of scores summarized in the frequency table. Or, as it is often stated, this area makes up 21.0% of the total area under the histogram. Noting the combined area of adjacent bars, we may observe that 67.5% of the total area under the curve (histogram) is contained between the continuous limits 99.5 and 114.5. In other words, 67.5% of the 224 reasoning ability test scores are between 99.5 and 114.5. Clearly, the total relative frequency under the entire histogram (sum of the relative frequencies represented by each bar) is equal to 1.000 or 100.0%. *The use of areas under a curve, such as a histogram, to represent frequencies and especially relative frequencies, is a basic notion in statistical inference*, as will become apparent in later chapters.

Figure 3.5.3 presents the *ogive*, which is a graphical representation of the cumulative frequencies. Two ogives are presented. One is for the *More than cum* f_i and the other is for the *Less than cum* f_i. The score scale along the abscissa is marked off to show the continuous class limits. The ordinate (left side) presents a scale of cumulative frequencies. Each cumulative frequency, as shown in the cumulative frequency columns in Table 3.3.1, is plotted above the corresponding continuous class limit at the proper height and the plotted points are connected by straight lines. It will be observed that the *Less than cum* f_i curve begins at 0 frequency for the lowest continuous class limit (84.5) and rises continuously to 224 (the total number of scores summarized in the frequency table) for the highest continuous class limit (129.5), as noted in the corresponding cumulative frequency column in Table 3.3.1. The ogive for the *More than cum* f_i, on the other hand, begins with the highest cumulative frequency (224) for the lowest continuous class limit (84.5) and declines continuously to 0 frequency for the highest continuous class limit (129.5). The right-hand ordinate scale shows the *relative cumulative frequency* scale from 0 to 1.00 and is to be used when plotting the relative cumulative frequencies presented in the appropriate columns in Table 3.3.2.

The three graphs presented serve to introduce the usual methods used to exhibit the distribution of data summarized in a frequency table. Although

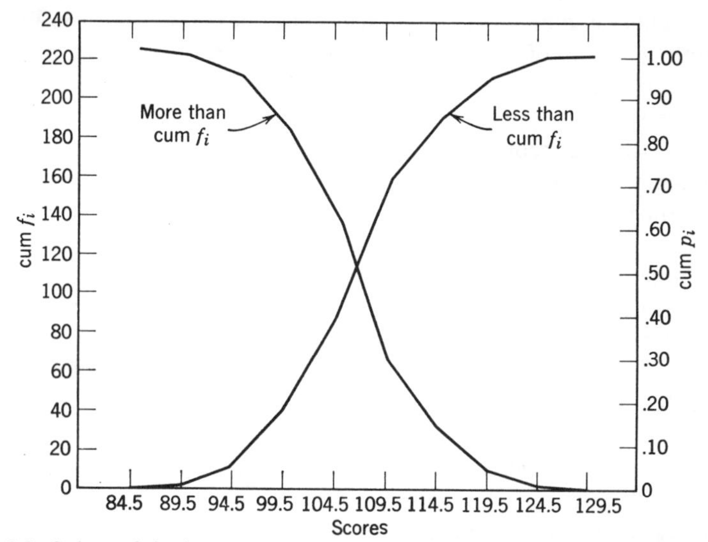

Fig. 3.5.3. Ogives of the frequency distribution of scores on a reasoning ability test for 224 subjects.

each graph presents two ordinate scales (frequency and relative frequency), usually it is necessary to use only one. Clearly, the distribution will look exactly the same, no matter which scale is used. The one selected will depend on whether it is desired to emphasize the frequencies or the relative frequencies associated with each class interval. In certain instances it may be desirable to show both scales, as was done in the illustrative graphs presented.

The shape of a frequency distribution may be expected to vary for different sets of data summarized into frequency tables. Figures 3.5.4 through 3.5.10 present the histogram, part *A*, and the less than cumulative frequency ogive, part *B*, for various distribution types. Figure 3.5.4 presents a *rectangular distribution* in which the class frequencies are all equal. This is also called a *uniform distribution.* The histogram presents bars of equal height, indicating that the class frequencies (and relative frequencies) are

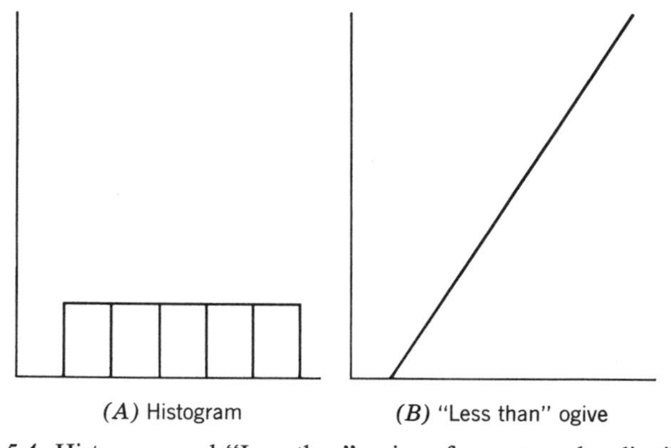

(A) Histogram (B) "Less than" ogive

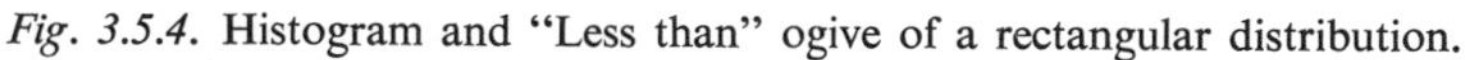

Fig. 3.5.4. Histogram and "Less than" ogive of a rectangular distribution.

equal. The ogive appears as a straight line, reflecting the equal amounts by which the cumulative frequency increases from the lowest continuous class limit to the highest continuous class limit.

Figure 3.5.5 presents a *symmetrical distribution with a central peak.* That is, if a vertical line is drawn through the midpoint of the middle class interval in part *A*, the histogram would be divided into two equal parts in such a way that each half is a mirror-image of the other. In this distribution, class frequencies continuously decline as one moves away from the middle class interval in either direction. The ogive presents an S-shape, reflecting the rise in class frequencies up to the middle class and the decline thereafter. Since cumulative frequencies are determined by adding frequencies, class by class, this decline in class frequencies shows up in the ogive as a slower rise (or a flattening) at the upper end of the curve.

Figure 3.5.6 presents a *skewed distribution.* It will be observed from the histogram that the class containing the highest frequency is not centrally

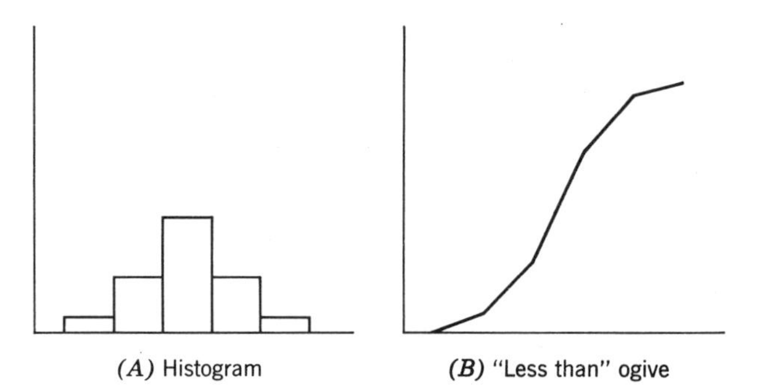

(A) Histogram (B) "Less than" ogive

Fig. 3.5.5. Histogram and "Less than" ogive of a symmetrical distribution with a central peak.

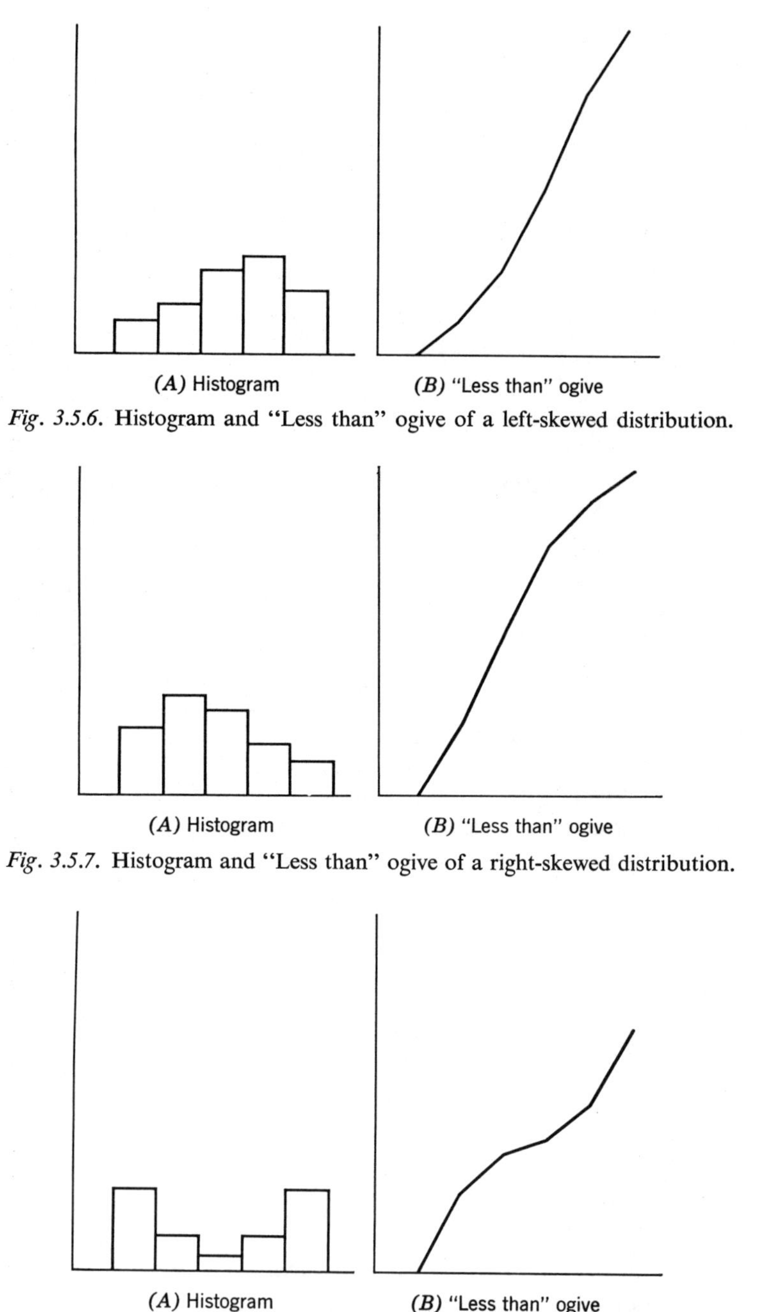

Fig. 3.5.6. Histogram and "Less than" ogive of a left-skewed distribution.

Fig. 3.5.7. Histogram and "Less than" ogive of a right-skewed distribution.

Fig. 3.5.8. Histogram and "Less than" ogive of the U-distribution.

located and that class frequencies continuously decline in either direction from this class. Moreover, the classes stretch out further in the downward direction, forming what may be called a "tail" of the distribution. Since this tail is in the left-hand portion of the histogram, this is called a *left-skewed distribution* or a *negatively skewed* distribution. The ogive appears S-shaped, with the top part cut off. This reflects the lack of a "tail" in the

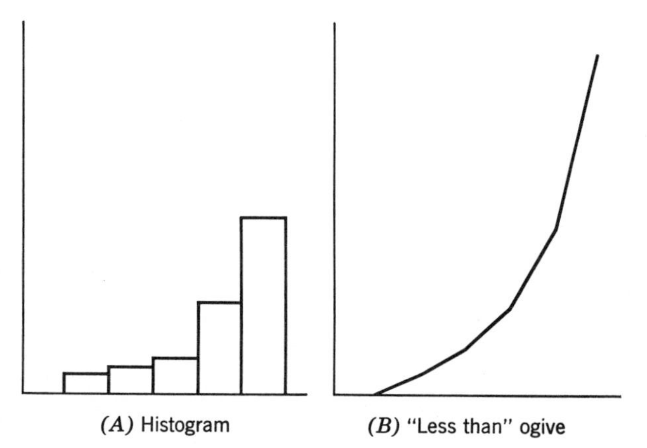

(A) Histogram *(B)* "Less than" ogive

Fig. 3.5.9. Histogram and "Less than" ogive of the J-distribution.

upper end of the histogram. Figure 3.5.7 presents a *right-skewed* or *positively skewed distribution.* This distribution has the "tail" in the upper end of the histogram and is a mirror-image of a left-skewed distribution. The ogive appears S-shaped, with the bottom part cut off, reflecting the lack of a "tail" in the lower end of the histogram.

Figure 3.5.8 presents a *U-distribution.* This is a symmetrical distribution, with class frequencies declining continuously as you move toward the middle of the distribution from either end. The histogram has the general shape of the letter U. The ogive tends to flatten (or rise more slowly) in the middle, reflecting the lower frequencies of the middle classes, as shown in the histogram.

Figure 3.5.9 presents a *J-distribution*, so-called because class frequencies rise continuously from the lowest class interval to the highest in such a way that the histogram resembles the letter J. The ogive rises, first slowly and then rapidly, reflecting the rising class frequencies as indicated in the histogram. Figure 3.5.10 presents the mirror-image of a J-distribution. As indicated in the histogram, the lowest class has the highest frequency. As you move up, class frequencies decline continuously. As a result of this pattern of frequencies, the ogive rises sharply, then tends to flatten out.

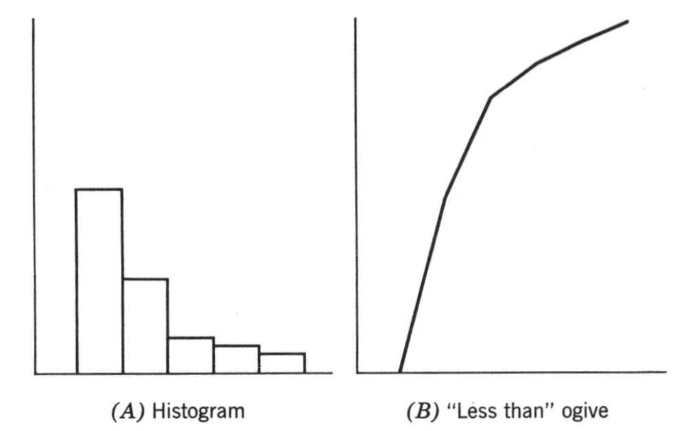

(*A*) Histogram (*B*) "Less than" ogive

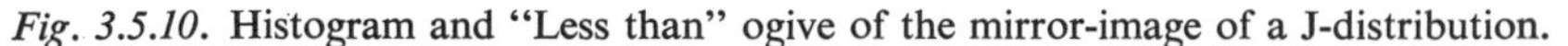

Fig. 3.5.10. Histogram and "Less than" ogive of the mirror-image of a J-distribution.

The distributions presented are meant to illustrate some of the distribution types which may be encountered by students in psychology and education. It is useful for the reader to observe the relationship between the pattern of class frequencies as presented in the histogram and the shape of the corresponding less than cumulative frequency ogive. Of course, we could just as well have studied and compared these distributions by presenting the frequency polygons and the corresponding more than cumulative frequency ogives.

PROBLEMS FOR PRACTICE AND REVIEW

1. Construct: (a) histogram, (b) frequency polygon, (c) more than ogive for the frequency distribution in Problem 7 (following Section 3.3).

2. Construct: (a) histogram, (b) frequency polygon, (c) less than ogive for the frequency distribution in Problem 8 (following Section 3.3).

3. Construct: (a) histogram, (b) frequency polygon, (c) more than ogive, (d) less than ogive for the frequency distribution in Problem 9 (following Section 3.3).

4. Construct a histogram for the frequency distribution in Problem 10 (following Section 3.3).

5. Construct: (a) histogram, (b) frequency polygon, (c) more than ogive, (d) less than ogive for the frequency distribution constructed in Problem 4 (following Section 3.4).

6. Construct: (a) histogram, (b) frequency polygon, (c) more than ogive, (d) less than ogive for the frequency distribution constructed in Problem 5 (following Section 3.4).

7. Construct: (a) histogram, (b) frequency polygon, (c) more than ogive, (d) less than ogive for the frequency distribution constructed in Problem 6 (following Section 3.4).

8. Construct: (a) histogram, (b) frequency polygon, (c) more than ogive, (d) less than ogive for the frequency distribution constructed in Problem 7 (following Section 3.4).

3.6 THE UNDERLYING DISTRIBUTION

Statistical methods, whether descriptive or inductive, are directed toward description of a distribution. *The idea of a distribution provides the basis for development of all statistical methods.* Statistical methods deal with more than one kind of distribution. For example, we have been discussing *frequency distributions.* In later chapters, we will encounter *probability distributions* and *sampling distributions.*

From the statistical point of view, any interest in a set of data relates to the distribution underlying the data. In the case of population data, the statistician is interested in various measures which characterize the distribution of the data. For example, in the case of a population of IQ scores, from the statistical point of view, the interest may be in the average score, how much variation there is among the scores, or the score range.

In the case of sample data, the statistician is interested in various measures which characterize the distribution *in the population from which the sample was selected.* As an illustration, suppose an educational research worker selects a sample of college seniors and asks each senior whether: (1) he plans to take a job in industry or government; (2) he plans to continue with his education; or (3) he has other plans. The research worker is interested in the sample information only in so far as it can be used to estimate the distribution of the population (say, all college seniors in the United States) with respect to these three categories. That is, he is interested in estimating how many college seniors *in the population* fall into each category.

Construction of a frequency table allows considerable room for discretion. Differences in how a set of data is summarized into a frequency table affect the appearance of the distribution as exhibited by the table. For example, the use of fewer classes may be expected to result in a different pattern of class frequencies than if a larger number of classes is used, even though the distributions exhibited by the tables will tend to have the same general shape.

Figure 3.6.1 presents the histograms for three different degrees of summarization of a set of data. In each histogram, the class frequencies are noted just above the rectangular bars representing the classes. There are 20 classes in part *A*, 10 classes in part *B*, and 5 classes in part *C*. The irregularity in the pattern of class frequencies is reduced as the data are condensed into fewer and fewer class intervals. However, it will be observed that the general shape of a positively skewed distribution is discernable in all three histograms. That is, the distribution of the data shows a general tendency for the frequencies to increase up to a point and then to decrease, stretching out into a tail in the upper end of the distribution. Even in part *A*, where 20 class intervals are used and the pattern of class frequencies is quite irregular, the general appearance of a positively skewed distribution

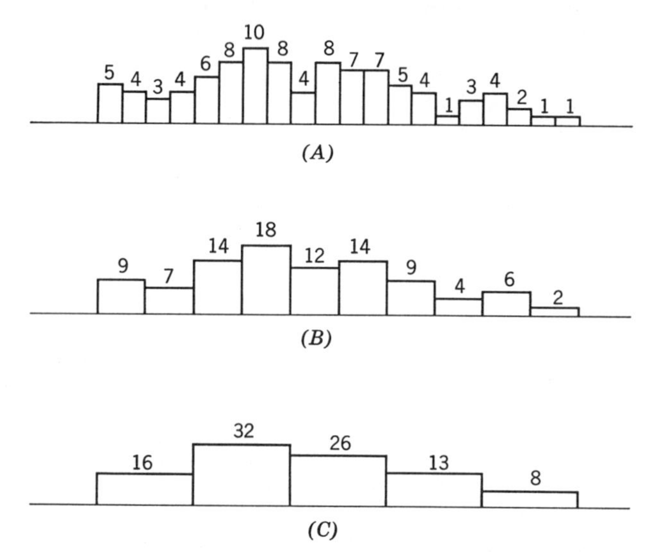

Fig. 3.6.1. Change in pattern of class frequencies as the number of classes are reduced.

is discernable. Clearly, the shape of the distribution is considerably sharper in part *C*, where five classes are used, than in part *A* or part *B*.

While the distribution of a set of data can be exhibited by a variety of histograms, a collection of data has a specific distribution. In the case of a set of scores or other items comprising a *population*, the simple grouping table presents the true distribution. Simple grouping identifies the specific item values occurring in the population and the frequencies with which they occur. The proper graphic representation of the distribution of data organized into a simple grouping table is a *bar chart*. For example, Figure 3.6.2 presents a bar chart of the simple grouping table of scores on a psychometric test. Observe that the bars are separated, reflecting the discontinuities of the discrete scale of measurement in which recorded data are expressed.

The width of the bars is of no particular significance. However, the bars must be of equal width and spaced at unit intervals, with spaces reserved for items with zero frequency. For example, the bar chart in Figure 3.6.2 indicates that the scores range from a low of 28 to a high of 42 and the scores of 29, 36, 38, and 40 have zero frequency. The height of each bar indicates the frequency of a given score. For example, the height of the bar at score 32 indicates that ten subjects obtained that score. The frequency is read from the left vertical scale, while the relative frequency is read from the right vertical scale. Of course, it is not necessary to show *both* frequency and relative frequency scales.

In the typical situation, the number of different scores making up a set of population data is large and score frequencies are often small and highly

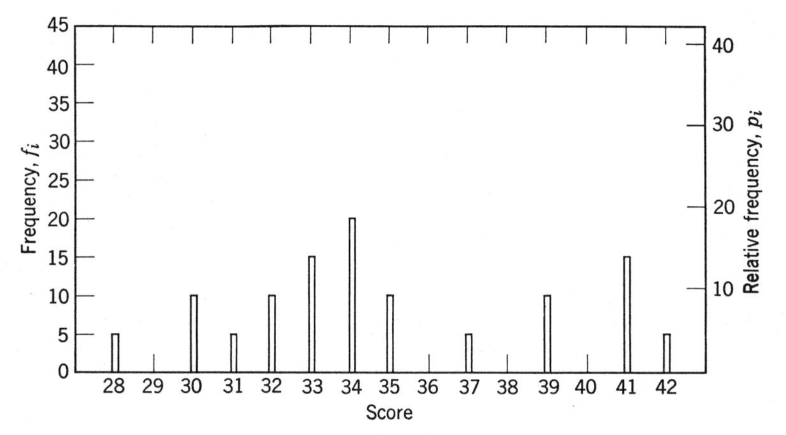

Fig. 3.6.2. Bar chart of the simple grouping table of scores on a psychometric test.

irregular. A simple grouping frequency table, under such circumstances, looks "stretched out" in both table and bar chart form, making it difficult to discern the nature of the distribution of the data. Hence, to assist the eye in visualizing the distribution underlying the data, further summarization into a frequency table using fewer classes is required, as discussed earlier in this chapter.

Either a frequency polygon or a histogram could be used to exhibit the distribution graphically. The histogram is generally preferred since its use reflects the assumption that the items in a class are evenly distributed over the class interval. While this assumption usually is not entirely true, it is, as a rule, more representative of the item distribution within a class than the assumption that all items in a class are equal to the class midpoint. Furthermore, an important property of the histogram is that areas under the curve represent frequencies or relative frequencies. It is sometimes considered helpful to approximate the histogram with a smooth, continuous curve. This is illustrated in Figure 3.6.3. The continuous curve may be sketched freehand and, for many purposes, this is adequate. Sometimes it is desirable to use a curve mathematically fitted to the data to approximate the shape of the distribution. However, a continuous curve, whether freehand or mathematical, only approximates the distribution of a given set of population data.

In the case of *sample* data, the distribution exhibited by a histogram may be considered representative of the distribution in the population from which the sample was selected. However, when dealing with sample data, it is always a question whether the observed pattern of class frequencies is characteristic of the population or merely a charactersitic of the

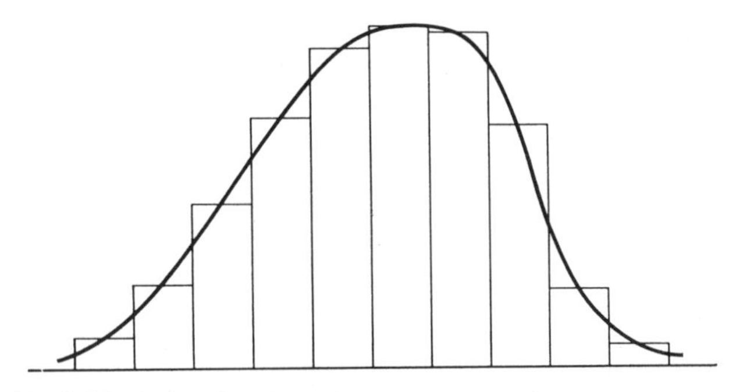

Fig. 3.6.3. Approximating a histogram with a continuous curve.

particular set of sample data under study. It is customary when dealing with sample data to utilize a theoretical distribution of an infinite population to represent the population under study. Sometimes a discrete theoretical distribution is appropriate, such as the *binomial population distribution.* In other cases, a continuous theoretical distribution is appropriate, such as the *normal distribution.* These theoretical distributions are presented and discussed in Chapter 8.

Figure 3.6.4 presents the process by which a theoretical continuous distribution curve is developed. Part *A* shows a histogram for a set of data. We know that, if the number of classes is increased for a given set of data, the pattern of class frequencies will tend to become more and more irregular. This, of course, reflects the reduction in class frequencies as the number of classes is increased. However, suppose the total number of items is also increased; then, it should not be expected that the greater number of classes would be accompanied by an increased irregularity in the pattern of class frequencies. Quite the contrary, as indicated in part *B*, the larger total number of items would tend to fill out the narrower classes, resulting in a *smoother* pattern of class frequencies.

If the total number of items is considered to be continuously increased, while the length of class interval is continuously decreased, the pattern of class frequencies would tend to become smoother and smoother, as indicated in part *C*. If we visualize class lengths becoming infinitesimally small (so that the bar representing a class interval may be visualized as a thin vertical line), while the total number of items becomes indefinitely large (infinite), it is easy to see that the outline of the histogram tends to become perfectly smooth. Carrying this process to the limit results in the continuous distribution curve presented in part *D*.

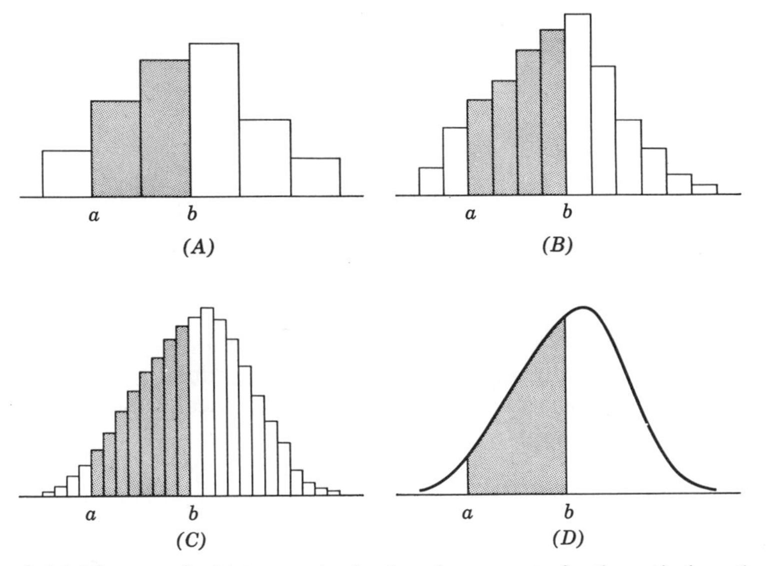

Fig. 3.6.4. The use of a histogram to develop the concept of a theoretical continuous distribution.

The continuous distribution curve just developed is a theoretical concept and is determined mathematically. Let us point out a most important aspect of such theoretical distribution curves. We have learned that the area under a histogram is equal to 1.00 or 100% and that the proportion of the area contained between two continuous class limits represents the relative frequency or the proportion of the total number of items which are included between the two limits. For example, in Figure 3.6.4, part *A*, the proportion of the total area which is shaded represents the relative frequency of the total distribution included in the range *a* to *b*. This relationship between the area under the curve and the relative frequency continues to hold for all the parts of the figure. More specifically, in the continuous distribution curve, part *D*, the total area under the curve is also equal to 1.00 or 100%. Furthermore, the proportion of the area under this curve between any two limits represents the relative frequency of the items which fall in the interval determined by these limits. In part D, the proportion of the total area included between a and b (shaded area) represents the relative frequency of items with values in the range a to b.

In a continuous distribution curve, *any* point along the abscissa can be designated as a limit and the proportion of the area contained between any two limits represents a relative frequency. As an additional illustration, suppose, in part D, that the area to the left of a makes up 7% of the total area under the curve. This indicates that 7% of the total number of items has a value less than a. *Interpretation of areas under a continuous distribution curve as relative frequencies is of paramount importance in statistical inference.* More will be said about this in later chapters.

3.7 NOMINAL AND ORDINAL SCALE DATA

The discussion of data organization and frequency distributions so far presented is applicable only to interval and ratio scale data. The attention given to class limits and length of class interval implies an ability to assign a numerical value to each item and to measure the distance between item values. These properties are found only in interval and ratio scale data.

How do we go about organizing nominal and ordinal scale data and constructing frequency distributions? Actually, the problem here is considerably simpler. Suppose we have the records of 237 graduate students in a given college, showing each student's major subject, in addition to other information. Let us suppose that the college president wishes to know how these students are distributed by major subject, a nominal scale. All that is required is to sort the records by major and count the number of students in each major category. A more convenient procedure, in many instances, is to set up a tally table as indicated in Table 3.7.1. (This is similar to the tally table presented for interval and ratio scale data in Table 3.4.2.) After tallying and determining the class frequencies (f_i), a frequency distribution table may be set up as indicated in Table 3.7.2. This table also presents a relative frequency column (p_i), which is often used to add to the informative value of the table.

Note that the major subjects are listed in alphabetical order. This is not necessary, although it is often a convenient arrangement since it facilitates finding a particular subject. However, sometimes it might be more useful to arrange the subjects in some other order. For example, it may be helpful to group the subjects into certain major areas, such as social sciences, physical sciences, etc. The arrangement of the subjects should be determined by the purposes for which the table is constructed. Furthermore, depending on the needs involved, the nominal scale (subject categories) may be refined into more definite classes, thus establishing a different,

Table 3.7.1 TALLY TABLE: DISTRIBUTION OF 237 GRADUATE STUDENTS BY MAJOR SUBJECT

Major Subject	Tally	Frequency, f_i
Accounting	𝍸 𝍸 𝍸 𝍸 𝍸	25
Biology	𝍸 𝍸 𝍸 /	16
Chemistry	𝍸 𝍸 𝍸 ////	19
Economics	𝍸 𝍸 𝍸 𝍸	20
Education	𝍸 𝍸 𝍸 𝍸 𝍸 𝍸 //	32
Mathematics	𝍸 𝍸 𝍸 𝍸 /	21
Physics	𝍸 𝍸 𝍸 𝍸 //	22
Psychology	𝍸 𝍸 𝍸 𝍸 𝍸 𝍸 𝍸 ///	38
Sociology	𝍸 𝍸 𝍸 ///	18
Statistics	𝍸 𝍸 𝍸 𝍸 𝍸 /	26

more refined nominal scale. For example, if useful for the purposes intended, "physics" may be divided into nuclear physics, biophysics, etc. It is only necessary that the essential property of a nominal scale be preserved. That is each class should be distinct, with no overlapping between classes.

Table 3.7.3 presents a frequency distribution table summarizing the attitudes of 430 voters toward a certain issue. The attitude scale represents an ordinal scale, since successive categories imply more or less feeling toward the issue. Such tables can be most easily constructed from the raw data by the tallying method illustrated in Table 3.7.1. In the case of

Table 3.7.2 FREQUENCY DISTRIBUTION OF 237 GRADUATE STUDENTS BY MAJOR SUBJECT

Major Subject	Frequency, f_i	Relative Frequency, p_i
Accounting	25	.11
Biology	16	.07
Chemistry	19	.08
Economics	20	.08
Education	32	.14
Mathematics	21	.09
Physics	22	.09
Psychology	38	.15
Sociology	18	.08
Statistics	26	.11

Table 3.7.3 FREQUENCY DISTRIBUTION OF 430 VOTERS BY ATTITUDE TOWARD A CERTAIN ISSUE

Attitude	Frequency, f_i	Relative Frequency, p_i
Very much opposed	63	.15
Opposed	94	.22
Neutral	23	.05
In favor	132	.31
Very much in favor	118	.27

ordinal scale data, the ordering of the categories is largely determined by the scale itself. For example, the categories should be listed to reflect the proper sequence of attitude, as shown in Table 3.7.3. It would not be useful to rearrange the order, say, as follows: opposed, neutral, very much opposed, etc. Clearly, it is quite illogical to list "neutral" between "opposed" and "very much opposed." A useful alternative arrangement of categories is to reverse the listing order shown in the table: that is, very much in favor, in favor, etc. The relative frequency (p_i), as well as class frequency (f_i), is presented in the table to add to the information provided.

The graphing devices presented for interval and ratio scale data (histogram, frequency polygon, ogive) are not suitable for nominal scale data. A useful form of graphic presentation for such data is the *bar chart*. Figure 3.7.1 presents a bar chart for the 237 graduate students in Table 3.7.2. It will be observed that the bars are separated by gaps, since the idea

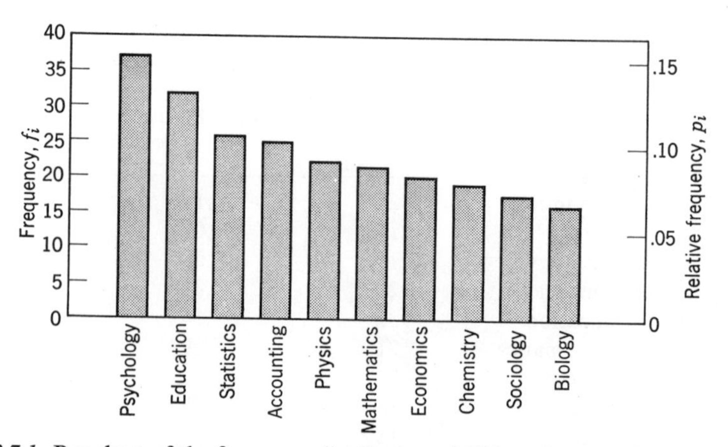

Fig. 3.7.1. Bar chart of the frequency distribution of 237 graduate students, by major subject.

of continuity is not applicable in a nominal scale. The width of a bar and the space between bars have no significance and are selected solely for eye appeal. The subjects are arranged in order of frequency to assist in visualizing the relationship among category frequencies. Other arrangements may be more desirable for particular uses of the chart. For example, if it is desired to study this data by major areas (e.g., social sciences, physical sciences, etc.), it may be more helpful to group the bars accordingly. The best presentation in a bar chart is the one which offers the most assistance to the user of the chart.

In the case of ordinal scale data, the bar chart is also a proper form of graphic presentation of the frequency distribution. However, the logical order of scale categories should be used for the order in which categories are presented in a bar chart, as was discussed for the construction of the frequency table for ordinal scale data. For example, the sequence of attitude categories presented in Table 3.7.3 for the 430 voters should be used if a bar chart is constructed to exhibit the distribution of the voters by attitude category.

PROBLEMS FOR PRACTICE AND REVIEW

1. The following data appear on cards maintained for 50 laboratory animals in an experimental psychology laboratory:

Animal Serial Number	Sex	Type	Learning Category	Response to Drug A
106	M	A	Highest	Strong
110	M	B	Highest	Weak
112	M	D	Low	Weak
119	F	A	High	Weak
123	M	B	Medium	Mild
127	F	B	Low	Very strong
129	F	B	High	Strong
130	M	C	Medium	Very strong
131	F	C	High	Very weak
134	F	B	Highest	Mild
136	M	A	Lowest	Weak
142	F	B	Lowest	Weak
143	F	C	Low	Mild
144	F	C	Highest	Strong
145	F	C	Medium	Very weak
147	F	D	High	Very weak
149	M	B	Medium	Mild
150	M	A	Highest	Strong
151	M	D	Medium	Mild
154	F	D	Medium	Very strong
156	F	C	Low	Strong

Animal Serial Number	Sex	Type	Learning Category	Response to Drug A
157	M	C	Lowest	Weak
159	F	D	High	Very strong
160	F	A	Medium	Strong
162	M	A	Medium	Very weak
163	M	B	Low	Very weak
165	F	B	Low	Weak
167	F	B	High	Mild
172	F	A	Lowest	Mild
173	F	A	Medium	Strong
177	M	D	Low	Very weak
178	M	C	Highest	Mild
179	F	D	Lowest	Very strong
181	M	D	Highest	Very strong
183	M	C	High	Mild
184	M	B	Medium	Strong
185	F	A	Medium	Strong
187	M	B	Low	Weak
188	F	B	Low	Weak
189	M	B	Highest	Mild
190	F	A	Medium	Very strong
193	F	C	High	Very weak
197	M	A	High	Mild
198	F	B	Lowest	Strong
199	F	A	High	Strong
203	M	D	Medium	Weak
204	M	A	Low	Very weak
207	M	D	High	Very weak
208	F	A	High	Mild
212	F	B	Low	Strong

Prepare a frequency table and a bar chart showing the laboratory animals: (a) by sex; (b) by type; (c) by learning category; (d) by response to drug A.

4

MEASURES OF CENTRAL TENDENCY

4.1 INTRODUCTION

Statistical methods provide a variety of measures to describe a distribution. The most often used descriptive measure is one which determines the *central tendency* of the distribution of a set of data. A more popular term for a measure of central tendency is an *average*. People generally talk about the average price, average height, average score, etc. What do we mean by an "average"? Usually, we mean some measure which is *typical* of a set of items or, in some way, *situated in the center* of the items. *Generally, an "average" is a single value which, in some sense, summarizes a set of data*. For example, if we are told that the average IQ of a group of students is 118, this single figure leads us to think of this group as generally bright. We know that not all the students in the group have an IQ of 118. Some have a lower IQ and some have a higher IQ. However, knowledge of the average IQ for the group permits us to gain a general impression of the intelligence level of the group of students as a whole.

Actually, there is more than one average which may be computed for a set of data. We will study three averages: *arithmetic mean*, *median*, and *mode*. The arithmetic mean is by far the most frequently used and most important of the three. The median is also an important type of average, frequently used in the fields of psychology and education. The mode is, generally, the simplest of the three to determine. However, it is of limited value. There are other averages (e.g., *harmonic mean*, *geometric mean*), but they are useful only in special circumstances. It is not worthwhile to take the time in an introductory text to discuss them.

Each of the averages we will study provides a measure of the central tendency of a set of numerical data. However, the notion of central tendency is different in each case. It should be noted that, although all averages may represent "typical values" of a set of data, this is not *always* the case for any average. For example, consider the following four scores: 10, 15, 90, 95. It is possible, of course, to find a central value for these four scores. Such a value would be somewhere between 15 and 90. However, it is clearly impossible to find any single value which is *typical* of all four scores.

4.2 ARITHMETIC MEAN: DEFINITION

When people speak about an average, they nearly always think about the *arithmetic mean.* Statisticians usually refer to the arithmetic mean merely as the *mean.* Suppose we have a set of four scores: 20, 35, 32, 28. The arithmetic mean (or the mean) is computed by adding these scores and dividing the sum (115) by the number of scores in the set (4), resulting in a mean of 28.75. *The arithmetic mean of a set of values is equal to the sum of the values divided by the number of values included in the summation.* We will use the symbol $\bar{X}$ (read "X bar") to represent the mean of a set of sample data, and the symbol μ (the Greek letter mu) to denote the mean of a set of population data. At this point, it may seem unnecessary to have two symbols for the mean. However, later in the text, the usefulness of two symbols will become apparent.

In statistics, as in all branches of mathematics, it is not only convenient, but extremely useful, to express computational procedures in generalized symbolic notation. This facilitates comprehension of the procedure and permits easier application in a variety of problems. The computation of the arithmetic mean of a set of N scores (X_i), in symbolic notation, is

Population
$$\mu = \frac{X_1 + X_2 + X_3 + \cdots + X_N}{N} \tag{4.2.1}$$

$$\mu = \frac{\sum_{i=1}^{N} X_i}{N} \tag{4.2.2}$$

Sample
$$\bar{X} = \frac{X_1 + X_2 + X_3 + \cdots + X_n}{n} \tag{4.2.3}$$

$$\bar{X} = \frac{\sum_{i=1}^{n} X_i}{n} \tag{4.2.4}$$

For population data, we will use N to denote the number of items in the population. In the language of statisticians, we may say that we have a population of size N. As indicated in Equation 4.2.1, the population mean (μ) is determined by adding all N (X_i) values in the population and dividing by N. This procedure is more compactly stated in Equation 4.2.2 by use of the summation notation discussed in Chapter 2, Section 2.6. As an illustration, if we wish to obtain the arithmetic mean for a population of 1000 scores on a personality inventory, we apply Equation 4.2.2 (or Equation 4.2.1), where $N = 1000$ and X_i = personality inventory score. Equation 4.2.2 becomes

$$\mu = \frac{\sum_{i=1}^{1000} X_i}{1000}$$

If these 1000 scores sum to 126,550, we obtain

$$\mu = \frac{126{,}550}{1000} = 126.55$$

For sample data, we will use n to denote the number of items in the sample. That is, we may speak of a sample of size n. Other than the use of $\bar{X}$ instead of μ to denote the arithmetic mean and n instead of N to denote the total number of items included, the equations shown above for sample data are identical to those shown for population data. That is, the arithmetic mean is computed in an identical manner whether dealing with a sample or with the entire population. However, there is an important difference in the *interpretation* of the computed result. In the case of a population, μ is the arithmetic mean for the population and represents a measure of central tendency for the population distribution. The sample mean ($\bar{X}$) may be considered as the arithmetic mean for the set of sample items. When so interpreted, it is similar to the interpretation of μ as the mean for a set of population items. However, as previously noted, when sample data are collected, it is generally not because there is an interest in the particular items which happen to be included in the sample. The interest in a sample is only for the information it can provide about the population from which it was selected.

It has been proven by mathematical statisticians that *the mean* ($\bar{X}$) *computed on the basis of sample data can be interpreted as an estimate of the mean* (μ) *in the population from which the sample was selected.* For example, suppose we obtain the spatial perception test scores for a sample of 50 male students selected from the male enrollment in a large university. We may compute the mean score ($\bar{X}$) for the sample by using Equation 4.2.4 (or Equation 4.2.3), where $n = 50$ and X_i = spatial perception test score. If these 50 scores sum to 4381.50, we obtain $\bar{X} = 4381.50/50 = 87.63$. Using this sample result, we estimate that the mean score (μ) in the population (all male students in the university) is 87.63. This is the usual interpretation of interest when $\bar{X}$ is computed.

It is convenient to abbreviate the notation as much as possible. For this reason, where it is clear what is meant, Equation 4.2.2 may be written as

$$\mu = \frac{\sum X_i}{N} \quad \text{or} \quad \frac{\sum X}{N},$$

and Equation 4.2.4 as

$$\bar{X} = \frac{\sum X_i}{n} \quad \text{or} \quad \frac{\sum X}{n}.$$

Since the arithmetic mean is computed in an identical way, whether you are computing μ or $\bar{X}$, we will continue our discussion by speaking of the mean of a set of data generally, without specifying whether we refer to population data or sample data. Where it is necessary to discuss the arithmetic mean separately for population data and sample data, it will be indicated specifically. Throughout the rest of this chapter, where equations are presented which relate to the mean, the symbol μ will be used. However, in all these cases, the equations are applicable *equally* to the population mean μ and the sample mean $\bar{X}$. The reader will find it very helpful to rewrite each of these equations in terms of $\bar{X}$ by substituting $\bar{X}$ for μ and n for N in each of them.

The reader will find it worthwhile to learn the algebraic proofs presented for many of the equations. These proofs appear in Section 4.10, *Algebraic Notes*. The reason for separate presentation is twofold. First, the simpler presentation made possible by this procedure should assist the reader in learning the relationships expressed by the various equations and in understanding their use and significance. Second, it may be helpful for those readers who have difficulty with algebraic operations to master the material first by ignoring the proofs. Then, on a second reading, study of Section 4.10 could be included. Only the simpler proofs are presented. Study of Section 4.10 will show the reader how algebraic operations and the summation rules are used and, in a substantial way, contribute to the meaning and understanding of the relationships expressed by the equations.

4.3 ARITHMETIC MEAN: SPECIAL SITUATIONS

One of the attractions which makes the arithmetic mean such a frequently used measure of central tendency is the ease with which it can be treated algebraically. That is, the equations for the mean (μ and $\bar{X}$) can be algebraically manipulated in accordance with the needs of a given situation.

Consequently, it is possible to determine special-purpose equations for computing the arithmetic mean which are useful and convenient in special situations. Several special-purpose equations will be presented in this section.

Situation 1: Given a set of N scores, $X_1, X_2, X_3, \ldots, X_N$, with mean μ. If a constant k is added to each score, so that each score becomes $X_i + k$, or, subtracted from each score, so that each score becomes $X_i - k$, the mean of the newly formed scores becomes

$$\mu_{(X+k)} = \mu + k \tag{4.3.1}$$

$$\mu_{(X-k)} = \mu - k \tag{4.3.2}$$

(For proofs see Section 4.10, *Notes* 4.1 *and* 4.2.)

Note that we use the subscript $(X + k)$ to form the convenient symbol $\mu_{(X+k)}$, read "μ sub $(X + k)$," to represent the mean for the newly formed scores $(X_i + k)$. In the same way, $\mu_{(X-k)}$ is used to represent the mean for the newly formed scores $(X_i - k)$. As an illustration, consider the set of 3 scores: 62, 75, 80. Applying Equation 4.2.1, we compute the mean $\mu = (62 + 75 + 80)/3 = 72.3$. Now, suppose each score is increased 5 points, resulting in the 3 larger scores: 67, 80, 85. The mean of these newly formed scores may be computed, according to Equation 4.3.1, as $\mu_{(X+5)} = 72.3 + 5 = 77.3$. We may verify this by computing $\mu_{(X+5)}$ directly as $(67 + 80 + 85)/3 = 77.3$. Suppose, now, that each of the 3 original scores is decreased by 5, resulting in the 3 smaller scores: 57, 70, 75. The mean of these newly formed scores may be computed, using Equation 4.3.2, as $\mu_{(X-5)} = 72.3 - 5 = 67.3$. This may be verified by computing $\mu_{(X-5)}$ directly as $(57 + 70 + 75)/3 = 67.3$.

The special-purpose equations presented for *Situation* 1 are useful in facilitating the computation of the mean in certain situations. For example, suppose it is desired to compute the mean μ for the 8 scores on a word association test presented in Table 4.3.1. We may reduce the computational labor by subtracting some appropriate constant, k, from each score. This will result in the 8 smaller scores, $X_i - k$, which should be easier to handle computationally. Then, compute the mean $\mu_{(X-k)}$ by adding these 8 smaller scores and dividing by 8. Finally, determine μ, the mean of the original X_i scores, as

$$\mu = \mu_{(X-k)} + k \tag{4.3.3}$$

Equation 4.3.3 is obtained by solving Equation 4.3.2 for μ.

We will use this approach to determine the mean μ for the 8 scores in Table 4.3.1. Since 136 is the lowest score, we could subtract this amount

Table 4.3.1 COMPUTATION OF THE MEAN: SCORES ON A WORD ASSOCIATION TEST

	Score, X_i	$X_i - 130$
	147	17
	139	9
	141	11
	136	6
	150	20
	145	15
	146	16
	138	8
Total		102

from each score. Or, we could decide to subtract the round figure 130 from each score. Suppose we choose the latter approach and set up the $X_i - 130$ column shown in the table. Noting that the sum of the 8 $(X_i - 130)$ scores is 102, we compute

$$\mu_{(X-130)} = \frac{102}{8} = 12.75$$

Finally, using Equation 4.3.3, we obtain

$$\mu = 12.75 + 130 = 142.75$$

The reader should verify this result by computing μ directly from the original X_i scores shown in the table.

The process of forming new scores by adding or subtracting a constant is referred to as *transforming* the scores. For example, in Table 4.3.1 we have transformed the score of 147 for subject A to a score of 17. More specifically, we have transformed the scores *by shifting the zero point*. For example, the original score for subject A is 147 units above a possible score of 0. In subtracting 130, we shifted the zero point 130 units *up the scale*, so that a score of 130, when transformed, becomes a score of zero. Consequently, the transformed score (17) is only 17 units above the new zero point. In some texts, a transformation process such as this is called *coding*. That is, 17 is called the coded score for subject A. In the same way, if, say, 100 is *added* to each score in a set, the zero point is shifted 100 units *down the scale*, so that a score of zero now becomes a score of 100. That is, the original score of zero is now 100 units above the new zero point.

Situation 2: Given a set of N scores, $X_1, X_2, X_3, \ldots, X_N$, with mean μ. If each score is multiplied by a constant g, so that each score becomes gX_i or, divided by a constant g, so that each score becomes X_i/g, the mean of the newly formed scores becomes

$$\mu_{gX} = g\mu \tag{4.3.4}$$

$$\mu_{X/g} = \frac{\mu}{g} \tag{4.3.5}$$

(For proofs see Section 4.10, *Notes* 4.3 *and* 4.4.)

As an illustration, consider the set of 4 scores: 24, 30, 36, 18. The mean of these scores is $\mu = 27$. Now, suppose each score is doubled, resulting in the newly formed scores: 48, 60, 72, 36. The mean of these newly formed scores may be determined, according to Equation 4.3.4, as $\mu_{2X} = (2)(27) = 54$. Suppose, on the other hand, these scores are each divided by 2, resulting in the scores: 12, 15, 18, 9. The mean of these smaller scores may be determined, using Equation 4.3.5, as $\mu_{X/2} = \frac{27}{2} = 13.5$.

The special-purpose equations presented in *Situation* 2 are also useful in some situations to reduce the computational labor in obtaining the mean. For example, say it is desired to compute the mean for a set of N scores (X_i), where each score is a large number. The first step is to divide each score by a convenient constant, g, to form the smaller scores X_i/g. Then, compute the mean $\mu_{X/g}$ by adding these N smaller scores and dividing by N. Finally, determine μ, the mean of the original X_i scores, as

$$\mu = g\mu_{X/g} \tag{4.3.6}$$

Equation 4.3.6 is obtained by solving Equation 4.3.5 for μ.

Let us use this approach to obtain the mean μ for the 10 scores on a mechanical skill test presented in Table 4.3.2. We observe that each score is a multiple of 12; therefore, we can reduce the labor of computation by dividing each score by 12 to obtain the $X_i/12$ column of scores shown in the table. Then, noting that the 10 $X_i/12$ scores sum to 37, we compute

$$\mu_{X/12} = \frac{37}{10} = 3.7$$

Finally, using Equation 4.3.6, we obtain

$$\mu = (12)(3.7) = 44.4$$

It is suggested that the reader verify this result by computing μ directly from the original X_i scores shown in the table.

The process of forming new scores by multiplying or dividing by a constant g also constitutes a transformation. However, here we are

Table 4.3.2 COMPUTATION OF THE MEAN: SCORES ON A MECHANICAL SKILL TEST

	Score, X_i	$\frac{X_i}{12}$
	24	2
	48	4
	36	3
	60	5
	24	2
	36	3
	84	7
	72	6
	48	4
	12	1
Total		37

transforming the original scores *by changing the unit of measurement*. For example, the score of 24 for subject A in Table 4.3.2 represents 24 score units, where the unit is 1 point. On the other hand, after transformation, the score of 2 represents 2 units, where each unit is equal to 12 points. This may be a little difficult to grasp. Suppose we consider the original score to represent 24 inches, instead of 24 points. Then, division by 12 constitutes a transformation by changing from inches to feet. We can now interpret the transformed score as 2 feet instead of 2 units of 12 points each. Clearly, division by 12 results in a new unit (feet) which is 12 times as large as the original unit (inches). Then, *division* by a constant g results in *multiplying* the unit of measurement by g. On the other hand, if each score in a set is *multiplied* by a constant g, the result is to *divide* the unit of measurement by g. For example, say we have a set of time-reaction scores and each score is in minutes. If we multiply each score by 60, the result will be to express each score in a new unit, seconds, which is $\frac{1}{60}$ as large.

Situation 3: Sometimes it is desirable to transform a set of scores *both* by shifting the zero point *and* by changing the unit of measurement. Given a set of N scores, $X_1, X_2, X_3, \ldots, X_N$, with mean μ, a double transformation is performed, first by subtracting from each score a constant k and then by dividing by a second constant g, so that each score becomes $(X_i - k)/g$.

It is convenient to use the symbol u_i to represent the scores resulting from the double transformation. Then,

$$u_i = \frac{X_i - k}{g} \qquad (4.3.7)$$

This double transformation procedure is useful in reducing the work involved in computing the mean μ in many situations. Application of this

Table 4.3.3 COMPUTATION OF THE MEAN: SCORES ON AN APTITUDE TEST

	Score, X_i	$u_i = \frac{X_i - 100}{3}$
	115	5
	124	8
	130	10
	118	6
	127	9
	106	2
	124	8
	121	7
Total	965	55

computing aid involves, first, transforming the original X_i scores to u_i scores by use of Equation 4.3.7; then, computing $\bar{u}$, the mean of the u_i scores, by using Equation 4.2.2 and substituting the variable u_i for X_i. This gives

$$\bar{u} = \frac{\sum_{i=1}^{N} u_i}{N} \qquad (4.3.8)$$

Finally, compute

$$\mu = g\bar{u} + k \qquad (4.3.9)$$

(For proof see Section 4.10, *Note* 4.5.)

We will use this approach to compute the mean μ for the 8 aptitude test scores presented in Table 4.3.3. These scores can be transformed to considerably smaller numbers if, from each score, we first subtract 100 and then divide the result by 3. This is accomplished by substituting $k = 100$ and $g = 3$ into Equation 4.3.7 to obtain

$$u_i = \frac{X_i - 100}{3}$$

Then, substituting each X_i score into the above equation, in turn, the u_i scores shown in Table 4.3.3 are computed. For example, substituting $X_i = 115$, we obtain the transformed score u_{115} as

$$u_{115} = \frac{115 - 100}{3} = 5$$

Noting in the table that $\Sigma u_i = 55$, we apply Equation 4.3.8 to obtain

$$\bar{u} = \frac{55}{8} = 6.88$$

Finally, applying Equation 4.3.9 and remembering that $k = 100$ and $g = 3$, we obtain

$$\mu = (3)(6.88) + 100 = 120.64$$

We can verify this result by computing μ directly from the X_i scores by Equation 4.2.2. Noting from Table 4.3.3 that $\Sigma X_i = 965$, we obtain

$$\mu = \frac{965}{8} = 120.63$$

Except for a slight difference due to rounding, the same result is obtained for μ using either approach.

Situation 4: Given a set of N scores $X_1, X_2, X_3, \ldots, X_N$, with weights $w_1, w_2, w_3, \ldots, w_N$, respectively, it is desired to determine the weighted mean, μ_w for the N scores.

The need to compute a weighted mean often arises in the fields of psychology and education. For example, suppose a four-test battery is administered to entering freshmen in a university and it is desired to compute a battery average for each student. Special attention is required if the four test scores are considered to have *different* degrees of importance. Table 4.3.4 presents the four test scores obtained by a given freshman and the weights (measures of importance) assigned to each test in the battery. These weights might have been determined on a judgment basis, a statistical basis, or a combination of the two. The weighted mean, μ_w, is obtained as

$$\mu_w = \frac{\sum_{i=1}^{N} X_i w_i}{\sum_{i=1}^{N} w_i} \tag{4.3.10}$$

Applying Equation 4.3.10 to the scores for a given freshman in Table 4.3.4, we compute the weighted mean (battery average) as

$$\mu_w = \frac{780}{10} = 78.0$$

Let us consider a different type of situation where the same approach is used in the computation of the arithmetic mean. Table 4.3.5 presents the scores on a sentence completion test for 30 subjects. Note that the first two columns comprise essentially a simple grouping table. The only difference is that the scores listed in the first column are those which have a frequency of one or more. Scores, such as 24, 25, and 26, are not listed

Table 4.3.4 COMPUTATION OF THE WEIGHTED MEAN: SCORES ON A FOUR-TEST BATTERY FOR A GIVEN FRESHMAN

Test	Score, X_i	Weight, w_i	$X_i w_i$
A	85	2	170
B	70	5	350
C	92	1	92
D	84	2	168
Total		10	780

since none of the 30 subjects obtained these scores. Our present interest is in determining the mean score for the 30 subjects. For this purpose, a full simple grouping table is not needed.

If we listed the 30 scores individually, it is clear that we could add all 30 scores and divide by 30 to obtain the arithmetic mean μ. In other words, we could use Equation 4.2.2. However, the table indicates that 3 subjects obtained a score of 30, 5 obtained a score of 31, etc. Therefore, summing the 30 individual scores amounts to adding in (3)(30) = 90 and (5)(31) = 155 to account for the 3 scores of 30 and the 5 scores of 31. Clearly, then, if we multiply each score by its frequency, as indicated in the column headed $X_i f_i$ in Table 4.3.5, the sum of these products (1059) is *identical* with the sum we would obtain if we added the 30 individual scores. Therefore, dividing this sum by $N = 30$ (total of the f_i column), we obtain the mean μ. Symbolically, we have

$$\mu = \frac{\sum_{i=1}^{c} X_i f_i}{\sum_{i=1}^{c} f_i} = \frac{\sum_{i=1}^{c} X_i f_i}{N} \tag{4.3.11}$$

Table 4.3.5 COMPUTATION OF THE ARITHMETIC MEAN: SCORES ON A SENTENCE COMPLETION TEST TAKEN BY 30 SUBJECTS

Score, X_i	f_i	X_if_i	p_i	X_ip_i
23	1	23	.033	.759
28	1	28	.033	.924
30	3	90	.100	3.000
31	5	155	.167	5.177
35	8	280	.267	9.345
39	7	273	.233	9.087
42	5	210	.167	7.014
Total	30	1059	1.000	35.306

Observe that in Equation 4.3.11 the summations go from $i = 1$ to c, instead of $i = 1$ to N, as previously. Recall that N stands for the number of scores in a set. However, in this equation, we are *not* adding the individual scores. For example, in the numerator we are adding the X_if_i products and there are as many products as there are *different* score values in the set. In the denominator we are adding the score frequencies f_i and, again, there are as many score frequencies as there are *different* score values. Therefore, c represents the number of *different* score values (X_i) in the set. Referring to the illustration in Table 4.3.5, we compute the mean according to Equation 4.3.11, as

$$\mu = \frac{\sum_{i=1}^{7} X_if_i}{\sum_{i=1}^{7} f_i} = \frac{1059}{30} = 35.3$$

The equation for μ presented in Equation 4.3.11 is similar to Equation 4.3.10 for the weighted mean, μ_w. The only difference is the use of score frequencies (f_i) instead of weights (w_i). Actually, the frequencies play the same role as weights. For example, a score with a frequency of 5 has more weight in determining μ than does a score with a lower frequency, say, 3 or 1. Sometimes μ computed according to Equation 4.3.11 is referred to as a weighted mean; however, it is usually considered as a mean just as if it were computed directly by Equation 4.2.2.

Notice that the equation for μ presented in Equation 4.3.11 is expressed in two forms. The first form, which is similar to the equation for μ_w, has Σf_i in the denominator. The second form takes into consideration that

$\Sigma f_i = N$. Noting that N is a constant, we may apply Summation Rule 2 (Chapter 2, Section 2.6) *in reverse* to the second form and put N *into* the summation, writing

$$\mu = \sum_{i=1}^{c} \frac{X_i f_i}{N} = \sum_{i=1}^{c} X_i \frac{f_i}{N} = \sum_{i=1}^{c} X_i p_i \qquad (4.3.12)$$

The ratio f_i/N expresses the class frequency f_i as a proportion of the total number of items (total frequency). It will be recalled that we discussed such proportions in Chapter 3, Section 3.3, where they were called *relative frequencies* and identified by the symbol p_i. Equation 4.3.12, in the extreme right form, uses p_i instead of f_i/N to denote the relative frequency in a class. This equation indicates that μ can be computed by adding the products obtained by multiplying each X_i score by its relative frequency (p_i). Referring to Table 4.3.5, we may apply Equation 4.3.12 to obtain

$$\mu = \sum_{i=1}^{7} X_i p_i = 35.306$$

This, of course, gives the same result as the computation according to Equation 4.3.11, except for possible rounding differences. When score frequencies (f_i) are available, it is not recommended that relative frequencies be computed for the sole purpose of computing μ according to Equation 4.3.12. However, this equation indicates how to determine the mean if the only frequencies available are the relative frequencies. Furthermore, this computational method will be useful in connection with discussions later in the text.

Situation 5: Given the means of subsets of scores (μ_i) and the number of items included in each subset (N_i), it is desired to determine the general mean (μ) for the scores in all subsets combined.

Computation of a *general mean* is often required in the fields of psychology and education. For example, suppose there are four sections in English II in a university, with mean grade per student in each section as indicated in Table 4.3.6. If it is desired to determine the general mean grade (μ) for all the students in the four sections combined, this can be computed based on the section means (μ_i) and the number of grades for each section (N_i) using the following equation:

$$\mu = \frac{\sum_{i=1}^{c} \mu_i N_i}{\sum_{i=1}^{c} N_i} \qquad (4.3.13)$$

(For proof see Section 4.10, *Note* 4.6.)

Notice that the summations in Equation 4.3.13 go from $i = 1$ to c, where c stands for the number of subsets to be combined. Applying this equation to the data in Table 4.3.6, we obtain

$$\mu = \frac{\sum_{i=1}^{4} \mu_i N_i}{\sum_{i=1}^{4} N_i} = \frac{5350}{65} = 82.3$$

Table 4.3.6 COMPUTATION OF THE GENERAL MEAN: MEAN GRADES IN ENGLISH II FOR FOUR SECTIONS

English II Sections	Number in Each Section, N_i	Mean Grade in Each Section, μ_i	$\mu_i N_i$
1	20	84	1680
2	15	70	1050
3	10	92	920
4	20	85	1700
Total	65		5350

The general mean 82.3 represents the mean grade for the 65 students in the four sections combined. That is, if we know the 65 individual grades and computed μ using Equation 4.2.2, we would obtain $\mu = 82.3$.

Situation 6: Given a pair of scores, an X_i score and a Y_i score, for each of N subjects, as follows: $X_1, X_2, X_3, \ldots, X_N$, with mean μ_X, and $Y_1, Y_2, Y_3, \ldots, Y_N$, with mean μ_Y, where the X_i and Y_i scores pertain to the ith subject. Let S_i denote the sum of the scores $(X_i + Y_i)$ for a subject and D_i, the difference between the scores $(X_i - Y_i)$. Then, μ_S, the mean of the sums, and μ_D, the mean of the differences, can be obtained as follows:

$$\mu_S = \mu_X + \mu_Y \tag{4.3.14}$$

$$\mu_D = \mu_X - \mu_Y \tag{4.3.15}$$

(For proof see Section 4.10, *Notes* 4.7 *and* 4.8.)

A situation may arise, for example, where it is desired to determine the mean of the total score for a two-part test administered to a group of subjects, when the mean is known for each part separately. This can be illustrated by using the data in Table 4.3.7 for four subjects. It can be determined that the mean score for Part 1 (μ_X) is 60.50, and the mean score for Part 2 (μ_Y) is 34.25. Therefore, we may determine the mean test score (including both parts) as

$$\mu_S = 60.50 + 34.25 = 94.75$$

Table 4.3.7 COMPUTATION OF THE MEAN OF SUMS OR DIFFERENCES: SCORES ON A TWO-PART TEST FOR FOUR SUBJECTS

Subject	Score on Part 1, X_i	Score on Part 2, Y_i	$S_i = X_i + Y_i$	$D_i = X_i - Y_i$
A	62	36	98	26
B	69	28	97	41
C	58	42	100	16
D	53	31	84	22
Total	242	137	379	105

This result can be verified by obtaining the mean μ_S directly from the S_i column in the table. We may determine the mean difference between Part 1 and Part 2 scores, where each difference is determined as $D_i = X_i - Y_i$, as

$$\mu_D = 60.50 - 34.25 = 26.25$$

This result may be verified by computing μ_D from the individual differences D_i shown in the last column of Table 4.3.7.

PROBLEMS FOR PRACTICE AND REVIEW

1. Compute the arithmetic mean for the following sample of 12 quiz grades: 9.3, 7.8, 9.0, 8.7, 3.9, 2.1, 6.7, 7.9, 8.9, 8.7, 9.8, 10.0.

2. The scores on a clerical quiz obtained for a population of seven clerks were recorded as: 5, 7, 2, 6, 8, 3, 6.

(a) Compute the mean.

(b) If 20 points are added to each score, find the new mean. (Do not use the individual increased scores for this computation.)

(c) If, instead, each score is reduced by two points, find the new mean. (Do not use the individual reduced scores for this computation.)

3. The scores on an anxiety scale for a sample of nine subjects are: 67, 75, 63, 72, 77, 78, 81, 77, 81.

(a) Compute the mean score.

(b) If ten points are added to each score, compute the new mean. (Do not use the individual increased scores for this computation.)

(c) If, instead, the original scores are doubled, compute the new mean. (Do not use the individual increased scores for this computation.)

4. The reaction times (in minutes) were recorded for a population of ten students as: .022, .020, .025, .022, .025, .021, .025, .025, .019, .025. Compute the mean. However, to simplify the computations, first multiply each reaction time by 1000 (in order to obtain whole-number scores), obtain the mean for these increased scores, and, then, determine the mean for the original scores.

5. Aptitude test scores for a sample of eight subjects are: 108, 103, 102, 107, 106, 102, 104, 105. Compute the mean aptitude test score. However, in order to reduce the computational labor, first reduce each score by 100 points.

6. A vocabulary recall test administered to a population of 15 college freshmen resulted in scores, as follows: 160, 80, 200, 280, 280, 480, 160, 280, 520, 160, 400, 280, 160, 200, 160. Compute the mean. However, in order to reduce the computational labor, first divide each score by 40.

7. Grades on a midterm examination in a French class of nine students are 72, 68, 58, 70, 74, 72, 64, 66, 70. Compute the mean grade. (Transform each grade X_i to a u_i grade by subtracting 50 and then dividing the result by 2.)

8. Compute the mean for the following sample of 11 aptitude test scores selected from a large population: 142, 114, 107, 163, 156, 121, 149, 107, 135, 149, 163. (Transform each score by subtracting 100 and then dividing by 7.)

9. A test battery consists of five tests with weights as follows: vocabulary recall 3, spatial perception 1, research aptitude 2, reading comprehension 3, and personality inventory 1. If a subject scored 159, 123, 112, 168, 103 on these tests, respectively, compute his battery (weighted mean) score.

10. The following four tests are administered to applicants by a trade school: mechanical ability, finger dexterity, spatial perception, mechanical speed, with weights 4, 4, 2, 1 respectively. What is the weighted mean score on these tests for an applicant who obtains 37, 22, 31, 29 (listed in the same order as the tests).

11. The number of errors recorded for a sample of 37 subjects in performing a specified task are 14 for 4 subjects, 16 for 6 subjects, 17 for 10 subjects, 18 for 7 subjects, 20 for 3 subjects, 21 for 3 subjects, 23 for 2 subjects, 26 for 1 subject, and 27 for 1 subject. Find the mean number of errors recorded for the 37 subjects.

12. An article in an educational psychology research journal noted that a large population of junior high school students were tested on "attitude toward adults" and .02 of this population scored 103, .06 scored 106, .10 scored 107, .25 scored 109, .35 scored 110, and .22 scored 112. Compute the mean score obtained by these students.

13. The same achievement test was given to each of five sections in English literature. The 32 students in Section A obtained a mean grade of 73, the 35 in Section B obtained a mean of 84, the 26 in Section C obtained a mean of 70, the 15 in Section D obtained a mean of 92, and the 12 students in Section E obtained a mean grade of 90. Compute the general mean grade for the 120 students in all five sections.

14. Three samples of white rats were selected for an experiment. The 50 rats in sample 1 obtained a mean score of 32 on a learning test; the 100 rats in sample 2 obtained a mean score of 28; and the 125 rats in sample 3 obtained a mean score of 23. Determine the general mean for the 275 rats considered as a single sample.

15. A two-part final examination was given to a class of 25 students in geology. The mean score was 24 on part 1 and 63 on part 2. Compute the mean for the full test (both parts) for this class.

16. A two-test battery was made up of a memory test and a reading comprehension test. The mean score for 100 subjects was 131 for the test battery and 78 for the reading comprehension test. If the test battery score for each subject was computed as the sum of the scores on the two tests, compute the mean score for the memory test for these 100 subjects.

4.4 ARITHMETIC MEAN: FREQUENCY DISTRIBUTIONS

Situations often arise in which it is necessary to compute the arithmetic mean for data organized into a frequency distribution. This may occur where the raw data are not available or where it is inconvenient to work directly with a large volume of unorganized data. Computation of the mean from a frequency table represents another type of special situation for which it is useful to develop special-purpose equations. Therefore, let us continue our enumeration of special situations by presenting *Situation* 7 and *Situation* 8 relating to frequency distributions.

***Situation** 7:* Given a set of N scores organized into a frequency table with c classes, it is desired to determine the mean score.

Table 4.4.1 presents a frequency table for scores on a word association test administered to 60 subjects. Of course, if we knew the 60 individual scores, we could compute the mean by adding the scores and dividing by 60. However, since it is not possible from a frequency table to know the individual scores included, it is necessary to make some assumption

Table 4.4.1 COMPUTATION OF THE ARITHMETIC MEAN: FREQUENCY TABLE OF SCORES ON A WORD ASSOCIATION TEST ADMINISTERED TO 60 SUBJECTS

Discrete Class Limits	Midpoint, X_i	f_i	$X_i f_i$	p_i	$X_i p_i$
30–39	34.5	3	103.5	.050	1.725
40–49	44.5	11	489.5	.183	8.144
50–59	54.5	18	981.0	.300	16.350
60–69	64.5	15	967.5	.250	16.125
70–79	74.5	9	670.5	.150	11.175
80–89	84.5	4	338.0	.067	5.662
	Total	60	3550.0	1.000	59.181

regarding these scores. *The assumption usually made is that the scores in a class interval are equal to the class midpoint.* Referring to Table 4.4.1, we assume that the 3 scores in the 30–39 class have the value 34.5, the 11 scores in the 40–49 class have the value 44.5, etc. Therefore, based on this assumption, it is possible to compute the mean μ by adding the 60 assumed scores and dividing by 60. However, 3 of these assumed scores are equal to 34.5, 11 are equal to 44.5, etc. Therefore, adding these 60 scores amounts to adding in (3)(34.5) = 103.5 and (11)(44.5) = 489.5 to account for the 3 scores of 34.5 and the 11 scores of 44.5. Clearly, then, if we multiply each assumed score (the class midpoint X_i) by its frequency f_i, as indicated in the X_if_i column in Table 4.4.1, the sum of these products (3550.0) is *identical* with the sum we would obtain if we added the 60 assumed scores. Therefore, dividing this sum by $N = 60$ (the total of the f_i column), we obtain the mean μ. That is, we may compute the mean as

$$\mu = \frac{\sum_{i=1}^{c} X_i f_i}{\sum_{i=1}^{c} f_i} = \frac{\sum_{i=1}^{c} X_i f_i}{N} \qquad (4.4.1)$$

Observe that the summations in Equation 4.4.1 go from $i = 1$ to c, since we are adding over c classes. The second form of this equation is, of course, equivalent to the first form, since $\Sigma f_i = N$. Applying this equation to the data in Table 4.4.1, we obtain

$$\mu = \frac{\sum_{i=1}^{6} X_i f_i}{\sum_{i=1}^{6} f_i} = \frac{3550.0}{60} = 59.17$$

The similarity between Equation 4.3.11 in Section 4.3 (*Situation* 4) and Equation 4.4.1 should be noted. Equation 4.3.11 involves computation of the mean for a set of c scores (X_i) with associated frequencies (f_i). Equation 4.4.1 involves computation of the mean for a set of c midpoints (X_i) with associated class frequencies (f_i). However, we may look upon the class midpoints as a set of c scores. Therefore, it is not surprising that Equation 4.4.1, where X_i denotes the class midpoint and c, the number of classes, is equivalent to Equation 4.3.11, where X_i denotes specified scores and c, the number of different scores. In the same way, we can set up an equation equivalent to Equation 4.3.12 in *Situation* 4 to express the mean for a frequency table with c classes in terms of the class midpoints and the *relative frequencies* (p_i) as

$$\mu = \sum_{i=1}^{c} X_i p_i \qquad (4.4.2)$$

Applying Equation 4.4.2 to the data in Table 4.4.1, we obtain

$$\mu = \sum_{i=1}^{6} X_i p_i = 59.181$$

The result obtained by the use of Equation 4.4.2, of course, is always the same as that obtained by the use of Equation 4.4.1, except for a possible rounding difference.

As noted in Chapter 3, Section 3.3, the assumption that all scores in a class are equal to the class midpoint will usually lead to some discrepancy in the mean computed from a frequency table compared with the mean which would be obtained if the actual scores were used in the computation. However, as previously discussed, with a well-constructed frequency table, the discrepancy is usually not important.

Situation 8: It is often quite laborious to compute the mean for a frequency table in the manner indicated in *Situation* 7. Given a set of N scores organized into a frequency table with c classes, it is often convenient to transform the class midpoints X_i to u_i, using the double transformation procedure presented in *Situation* 3, and then to compute the mean μ based on the transformed u_i scores.

Application of this computing aid involves, first, transforming the class midpoints X_i to u_i scores, as follows:

$$u_i = \frac{X_i - k}{g} \tag{4.4.3}$$

Equation 4.4.3 is like Equation 4.3.7 presented for *Situation* 3, except that here X_i represents the class midpoints instead of the individual scores. The constants k and g should be selected in a certain way if the greatest computational convenience is to be obtained. *The constant k should be put equal to the midpoint* (X_i) *which is associated with the largest class frequency and which is also centrally located in the frequency table.* It is not always possible to select a midpoint which meets *both* of these requirements. However, the midpoint which comes closest to meeting these requirements should be selected as the value of k. *The constant g should be put equal to the length of class interval.* Then, compute $\bar{u}$, the mean of the u_i scores, as follows:

$$\bar{u} = \frac{\sum_{i=1}^{c} u_i f_i}{\sum_{i=1}^{c} f_i} = \frac{\sum_{i=1}^{c} u_i f_i}{N} \tag{4.4.4}$$

The equation for $\bar{u}$ is obtained by substituting u_i for X_i in Equation 4.4.1 (*Situation* 7). Finally, compute

$$\mu = g\bar{u} + k \tag{4.4.5}$$

This equation, it will be noted, is the same as Equation 4.3.9 in *Situation* 3.

Table 4.4.2 presents the class midpoints and frequencies for the 60 scores on a word association test from Table 4.4.1. The double transformation

Table 4.4.2 COMPUTATION OF THE MEAN, AFTER TRANSFORMATION OF THE CLASS MIDPOINTS X_i TO u_i: FREQUENCY TABLE OF SCORES ON A WORD ASSOCIATION TEST ADMINISTERED TO 60 SUBJECTS

Midpoint, X_i	f_i	u_i	$u_i f_i$
34.5	3	−2	−6
44.5	11	−1	−11
(54.5)	18	0	0
64.5	15	1	15
74.5	9	2	18
84.5	4	3	12
Total	60		28

procedure will be used to compute the mean of these scores. We begin by selecting the values for k and g. Let $k = 54.5$ since this midpoint has the highest class frequency (18) and it is also in the central part of the frequency table. It is a good idea to put parentheses around the midpoint selected, as indicated in the table. This will identify it for later reference. Let $g = 10$, the length of class interval. Then, substituting these values for k and g into Equation 4.4.3, we obtain

$$u_i = \frac{X_i - 54.5}{10}$$

Now, substituting each midpoint in turn into the above equation, we compute the transformed u_i scores as shown in the u_i column in Table 4.4.2. For example, substituting the first midpoint, 34.5, into this equation, we compute the corresponding transformed score $u_{34.5}$ as

$$u_{34.5} = \frac{34.5 - 54.5}{10} = -2$$

The mean of the u_i scores, $\bar{u}$, is computed, according to Equation 4.4.4, as

$$\bar{u} = \frac{\sum_{i=1}^{6} u_i f_i}{\sum_{i=1}^{6} f_i} = \frac{28}{60} = .467$$

Finally, using Equation 4.4.5,

$$\mu = 10\bar{u} + 54.5 = (10)(.467) + 54.5 = 59.17$$

This, of course, is the same result obtained previously when μ was computed directly from the class midpoints (*Situation* 7).

Selection of the two constants k and g in the prescribed manner results in conveniently simple u_i scores, as shown in the u_i column in Table 4.4.2. For example, the u_i score obtained for the midpoint selected for the value of k (54.5) is 0, as shown in the table. This score, $u_{54.5}$, is obtained by substituting $X_i = 54.5$ and the selected values for k and g into Equation 4.4.3, as follows:

$$u_{54.5} = \frac{54.5 - 54.5}{10} = 0$$

The transformed u_i score for the class midpoint which is selected as the value of k is always equal to 0. It will be observed from Table 4.4.2 that for midpoints which are *higher-valued* than 54.5, the u_i scores are 1, 2, 3. In the case of midpoints which are *lower-valued* than 54.5, the u_i scores follow the same numerical sequence but are *negative*.

As noted in *Situations* 1 *and* 2, the effect of the double transformation is to shift the zero point and change the unit of measurement. The double transformation procedure just presented shifts the zero point for the scores in the frequency table to the midpoint selected for k and changes the unit of measurement to the length of class interval, g. Therefore, we may interpret the transformed u_i scores as follows: a *negative* u_i score indicates how many class intervals the corresponding midpoint is *less than* the midpoint used for k. For example, the u_i score of -2 in Table 4.4.2 indicates that the corresponding midpoint (34.5) is two class intervals (or 20 points) less than 54.5. A *positive* u_i score indicates how many class intervals the corresponding midpoint is *more than* the midpoint used for k. As an example, the u_i score of 2 in the table indicates that the corresponding midpoint (74.5) is two class intervals (or 20 points) more than 54.5.

Therefore, a set of midpoints can be transformed to u_i scores *immediately*, without any computations. First, select the midpoint to use for k. Put parentheses around this midpoint (to identify it for later reference) and place a 0 in the u_i column for the midpoint. As you move away from this midpoint in the direction of *decreasing* midpoint values, enter the *negative* sequence -1, -2, etc., in the u_i column until a u_i score is assigned to all *lower-valued* midpoints. Then, as you move away from the midpoint in parentheses in the direction of *increasing* midpoint values, enter the *positive* sequence 1, 2, etc., in the u_i column until a u_i score is assigned to all *higher-valued* midpoints.

Actually, μ can be conveniently computed no matter which midpoint in a frequency table is selected for k. However, the u_i scores and the computations will be most convenient if the midpoint selected for k is *centrally located* in the table. For example, referring to Table 4.4.2, if k is put equal to 34.5, then the u_i score for this midpoint becomes 0 and, for the other midpoints (all higher in value), u_i scores become 1, 2, 3, 4, 5. That is, the u_i score for, say, the midpoint 64.5 will become 3 in place of 1 (as shown in the table). Therefore, in computing u_if_i for the last column of the table, we must multiply the class frequency 15 by 3 instead of by 1.

This may not seem to involve much of a difference in computational labor for the illustration we are using. However, when you are dealing with larger class frequencies, the difference may be important. Furthermore, if the class midpoint with the *largest frequency* is selected for the value of k, then the corresponding u_i score will be zero, resulting in $u_if_i = 0$ for this class. When the frequency for this class is large, multiplication by zero is a convenience. Finally, since the sum of the u_if_i products is required (Equation 4.4.4), the smaller we can make the individual u_if_i products, the more convenient is it to obtain the summation. Of course, it is not always possible to choose a midpoint which meets both requirements. However, in a given situation, the midpoint which is closest to meeting these requirements is the one to choose for the value of k.

It should be noted that the method just presented for computing the mean from data grouped into a frequency table is applicable *only when the table contains equal class intervals*. A modification of this method is available for unequal classes. However, since this text is concerned only with equal class intervals, we will not take the time to present this modification.

We will apply this double transformation procedure to another illustration. Table 4.4.3 presents a frequency table of the scores on a clerical aptitude test for 85 subjects. We note that there is no midpoint which is both centrally located and associated with the highest frequency. Let us select 120.5 for the value of k since the associated class frequency is second highest and it is not too far from the center of the table (though 125.5 could serve just as well). Place parentheses around this midpoint. Let $g =$ 5 (the length of class interval). Now we can immediately write the u_i scores corresponding to each midpoint. First, the u_i score for 120.5 is 0. Then, for succeeding lower-valued midpoints, the u_i scores are -1, -2,

Table 4.4.3 COMPUTATION OF THE MEAN, AFTER TRANSFORMATION OF THE CLASS MIDPOINTS X_i TO u_i: FREQUENCY TABLE OF SCORES ON A CLERICAL APTITUDE TEST ADMINISTERED TO 85 SUBJECTS

Midpoint, X_i	f_i	u_i	$u_i f_i$
105.5	3	−3	−9
110.5	9	−2	−18
115.5	14	−1	−14
(120.5)	21	0	0
125.5	38	1	38
Total	85		−3

−3, and, for the higher-valued midpoint, the u_i score is 1. These scores are shown in the u_i column in the table. Using Equation 4.4.4, we compute

$$\bar{u} = \frac{\sum_{i=1}^{5} u_i f_i}{\sum_{i=1}^{5} f_i} = \frac{-3}{85} = -.035$$

Finally, using Equation 4.4.5, we obtain

$$\mu = (5)(-.035) + 120.5 = 120.3$$

PROBLEMS FOR PRACTICE AND REVIEW

1. Compute the mean for the frequency distribution of the population of scores on a reading speed test in Problem 7 (following Section 3.3). Do this two ways, based upon the reading speed test scores X_i and, then, after transforming these to u_i scores.

2. Given the following frequency distribution of a population of 27 quiz grades:

Grades	Number of Students
12.0–15.9	6
16.0–19.9	10
20.0–23.9	7
24.0–27.9	4

Compute the mean in two ways, using the quiz grades X_i and, then, after transforming these grades to u_i values.

3. Given the following frequency distribution of a sample of 41 scores on a personality scale:

Scores	Frequency
115–117	3
118–120	7
121–123	12
124–126	10
127–129	9

Compute the mean in two ways, using the personality scale scores X_i and, then, after transforming these to u_i scores.

4. Given the following data on the number of errors made by a sample of 162 subjects in a foreign language typing test:

Number of Errors	Number of Subjects
20–24	3
25–29	8
30–34	12
35–39	21
40–44	29
45–49	32
50–54	30
55–59	27

compute the mean number of errors per subject. Do this in two ways, using the number of errors X_i and, then, after transforming X_i to u_i.

5. Compute the mean for the frequency distribution of the population of anxiety scale scores in Problem 8 (following Section 3.3).

6. The reaction times (minutes) to a new drug administered to a sample of 223 subjects are:

Reaction Times (Minutes)	Number of Subjects
.00–.09	31
.10–.19	42
.20–.29	47
.30–.39	44
.40–.49	39
.50–.59	20

Estimate the population mean.

7. Compute the mean for the population of times required in Problem 9 (following Section 3.3).

8. Compute the mean for the following population of 39 scores on a social science research aptitude test:

Scores	Frequency
125.0–125.4	2
125.5–125.9	3
126.0–126.4	5
126.5–126.9	7
127.0–127.4	10
127.5–127.9	12

9. Compute the mean for the following population of scores on a running speed test:

Running Speed Minutes	Relative Frequency, p_i
2.25–2.49	.18
2.50–2.74	.15
2.75–2.99	.10
3.00–3.24	.07
3.25–3.49	.10
3.50–3.74	.19
3.75–3.99	.21

10. Compute the mean for the following sample of scores on a mechanical performance test:

Scores	Frequency
12.000–12.019	18
12.020–12.039	21
12.040–12.059	28
12.060–12.079	25
12.080–12.099	19
12.100–12.119	11
12.120–12.139	7
12.140–12.159	2

4.5 MEDIAN: DEFINITION

Compared with the arithmetic mean which is a computed average and can be treated algebraically, *the median is a measure of position*. That is, *in a set of scores, the median is the score value centrally located so that the number of scores in the set with a higher value is equal to the number with a lower value.* We will use the symbol M to represent the median, whether determined from a set of sample data or from the full population. As in the case of the mean, the median is determined in the same manner for sample data and population data.

Suppose we have a set of 5 scores on a science test as follows: 85, 72, 91, 69, 83. The first step in determining the median is to *rank* the scores.

Arranging the scores from lowest to highest, we have: 69, 72, 83, 85, 91. The next step is to determine the *position* of the median in the ranked set of scores. This is easily determined as $\frac{1}{2}(N + 1)$, where N represents the number of items included in the set. (Note that, in our discussion of the median in this chapter, we will use N to represent the number of items, whether the set represents a sample or a population.) Performing this computation for the set of 5 scores in our illustration, we obtain $\frac{1}{2}(5 + 1) = 3$. This indicates that the score which occupies the third position *after the scores are ranked* is the median. We could start with the lowest score (69) and count until we reach the third score from the bottom; or we could start with the highest score (91) and count until we reach the third score from the top. Either way, the result will be the same since the median is in the center. In our illustration, the third score is 83, which is the median for this set of 5 scores. Note that this score is centrally located in the ranked sequence. That is, the number of scores in the set with a higher value (2 scores) is equal to the number with a lower value.

Sometimes a set of scores contains ties. For example, suppose a set of 9 scores on a midterm examination are: 98, 99, 68, 84, 71, 84, 71, 84, 79. How do we find the median? The first step is to rank these scores: 68, 71, 71, 79, 84, 84, 84, 98, 99. It does not matter which of the tied scores are written first. Then, we determine the position of the median as $\frac{1}{2}(9 + 1) = 5$. Counting until we get to the fifth position in the ranked sequence of scores, we determine that 84 is the median. It will be apparent to the reader that, in this illustration, there are 4 scores with a lower value than the median and only 2 with a higher value. This discrepancy is usually explained away by taking individual differences into consideration. That is, it is considered unlikely that the three scores of 84 would remain equal if the scores were more precisely determined. Hence, we make the assumption that the three scores of 84 are not equal and that the 84 which happens to be listed first actually represents a lower score than the other two 84 scores. Then, we are able to state that there are 4 scores with a higher value than the median, just as there are 4 with a lower value.

So far, we have illustrated the determination of the median for an odd number of scores. When a set contains an even number of scores, an additional step is needed to determine the median. For example, let us find the median for the following 6 quiz grades obtained by a group of biology students: 82, 70, 79, 87, 91, 78. First, ranking the grades, we have: 70, 78, 79, 82, 87, 91. Then, we determine the position of the median as $\frac{1}{2}(6 + 1) = 3.5$. This indicates that the median is located *midway* between the grades in the third and fourth positions in the ranked sequence. In the illustration, the grades 79 and 82 occupy the third and fourth positions. Then, *the median is computed as the mean of these two grades, since the mean is located midway between them.* In the illustration, we obtain the median as $\frac{1}{2}(79 + 82) = 80.5$. It will be noted that 3 grades are below the median and 3 are above.

Let us determine the median for an even-numbered set of scores which contains ties. Suppose we have a set of 8 scores on an attitude scale, as follows: 28, 32, 28, 31, 26, 28, 23, 28. Ranking them, we obtain: 23, 26, 28, 28, 28, 28, 31, 32. The position of the median is determined as $\frac{1}{2}(8 + 1) = 4.5$, indicating that the median is located midway between the scores in the fourth and fifth ranked positions (28 and 28). Hence, the median is $\frac{1}{2}(28 + 28) = 28$. Clearly, for a set which contains an even number of items, the median is not equal to any of the scores in the set, except in the special type of situation illustrated above.

4.6 MEDIAN: FREQUENCY DISTRIBUTIONS

A situation often encountered by students in psychology and education is the need to determine the median for a set of data that is organized into a frequency distribution. For example, Table 4.6.1 presents a frequency distribution for the scores obtained by 81 job applicants on a research aptitude test. Of course, if the 81 individual scores were known, we could

Table 4.6.1 FREQUENCY DISTRIBUTION FOR SCORES ON A RESEARCH APTITUDE TEST FOR 81 JOB APPLICANTS

Discrete Class Limits	Continuous Class Limits	f_i	Less than cum f_i	More than cum f_i
	79.5		0	81
80–83		5		
	83.5		5	76
84–87		9		
	87.5		14	67
88–91		17		
	91.5		31	50
92–95		(24)		
	95.5		55	26
96–99		12		
	99.5		67	14
100–103		11		
	103.5		78	3
104–107		3		
	107.5		81	0

determine the median in the manner just described. The approach used to determine the median when dealing with a frequency table is best visualized by referring to the histogram.

Figure 4.6.1 presents the histogram for the 81 scores in Table 4.6.1. It will be recalled that each rectangular bar in the histogram represents (is proportional to) the frequency in the corresponding class interval, and the entire area under the histogram represents the total number of scores. The area under the histogram in Figure 4.6.1 represents the 81 scores in

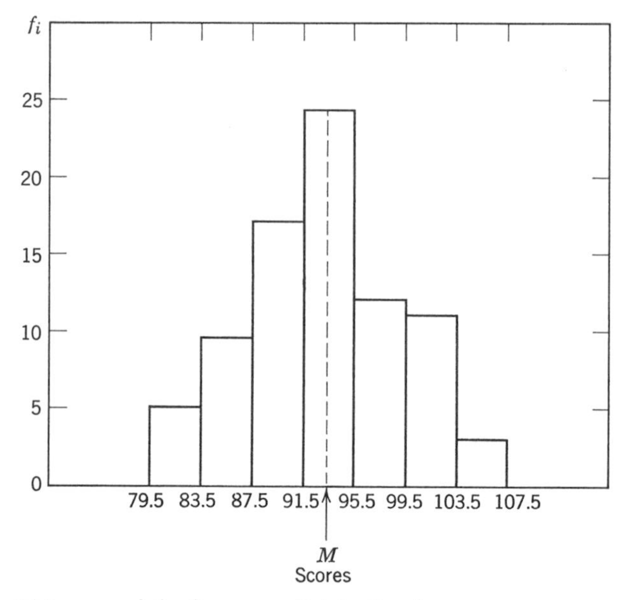

Fig. 4.6.1. Histogram of the frequency distribution for scores on a research aptitude test for 81 job applicants.

Table 4.6.1. Now, construct a vertical line (an ordinate) which will divide the area under the histogram into two equal parts. The vertical line of dashes in Figure 4.6.1 is such an ordinate; that is, the area under the histogram to the right of this ordinate is equal to the area to the left. In other words, each half area under the histogram represents half of the total number of scores or $N/2$ scores. The point on the score scale at which this ordinate is constructed, indicated as M in Figure 4.6.1, is the median. Clearly, then, *the median M for a set of N scores organized into a frequency table is that score value where half the scores* ($N/2$) *have a lower value* (*or, where half the scores have a higher value*).

How is the median determined from a frequency table? The continuous class limits and one of the cumulative frequency columns are used for this purpose. Let us use the *Less than cum* f_i column. The first step is to compute $N/2$. In our illustration (Table 4.6.1), we have $\frac{81}{2} = 40.5$. This tells how many scores make up half the scores. Now we must determine that score value M (the median) where exactly 40.5 scores are less than M. Looking down the *Less than cum* f_i column, we note that 31 scores are less than the continuous class limit 91.5, and 55 scores are less than the next continuous class limit, 95.5. Then, 91.5 cannot be the median since 31 are *too few* scores. Neither is 95.5 the median since 55 are *too many* scores. Somewhere between these two limits must lie that score value (M) where exactly 40.5 scores have a lower value (see Figure 4.6.1). In order to locate M within the continuous class interval 91.5–95.5, *we make the assumption that the scores in this class (the median class) are evenly distributed over the class interval.* Then, we proceed to determine M by the *method of linear interpolation.* Write the continuous class limits for the median class and the associated less than cum f_i as follows:

$$\left(\begin{array}{l}\left.\begin{array}{l}91.5\\ M\end{array}\right)\\ 95.5\end{array}\right) \qquad \left(\begin{array}{l}\left.\begin{array}{l}31\\ 40.5\end{array}\right)\\ 55\end{array}\right)$$

Notice that we entered M between the class limits and 40.5 between the cumulative frequencies. The method of linear interpolation requires equating ratios of differences. The parentheses shown above indicate how these differences are formed. More specifically, we set up an equation as follows:

$$\frac{M - 91.5}{95.5 - 91.5} = \frac{40.5 - 31}{55 - 31} \tag{4.6.1}$$

The relation between the four parentheses shown above and the four differences shown in Equation 4.6.1 should be apparent. For example, the numerator on the left side of the equation is the difference formed by using 91.5 and M which are joined together above. It will be noted that the numerators in Equation 4.6.1 correspond to the short parentheses and the denominators correspond to the long parentheses.

Carrying out the subtractions indicated in Equation 4.6.1 as far as possible, we obtain

$$\frac{M - 91.5}{4} = \frac{9.5}{24} \tag{4.6.2}$$

Notice that the denominator on the left side (4) is the length of class interval, whereas the denominator on the right side (24) is the frequency in the median class. Now, solving Equation 4.6.2 for M, we obtain as the median for the scores in Table 4.6.1

$$M = (4)\frac{9.5}{24} + 91.5 = 93.08 \tag{4.6.3}$$

Based on this result, we can set up *a general equation for computing the median for a frequency table based on the continuous class limits and the less than cumulative frequencies* as

$$M = L + g\frac{d}{f_M} \tag{4.6.4}$$

where L = lower continuous class limit of the median class. (In Equation 4.6.3, $L = 91.5$.)
g = length of class interval. (In Equation 4.6.3, $g = 4$.)
d = difference between $N/2$ and the less than cum f_i associated with L. (In Equation 4.6.3, $d = 40.5 - 31 = 9.5$.)
f_M = frequency of the median class. (In Equation 4.6.3, $f_M = 24$.)

It is a good idea to bracket the continuous class limits of the median class and the associated less than cumulative frequencies and place parentheses around the frequency of this class, as indicated in Table 4.6.1. This will identify the various items needed for computation of the median. For example, the various items in Table 4.6.1 going into Equation 4.6.4 may be identified as

L = the smaller of the two limits in the bracket, 91.5.
g = the difference between the two limits in the bracket ($95.5 - 91.5 = 4$).
d = the difference between $N/2 = 40.5$ and the less than cum f_i associated with L, 31 ($40.5 - 31 = 9.5$).
f_M = the class frequency in parentheses, 24.

We will use Equation 4.6.4 to obtain the median for the frequency distribution of 68 final examination grades presented in Table 4.6.2. If we are given only the first two columns of information (discrete class limits and class frequencies), we need to compute the continuous class limits and a cumulative frequency column. *Since we wish to apply Equation* 4.6.4, *we need the less than cumulative frequency column.*

After determining this additional information, the first step in determining the median is to compute $N/2 = \frac{68}{2} = 34$. Then, starting at the top, look down the less than cumulative frequency column in Table 4.6.2. Note that 34 is between the two less than cumulative frequencies 23 and 42. Bracket these cumulative frequencies, as shown in the table. The corresponding continuous class limits identify the median class ($74.5 - 79.5$). Bracket these limits. Place parentheses around the frequency of the

Table 4.6.2 FREQUENCY DISTRIBUTION FOR FINAL EXAMINATION GRADES FOR 68 COLLEGE SENIORS

Discrete Class Limits	f_i	Continuous Class Limits	Less than cum f_i
		54.5	0
55–59	1		
		59.5	1
60–64	3		
		64.5	4
65–69	7		
		69.5	11
70–74	12		
		74.5	23
75–79	(19)		
		79.5	42
80–84	10		
		84.5	52
85–89	9		
		89.5	61
90–94	7		
		94.5	68

median class (19). Then, noting that $L = 74.5$, $g = 79.5 - 74.5 = 5$, $d = 34 - 23 = 11$, and $f_M = 19$, compute the median, using Equation 4.6.4, as

$$M = 74.5 + (5)\frac{11}{19} = 77.39$$

Sometimes a frequency table may show *relative frequencies* (p_i) in place of frequencies. In such case, we must think of the area under the histogram as equal to 1 (instead of N) and half the area under the histogram as .5 (instead of $N/2$). Then, an equation for the median similar to Equation 4.6.4 but based on less than cumulative relative frequencies, is

$$M = L + g\frac{d_p}{p_M} \qquad (4.6.5)$$

L and g have the same meaning as for Equation 4.6.4 and the other symbols have the following meaning:

d_p = difference between .5 and the less than cum p_i associated with L.
p_M = relative frequency of the median class.

Table 4.6.3 presents the relative frequency distribution for the 81 scores on a research aptitude test from Table 4.6.1. Let us obtain the median according to Equation 4.6.5, using the continuous class limits and the less than cum p_i. Starting at the top, look down the *Less than cum* p_i column. We note that .5 is between .383 and .679 (bracket these less than cum p_i

Table 4.6.3 RELATIVE FREQUENCY DISTRIBUTION FOR SCORES ON A RESEARCH APTITUDE TEST FOR 81 JOB APPLICANTS

Continuous Class Limits	p_i	Less than cum p_i	More than cum p_i
79.5		0	1.000
	.062		
83.5		.062	.938
	.111		
87.5		.173	.827
	.210		
91.5 ⎤		.383 ⎤	.617 ⎤
	(.296)		
95.5 ⎦		.679 ⎦	.321 ⎦
	.148		
99.5		.827	.173
	.136		
103.5		.963	.037
	.037		
107.5		1.000	0

values). The corresponding continuous class limits identify the median class 91.5–95.5. Bracket these limits. Place parentheses around the median class relative frequency (.296). Then, the various values which go into Equation 4.6.5 are: $L = 91.5$, $g = 4$, $d_p = .500 - .383 = .117$, and $p_M = .296$. Using Equation 4.6.5, we obtain the median as

$$M = 91.5 + (4)\frac{.117}{.296} = 93.080$$

This result, of course, is the same as obtained previously when Equation 4.6.4 was used to determine the median.

An equation, corresponding to Equation 4.6.4, for computing the median for a frequency table based on the continuous class limits and the *more than cumulative frequencies* is

$$M = U - g\frac{d'}{f_M} \tag{4.6.6}$$

The symbols g and f_M have the same meaning as in Equation 4.6.4 and the other symbols have the following meaning:

U = upper continuous class limit of the median class.
d' = difference between $N/2$ and the more than cum f_i associated with U.

Let us begin again and compute the median for the 81 scores in Table 4.6.1, using Equation 4.6.6. The first step is to compute $N/2 = 81/2 = 40.5$. Then, starting at the bottom let us look up the *More than cum* f_i column in Table 4.6.1. We note that 40.5 is between the two more than cumulative frequencies 26 and 50. Bracket these cumulative frequencies, as shown in the table. The corresponding continuous class limits identify the median class 91.5–95.5. Bracket these limits. Place parentheses around the frequency of the median class (24). The values of the various items which go into Equation 4.6.6 are: $U = 95.5$, $g = 4$, $d' = 40.5 - 26 = 14.5$, and $f_M = 24$. Then, we obtain the median as

$$M = 95.5 - (4)\frac{14.5}{24} = 93.08$$

Of course, the median is the same whether computed from Equation 4.6.4 or Equation 4.6.6.

An equation for the median similar to Equation 4.6.6 but based on the more than cumulative relative frequencies is

$$M = U - g\frac{d'_p}{p_M} \tag{4.6.7}$$

U and g have the same meaning as for Equation 4.6.6 and the other symbols have the following meaning:

d'_p = difference between .5 and the more than cum p_i associated with U.
p_M = relative frequency of the median class.

Let us start over again and use Equation 4.6.7 to determine the median for the relative frequency distribution presented in Table 4.6.3. Starting at the bottom look up the *More than cum* p_i column in the table. Note that .5 is between .321 and .617. Bracket these more than cum p_i values, as shown in the table. The corresponding continuous class limits identify the median class 91.5–95.5. Bracket these limits. Place parentheses around the relative frequency of the median class (.296). Then, the values needed for Equation 4.6.7 are: $U = 95.5$; $g = 4$; $d'_p = .500 - .321 = .179$; $p_M = .296$. Using Equation 4.6.7, we obtain the median as

$$M = 95.5 - (4)\frac{.179}{.296} = 93.080$$

This result, as expected, is the same as previously obtained.

The various methods presented for obtaining the median for a frequency distribution are applicable whether or not equal class intervals are used in setting up the frequency distribution. This is so since the only class interval involved when computing the median is the interval for the median class.

PROBLEMS FOR PRACTICE AND REVIEW

1. Determine the median for each of the following sets of scores:
(a) 7, 15, 10, 8, 11, 14, 16, 13, 4
(b) 109, 100, 97, 112, 98, 93, 101
(c) .07, .01, .09, .03, .03, .07, .07, .07, .09, .05, .08, .07, .04, .03, .02
(d) 57.03, 54.97, 58.00, 58.01, 57.00, 57.03, 55.66, 54.99, 55.00, 56.87, 57.00, 57.00, 54.97, 54.97, 58,01, 58.00, 58.01, 57.03

2. Determine the median for the response scale scores obtained for 28 subjects, as follows:

Score	Number of Subjects
100	5
101	7
102	4
103	3
104	3
105	3
106	1
107	1
108	1

3. Determine the median score for the following simple grouping table:

Score	Relative Frequency
10	.06
11	.14
12	.10
13	.10
14	.09
15	.09
16	.07
17	.07
18	.08
19	.09
20	.11

4. Compute the median for the 27 quiz grades in Problem 2 (following Section 4.4). Do this two ways, first based upon the less than cum f_i and, then, based on the more than cum f_i.

5. Compute the median for the 41 personality scale scores in Problem 3 (following Section 4.4). Do this two ways, first based upon the less than cum f_i and, then, based upon the more than cum f_i.

6. Compute the median for the frequency distribution in Problem 4 (following Section 4.4).

7. Compute the median for the 223 reaction times in Problem 6 (following Section 4.4).

8. Compute the median for the 39 scores in Problem 8 (following Section 4.4).

9. Compute the median for the frequency distribution in Problem 9 (following Section 4.4).

10. Compute the median for the frequency distribution in Problem 10 (following Section 4.4).

4.7 PERCENTILES, QUARTILES, DECILES

The median is not the only measure of position which can be determined for a distribution. Other measures of position along the score scale, useful in the fields of psychology and education, are percentiles, quartiles, and deciles. It is appropriate to introduce these measures at this point, even though they are not measures of central tendency, because they are similar in concept and method of computation to the median. We will consider these positional measures only for data organized into a frequency distribution, as they are not usually used with small sets of data.

Clearly, the median is the half-way or 50% point on the score scale. This follows from the definition of the median of a frequency distribution as that score value M where half the scores ($N/2$) have a lower value. For this reason, *the median is also called the 50th percentile, for which we use the symbol* P_{50}. *We define* P_{50} *(the 50th percentile) as that score value where 50% of the scores* ($.50N$) *have a lower value.* In the same way, we can determine a percentile so that any given proportion of the N scores has a lower value. For example, the 6th percentile (P_6) is that score value where 6% of the scores ($.06N$) have a lower value. P_{75} (the 75th percentile) is that score value where 75% of the scores ($.75N$) have a lower value. In general, *we define* P_i *(the ith percentile) as that score value where* $i\%$ *of the scores have a lower value.* P_i may be computed as follows:

$$P_i = L + g\frac{d}{f_i} \tag{4.7.1}$$

The symbols have the following meaning:

L = Lower continuous class limit of the ith percentile class.
g = length of class interval.
d = difference between $i\%$ of the scores and the less than cum f_i associated with L.
f_i = frequency of the ith percentile class.

Notice the similarity between Equation 4.7.1 and Equation 4.6.4 presented for the median in Section 4.6. Let us use Equation 4.7.1 to determine the 25th percentile (P_{25}) for the frequency distribution of the 97 scores on a spatial perception test presented in Table 4.7.1. First, determine $.25N = .25(97) = 24.25$. This tells us that we must find the score value P_{25} so that exactly 24.25 scores have a lower value. Looking down the

Table 4.7.1 FREQUENCY DISTRIBUTION FOR SCORES ON A SPATIAL PERCEPTION TEST ADMINISTERED TO 97 SUBJECTS

Continuous Class Limits	f_i	Less than cum f_i
79.5		0
	8	
83.5		8
	9	
[87.5]		[17]
	(11)	
[91.5]		[28]
	13	
95.5		41
	16	
99.5		57
	22	
103.5		79
	18	
107.5		97

Less than cum f_i column in Table 4.7.1, we note that 24.25 is between the two less than cumulative frequencies 17 and 28. Bracket these cumulative frequencies, as shown in the table. The corresponding continuous class limits identify the 25th percentile class, 87.5–91.5. Bracket these limits. Place parentheses around the frequency of the P_{25} class (11). The values of the various items which go into Equation 4.7.1 are: $L = 87.5$; $g = 91.5 - 87.5 = 4$; $d = 24.25 - 17 = 7.25$; $f_i = 11$. Therefore, we obtain the 25th percentile as

$$P_{25} = 87.5 + (4)\frac{7.25}{11} = 90.14$$

Special names are often used for two sets of percentiles. *P_{25}, P_{50}, and P_{75} are also called quartiles.* The 25th percentile is called the *first quartile* (or the *lower quartile*) and identified by the symbol Q_1. The 50th percentile (the median) is called the *second quartile* and identified as Q_2. The 75th percentile is called the *third quartile* (or the *upper quartile*) and identified as Q_3. The quartiles divide the total set of N scores into four equal parts. For example, one-fourth of the scores in a set are less than Q_1 and one-half are

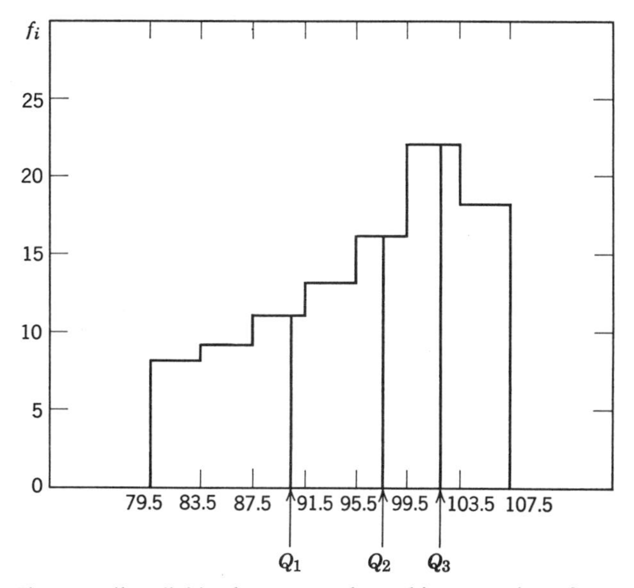

Fig. 4.7.1. The quartiles divide the area under a histogram into four equal parts.

less than Q_2 (the median). Therefore, one-fourth of the scores are between Q_1 and Q_2. Three-fourths of the scores are less than Q_3, so that one-fourth are between Q_2 and Q_3 and one-fourth are higher than Q_3. Figure 4.7.1 presents the histogram for the 97 scores in Table 4.7.1. The ordinates constructed at the quartile points (Q_1, Q_2, Q_3) divide the area under the histogram into four equal parts.

$P_{10}, P_{20}, P_{30}, \ldots, P_{90}$ are also called deciles. These percentile points on the score scale divide the total set of N scores into ten equal parts. For example, one-tenth of the scores are less than P_{10} and two-tenths are less than P_{20}. Therefore, one-tenth are between P_{10} and P_{20}. P_{10} is called the *first decile* and identified as D_1. P_{20} is called the *second decile* and identified as D_2. There are 9 deciles: $D_1, D_2, D_3, \ldots, D_9$. If ordinates are constructed at the 9 decile points in a histogram, the total area will be divided into ten equal parts.

PROBLEMS FOR PRACTICE AND REVIEW

1. Determine Q_1, Q_3, and P_{46} for the 27 quiz grades in Problem 2 (following Section 4.4).

2. Compute Q_1, Q_3, D_1, P_{35}, and P_{69} for the frequency distribution in Problem 4 (following Section 4.4).

3. Compute Q_1, Q_3, D_3, D_8, P_{18}, and P_{55} for the reaction times in Problem 6 (following Section 4.4).

4. Compute Q_1, Q_3, D_4, D_7, and P_{22} for the scores on a running speed test in Problem 9 (following Section 4.4).

5. Compute Q_1, Q_3, D_6, D_9, P_{77}, and P_{95} for the 131 mechanical performance test scores in Problem 10 (following Section 4.4).

4.8 MODE

In a set of scores, *the mode is that score which appears most often.* Hence, generally speaking, the mode is the easiest measure of central tendency to determine. For example, suppose we have the following scores on an arithmetic speed test for 15 sixth-grade pupils: 85, 74, 68, 71, 74, 74, 79, 85, 93, 74, 74, 71, 74, 79, 79. Since 74 appears most often (six times), it is the mode of this set of scores. When the number of scores in a set is large, the mode is most easily found by organizing the data into a simple grouping table (see Chapter 3, Section 3.2). This not only provides a convenient means to determine the mode but gives some idea as to how the data are distributed as well.

Sometimes a set of data does not have a mode. For example, consider the following set of 8 grades on a history examination: 72, 85, 93, 81, 93, 81, 72, 85. It will be observed that each grade appears twice. Hence, there is no mode since no grade appears more often than the others. *In such a case, the mode is not zero; it just does not exist.* A set of scores may have two or more modes. For example, Table 4.8.1 presents a simple grouping table summarizing 158 scores on a word recognition test. Observing the total frequency column, we note that the score of 22 has a frequency (21) which is the maximum for the lower part of the score scale, and the score of 27 has a frequency (25) which is the maximum for the upper part of the score scale. This is an illustration of a *bimodal* (two modes) distribution. To be a mode, a score need not have a frequency which is the maximum when all scores along the score scale are considered. Actually, *a modal score is one which has a maximum frequency along some portion of the score scale.* The bimodality of the distribution of the 158 scores is clearly apparent in Figure 4.8.1. A distribution which contains two or more modes is called a *multimodal* distribution.

A distribution may be bimodal due to the heterogeneous nature of the data. For example, as indicated in Table 4.8.1 and Figure 4.8.1, the 158 word recognition test scores represent a heterogeneous collection of scores. That is, these scores include two distinct groups, high school students and college students. It is to be expected that the college students will tend to score higher on this test than the high school students. If the scores for these groups are separated, the resulting separate score distributions are clearly *unimodal* (contain a single mode each).

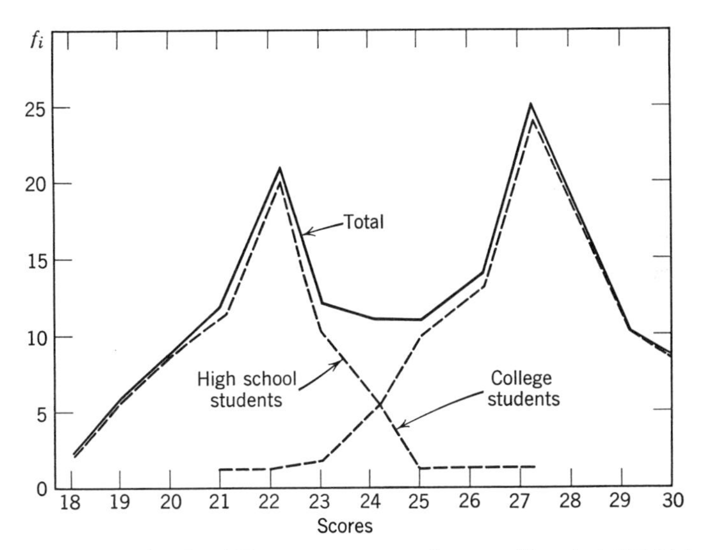

Fig. 4.8.1. Line graphs for 158 scores on a word recognition test (67 high school students, 91 college students). An illustration of a bimodal distribution, where the bimodality is caused by the heterogeneity of the data.

There appears to be no generally accepted method of determining the mode for a frequency distribution. For example, consider the scores for 126 college seniors on a reading comprehension test presented in Table 4.8.2. Examination of the class frequencies indicates that 95.0–99.9 is the *modal class* since it is the class with the largest frequency (32). The midpoint of this class (97.45) is called the *crude mode* of the distribution. Recall that organization of a collection of data into a frequency distribution involves a number of decisions, with considerable room for the use of judgment. Any change in the manner of data organization may lead to different classes and different midpoints. Therefore, the use of the midpoint of the modal class as the mode involves a degree of arbitrariness.

Various methods are used to refine the crude mode, none especially

Table 4.8.1 SIMPLE GROUPING TABLE OF 158 SCORES ON A WORD RECOGNITION TEST

	Frequency		
Score	Total	High School Students	College Students
18	2	2	–
19	6	6	–
20	9	9	–
21	12	11	1
22	21	20	1
23	12	10	2
24	11	6	5
25	11	1	10
26	14	1	13
27	25	1	24
28	17	–	17
29	10	–	10
30	8	–	8
Total	158	67	91

outstanding. This text suggests the following as an approach that is easy to understand and use. It is assumed that the true mode lies somewhere within the continuous limits of the modal class. A more refined mode for a frequency distribution may be determined on the basis of the midpoints (X_i) and class frequencies (f_i) for the following three classes: the modal

Table 4.8.2 FREQUENCY DISTRIBUTION FOR SCORES ON A READING COMPREHENSION TEST FOR 126 COLLEGE SENIORS

Discrete Class Limits	f_i	Midpoint, X_i
85.0–89.9	19	87.45
90.0–94.9	27	92.45
95.0–99.9	32	97.45
100.0–104.9	20	102.45
105.0–109.9	17	107.45
110.0–114.9	9	112.45
115.0–119.9	2	117.45

class, the class just below, and the class just above. More specifically, the mode may be obtained as

$$\text{Mode} = \frac{\sum X_i f_i}{\sum f_i} \quad \text{(summation over three classes)} \qquad (4.8.1)$$

Let us use Equation 4.8.1 to obtain the mode for the frequency distribution in Table 4.8.2. The three classes to be used are the modal class (95.0–99.9), the next lower class (90.0–94.9), and the next higher class (100.0–104.9). It is a good idea to bracket the midpoints and class frequencies for these classes, as indicated in Table 4.8.2. Then, using Equation 4.8.1, we obtain

$$\text{Mode} = \frac{(92.45)(27) + (97.45)(32) + (102.45)(20)}{27 + 32 + 20} = 97.01$$

We can demonstrate that Equation 4.8.1 results in a modal score within the continuous limits of the modal class by considering the *extreme possibilities*. For example, since the class frequency is highest for the modal class (by definition), other class frequencies in the distribution must be smaller. Since the modal class frequency in Table 4.8.2 is 32, the highest possible frequency for another class in this distribution is 31. Of course, the lowest possible frequency for a class is 0. Therefore, for the three classes used in computing the mode, let us consider the extreme possibility where we have the maximum nonmodal frequency (31) for one of the two nonmodal classes, the minimum frequency (0) for the other, and 32 for the modal class, as follows:

X_i	f_i
92.45	31
97.45	32
102.45	0

Applying Equation 4.8.1, we obtain

$$\text{Mode} = \frac{(92.45)(31) + (97.45)(32) + (102.45)(0)}{31 + 32 + 0} = 94.99$$

We will now consider the opposite extreme possibility by reversing the nonmodal class frequencies, as follows:

X_i	f_i
92.45	0
97.45	32
102.45	31

Applying Equation 4.8.1, we now obtain

$$\text{Mode} = \frac{(92.45)(0) + (97.45)(32) + (102.45)(31)}{0 + 32 + 31} = 99.91$$

Clearly, then, the extreme values possible for the mode, 94.99 and 99.91, are contained within the continuous limits of the modal class, 94.95–99.95. It might be noted that when the two nonmodal classes have the same frequency, the refined mode computed by the use of Equation 4.8.1 is identical with the crude mode. For example, using 31 as the frequency for each of the two nonmodal classes, we have

X_i	f_i
92.45	31
97.45	32
102.45	31

Applying Equation 4.8.1, we find that the refined mode is 97.45, the same as the crude mode.

It may have been noted by the reader that Equation 4.8.1 is similar to the equation for the mean computed for a frequency distribution (Equation 4.3.16, Section 4.3 of this chapter). In other words, computation of the mode by the use of Equation 4.8.1 amounts to computing the mean for the scores contained in the modal class and the two bordering class intervals.

PROBLEMS FOR PRACTICE AND REVIEW

1. Determine the mode for each of the following sets of scores:

(a) 12, 10, 14, 10, 9, 12, 9, 10, 14, 10, 12, 10, 12, 10, 18, 9, 10

(b) 120, 111, 123, 122, 121, 123, 121, 123, 116, 123, 120, 111, 123, 120, 123, 114, 123, 115, 115, 111, 123, 118, 111, 110, 123, 116, 123, 121, 125, 127, 123, 118, 118, 123, 127, 130

(c) 76, 70, 70, 76, 71, 81, 75, 70, 71, 81, 76, 81, 75, 71, 75, 83, 83, 83, 75, 76, 81, 70, 71, 83

(d) 21, 18, 15, 18, 13, 11, 21, 15, 14, 15, 18, 20, 21, 23, 24, 21, 20, 21, 22, 18, 21, 15, 13, 21, 21, 15, 21, 20, 13, 18, 11, 15, 10, 15, 15, 21, 22, 25, 27, 21, 15, 15, 14, 15

(e) 0, 10, 2, 1, 2, 7, 10, 8, 9, 10, 7, 0, 1, 3, 7, 2, 4, 5, 7, 10, 7, 8, 9, 10, 7, 2, 0, 1, 10, 2, 8, 6, 4, 2, 2, 0

2. Determine the mode (crude and refined) for the 27 quiz grades in Problem 2 (following Section 4.4).

3. Determine the mode (crude and refined) for the 41 scores in Problem 3 (following Section 4.4).

4. Determine the mode (crude and refined) for the frequency distribution in Problem 4 (following Section 4.4).

5. Determine the mode (crude and refined) for the frequency distribution in Problem 6 (following Section 4.4).

4.9 PROPERTIES AND COMPARISONS

Clearly, each of the three averages we have studied qualifies as a measure of central tendency and/or of the typicalness of a set of data. Nevertheless, they are quite different. What are the properties of each of these averages? How do they compare? In a given situation, which should you use?

The arithmetic mean represents the equilibrium point of a set of data. For example, the mean of the set of three scores 4, 5, 9 is 6. Suppose we have a weightless bar, scaled off as in Figure 4.9.1, and three cylinders of

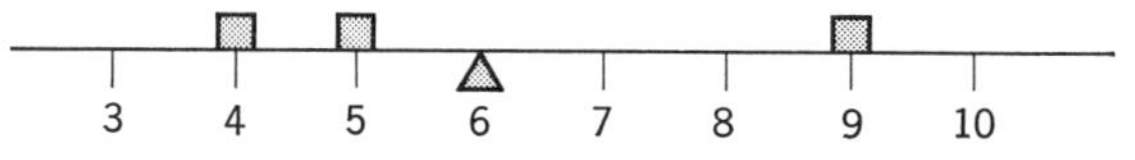

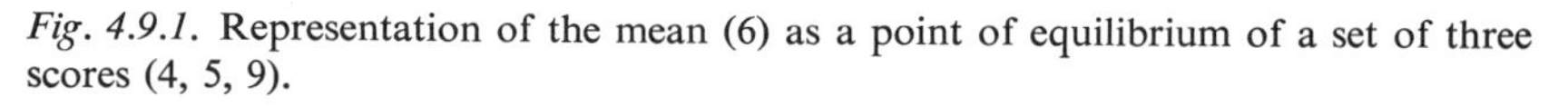

Fig. 4.9.1. Representation of the mean (6) as a point of equilibrium of a set of three scores (4, 5, 9).

equal weight. We place one cylinder at each of the scale positions corresponding to the scores 4, 5, 9. If a fulcrum is placed at the mean (6), the bar will be in perfect balance. In this sense, the mean of a set of values is the point of balance or equilibrium of the set.

The mean is determined by every item in a set of values. Therefore, it is the most sensitive of the three averages. If we change one or more scores in a set, the mean will change. For example, in the set 4, 5, 9, if we change 9 to 10, the mean will change from 6 to 6.33. This is an important and usually desirable property of the mean. However, this property makes the mean less desirable as an average for a set which contains extreme values. For example, consider the set of scores 12, 11, 18, 16, 100. The mean is 31.4. This is not a desirable average for this set, generally speaking, since it is not representative of any of the scores in the set.

A most important property of the mean is that it can be treated algebraically. This has already been noted in our discussion of the mean. If we subtract the mean (μ) from any score (X_i) in a set, we obtain the *deviation from the mean* ($X_i - \mu$). This is a very important concept in statistical theory. We will use the lower-case letter x_i to represent the deviation from the mean ($X_i - \mu$). *The sum of the deviations of a set of N scores from their mean is zero*. We can express this property of the mean symbolically as

$$\sum_{i=1}^{N} x_i = \sum_{i=1}^{N}(X_i - \mu) = 0 \qquad (4.9.1)$$

(For proof see Section 4.10, *Note* 4.9.)

We will illustrate this property of the mean by considering the set of four scores 3, 7, 8, 2. The mean is 5. The deviations from the mean for this set are: $3 - 5 = -2$, $7 - 5 = 2$, $8 - 5 = 3$, $2 - 5 = -3$. The algebraic sum of these deviations (the sum which takes into consideration the plus and minus signs of the deviations) is: $(-2) + (2) + (3) + (-3) = 0$.

Suppose we select a constant k and determine, for each score (X_i) in a set of N scores, the deviation ($X_i - k$). Then, let us square each deviation, obtaining $(X_i - k)^2$, and add the N squared deviations for the set. *This sum of squared deviations from a constant k is a minimum if the value we choose for k is the mean μ for the set of scores*. This is known as the *least squares property of the mean*. We may show this symbolically as

$$\sum_{i=1}^{N} (X_i - k)^2 \quad \text{is a minimum if} \quad k = \mu \qquad (4.9.2)$$

Let us demonstrate the truth of Equation 4.9.2. The mean of the 5 scores, 36, 31, 24, 30, 29, is 30. The deviations from the mean are 6, 1, −6, 0, −1, respectively. The sum of the squared deviations is 74. Let us compare this result with the sum of the squared deviations of these 5 scores from some other value, say, 29. These deviations are 7, 2, −5, 1, 0, respectively. The sum of the squares of these deviations is 79, which, of course, is greater than 74.

The arithmetic mean is unique for a set of data. That is, for a given set of scores, there is *one* and *only one* mean. Furthermore, the mean can always be computed. Even if the individual scores in a set are not known, the mean can be determined if we know the number of scores included (N) and the sum of the scores (ΣX_i). This follows from the definition of the mean (see Equation 4.2.2 in Section 4.2). If a frequency table is open at one or both ends, it is not possible to compute the mean unless the open class intervals are closed. This may be done by going back to the raw data (which is usually not practical or not possible) or making an assumption as to the length of the open class intervals.

The median represents the midrank value of a set of data. That is, the median is centrally positioned in a set of scores in the sense that the number of scores with a lower value is equal to the number with a higher value. *The median is considerably less sensitive to the particular values of the data included in a set than is the mean*. For example, the median of the five scores 30, 45, 50, 33, 49 is 45. If 50 were changed to 500, 45 would still be the median since it would still be centrally located. However, if a score is changed in such a way that it results in a change in the middle score, then the median will be affected. For example, if the score of 50 in this illustration is changed to 5, then 33 becomes the median instead of 45.

A deviation of a score (X_i) from some value, say, k, may be positive or negative. This was observed when we discussed deviations such as ($X_i - k$). Sometimes one is interested in the *magnitude* of a deviation, *not the direction* (plus or minus). In this case, the interest is in the *absolute* deviation. For example, the deviations of scores 5 and 10 from 7 are $5 - 7 = -2$ and $10 - 7 = 3$. However, the *absolute* deviations of these scores from 7 are 2 and 3, respectively. Clearly, to obtain absolute deviations, we must consider all deviations as positive, regardless of sign. *The sum of the absolute deviations of a set of N scores from a constant k is a minimum if k is the median for the set.* This property of the median can be shown in symbols as

$$\sum_{i=1}^{N} |X_i - k| \quad \text{is a minimum if} \quad k = M \tag{4.9.3}$$

The symbol $|X_i - k|$ is used to represent the absolute deviation of X_i from k. Let us demonstrate the truth of Equation 4.9.3. Consider the 5 scores 105, 110, 95, 107, 112. The median is 107. The absolute deviations from the median are 2, 3, 12, 0, 5, respectively. The sum of these deviations is 22. Let us now determine the sum of the absolute deviations from some other value, say, 105. The absolute deviations from 105 are 0, 5, 10, 2, 7, respectively, and the sum of these deviations is 24, which is greater than 22.

The median can always be computed, even for frequency tables which are open at one or both ends. That is, computation of the median for a frequency distribution is based on the continuous limits of the median class, plus other information. The limits of other class intervals in a frequency distribution are not involved in this computation.

In a set of scores, *the mode represents the score with the maximum frequency*. The mode is practically insensitive to the particular values included in a set. That is, changes in the value of items in a set have no effect on the mode, except insofar as they affect the item with the maximum frequency. For example, consider this set of 7 scores: 131, 139, 127, 131, 125, 126, 131. The mode is 131. If we change any or all of the scores, the mode will not change, unless, as a result of these changes, 131 no longer has the maximum frequency.

In a unimodal, symmetrical distribution, as shown in Figure 4.9.2, part A, the three averages (mean, median, mode) are equal. Therefore, in such a situation, there is no problem as to which average is best to use. In a positively skewed, unimodal distribution, as shown in part B, the concentration of items is in the lower end of the score scale. Some items are strung out in a tail at the upper end of the scale. These extreme items in the tail influence the mean, pulling it upward, but have no effect on the other two averages. In such distributions, the mean has the highest value,

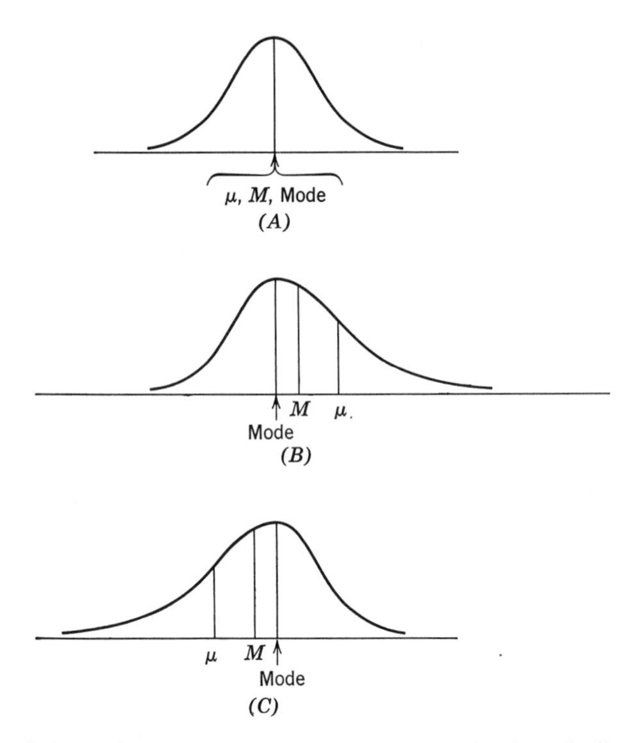

Fig. 4.9.2 Relative position of the mean, median and mode for three distribution types. (*A*) Symmetrical, unimodal distribution (*B*) Positively skewed, unimodal distribution (*C*) Negatively skewed, unimodal distribution.

the mode has the lowest value, and the median is somewhere between the two, as indicated in part *B*. In a negatively skewed, unimodal distribution, illustrated in part *C*, the reverse is true. Here, the tail is in the lower end of the score scale, resulting in a downward pull on the mean. Hence, the mean has a lower value than either of the other two averages in such distributions. It is apparent from the illustration that, here, the mode has the highest value and the median lies somewhere in between.

Generally speaking, the mean is the preferred average because it is more rigorously defined, it can be treated algebraically, and when it is used, there is a tendency toward less sampling variability than for the other averages. This latter point needs further explanation. It has already been noted that a most important application of statistical methods is the development of statistical inferences relating to a population based on information obtained from a sample. This will be more fully treated in later chapters. However, it might be noted at this point that the theory underlying statistical inferences is based on the notion of *repeated sampling*.

For example, suppose the superintendent of a large school system must estimate the average IQ for high school freshmen currently enrolled. Say, it is decided to select a sample of 50 freshmen and, based on the average IQ in the sample, to make an inference as to the average in the population. Of course, the superintendent will select only one sample of 50 students. However, the statistical theory used in making the inference is based on the idea of selecting a large number of samples of 50 students each, determining the average from each sample, and taking into consideration how the average varies from sample to sample. According to statistical theory to be discussed later in the text, the less variation there is among sample averages, the more likely is it that the average computed for the particular sample selected by the superintendent will be a good estimate of the population average.

In the usual situation of concern to workers in psychology and education, *sampling variability of an average, in the sense just described, is less if the average used is the arithmetic mean.* This is a critically important advantage of the mean over the other averages where statistical inferences are to be made based on sample data.

Generally, when an average is required for data containing extreme values, such as in a highly skewed distribution, the median is the preferred average. The mean is too sensitive to extreme values, and the mode merely reflects the value with the maximum frequency. In such situations, the median is the most typical average and most representative of the distribution.

The mean can be determined only for ratio and interval scale data. The median can be determined for ratio, interval, and ordinal scale data. The mode, on the other hand, can be determined for data measured on any scale, including the nominal scale. Table 4.9.1 presents the final grade distribution in history for 148 high school honor students. The grade scale is an ordinal scale, permitting a ranking arrangement, as shown in the table. The *cum* f_i column is somewhat different from the cum f_i presented previously. The first frequency in this column indicates that 59 students received a final grade of A. The second frequency indicates that 82 students received a grade of A− or better, etc. Since there are 148 grades, the median position is $\frac{1}{2}(148 + 1) = 74.5$. Therefore, looking down the *cum* f_i column, since 82 students received a grade of A− or better (including the 74th and 75th grades), the median grade is A−. The modal grade is A

Table 4.9.1 FINAL GRADES IN HISTORY FOR 148 HIGH SCHOOL HONOR STUDENTS

Grade	Number of Students, f_i	Cum f_i
A	59	59
A–	23	82
B+	5	87
B	52	139
B–	3	142
C+	1	143
C	5	148

since more students received this grade than any other in the set. As indicated in the table, B is also a mode. Hence, this is a bimodal distribution.

Table 4.9.2 presents the distribution of 100 subjects according to the experimental form of reading comprehension test taken. The scale of measurement for this distribution (test form) is a nominal scale. The only average which can be determined for this distribution is the mode. Clearly, test form RC-15 is the modal form.

Table 4.9.2 DISTRIBUTION OF 100 SUBJECTS ACCORDING TO EXPERIMENTAL FORM OF READING COMPREHENSION TEST

Test Form	Number of Subjects
RC–12	18
RC–13	12
RC–14	16
RC–15	39
RC–16	15

PROBLEMS FOR PRACTICE AND REVIEW

1. List the properties of the mean, median, mode.

2. Using the set of scores: 108, 106, 111, 109, 110, 104, 108:

(a) verify Equation 4.9.1.

(b) show that the sum of the deviations from a value not equal to the mean, say 105, is not equal to zero.

3. Using the set of scores in Problem 2, verify Equation 4.9.6 by comparing the results when k is put equal to the mean and when $k = 105$.

4. Given the set of scores: 74, 61, 62, 74, 50, 74, 62, 65, 74, 50, 47, 46, 74, 74, 46, 41, 40, verify Equation 4.9.7 by comparing the results for $k = M$, $k = \mu$, $k =$ mode, $k = 40$.

5. Given the set of midterm examination grades for a class: 23, 93, 31, 90, 97, 96, 88, 100, 19, 98, 100, 96, 90, 91, 89, which is the most suitable average to use to represent the class performance on this examination? Why?

6. The following data appeared in a psychological research journal:

Response to Therapy	Number of Subjects
Excellent	10
Very good	14
Good	11
No apparent response	5

Determine the median response by the 40 subjects. Determine the modal response.

4.10 ALGEBRAIC NOTES

This section presents algebraic proofs of certain equations introduced in this chapter. The background required to follow these proofs includes a knowledge of the basic operations of elementary algebra, as sketched in Appendix A, and the three rules of summation presented in Chapter 2, Section 2.6. The proofs are presented in a series of *Notes*. In each *Note*, the equation which is the subject of the proof is identified, as well as the general location of the equation in the chapter. Reference should be made to the previous discussion of the equation before studying each *Note*. When equations which have already appeared in the text are presented, they are identified by the number originally assigned. For equations presented for the first time, new identifying numbers (keyed to this section) are assigned.

NOTE 4.1: To prove (*Situation* 1)

$$\mu_{(X+k)} = \mu + k \qquad (4.3.1)$$

The mean $\mu_{(X+k)}$ of a set of N $(X_i + k)$ scores can be obtained directly by substituting $X_i + k$ for X_i in Equation 4.2.2 to obtain

$$\mu_{(X+k)} = \frac{\sum_{i=1}^{N} (X_i + k)}{N} \qquad (4.10.1)$$

Applying Summation Rule 1 to the numerator of Equation 4.10.1, we obtain

$$\mu_{(X+k)} = \frac{\sum_{i=1}^{N} X_i + \sum_{i=1}^{N} k}{N} = \frac{\sum_{i=1}^{N} X_i}{N} + \frac{\sum_{i=1}^{N} k}{N} \tag{4.10.2}$$

In the second form of Equation 4.10.2, the first term is the mean of the X_i scores μ (Equation 4.2.2). Then, substituting μ for the first term and applying Summation Rule 3 to the second term (k is a constant), we obtain

$$\mu_{(X+k)} = \mu + \frac{Nk}{N} = \mu + k \tag{4.10.3}$$

NOTE 4.2: To prove (*Situation* 1)

$$\mu_{(X-k)} = \mu - k \tag{4.3.2}$$

This proof is similar to *Note* 4.1. It begins by expressing the mean $\mu_{(X-k)}$ of a set of N $(X_i - k)$ scores according to Equation 4.2.2, substituting $X_i - k$ for X_i. This gives

$$\mu_{(X-k)} = \frac{\sum_{i=1}^{N} (X_i - k)}{N} \tag{4.10.4}$$

The balance of the proof will be left as an exercise for the reader.

NOTE 4.3: To prove (*Situation* 2)

$$\mu_{gX} = g\mu \tag{4.3.4}$$

The mean μ_{gX} of a set of N gX_i scores can be obtained directly by substituting gX_i for X_i in Equation 4.2.2, to obtain

$$\mu_{gX} = \frac{\sum_{i=1}^{N} gX_i}{N} \tag{4.10.5}$$

Noting that g is a constant, apply Summation Rule 2 to obtain

$$\mu_{gX} = \frac{g \sum_{i=1}^{N} X_i}{N} = g\left(\frac{\sum_{i=1}^{N} X_i}{N}\right) \tag{4.10.6}$$

In the second form of Equation 4.10.6, the term in parentheses is μ, the mean of the X_i scores (Equation 4.2.2). Therefore, substituting μ for this term, we obtain

$$\mu_{gX} = g\mu \tag{4.10.7}$$

NOTE 4.4: To prove (*Situation* 2)

$$\mu_{X/g} = \frac{\mu}{g} \tag{4.3.5}$$

The mean $\mu_{X/g}$ of a set of N X_i/g scores can be obtained directly by substituting X_i/g for X_i in Equation 4.2.2 to obtain

$$\mu_{X/g} = \frac{\sum_{i=1}^{N} \frac{X_i}{g}}{N} \tag{4.10.8}$$

The balance of the proof is similar to *Note* 4.3 and will be left as an exercise for the reader.

NOTE 4.5: To prove (*Situation* 3)

$$\mu = g\bar{u} + k \tag{4.3.9}$$

where

$$\bar{u} = \frac{\sum_{i=1}^{N} u_i}{N} \tag{4.3.8}$$

and

$$u_i = \frac{X_i - k}{g} \tag{4.3.7}$$

Solving Equation 4.3.7 for X_i, we obtain

$$X_i = gu_i + k \tag{4.10.9}$$

Then, in Equation 4.2.2, substituting for X_i in accordance with Equation 4.10.9, we obtain

$$\mu = \frac{\sum_{i=1}^{N} (gu_i + k)}{N} \tag{4.10.10}$$

Applying Summation Rule 1 to the numerator of Equation 4.10.10, we obtain

$$\mu = \frac{\sum_{i=1}^{N} gu_i + \sum_{i=1}^{N} k}{N} = \frac{\sum_{i=1}^{N} gu_i}{N} + \frac{\sum_{i=1}^{N} k}{N} \tag{4.10.11}$$

In the second form of Equation 4.10.11, noting that g and k are constants, apply Summation Rule 2 to the first term and Summation Rule 3 to the second term. This gives

$$\mu = \frac{g\sum_{i=1}^{N} u_i}{N} + \frac{Nk}{N} = g\left(\frac{\sum_{i=1}^{N} u_i}{N}\right) + k \tag{4.10.12}$$

In the second form of Equation 4.10.12, the term in parentheses is $\bar{u}$ (Equation 4.3.8), the mean of the u_i scores. Therefore, substituting $\bar{u}$ for this term, we obtain

$$\mu = g\bar{u} + k \tag{4.10.13}$$

NOTE 4.6: To prove (*Situation* 5)

$$\mu = \frac{\sum_{i=1}^{c} \mu_i N_i}{\sum_{i=1}^{c} N_i} \tag{4.3.13}$$

Solving Equation 4.2.2 for $\Sigma\, X_i$, we obtain

$$\sum_{i=1}^{N} X_i = N\mu \tag{4.10.14}$$

Equation 4.10.14 indicates that, for any collection of scores (X_i), the product of the mean (μ) and the number of scores included in the collection (N) is equal to the sum of all the scores in the collection ($\Sigma\, X_i$). In the same way, for a subset of N_i scores with mean μ_i the product $N_i\mu_i$ represents the sum of all the scores in the subset. If there are c subsets, then the sum of all scores in all subsets combined is $\sum_{i=1}^{c} N_i\mu_i$. Furthermore, the total number of scores in all subsets combined is $\sum_{i=1}^{c} N_i$. Therefore, since the mean is computed as the sum of the scores divided by the total number of scores included (Equation 4.2.2), we have

$$\mu = \frac{\sum_{i=1}^{c} \mu_i N_i}{\sum_{i=1}^{c} N_i} \tag{4.10.15}$$

NOTE 4.7: To prove (*Situation* 6)

$$\mu_S = \mu_X + \mu_Y \tag{4.3.14}$$

The mean μ_S of a set of N S_i $(= X_i + Y_i)$ scores can be obtained directly by substituting $X_i + Y_i$ for X_i in Equation 4.2.2, to obtain

$$\mu_S = \frac{\sum_{i=1}^{N} (X_i + Y_i)}{N} \tag{4.10.16}$$

Applying Summation Rule 1 to the numerator of Equation 4.10.16, we obtain

$$\mu_S = \frac{\sum_{i=1}^{N} X_i + \sum_{i=1}^{N} Y_i}{N} = \frac{\sum_{i=1}^{N} X_i}{N} + \frac{\sum_{i=1}^{N} Y_i}{N} \quad (4.10.17)$$

In the second form of Equation 4.10.17, the first term is the mean of the X_i scores, μ_X, and the second term is the mean of the Y_i scores, μ_Y (Equation 4.2.2). Therefore, substituting for these terms, we obtain

$$\mu_S = \mu_X + \mu_Y \quad (4.10.18)$$

NOTE 4.8: To prove (*Situation* 6)

$$\mu_D = \mu_X - \mu_Y \quad (4.3.15)$$

This proof is similar to *Note* 4.7. It begins by expressing the mean μ_D of a set of N D_i $(= X_i - Y_i)$ scores according to Equation 4.2.2, substituting $X_i - Y_i$ for X_i. This gives

$$\mu_D = \frac{\sum_{i=1}^{N} (X_i - Y_i)}{N} \quad (4.10.19)$$

The balance of the proof will be left as an exercise for the reader.

NOTE 4.9: To prove (Section 4.9)

$$\sum_{i=1}^{N} x_i = \sum_{i=1}^{N} (X_i - \mu) = 0 \quad (4.9.1)$$

Applying Summation Rule 1 to the second summation in Equation 4.9.1, we obtain

$$\sum_{i=1}^{N} x_i = \sum_{i=1}^{N} X_i - \sum_{i=1}^{N} \mu \quad (4.10.20)$$

Noting that μ is a constant for a given set of scores, apply Summation Rule 3 to obtain

$$\sum_{i=1}^{N} x_i = \sum_{i=1}^{N} X_i - N\mu \quad (4.10.21)$$

Referring to Equation 4.10.14, we may substitute $\sum X_i$ for $N\mu$ and obtain

$$\sum_{i=1}^{N} x_i = \sum_{i=1}^{N} X_i - \sum_{i=1}^{N} X_i = 0 \quad (4.10.22)$$

5

MEASURES OF VARIATION

5.1 INTRODUCTION

Typically, measurements of any kind exhibit variation. Quiz grades for a class vary from pupil to pupil. Scores on a psychometric test vary from subject to subject. Reaction time to a stimulus varies from subject to subject and even from trial to trial for the same subject. *Variation is the most important characteristic of a distribution, from the point of view of statistical methods.* For example, consider a collection of, say, 1000 scores on a psychometric test. If it is determined that there is no variation at all among these scores and that they are all equal to, say, 129, we then have complete information concerning the score distribution. There is no need whatsoever for statistical methods. However, in the typical situation, where variation does exist among the scores in a collection, statistical methods are required to describe the score distribution.

The extent of variation among the scores in a set is of primary importance in any application of statistical methods. For example, consider the two sets of scores: 150, 151, 153, 154 (set A); and 70, 101, 204, 233 (set B). In both sets, the mean is 152. However, set A is considerably more homogeneous than set B (i.e., contains considerably less variation among the scores in the set). Consequently, knowledge of the mean for set A conveys more information concerning the individual scores in the set than is the case for set B. *The extent of variation among the scores in a population is of major importance in sampling and statistical inference.* This will be discussed in later chapters.

One of the simplest measures of variation is the *range* (*the distance between the highest and lowest values in a set*). In the example, the highest score in set A is 154 and the lowest is 150. Hence, we determine the range as 4, the difference between the two extreme scores.

The *score interval*, 150–154, as well as the *distance*, 4, is referred to as the range. In set B, the range is 70–233 or 163. Suppose we did not know the individual scores included in each set and are told that set A has a mean of 152 and a range of 4, whereas set B has the same mean but a range of 163. This would certainly provide more illuminating knowledge concerning the score distribution in each set than if we only knew that the mean of each set is 152. Clearly, the combined knowledge of an average and a measure of variation provides substantially more descriptive information concerning a distribution than is provided by an average alone.

Fundamentally, measures of variation are of a different nature than measures of central tendency. That is, *an average represents a point on the score scale, whereas a measure of variation represents a distance along the score scale*. For example, in previously discussed sets A and B the mean (152) represents a central point on the score scale, whereas the range (4 for set A and 163 for set B) represents the distance along the score scale between the highest and lowest scores for a set.

Although the range is the simplest measure of variation to compute, it is usually of limited value because it depends solely on the two extreme values of a set, the highest value and the lowest value. The distribution of the other scores in a set has no effect on the range. For example, the two sets of scores 50, 100, 150, 200 and 50, 51, 52, 200 have the same range (150). However, the score distributions are quite different. In the first set, the four scores are evenly spaced over the 50–200 range. In the second set, the first three scores are closely grouped, whereas the fourth score stands alone at the upper end of the range.

The most important measures of variation used in statistics represent, in some sense, *the average distance of the scores in a set from a point of reference*. For example, consider the set of five scores: 92, 98, 103, 105, 110. Let us, arbitrarily, select 80 as a point of reference. Then, the distances of these scores from 80 are 12, 18, 23, 25, 30. The mean of these distances, 21.6, represents a measure of variation of the set of five scores *from the arbitrary point of reference*. In other words, on the average, these scores vary (deviate) from 80 by 21.6 points. A measure of variation computed in this manner represents an improvement over the range in that all the scores in a set are involved in the computation. However, a serious weakness in the approach used is the arbitrary nature of the point of reference selected. That is, there is no particular significance in the average distance of a set of scores from some arbitrarily designated value.

We will study the *standard deviation* and the *quartile deviation*, two measures of variation important in statistics. Both of these measures are based on the notion of an average deviation (distance) of a set of scores from a point of reference. However, *the point of reference used in each case is a measure of central tendency*, resulting in a measure of variation which is meaningful and highly useful. This will become clearer in the following discussion.

5.2 STANDARD DEVIATION: DEFINITION

The *standard deviation* is, by far, the most important and most used measure of variation in statistics. *This measure of variation is based on the arithmetic mean as the point of reference.* Therefore, the standard deviation is the appropriate measure of variation to use when the mean is used as the average.

Let us consider the set of four scores: 24, 28, 31, 37. Using the mean (30) as the point of reference, we determine the deviation of each score from the mean as: $24 - 30 = -6$, $28 - 30 = -2$, $31 - 30 = 1$, $37 - 30 = 7$. We may attempt to construct a measure of variation, following the procedure presented previously, by computing the mean of these deviations from the mean. That is, add the four deviations and divide by 4. However, we note that the deviations add to zero, so that the mean is zero. Furthermore, if we tried this again using another set of scores, the sum of the deviations from the mean would again turn out to be zero.

Of course, this should occasion no surprise, since we noted in Chapter 4, Section 4.9 that the sum of the deviations of a set of scores from their mean is always zero. This property of the mean was expressed algebraically in Equation 4.9.1 where we used the symbol x_i to represent $X_i - \mu$, the deviation of a score (X_i) from the mean (μ) for the set. We will use x_i to represent the deviation from the mean for sample data as well as population data. That is, for sample data, $x_i = X_i - \bar{X}$. Clearly, this property of the mean makes this procedure for constructing a measure of variation worthless, since the measure will always be zero.

A slight modification of this approach provides a highly useful measure of variation. This modification involves *squaring the deviations from the mean and then obtaining the mean of the squared deviations.* Using this modified approach, we obtain the following measures of variation:

Population
$$\sigma^2 = \frac{\sum_{i=1}^{N}(X_i - \mu)^2}{N} = \frac{\sum_{i=1}^{N} x_i^2}{N} \tag{5.2.1}$$

$$\sigma = \sqrt{\sigma^2} \tag{5.2.2}$$

$$\text{Sample} \qquad s^2 = \frac{\sum_{i=1}^{n}(X_i - \bar{X})^2}{n-1} = \frac{\sum_{i=1}^{n} x_i^2}{n-1} \qquad (5.2.3)$$

$$s = \sqrt{s^2} \qquad (5.2.4)$$

Let us first consider the equations for population data and apply them to the population of ten scores on a digital dexterity test, as shown in Table 5.2.1. Using the total of the score column in the table, compute $\mu = \frac{414}{10} =$

Table 5.2.1 COMPUTATION OF THE VARIANCE AND THE STANDARD DEVIATION: SCORES ON A DIGITAL DEXTERITY TEST FOR A POPULATION OF TEN SUBJECTS

	Score, X_i	$x_i = X_i - 41.4$	x_i^2
	38	–3.4	11.56
	41	–.4	.16
	32	–9.4	88.36
	39	–2.4	5.76
	40	–1.4	1.96
	42	.6	.36
	51	9.6	92.16
	58	16.6	275.56
	43	1.6	2.56
	30	–11.4	129.96
Total	414		608.40

41.4. Then, determine the deviation of each score from the mean, $x_i = X_i - 41.4$, as shown in the table. Square these deviations to obtain x_i^2, as shown in the last column of the table. Then, applying Equation 5.2.1, we obtain σ^2 (σ is the lower-case Greek letter *sigma*) as follows:

$$\sigma^2 = \frac{\sum_{i=1}^{10} x_i^2}{10} = \frac{608.40}{10} = 60.84$$

The result (σ^2), which is *the mean of the squared deviations from the mean, is called the variance.* The variance is an important measure of variation in statistics. However, σ^2 measures the variation of a set of scores in terms of the *squares* of the deviations from the mean. It is general practice to compute σ, the square root of the variance (Equation 5.2.2). This measure of variation, σ, is called the *standard deviation.* In our illustration, $\sigma = \sqrt{60.84} = 7.8$.

It should be noted that it is the *distance* of each score from the mean and not the *direction* which is considered in the computation of the standard deviation, σ. This is accomplished when the deviations are squared. For example, if the mean of a population of scores is 50, the deviation of a score of 40 from the mean is -10 (or 10 points *below* the mean), while the deviation of a score of 60 is 10 (or 10 points *above* the mean). However, the squared deviations from the mean are the same (100) for both scores. In other words, the squared deviation takes into account only the *magnitude* of the deviation (10) and not the *direction* of the deviation (above, + or below, −).

It is important for the reader to understand the meaning of the standard deviation. *It is a measure of how much, on the average, the scores in a set deviate from the mean.* In other words, it is a measure of how far, on the average, the scores are dispersed or scattered about the mean. A larger value of σ means that the scores in a population are more dispersed about the mean, on the average, than would be indicated by a smaller value of σ. In fact, the more closely the scores in a population are concentrated around the mean, the smaller is the value of σ. As an extreme, if $\sigma = 0$, it means that all the scores are at the mean; that is, there is no variation at all among the scores. In our illustration (Table 5.2.1), the standard deviation indicates that, on the average, the scores differ from the mean by 7.8 points. Referring to the column of deviations from the mean in the table, the magnitudes of the deviations (signs ignored) range from .4 point to 16.6 points. The standard deviation of 7.8 points is a measure of the average magnitude of the deviations in this column, where the average is determined according to Equations 5.2.1 and 5.2.2.

Many readers may find it difficult to grasp the meaning of the standard deviation as a measure of variation (also called a measure of dispersion). It is worthwhile to examine two sets of scores, with contrasting score variation, which should assist the reader in mastering the meaning of this highly important concept. These sets (1 and 2), composed of 12 scores each, are graphically presented in Figure 5.2.1. Set 1 is composed of the scores 20, 30, 30, 40, 40, 40, 60, 60, 60, 70, 70, 80. Set 2 is composed of the scores 20, 20, 20, 30, 30, 40, 60, 70, 70, 80, 80, 80. The mean of each set is 50. As indicated in the figure, set 1 scores are more concentrated around the mean than are set 2 scores. Therefore, it is to be expected that σ will have a lower value for set 1 than for set 2. Table 5.2.2 presents the scores in set 1 and also the computations required to obtain σ. As shown in the

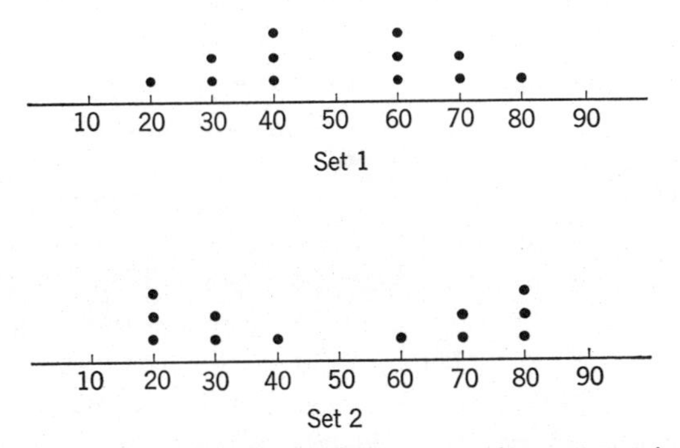

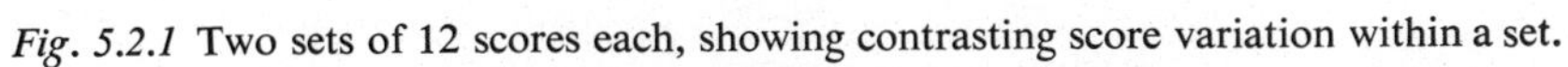
Fig. 5.2.1 Two sets of 12 scores each, showing contrasting score variation within a set.

Table 5.2.2 COMPUTATION OF THE STANDARD DEVIATION: SCORES IN A POPULATION OF $N = 12$ (SET 1)

	Score, X_i	x_i	x_i^2
	20	–30	900
	30	–20	400
	30	–20	400
	40	–10	100
	40	–10	100
	40	–10	100
	60	10	100
	60	10	100
	60	10	100
	70	20	400
	70	20	400
	80	30	900
Total	600		4000

$$\mu = \frac{600}{12} = 50$$

$$\sigma^2 = \frac{4000}{12} = 333.33$$

$$\sigma = \sqrt{333.33} = 18.3$$

table, $\sigma = 18.3$. The standard deviation for set 2 is larger, 24.5. (It will be left as an exercise for the reader to set up a table for set 2 and carry out the computations for σ.)

It is possible to evaluate a set of scores to gain an idea as to the value to be expected for σ. Such evaluation is also useful to check whether a gross error has been made in computing σ for a set of data. Let us try this for the aforementioned set 1. This evaluation can be made from the score column in Table 5.2.2 or from the graphic presentation of the scores in set 1 shown in Figure 5.2.1. Note that the smallest score in the set (20) is 30 points away from the mean (50), and the highest score in the set (80) is also 30 points away from the mean. The scores closest to the mean, 3 scores of 40 and 3 scores of 60, are all 10 points away from the mean. Therefore, σ, which is a kind of average of the deviations from the mean, must have a value somewhere between the largest deviation from the mean (30) and the smallest deviation from the mean (10). It is apparent from Figure 5.2.1 and Table 5.2.2 that the scores tend to concentrate relatively close to the mean, so that σ may be expected to be closer to 10 than to 30. Therefore, we may accept the result $\sigma = 18.3$ as reasonable. (It is a good idea for the reader to evaluate the score distribution in set 2 in a similar manner to check the reasonableness of 24.5 as a value for σ.)

In Chapter 4, Section 4.9, it was noted that the sum of squares of the deviations of a set of scores from the mean is less than the sum of squares of the deviations of the scores from any other point of reference. This was referred to as the *least squares property of the mean* and was expressed algebraically in Equation 4.9.6. Therefore, since the standard deviation is based on the sum of squares of the deviations from the mean, it provides a measure of variation of a set of scores which is *optimum in the least squares sense*. That is, *the standard deviation computed for a set of scores is less than any other measure of variation computed according to Equations* 5.2.1 *and* 5.2.2, *but with the use of a value other than the mean as the point of reference.*

It will be recalled that, in our discussion of the arithmetic mean, a distinction was made between the mean computed from population data and the mean computed from sample data. This was due to the difference in the interpretation of μ and $\bar{X}$. A similar situation arises in the case of the standard deviation. *The standard deviation computed for population data* (σ) *is interpreted as a measure of the variation of a population of scores about their mean.* It is possible to compute σ for a set of sample data as well, and interpret it as a measure of the variation in the sample set of scores. However, this is rarely of interest. As noted in the discussion of the mean, the interest in a sample is, generally, only for the information it provides relating to the population from which it was selected. It has been shown by mathematical statisticians that *the standard deviation computed from sample data according to Equations* 5.2.3 *and* 5.2.4 *and denoted by the symbol s can be interpreted as an estimate of the standard deviation* (σ) *in the population from which the sample was selected.*

For example, suppose a vocabulary recall test is administered to a sample of 40 junior high school students selected from the population of junior high school students in a given city. Say, the standard deviation (s) computed for the test scores for this sample is 8.73. Using this sample result, we estimate that, if the same vocabulary recall test were administered to all the junior high school students in the city, the standard deviation of the test scores for this population would be 8.73. This is the usual interpretation of interest when the standard deviation is computed from a set of sample data.

For the arithmetic mean, it will be recalled that the computation is the same for both population data and sample data. Only the symbols used are different. For the standard deviation, however, both the symbols and the computation are different. In Equations 5.2.3 and 5.2.4 for sample data, s^2 denotes the variance and s the standard deviation. As before, n denotes the sample size and $\bar{X}$ the sample mean. Furthermore, s^2 is computed by dividing the sum of the squared deviations from the mean by $n - 1$. This compares with σ^2 which is computed by dividing the sum of the squared deviations from the mean by N. It has been proved by mathematical statisticians that, if the standard deviation is computed for sample data using Equations 5.2.1 and 5.2.2, the resulting measure *tends to be too small* when used as an estimate of the standard deviation in the population. In the language of the statisticians, this measure has a *downward bias.* We correct for this bias in the computation of s (Equations 5.2.3 and 5.2.4) by dividing the sum of squared deviations from the mean by $n - 1$ instead of n.

Table 5.2.3 presents scores on a memory test for a sample of 8 students selected from the population of freshmen enrolled in a large college. Using the total of the score column in the table, compute $\bar{X} = 808/8 = 101$. Then, determine the deviation of each score from the mean, $x_i = X_i - 101$, as shown in the table. Square these deviations to obtain x_i^2, as shown in the last column of the table. Then, applying Equation 5.2.3, compute

$$s^2 = \frac{\sum_{i=1}^{8} x_i^2}{8 - 1} = \frac{316}{7} = 45.1429.$$

Finally, using Equation 5.2.4, compute the standard deviation as follows:

$$s = \sqrt{45.1429} = 6.72$$

Table 5.2.3 COMPUTATION OF THE VARIANCE AND THE STANDARD DEVIATION: SCORES ON A MEMORY TEST FOR A SAMPLE OF EIGHT COLLEGE FRESHMEN

	Score, X_i	$x_i = X_i - 101$	x_i^2
	106	5	25
	95	−6	36
	110	9	81
	92	−9	81
	95	−6	36
	99	−2	4
	103	2	4
	108	7	49
Total	808		316

Based on the result that $s = 6.72$, we may estimate that σ, the standard deviation of the memory test scores for all the freshmen enrolled in the college, is equal to 6.72.

5.3 STANDARD DEVIATION: SPECIAL SITUATIONS

An important advantage of the standard deviation as a measure of variation is the ease with which it can be treated algebraically. The standard deviation shares this advantage with the mean. The equations for the standard deviation (σ and s), like those for the mean, can be modified algebraically to provide special-purpose equations which are convenient and useful in special situations. Several special-purpose equations will be presented in this section.

Situation A: Equations 5.2.1 and 5.2.2 for σ and Equations 5.2.3 and 5.2.4 for s are *definitional* equations since they define the standard deviation. However, they are rarely convenient to use computationally, except in the simplest situation. Given a set of scores (X_1, X_2, X_3, etc.), the following more convenient *computational* equations are generally used:

$$\text{Population} \qquad \sigma = \frac{1}{N}\sqrt{N\sum_{i=1}^{N} X_i^2 - \left(\sum_{i=1}^{N} X_i\right)^2} \qquad (5.3.1)$$

$$\text{Sample} \qquad s = \sqrt{\frac{n \sum_{i=1}^{n} X_i^2 - \left(\sum_{i=1}^{n} X_i\right)^2}{n(n-1)}} \tag{5.3.2}$$

(For proofs see Section 5.8, *Notes* 5.1 *and* 5.2.)

These equations may, at first, look formidable to the reader. However, each equation requires the determination of only three items of information for a set of scores: the number of items included (N or n), the sum of the

Table 5.3.1 COMPUTATION OF THE STANDARD DEVIATION: SCORES ON A READING SPEED TEST FOR A POPULATION OF FIVE SUBJECTS

	Score, X_i	X_i^2
	21	441
	27	729
	22	484
	25	625
	28	784
Total	123	3063

scores in the set (ΣX_i), and the sum of the square of each score in the set (ΣX_i^2). An illustration or two will indicate that these equations are simple to use. Let us compute the standard deviation for the population of five scores (X_i) on a reading speed test presented in Table 5.3.1. First, as shown in the table, compute the square of each score (X_i^2), then obtain the total for each of the two columns in the table. Now, in Equation 5.3.1 substitute $N = 5$, $\Sigma X_i^2 = 3063$, and $\Sigma X_i = 123$ (as shown in Table 5.3.1) to obtain

$$\sigma = \tfrac{1}{5}\sqrt{5(3063) - (123)^2} = \tfrac{1}{5}\sqrt{186} = 2.7$$

As a second illustration, let us compute the standard deviation (s) for the scores (X_i) on a spatial perception test for a sample of six teenage boys, as shown in Table 5.3.2. Following the same procedure as before, first compute the square of each score (X_i^2), then compute the total for each of the two columns in the table. Noting that $n = 6$, $\Sigma X_i^2 = 18{,}364$, and

Table 5.3.2 COMPUTATION OF THE STANDARD DEVIATION: SCORES ON A SPATIAL PERCEPTION TEST FOR A SAMPLE OF SIX TEENAGE BOYS

	Score, X_i	X_i^2
	47	2209
	58	3364
	61	3721
	51	2601
	50	2500
	63	3969
Total	330	18,364

$\Sigma X_i = 330$ (as shown in Table 5.3.2), apply Equation 5.3.2 to obtain

$$s = \sqrt{\frac{6(18{,}364) - (330)^2}{(6)(5)}} = \sqrt{42.8} = 6.5$$

Situation B: Given a set of scores (X_1, X_2, X_3, etc.) with standard deviation σ (population) or s (sample). If a constant k is added to (or subtracted from) each score, so that each score becomes $X_i + k$ (or $X_i - k$), the standard deviation of the newly formed scores is the same as for the original scores.

We may express these relationships algebraically as follows:

$$\text{Population} \qquad \sigma_{(X \pm k)} = \sigma \tag{5.3.3}$$

$$\text{Sample} \qquad s_{(X \pm k)} = s \tag{5.3.4}$$

(For proofs see Section 5.8, *Notes* 5.3, 5.4, 5.5, and 5.6).

A word of explanation is required for the notation used in Equations 5.3.3 and 5.3.4 and throughout this chapter. We shall use σ or s for the standard deviation of the original set of scores (X_i). We shall use appropriate subscripts to identify the standard deviation for newly formed variables in the same manner as for the mean in Chapter 4. For example, $\sigma_{(X+k)}$ denotes the standard deviation for the $X_i + k$ scores and $\sigma_{(X-k)}$ denotes the standard deviation for the $X_i - k$ scores. We refer to these standard deviations simultaneously by the symbol $\sigma_{(X \pm k)}$. The subscript

$(X \pm k)$ is read "$X +$ or $-k$". In other words, this subscript provides for *both* possibilities: $(X + k)$ and $(X - k)$. For example, Equation 5.3.3 states that $\sigma_{(X \pm k)}$, the standard deviation of the newly formed variable $X_i + k$ and the standard deviation of the newly formed variable $X_i - k$, are each equal to σ, the standard deviation of the original variable X_i.

These relationships are useful in various situations. For example, a teacher may decide that a certain examination, resulting in a mean grade of 60 and a standard deviation of 12, was too difficult. He may wish to

Table 5.3.3 COMPUTATION OF THE STANDARD DEVIATION: GRADES ON A MIDTERM EXAMINATION FOR A POPULATION OF FIVE STUDENTS

Grade, X_i	$X'_i = X_i - 80$	$(X'_i)^2$
88	8	64
84	4	16
92	12	144
88	8	64
84	4	16
	Total 36	304

adjust the grades upward, without affecting the variation among the grades. Therefore, he could decide to add a constant number of points to each grade, say, 10 points, thus raising the general level of class grades. The mean grade will then be increased 10 points to a mean of 70 (Equation 4.3.1), but the standard deviation will still be 12, according to Equation 5.3.3.

The reader will recognize that *Situation B* is similar to *Situation* 1 presented for the mean in Chapter 4, Section 4.3. As then noted, adding or subtracting a constant to each score in a set involves a transformation of the scores by shifting the zero point. This procedure is of considerable help in reducing the labor of computing the standard deviation in certain situations. For example, let us compute the standard deviation σ for the population of 5 midterm examination grades (X_i) presented in Table 5.3.3. First, transform X_i to a new variable $X_i - 80$ and, for convenience, let us call this new variable X'_i, as shown in the table (X'_i is read "X prime sub i"). Clearly, the new variable X'_i involves far smaller numbers, thus considerably simplifying the computations. Substituting X'_i for X_i in

Equation 5.3.1, we can write the equation for $\sigma_{(X-80)}$, the standard deviation of the newly formed variable X'_i, as follows:

$$\sigma_{(X-80)} = \frac{1}{N}\sqrt{N\sum_{i=1}^{N}(X'_i)^2 - \left(\sum_{i=1}^{N}X'_i\right)^2}$$

Now, substituting $N = 5$, $\Sigma\,(X'_i)^2 = 304$, and $\Sigma\,X'_i = 36$ (as shown in Table 5.3.3) into the above equation, we obtain

$$\sigma_{(X-80)} = \tfrac{1}{5}\sqrt{5(304) - (36)^2} = \tfrac{1}{5}\sqrt{224} = 2.99$$

Table 5.3.4 COMPUTATION OF THE STANDARD DEVIATION: SCORES ON A MEMORY TEST OBTAINED BY A SAMPLE OF SEVEN SUBJECTS

Score, X_i	$X'_i = X_i - 114$	$(X'_i)^2$
123	9	81
114	0	0
120	6	36
114	0	0
126	12	144
120	6	36
129	15	225
	Total 48	522

Then, according to Equation 5.3.3, 2.99 is also the value of σ, the standard deviation of the original grades (X_i), which we wanted to determine.

As a second illustration, let us compute the standard deviation s for the sample of seven memory test scores (X_i) shown in Table 5.3.4. In order to simplify the computations, transform the scores by subtracting 114. This results in the new scores $X_i - 114$, which we will denote by the symbol X'_i, as shown in the table. Substituting X'_i for X_i in Equation 5.3.2, we obtain the equation for $s_{(X-114)}$, the standard deviation of the newly formed variable X'_i, as

$$s_{(X-114)} = \sqrt{\frac{n\sum_{i=1}^{n}(X'_i)^2 - \left(\sum_{i=1}^{n}X'_i\right)^2}{n(n-1)}}$$

Now, substituting $n = 7$, $\Sigma\,(X'_i)^2 = 522$, and $\Sigma\,X'_i = 48$ (as shown in

Table 5.3.4) into the above equation, we obtain

$$s_{(X-114)} = \sqrt{\frac{(7)(522) - (48)^2}{(7)(6)}} = \sqrt{32.14} = 5.7$$

Then, according to Equation 5.3.4, 5.7 is also the value of s, the standard deviation of the original scores (X_i).

The reader may wish to verify the foregoing results by direct computation of σ for the X_i scores in Table 5.3.3 using Equation 5.3.1, and s for the X_i scores in Table 5.3.4 using Equation 5.3.2.

Situation C: Given a set of scores (X_1, X_2, X_3, etc.) with standard deviation σ (population) or s (sample). If each score is multiplied (or divided) by a constant g so that each score becomes gX_i (or X_i/g), the standard deviation of the newly formed scores becomes

Population $$\sigma_{gX} = g\sigma \qquad (5.3.5)$$

$$\sigma_{X/g} = \frac{\sigma}{g} \qquad (5.3.6)$$

Sample $$s_{gX} = gs \qquad (5.3.7)$$

$$s_{X/g} = \frac{s}{g} \qquad (5.3.8)$$

(For Proofs see Section 5.8, *Notes* 5.7, 5.8, 5.9, *and* 5.10.)

These relationships are often very useful. For example, a sample of scores (seconds) on a reaction-time test has a standard deviation of 30 seconds. It may be desired to change the unit of measurement from seconds to minutes by dividing each score by 60. If this is done, the standard deviation of the transformed scores will become $30/60 = .5$ minutes, according to Equation 5.3.8.

Situation C is similar to *Situation* 2 presented for the mean. As then noted, formation of new scores by multiplying or dividing by a constant involves a transformation by changing the unit of measurement. This was illustrated in the aforementioned case of the reaction-time scores which could be transformed from seconds to minutes by dividing each score by 60. Such transformation is of considerable value in reducing the computational labor involved in determining the standard deviation in certain situations.

As an illustration, let us compute the standard deviation σ of the population of 5 grades (X_i) presented in Table 5.3.5. (This is the same set of

Table 5.3.5 COMPUTATION OF THE STANDARD DEVIATION: GRADES ON A MIDTERM EXAMINATION FOR A POPULATION OF FIVE STUDENTS

Grade, X_i	$\frac{X_i}{4}$	$\left(\frac{X_i}{4}\right)^2$
88	22	484
84	21	441
92	23	529
88	22	484
84	21	441
Total	109	2379

grades presented in Table 5.3.3 and used as an illustration for *Situation B.*) First, to simplify the computations, divide each grade by 4. This results in the new variable $X_i/4$ as shown in Table 5.3.5. We can write the equation for $\sigma_{X/4}$, the standard deviation of the new variable, by substituting the new variable $X_i/4$ for X_i in Equation 5.3.1, as follows:

$$\sigma_{X/4} = \frac{1}{N}\sqrt{N\sum_{i=1}^{N}\left(\frac{X_i}{4}\right)^2 - \left(\sum_{i=1}^{N}\frac{X_i}{4}\right)^2}$$

Substituting $N = 5$, $\Sigma\,(X_i/4)^2 = 2379$, and $\Sigma\,(X_i/4) = 109$ (as shown in Table 5.3.5) into the preceding equation, we obtain

$$\sigma_{X/4} = \tfrac{1}{5}\sqrt{5(2379) - (109)^2} = \tfrac{1}{5}\sqrt{14} = .75$$

Then, to obtain σ use Equation 5.3.6, with $g = 4$ and $\sigma_{X/g} = \sigma_{X/4} = .75$, to obtain

$$.75 = \sigma/4$$

And finally

$$\sigma = 4(.75) = 3.00$$

This value for σ differs only slightly from the value obtained previously (2.99) because of rounding.

Let us use this same approach and compute the standard deviation s for the sample of seven memory test scores (X_i) in Table 5.3.6. (This is the same set of sample scores presented in Table 5.3.4 and used as an illustration for *Situation B.*) First, to simplify the computations, divide each score by 3 to obtain the new scores $X_i/3$, as shown in Table 5.3.6. Substitute

Table 5.3.6 COMPUTATION OF THE STANDARD DEVIATION: SCORES ON A MEMORY TEST OBTAINED BY A SAMPLE OF SEVEN SUBJECTS

Score, X_i	$\frac{X_i}{3}$	$\left(\frac{X_i}{3}\right)^2$
123	41	1,681
114	38	1,444
120	40	1,600
114	38	1,444
126	42	1,764
120	40	1,600
129	43	1,849
Total	282	11,382

the new variable $X_i/3$ for X_i in Equation 5.3.2 to obtain $s_{X/3}$, the standard deviation of the new variable, as follows:

$$s_{X/3} = \sqrt{\frac{n\sum_{i=1}^{n}\left(\frac{X_i}{3}\right)^2 - \left(\sum_{i=1}^{n}\frac{X_i}{3}\right)^2}{n(n-1)}}$$

Substituting into the above equation (from Table 5.3.6) $n = 7$, $\Sigma\,(X_i/3)^2 = 11{,}382$, and $\Sigma\, X_i/3 = 282$, we obtain

$$s_{X/3} = \sqrt{\frac{7(11{,}382) - (282)^2}{(7)(6)}} = \sqrt{3.57} = 1.9$$

Then, to determine s, use Equation 5.3.8, with $g = 3$ and $s_{X/g} = s_{X/3} = 1.9$, to obtain

$$1.9 = s/3$$

And finally

$$s = 3(1.9) = 5.7$$

This value for s is the same as obtained previously.

Situation D: Given a set of scores (X_1, X_2, X_3, etc.), with standard deviation σ (population) or s (sample), a double transformation is performed by subtracting a constant k from each score and, then, dividing by a second constant g, so that each score becomes $(X_i - k)/g$.

Situation D, which is the same as *Situation* 3 for the mean, involves transformation both by shifting the zero point and changing the unit of measurement. Let us follow the practice adopted in *Situation* 3 and use the symbol u_i to represent the scores after the double transformation. That is,

$$u_i = \frac{X_i - k}{g} \tag{5.3.9}$$

This is identical with Equation 4.3.7 presented in *Situation* 3. Then, substituting u_i for X_i in the computational equations for the standard deviation presented in *Situation A*, we arrive at equations for computing the standard deviation for the transformed scores u_i as follows:

$$\text{Population} \qquad \sigma_u = \frac{1}{N}\sqrt{N\sum_{i=1}^{N} u_i^2 - \left(\sum_{i=1}^{N} u_i\right)^2} \tag{5.3.10}$$

$$\text{Sample} \qquad s_u = \sqrt{\frac{n\sum_{i=1}^{n} u_i^2 - \left(\sum_{i=1}^{n} u_i\right)^2}{n(n-1)}} \tag{5.3.11}$$

In certain situations, this double transformation procedure is very useful in reducing the work involved in computing the standard deviation. In such situations, the original X_i scores may be transformed to u_i scores (by the use of Equation 5.3.9) and σ_u or s_u, as appropriate, computed. Then, the standard deviation for the original X_i scores (σ or s) is determined as follows:

$$\text{Population} \qquad \sigma = g\sigma_u \tag{5.3.12}$$

$$\text{Sample} \qquad s = gs_u \tag{5.3.13}$$

(For proofs see Section 5.8, *Notes* 5.11 *and* 5.12.)

Table 5.3.7 presents the scores (X_i) for a sample of 8 subjects on an aptitude test. Let us compute the standard deviation, s, using the double transformation procedure just explained. Inspection of the sample scores indicates that we can substantially reduce the magnitude of the scores and simplify the computations by subtracting 100 from each score and then dividing the result by 3. Therefore, substituting $k = 100$ and $g = 3$ in Equation 5.3.9, we set up the transformation equation

$$u_i = \frac{X_i - 100}{3}$$

Substituting each X_i value, in turn, into this transformation equation, we determine the corresponding u_i scores, as shown in Table 5.3.7. Applying

Equation 5.3.11 with $n = 8$, $\Sigma u_i^2 = 423$, and $\Sigma u_i = 55$, we obtain

$$s_u = \sqrt{\frac{(8)(423) - (55)^2}{(8)(7)}} = \sqrt{6.41} = 2.5$$

Then, the standard deviation, s, for the original set of sample scores is obtained by applying Equation 5.3.13 with $g = 3$ and $s_u = 2.5$ to obtain

$$s = 3(2.5) = 7.5$$

It is a good idea for the reader to compute s directly from the X_i scores in Table 5.3.7 to demonstrate the saving in computational effort achieved

Table 5.3.7 COMPUTATION OF THE STANDARD DEVIATION: SAMPLE OF SCORES ON AN APTITUDE TEST

Score, X_i	$u_i = \frac{X_i - 100}{3}$	u_i^2
115	5	25
124	8	64
130	10	100
118	6	36
127	9	81
106	2	4
124	8	64
121	7	49
Total	55	423

by converting to u_i scores. In the same way, Equations 5.3.10 and 5.3.12 are used with population data to reduce the effort required to compute σ.

Situation E: Given a set of scores (X_1, X_2, X_3, etc.) organized into a simple grouping table, it is desired to determine the standard deviation.

Table 5.3.8 presents the scores on a spelling test for a class of 16 pupils. These scores are organized into a simple grouping table showing only those scores which have a frequency of one or more. Scores with zero frequency, such as 20 and 22, are omitted. This table is similar to Table 4.3.5 presented in the discussion of *Situation* 4 pertaining to the mean. The reasoning used there in developing Equation 4.3.11 for computation of the mean from a simple grouping table will be followed here to develop computational equations for the standard deviation for use with simple grouping tables.

If the population of 16 scores were listed individually, without grouping, clearly Equation 5.3.1 presented in *Situation A* would be suitable for computation of the standard deviation σ. In this instance, we would enter Equation 5.3.1 with $N = 16$, ΣX_i = sum of the 16 scores, and ΣX_i^2 = sum of the squares of the 16 scores. Referring to Table 5.3.8, we note that 2 pupils obtained a score of 18, 2 obtained a score of 19, etc. Therefore, $\Sigma X_i = 18 + 18 + 19 + 19 + \cdots$. Or, we could obtain ΣX_i just as well

Table 5.3.8 COMPUTATION OF THE STANDARD DEVIATION: SCORES ON A SPELLING TEST FOR A CLASS OF SIXTEEN PUPILS

Score, X_i	f_i	$X_i f_i$	$X_i^2 f_i$	p_i	$X_i p_i$	$X_i^2 p_i$
18	2	36	648	.1250	2.2500	40.5000
19	2	38	722	.1250	2.3750	45.1250
21	3	63	1323	.1875	3.9375	82.6875
24	3	72	1728	.1875	4.5000	108.0000
27	3	81	2187	.1875	5.0625	136.6875
29	2	58	1682	.1250	3.6250	105.1250
32	1	32	1024	.0625	2.0000	64.0000
Total	16	380	9314	1.0000	23.7500	582.1250

by adding $2(18) + 2(19) + \cdots$. That is, we could multiply each score (X_i) by its frequency (f_i) to obtain $X_i f_i$ and then add these products to obtain $\Sigma X_i f_i$. This sum is 380 for the 16 scores, as shown in the table. Similarly, we obtain ΣX_i^2 by adding $2(18)^2 + 2(19)^2 + \cdots$. That is, we multiply the square of each score (X_i^2) by its frequency (f_i) to obtain $X_i^2 f_i$ and then add these products to obtain $\Sigma X_i^2 f_i$. This sum, as shown in the table, is 9314 for the 16 scores.

Therefore, substituting $\Sigma X_i f_i$ for ΣX_i and $\Sigma X_i^2 f_i$ for ΣX_i^2 in Equation 5.3.1, we obtain the following computational equation for σ appropriate for a simple grouping table:

$$\text{Population} \qquad \sigma = \frac{1}{N}\sqrt{N \sum_{i=1}^{c} X_i^2 f_i - \left(\sum_{i=1}^{c} X_i f_i\right)^2} \qquad (5.3.14)$$

Applying Equation 5.3.14 to the scores in Table 5.3.8, we obtain

$$\sigma = \tfrac{1}{16}\sqrt{16(9314) - (380)^2} = \tfrac{1}{16}\sqrt{4624} = 4.25$$

Note that in Equation 5.3.14 the summation goes from $i = 1$ to c. That is, we use c instead of N because we are adding over the c different score values in the set of N scores. In our illustration, the set of 16 scores includes 7 different score values, as listed in the first column of Table 5.3.8. Therefore, $c = 7$. This use of c in the summation was explained in the discussion of Table 4.3.5 in *Situation* 4 for the mean.

In the same way, we can show that the standard deviation for a sample set of data organized into a simple grouping table can be determined as follows:

$$\text{Sample} \qquad s = \sqrt{\frac{n \sum_{i=1}^{c} X_i^2 f_i - \left(\sum_{i=1}^{c} X_i f_i\right)^2}{n(n-1)}} \qquad (5.3.15)$$

Equation 5.3.15 is obtained by substituting $\Sigma X_i f_i$ for ΣX_i, and $\Sigma X_i^2 f_i$ for ΣX_i^2 in Equation 5.3.2 from *Situation A* and adding from $i = 1$ to c, as was done in Equation 5.3.14 for σ.

It will be recalled that in the discussion of *Situation* 4 we showed that the mean can be computed for a simple grouping table using the *relative frequency* or *proportion* p_i in a class in place of the class frequency f_i (Equation 4.3.12). The standard deviation for a simple grouping table also can be determined using relative frequencies instead of frequencies, as follows:

$$\text{Population} \qquad \sigma = \sqrt{\sum_{i=1}^{c} X_i^2 p_i - \left(\sum_{i=1}^{c} X_i p_i\right)^2} \qquad (5.3.16)$$

$$\text{Sample} \qquad s = \sqrt{\frac{n}{n-1}\left[\sum_{i=1}^{c} X_i^2 p_i - \left(\sum_{i=1}^{c} X_i p_i\right)^2\right]} \qquad (5.3.17)$$

Let us use Equation 5.3.16 to obtain the standard deviation for the population of 16 scores in Table 5.3.8. Using the summations $\Sigma X_i p_i = 23.7500$ and $\Sigma X_i^2 p_i = 582.1250$ from the table, we obtain

$$\sigma = \sqrt{582.1250 - (23.7500)^2} = \sqrt{18.0625} = 4.25$$

This, of course, is the same result obtained previously. Equations 5.3.16 and 5.3.17 will always give the same results as Equations 5.3.14 and 5.3.15, respectively, except for possible slight differences owing to rounding.

Let us compute the standard deviation for the sample of 10 scores on a personality quiz presented in Table 5.3.9. Since these 10 scores are organized into a simple grouping table, Equation 5.3.15 is the appropriate equation to use. Therefore, substituting $n = 10$, $\Sigma X_i^2 f_i = 878$, and $\Sigma X_i f_i = 92$, as shown in the table, we obtain

$$s = \sqrt{\frac{(10)(878) - (92)^2}{(10)(9)}} = \sqrt{3.51} = 1.9$$

Table 5.3.9 COMPUTATION OF THE STANDARD DEVIATION: SCORES ON A PERSONALITY QUIZ FOR A SAMPLE OF TEN CLERKS

Score, X_i	f_i	$X_i f_i$	$X_i^2 f_i$	p_i	$X_i p_i$	$X_i^2 p_i$
7	3	21	147	.3	2.1	14.7
9	3	27	243	.3	2.7	24.3
10	2	20	200	.2	2.0	20.0
12	2	24	288	.2	2.4	28.8
Total	10	92	878	1.0	9.2	87.8

The standard deviation for this sample of 10 scores could also be determined using Equation 5.3.17. Substituting $n = 10$, $\Sigma X_i^2 p_i = 87.8$, and $\Sigma X_i p_i = 9.2$, as shown in Table 5.3.9, we obtain

$$s = \sqrt{\tfrac{10}{9}\,[87.8 - (9.2)^2]} = \sqrt{3.51} = 1.9$$

PROBLEMS FOR PRACTICE AND REVIEW

1. Compute the standard deviation for the sample of 12 quiz grades in Problem 1 (following Section 4.3).

2. Given the population of scores for seven clerks in Problem 2 (following Section 4.3):
(a) compute the standard deviation.
(b) if 20 points are added to each score, what is the new standard deviation?

3. Given the scores on an anxiety scale for a sample of nine subjects in Problem 3 (following Section 4.3):
(a) compute the standard deviation.
(b) if each score is doubled, what is the standard deviation of the new scores?

4. Compute the standard deviation for the population of reaction times in Problem 4 (following Section 4.3). However, to simplify the computations, first multiply each reaction time by 1000, obtain the standard deviation for these increased values, and, then, determine the standard deviation for the original values.

5. Obtain the standard deviation for the sample of eight scores in Problem 5 (following Section 4.3). *Hint:* First reduce each score by 100 points.

6. Obtain the standard deviation for the population of 15 scores in Problem 6 (following Section 4.3). *Hint:* First divide each score by 40.

7. Compute the standard deviation for the grades in Problem 7 (following Section 4.3). *Hint:* First transform each grade X_i to a u_i grade by subtracting 50 and then dividing the result by 2.

8. Compute the standard deviation for the sample of scores in Problem 8 (following Section 4.3). *Hint:* Transform each score by subtracting 100 and then dividing by 7.

9. Compute the standard deviation for the sample of 37 error counts in Problem 11 (following Section 4.3).

10. Compute the standard deviation for the population of scores in Problem 12 (following Section 4.3).

5.4 STANDARD DEVIATION: FREQUENCY DISTRIBUTIONS

Computation of the standard deviation for data summarized into a frequency table represents another type of special situation for which it is useful to present special-purpose equations. Therefore, let us continue our list of special situations by adding *Situation F* and *Situation G* relating to frequency distributions. These correspond to *Situation* 7 and *Situation* 8, respectively, presented for the mean in Chapter 4, Section 4.4.

Situation F: Given a set of scores (X_1, X_2, X_3, etc.) organized into a frequency table with c classes, it is desired to determine the standard deviation.

Table 5.4.1 presents a frequency table for a population of 50 scores on a matching test. Clearly, if we knew the 50 individual scores, we could compute the standard deviation using the appropriate equation presented in *Situation A*. Of course, it is not possible to know the individual scores from the information presented in a frequency table. Hence, we must make some assumption regarding these scores. *The assumption usually made is that the*

Table 5.4.1 COMPUTATION OF THE STANDARD DEVIATION: FREQUENCY TABLE FOR A POPULATION OF 50 SCORES ON A MATCHING TEST

Discrete Class Limits	Midpoint, X_i	f_i	$X_i f_i$	$X_i^2 f_i$
110–119	114.5	10	1145.0	131,102.50
120–129	124.5	11	1369.5	170,502.75
130–139	134.5	13	1748.5	235,173.25
140–149	144.5	9	1300.5	187,922.25
150–159	154.5	4	618.0	95,481.00
160–169	164.5	2	329.0	54,120.50
170–179	174.5	1	174.5	30,450.25
	Total	50	6685.0	904,752.50

scores in a class interval are equal to the class midpoint. This is the same assumption made in *Situation* 7 for computing the mean for scores organized into a frequency table.

Referring to Table 5.4.1, we assume that the 10 scores in the 110–119 class each have the value 114.5, etc. Using this assumption amounts to converting a frequency table into a simple grouping table. That is to say, using this assumption, a frequency table (such as Table 5.4.1) may be considered to be made up of specified scores (class midpoints) and associated frequencies, as in the case of a simple grouping table. This is true, clearly, whether the scores in a frequency table are sample data or population data. Therefore, Equations 5.3.14 and 5.3.15 in *Situation E* for computing the standard deviation from a simple grouping table are immediately applicable to computation of the standard deviation from a frequency table. Then, with X_i representing the class midpoint, f_i representing the class frequency, and c equal to the number of classes, we have

$$\text{Population} \qquad \sigma = \frac{1}{N}\sqrt{N\sum_{i=1}^{c} X_i^2 f_i - \left(\sum_{i=1}^{c} X_i f_i\right)^2} \tag{5.4.1}$$

$$\text{Sample} \qquad s = \sqrt{\frac{n\sum_{i=1}^{c} X_i^2 f_i - \left(\sum_{i=1}^{c} X_i f_i\right)^2}{n(n-1)}} \tag{5.4.2}$$

Applying Equation 5.4.1 to compute the standard deviation for the population of 50 scores in Table 5.4.1 with $N = 50$, $\Sigma X_i f_i = 6685.0$, and $\Sigma X_i^2 f_i = 904{,}752.50$ (as shown in the table), we obtain

$$\sigma = \tfrac{1}{50}\sqrt{50(904{,}752.50) - (6{,}685.0)^2} = \tfrac{1}{50}\sqrt{548{,}400} = 14.8$$

In the same way, with X_i representing the class midpoint, p_i representing the relative frequency in a class, and c equal to the number of classes, we can immediately adapt Equations 5.3.16 and 5.3.17 to computation of the standard deviation from a *relative frequency* table, as follows:

$$\text{Population} \qquad \sigma = \sqrt{\sum_{i=1}^{c} X_i^2 p_i - \left(\sum_{i=1}^{c} X_i p_i\right)^2} \tag{5.4.3}$$

$$\text{Sample} \qquad s = \sqrt{\frac{n}{n-1}\left[\sum_{i=1}^{c} X_i^2 p_i - \left(\sum_{i=1}^{c} X_i p_i\right)^2\right]} \tag{5.4.4}$$

Table 5.4.2 presents the relative frequency table for the population of 50 scores from Table 5.4.1. Applying Equation 5.4.3 to compute the standard deviation, using $\Sigma X_i p_i = 133.70$ and $\Sigma X_i^2 p_i = 18{,}095.07$ from Table 5.4.2, we obtain

$$\sigma = \sqrt{18{,}095.07 - (133.70)^2} = \sqrt{219.38} = 14.8$$

This is, of course, the same result as obtained previously.

As noted for the mean (*Situation* 7), the assumption that all scores in a class are equal to the class midpoint will usually result in some discrepancy in the standard deviation computed for a frequency table compared with

Table 5.4.2 COMPUTATION OF THE STANDARD DEVIATION: RELATIVE FREQUENCY TABLE FOR A POPULATION OF 50 SCORES ON A MATCHING TEST

Midpoint, X_i	p_i	$X_i p_i$	$X_i^2 p_i$
114.5	.20	22.90	2,622.05
124.5	.22	27.39	3,410.06
134.5	.26	34.97	4,703.47
144.5	.18	26.01	3,758.45
154.5	.08	12.36	1,909.62
164.5	.04	6.58	1,082.41
174.5	.02	3.49	609.01
Total	1.00	133.70	18,095.07

the result which would be obtained if the actual scores were used in the computation. However, as previously observed, with a well-constructed frequency table, this discrepancy is usually not important.

Situation G: Given a set of scores (X_1, X_2, X_3, etc.) organized into a frequency table with c classes, it is often laborious to compute the standard deviation in the manner indicated in *Situation F*. It is often convenient to transform the midpoint X_i to $u_i = (X_i - k)/g$ as presented in *Situation D* and then to compute the standard deviation based on the transformed u_i scores.

As discussed in *Situation* 8 for the mean, the double transformation of the class midpoints X_i to u_i is easiest to accomplish and most convenient when k and g are selected in a certain way. The constant k is put equal to the midpoint which is both centrally located in the frequency table and associated with the largest class frequency, as far as possible. The constant g is put equal to the length of class interval. This transformation results in a frequency table made up of c classes, with midpoints in terms of the transformed u_i values. The next step is to compute the standard deviation of this frequency distribution, as follows:

$$\text{Population} \qquad \sigma_u = \frac{1}{N}\sqrt{N\sum_{i=1}^{c} u_i^2 f_i - \left(\sum_{i=1}^{c} u_i f_i\right)^2} \qquad (5.4.5)$$

$$\text{Sample} \qquad s_u = \sqrt{\frac{n\sum_{i=1}^{c} u_i^2 f_i - \left(\sum_{i=1}^{c} u_i f_i\right)^2}{n(n-1)}} \qquad (5.4.6)$$

These equations are obtained by substituting u_i for X_i in Equations 5.4.1 and 5.4.2 in *Situation F*. Finally, we compute the standard deviation for the

Table 5.4.3 COMPUTATION OF THE STANDARD DEVIATION AFTER TRANSFORMATION OF THE CLASS MIDPOINTS X_i TO u_i: FREQUENCY TABLE FOR A POPULATION OF 50 SCORES ON A MATCHING TEST

Midpoint, X_i	f_i	u_i	$u_i f_i$	$u_i^2 f_i$
114.5	10	−3	−30	90
124.5	11	−2	−22	44
134.5	13	−1	−13	13
(144.5)	9	0	0	0
154.5	4	1	4	4
164.5	2	2	4	8
174.5	1	3	3	9
Total	50		−54	168

original X_i scores by applying Equation 5.3.12 or Equation 5.3.13, from *Situation D*, as appropriate. Equation 5.3.12 is used for population data to determine σ. Equation 5.3.13 is used for sample data to determine s.

Table 5.4.3 presents the class midpoints and frequencies for the population of 50 scores on a matching test from Table 5.4.1. Let us apply the double transformation procedure to determine the standard deviation for this frequency distribution. First, let us select the midpoint 144.5 as the value of k. Place parentheses around this midpoint, as shown in Table 5.4.3, to identify it as the value of k. Let g equal 10, the length of class interval. Now, as explained in *Situation* 8 for the mean, we can immediately write the u_i value for each class midpoint X_i. First enter a 0 as the u_i value for the midpoint in parentheses. Then, enter −1, −2, −3 as the u_i values for succeeding smaller midpoints and 1, 2, 3 for succeeding larger midpoints, as shown in the table. Then, applying Equation 5.4.5 with $N = 50$, $\Sigma u_i^2 f_i = 168$, and $\Sigma u_i f_i = -54$ (as shown in Table 5.4.3), we obtain

$$\sigma_u = \tfrac{1}{50}\sqrt{50(168) - (-54)^2} = \tfrac{1}{50}\sqrt{5{,}484} = 1.48$$

Finally, we compute σ, the standard deviation for the original X_i scores, by applying Equation 5.3.12. Noting that $g = 10$ and $\sigma_u = 1.48$, we obtain

$$\sigma = 10\sigma_u = 10(1.48) = 14.8$$

This is the same result obtained previously, in *Situation F*, when the standard deviation was computed directly from the class midpoints X_i.

If we wish to compute the standard deviation for a sample set of scores organized into a frequency table, we follow the same procedure, transforming the class midpoints X_i to u_i values. Then, applying Equation 5.4.6, we compute s_u. Finally, applying Equation 5.3.12 from *Situation D*, we compute s based on the obtained value of s_u and the appropriate value of g (length of class interval).

PROBLEMS FOR PRACTICE AND REVIEW

1. Compute the standard deviation for the frequency distribution of the population of scores on a reading speed test in Problem 7 (following Section 3.3). Do this two ways, based upon the reading speed test scores X_i and, then, after transforming these scores to u_i scores.

2. Compute the standard deviation for the frequency distribution of the population of 27 quiz grades in Problem 2 (following Section 4.4). Do this two ways, based upon the quiz grades X_i and, then, after transforming these grades to u_i values.

3. Compute the standard deviation for the sample of 41 scores from Problem 3 (following Section 4.4). Do this in two ways, as noted for Problem 2.

4. Compute the standard deviation for the sample of 162 error counts in Problem 4 (following Section 4.4). Do this in two ways, as noted in Problem 2.

5. Compute the standard deviation for the population of anxiety scale scores in Problem 8 (following Section 3.3).

6. Compute the standard deviation for the sample of 233 reaction times in Problem 6 (following Section 4.4).

7. Compute the standard deviation for the population in Problem 9 (following Section 3.3).

8. Compute the standard deviation for the population of 39 scores in Problem 8 (following Section 4.4).

9. Compute the standard deviation for the population of scores in Problem 9 (following Section 4.4).

10. Compute the standard deviation for the sample of scores in Problem 10 (following Section 4.4).

5.5 OTHER MEASURES OF VARIATION

The *quartile deviation* is usually the appropriate measure of variation to employ when the median is used as the measure of central tendency. In a particular way, the quartile deviation may be considered to measure the variation of a set of scores from the median as the point of reference. It would seem logical to compute this measure of variation based on the *absolute deviations* of the scores in a set from the median. This would provide an optimum measure of variation in the sense of the least average absolute deviation. It will be recalled that the sum of the absolute deviations of a set of scores from a value k is a minimum if k is the median for the set (Chapter 4, Section 4.9). This property of the median was expressed algebraically in Equation 4.9.7.

The median, a positional measure, depends on the ranked sequence of scores in a set not on the particular numerical value of each score. Therefore, as might be expected, the quartile deviation is not actually based on the absolute deviations of the individual scores from the median, but on the absolute deviations of two other positional measures from the median, the first and third quartiles (Q_1 and Q_3). The absolute deviation of the upper quartile Q_3 from the median M is $|Q_3 - M|$. Obtaining absolute deviations, it will be recalled, amounts to considering all deviations as positive. Therefore, since Q_3 is always higher in value than M, we could write the absolute deviation as $(Q_3 - M)$ just as well, since this deviation will always be positive. The absolute deviation of the lower quartile Q_1 from M is $|Q_1 - M|$. Since Q_1 is always lower in value than M, we could express the absolute deviation as $(M - Q_1)$. The deviation obtained in this manner will always be positive. Then, the quartile deviation Q is computed as the mean of these two deviations, as follows:

$$Q = \frac{(Q_3 - M) + (M - Q_1)}{2} \tag{5.5.1}$$

When we remove the parentheses in the numerator of Equation 5.5.1, M cancels out, leaving

$$Q = \frac{Q_3 - Q_1}{2} \tag{5.5.2}$$

Therefore, the quartile deviation depends solely on the upper and lower quartiles and not at all upon the median. Actually, then, the same equation would result for Q if any value between Q_1 and Q_3 were selected as the point of reference. However, the logic behind the use of absolute deviations is dependent upon the consideration that the median is the point of reference.

As an illustration, let us compute Q for a set of scores for which $Q_1 = 18$ and $Q_3 = 62$. Applying Equation 5.5.2, we obtain

$$Q = \frac{62 - 18}{2} = 22$$

It will be observed from Equation 5.5.2 that Q is half the range between the upper and lower quartiles. More specifically, Q equals half the range of the middle 50% of the scores in a set. The quartile deviation is sometimes called the *semi-interquartile range*. The quartile deviation is not nearly as useful nor as frequently used a measure of variation as the standard deviation.

Sometimes other ranges between a pair of positional measures are used as a measure of variation. For example, the full range $(Q_3 - Q_1)$, not the half-range, is sometimes used. This is called the *interquartile range*, as might be expected. Another range which statisticians in the fields of psychology and education find useful is the difference between the ninth and first decile, $D_9 - D_1$.

5.6 RELATIVE VARIATION

The measures of variation just discussed are highly useful and provide a better understanding of the distribution of a set of numerical data than is possible without them. However, taken by themselves, they have serious limitations. For example, suppose we are told that $\sigma = 5$ points for the scores on a language aptitude test administered to a population of 60 students. Does this indicate considerable variation among the 60 scores or very little? Suppose we are told further that $\sigma = 25$ seconds for the scores on a typing speed test administered to this same student population. May we conclude that there is more variation in the typing speed test scores than in the scores on the language aptitude test?

Let us first consider the language test scores. If we discovered that these scores have a mean of 20, our evaluation of $\sigma = 5$ would be different than if we found that the mean was actually 220. That is, a standard deviation of 5 points looks a lot more important when the mean is only 20 than when it is 220. If the mean score were 1020, a standard deviation of 5 points would look quite insignificant, indicating hardly any variation at all around the mean. Clearly, evaluation of the extent of variation among a set of scores is meaningful only when compared with the average level of the scores in the set. The problem becomes compounded when we compare the variation of two sets of scores, especially when the scores are in different units of measurement. Referring to the illustration, how can we compare a standard deviation of 5 points with one of 25 seconds, even if we knew the value of the mean for each set of scores?

The statistical analyst copes with such problems by expressing the measure of variation as a percentage of the mean. That is, he converts the measure of variation to a measure of *relative variation* called the *coefficient of variation* (V). This is computed as

$$V = \frac{\text{standard deviation}}{\text{mean}} \cdot 100 \tag{5.6.1}$$

For example, referring to the language aptitude test scores with $\sigma = 5$, if $\mu = 20$, the coefficient of variation V is computed as $\frac{5}{20} \cdot 100 = 25\%$. However, if $\mu = 220$, $V = \frac{5}{220} \cdot 100 = 2.3\%$. Therefore, relative to the mean, the variation of these 60 scores is considerable (25%) if the mean is 20; but, if the mean is 220, the relative variation is not great (2.3%). If $\mu = 1020$ then $V = .5\%$, indicating that there is hardly any variation at all among the 60 scores. Let us compare the variation of the language aptitude test scores ($\sigma = 5$ points) and the typing speed test scores ($\sigma =$ 25 seconds) by converting these absolute measures of variation to relative measures. Suppose for the language aptitude scores, $\mu = 20$ points, and, for the typing speed scores, $\mu = 300$ seconds. Then, the coefficient of variation is 25% for the language scores compared with 8.3% for the typing speed scores, indicating considerably less relative variation among the scores on the typing speed test.

The use of Equation 5.6.1 to determine relative variation has been illustrated using population data. Of course, the same approach is applicable for sample data. For example, if a science aptitude test administered to a sample of 50 subjects showed $\bar{X} = 135$ and $s = 30$, the coefficient of variation, V, would be computed as $\frac{30}{135} \cdot 100 = 22.2\%$, indicating considerable relative variation among the scores.

In the same way, if the quartile deviation Q is used as the measure of variation of a set of scores and the median M as the measure of central tendency, relative variation can be computed by expressing Q as a percentage of M to obtain

$$\frac{Q}{M} \cdot 100 = \frac{(Q_3 - Q_1)/2}{M} \cdot 100 \tag{5.6.2}$$

In a *symmetrical distribution*, the median is midway between Q_1 and Q_3, so that

$$M = \frac{Q_3 + Q_1}{2} \tag{5.6.3}$$

This, of course, is only approximately true for distributions which are only approximately symmetrical. For other distributions, such as highly skewed distributions, the median may be quite distant from the midpoint between Q_1 and Q_3. However, it has become general practice, when Q is the computed measure of variation, to determine the relative variation by expressing the quartile deviation $(Q_3 - Q_1)/2$ as a percentage of the midpoint between Q_1 and Q_3. This percentage is denoted by V_Q and is obtained as follows:

$$V_Q = \frac{(Q_3 - Q_1)/2}{(Q_3 + Q_1)/2} \cdot 100 = \frac{Q_3 - Q_1}{Q_3 + Q_1} \cdot 100 \qquad (5.6.4)$$

V_Q is called the *coefficient of quartile deviation*. If $Q_1 = 58$ and $Q_3 = 72$ for a set of scores, we may compute the coefficient of quartile deviation as

$$V_Q = \frac{72 - 58}{72 + 58} \cdot 100 = 10.8\%$$

5.7 STANDARD SCORES

In Section 5.6, questions were raised concerning the evaluation of measures of variation. Similar questions need to be considered relating to the individual scores. For example, a senior high school student states that he obtained a score of 69 on a science aptitude test. Is this a high score or a low score? Suppose this student also obtained a score of 105 on a language aptitude test. Could you conclude that this student shows greater aptitude in languages than in science?

A score standing by itself is, usually, not meaningful. It must be evaluated with reference to the average level of scores on the same test obtained by others, as well as the variation among the scores. Clearly, if all senior high school students who took the science aptitude test obtained a mean score of 60, with a standard deviation of 10 points, a score of 69 would look quite good, since it would be nearly one standard deviation (9 points) above the mean. On the other hand, if all senior high school students who took the language aptitude test obtained a mean score of 120, with a standard deviation of only 5 points, a score of 105 would not look so good, since it would be three standard deviations (15 points) below the mean score for the group. Relationship to the group is important for any type of measurement. For example, a man 5 feet 10 inches tall feels quite short in a group of basketball players in which the shortest player is 6 feet 4 inches in height.

A widely used method for evaluating a score is to transform it to *standard units*. The original score is called a *raw score* and the transformed score is called a *standard score*. *A set of scores is transformed to standard scores (or standard units) when the mean and standard deviation of the set are made to equal predetermined values.* Generally, the predetermined values are zero for the mean and one for the standard deviation. This transformation is accomplished by the double transformation procedure presented in *Situation D* for the standard deviation and *Situation* 3 for the mean. This requires transforming the X_i scores to u_i scores according to Equation 5.3.9, where the constant k is put equal to the raw score mean (μ or $\bar{X}$) and the constant g is put equal to the raw score standard deviation (σ or s). Making the appropriate substitutions for k and g in Equation 5.3.9 and denoting the resulting transformed scores (standard scores) by z_i (instead of u_i), we obtain the following equations:

$$\text{Population} \qquad z_i = \frac{X_i - \mu}{\sigma} \tag{5.7.1}$$

$$\text{Sample} \qquad z_i = \frac{X_i - \bar{X}}{s} \tag{5.7.2}$$

Standard scores computed according to Equations 5.7.1 and 5.7.2 will have a mean of zero and a standard deviation of one. (For proofs see Section 5.8, *Note* 5.13.)

Suppose a population of raw scores has $\mu = 30$ and $\sigma = 5$. Substituting these values into Equation 5.7.1, we obtain

$$z_i = \frac{X_i - 30}{5}$$

The raw scores included in this population may be transformed to standard scores z_i by substituting in this equation. For example, suppose 20 and 45 are two scores from this population. We obtain the corresponding standard scores as

$$z_{20} = \frac{20 - 30}{5} = -2$$

$$z_{45} = \frac{45 - 30}{5} = 3$$

Observe that z_i scores may be negative as well as positive. Raw scores below the mean result in z_i scores which are negative. Raw scores above the mean result in z_i scores which are positive. A raw score which is equal to the mean results in a z_i score of zero. For example, if the foregoing population included a raw score of 30, the corresponding standard score would be computed as

$$z_{30} = \frac{30 - 30}{5} = 0$$

Standard scores z_i are in standard deviation units. For example, the raw score of 20 in the foregoing illustration is 10 points below the mean of 30, and 10 points amounts to two standard deviations ($\sigma = 5$). Therefore, the corresponding z_i score of -2 indicates that the raw score of 20 is two standard deviations below the mean. This demonstrates an important advantage of z_i scores over raw scores. For example, it is not possible to evaluate a raw score, say the raw score of 45 in this illustration, when it

Table 5.7.1 EVALUATION OF EXAMINATION GRADES OBTAINED IN FIVE SUBJECTS BY A GIVEN STUDENT IN A CLASS OF 35 STUDENTS

Subject	Raw Grade X_i	μ	σ	Standard Grade z_i
A	90	80	5	2.0
B	90	60	10	3.0
C	75	80	10	−.5
D	60	75	15	−1.0
E	50	20	20	1.5

stands alone. However, the corresponding z_i score of 3 is immediately meaningful, indicating a score which is three standard deviations above the mean.

It is instructive to apply this transformation procedure to the examination grades obtained by a student in five subjects, as presented in Table 5.7.1. Based on the raw grades, it appears that this student did very well in subjects *A* and *B* and quite poorly in subjects *D* and *E*. However, it is well known by students in psychology and education that some examinations are very easy, resulting in generally high grades, whereas some examinations are very difficult, resulting in generally low grades. A high grade on an easy examination, where most grades are high and closely grouped, does not necessarily indicate a high degree of achievement in the subject. Actually, such a grade may indicate less achievement than a much lower grade obtained in a really tough examination.

Table 5.7.1 also presents the mean and standard deviation of the grade distribution for each subject for the 35 students in the class. Clearly, a mean of 80 indicates that the grades were generally high for subjects *A* and *C*, whereas a mean of 20 for subject *E* indicates that grades were generally quite low for students in this subject. The standard deviation column indicates that the grades were fairly closely grouped for subject *A* ($\sigma = 5$), whereas they were considerably more dispersed for subject D ($\sigma = 15$) and subject E ($\sigma = 20$).

Taking into consideration these distribution measures (μ and σ), let us transform the raw grades in Table 5.7.1 to grades expressed in standard units, using Equation 5.7.1 which is applicable to population data. These standard grades, which appear in the last column of the table, provide a sounder basis for evaluating a particular grade and for making comparisons among them. For example, positive z_i grades for subjects A, B, and E indicate above average performance in these subjects, whereas negative z_i grades for subjects C and D indicate below average performance. The student's best performance compared with over-all class performance occurred in subject B, where the z_i grade of 3.0 indicates that his raw grade is as much as three standard deviations above the mean. His poorest performance relative to class performance occurred in subject D, since his z_i grade of -1.0 is lowest for this subject.

One characteristic of z_i scores, which is sometimes considered to be a disadvantage, is the fact that negative as well as positive scores occur. Sometimes the fact that z_i scores take on fractional values is also considered undesirable. Therefore, instead of standardizing on the basis of zero mean and unit standard deviation, other standardizing values are selected which always lead to positive standard scores. Such standard scores, where the mean and the standard deviation have values other than 0 and 1, respectively, will be denoted by the symbol z'_i (read z prime sub i). Values often found convenient are a mean of 50 and a standard deviation of 10, or a mean of 100 and a standard deviation of 20. Standard z'_i scores are generally rounded to the nearest whole number.

In general, a population of raw scores, with mean μ and standard deviation σ, may be transformed to standard z'_i scores, with mean μ' and standard deviation σ', as follows:

$$\text{Population} \qquad z'_i = \frac{\sigma'}{\sigma}(X_i - \mu) + \mu' \qquad (5.7.3)$$

Similarly, a sample of raw scores, with mean $\bar{X}$ and standard deviation s, may be transformed to standard z'_i scores, with mean $\bar{X}'$ and standard deviation s', as follows:

$$\text{Sample} \qquad z'_i = \frac{s'}{s}(X_i - \bar{X}) + \bar{X}' \qquad (5.7.4)$$

Refer to Section 5.8, *Note* 5.14, for proof that z'_i scores computed according to Equations 5.7.3 and 5.7.4 have a mean of μ' (population) or $\bar{X}'$ (sample) and a standard deviation of σ' (population) or s' (sample).

Suppose a population of raw scores has $\mu = 70$ and $\sigma = 8$. Say, it is desired to transform these scores to standard scores with mean $\mu' = 100$

and standard deviation $\sigma' = 20$. Substituting these values for μ, μ', σ, and σ' into Equation 5.7.3, we have

$$z'_i = \frac{20}{8}(X_i - 70) + 100$$

The raw scores included in the population may be transformed to standard scores z'_i by substituting in the foregoing equation. For example, suppose 40 and 87 are two scores from this population. We obtain the corresponding standard scores as

$$z'_{40} = \frac{20}{8}(40 - 70) + 100 = 25$$

$$z'_{87} = \frac{20}{8}(87 - 70) + 100 = 142.5$$

When they are rounded to the nearest whole number, the standard scores corresponding to the raw scores 40 and 87 are 25 and 143, respectively. Knowing that the scores have been standardized to a mean of 100 and a standard deviation of 20, these standard scores are immediately meaningful. For example, the standard score 25 is recognized as being 75 points or nearly four standard deviations below the mean. On the other hand, the standard score 143 is 43 points or over two standard deviations above the mean.

PROBLEMS FOR PRACTICE AND REVIEW

1. The number of errors on a mechanical skill test recorded for a sample of 11 subjects was: 6, 2, 1, 9, 8, 3, 7, 1, 5, 7, 9.

(a) Determine the coefficient of variation for this sample.

(b) Transform these scores to standard scores (z).

(c) Transform these scores to standard scores (z') with mean 50 and standard deviation 10.

2. A class of ten students in an intermediate accounting class obtained the following grades on two quizzes (quiz 1 on methods and quiz 2 on principles):

Quiz 1	Quiz 2
4	3
7	10
10	8
8	6
3	10
7	9
10	9
10	4
9	2
8	7

(a) Compare the variability of quiz 1 and quiz 2 grades by comparing the coefficient of variation computed for each quiz. Which quiz shows the most relative variability?

(b) Transform the quiz grades of 4 and 9 to standard units z. Do these grades indicate better performance in quiz 1 or quiz 2? Why?

3. A sample of eight subjects completed a reading speed test and a research aptitude test, obtaining the following scores:

Subject	Research Aptitude Test	Reading Speed Test
A	93	23
B	104	18
C	112	31
D	98	29
E	121	32
F	116	20
G	100	27
H	95	31

(a) Compare the variability of these two sets of scores by computing the coefficient of variation for each set.

(b) Transform the scores in each set to standard scores z.

(c) Transform the scores in each set to standard scores z' with mean 100 and standard deviation 20.

4. The 162 high school seniors in a city school system obtained the following scores on a social understanding test:

Scores	Number of Students
120–124	3
125–129	8
130–134	12
135–139	21
140–144	29
145–149	32
150–154	30
155–159	27

(a) Compute the quartile deviation.

(b) Compute the coefficient of quartile deviation.

5. The number of trials per subject required to perform a specified task successfully was as follows for a sample of 41 subjects:

Number of Trials per Subject	Number of Subjects
18–20	3
21–23	7
24–26	12
27–29	10
30–32	9

(a) Compute the quartile deviation.

(b) Compute the coefficient of quartile deviation.

(c) Compute the coefficient of variation.

5.8 ALGEBRAIC NOTES

This section presents algebraic proofs for various equations introduced in this chapter. Some of these proofs may appear to be more difficult to some readers than the proofs presented in the section on Algebraic Notes in Chapter 4. However, for the most part, it is merely that the equations look more complicated. Actually, a knowledge of elementary algebra as presented in Appendix A and the summation rules discussed in Chapter 2, Section 2.6 are sufficient background for following these proofs. It will pay the reader to study these notes carefully, since it will enrich his understanding of the various relationships presented in this chapter and provide a sounder basis for understanding and applying the introductory methods of statistics. Before studying any of the notes in this section, the reader should review the pertinent parts of this chapter in order to provide the proper frame of reference.

NOTE 5.1: To prove (*Situation A*):

$$\sigma = \frac{1}{N}\sqrt{N\sum_{i=1}^{N} X_i^2 - \left(\sum_{i=1}^{N} X_i\right)^2} \qquad (5.3.1)$$

The definitional equation for the variance (σ^2) of a population of N scores (X_i), with mean μ, is

$$\sigma^2 = \frac{\sum_{i=1}^{N} x_i^2}{N} \qquad (5.2.1)$$

Expressing the numerator in terms of the original scores (X_i) and expanding by squaring, we have

$$\sum_{i=1}^{N} x_i^2 = \sum_{i=1}^{N}(X_i - \mu)^2 = \sum_{i=1}^{N}(X_i^2 - 2X_i\mu + \mu^2) \qquad (5.8.1)$$

Applying Summation Rule 1 to the last form of Equation 5.8.1, we obtain

$$\sum_{i=1}^{N} x_i^2 = \sum_{i=1}^{N} X_i^2 - \sum_{i=1}^{N} 2X_i\mu + \sum_{i=1}^{N} \mu^2 \qquad (5.8.2)$$

Then, noting that 2 and μ are both constants, apply Summation Rule 2 to the middle summation on the right-hand side of Equation 5.8.2 and Summation Rule 3 to the last summation to obtain

$$\sum_{i=1}^{N} x_i^2 = \sum_{i=1}^{N} X_i^2 - 2\mu\sum_{i=1}^{N} X_i + N\mu^2 \qquad (5.8.3)$$

Substituting

$$\mu = \frac{\sum_{i=1}^{N} X_i}{N},$$

we obtain

$$\begin{aligned}
\sum_{i=1}^{N} x_i^2 &= \sum_{i=1}^{N} X_i^2 - 2\left(\frac{\sum_{i=1}^{N} X_i}{N}\right)\sum_{i=1}^{N} X_i + N\left(\frac{\sum_{i=1}^{N} X_i}{N}\right)^2 \\
&= \sum_{i=1}^{N} X_i^2 - \frac{2\left(\sum_{i=1}^{N} X_i\right)^2}{N} + \frac{N\left(\sum_{i=1}^{N} X_i\right)^2}{N^2} \\
&= \sum_{i=1}^{N} X_i^2 - \frac{2\left(\sum_{i=1}^{N} X_i\right)^2}{N} + \frac{\left(\sum_{i=1}^{N} X_i\right)^2}{N} \qquad (5.8.4)
\end{aligned}$$

Combining the last two terms in the last form of Equation 5.8.4, we obtain

$$\sum_{i=1}^{N} x_i^2 = \sum_{i=1}^{N} X_i^2 - \frac{\left(\sum_{i=1}^{N} X_i\right)^2}{N} = \frac{N\sum_{i=1}^{N} X_i^2 - \left(\sum_{i=1}^{N} X_i\right)^2}{N} \qquad (5.8.5)$$

Now, in Equation 5.2.1 for the variance, substitute for $\Sigma\, x_i^2$ according to Equation 5.8.5 to obtain

$$\begin{aligned}
\sigma^2 &= \frac{1}{N}\left[\frac{N\sum_{i=1}^{N} X_i^2 - \left(\sum_{i=1}^{N} X_i\right)^2}{N}\right] \\
&= \frac{N\sum_{i=1}^{N} X_i^2 - \left(\sum_{i=1}^{N} X_i\right)^2}{N^2} \qquad (5.8.6)
\end{aligned}$$

Finally, the standard deviation is obtained by taking the square root of the variance

$$\begin{aligned}
\sigma &= \sqrt{\frac{N\sum_{i=1}^{N} X_i^2 - \left(\sum_{i=1}^{N} X_i\right)^2}{N^2}} \\
&= \frac{1}{N}\sqrt{N\sum_{i=1}^{N} X_i^2 - \left(\sum_{i=1}^{N} X_i\right)^2} \qquad (5.8.7)
\end{aligned}$$

NOTE 5.2: To prove (*Situation A*):

$$s = \sqrt{\frac{n \sum_{i=1}^{n} X_i^2 - \left(\sum_{i=1}^{n} X_i\right)^2}{n(n-1)}} \qquad (5.3.2)$$

This proof is similar to *Note* 5.1. It begins by considering the definitional equation for the variance (s^2) computed for a sample of n scores (X_i), with mean $\bar{X}$, as follows:

$$s^2 = \frac{\sum_{i=1}^{n} x_i^2}{n-1} \qquad (5.2.3)$$

Expressing the numerator in terms of the original scores (X_i) and expanding by squaring, we have

$$\sum_{i=1}^{n} x_i^2 = \sum_{i=1}^{n}(X_i - \bar{X})^2 = \sum_{i=1}^{n}(X_i^2 - 2X_i\bar{X} + \bar{X}^2) \qquad (5.8.8)$$

The balance of the proof will be left as an exercise for the reader.

NOTE 5.3: To prove (*Situation B*):

$$\sigma_{(X+k)} = \sigma \qquad (5.3.3)$$

Given a population of N scores (X_i), with mean μ and standard deviation σ, if a constant k is added to each score, the mean of the $X_i + k$ scores, $\mu_{(X+k)}$, is $\mu + k$ (Equation 4.3.1). The standard deviation of the $X_i + k$ scores, $\sigma_{(X+k)}$, may be obtained directly by substituting $X_i + k$ for X_i and $\mu + k$ for μ in Equation 5.2.1 and taking the square root, as follows:

$$\sigma_{(X+k)} = \sqrt{\frac{\sum_{i=1}^{N} [(X_i + k) - (\mu + k)]^2}{N}} \qquad (5.8.9)$$

Removing the parentheses inside the brackets in the numerator, we obtain

$$\sigma_{(X+k)} = \sqrt{\frac{\sum_{i=1}^{N} (X_i + k - \mu - k)^2}{N}}$$

$$= \sqrt{\frac{\sum_{i=1}^{N} (X_i - \mu)^2}{N}}$$

$$= \sqrt{\sigma^2} = \sigma \qquad (5.8.10)$$

NOTE 5.4: To prove (*Situation B*):

$$\sigma_{(X-k)} = \sigma \tag{5.3.3}$$

This proof is similar to *Note* 5.3. Given a population of N scores (X_i), with mean μ and standard deviation σ, if a constant k is subtracted from each score, the mean of the $X_i - k$ scores, $\mu_{(X-k)}$, is $\mu - k$ (Equation 4.3.2). The standard deviation of the $X_i - k$ scores, $\sigma_{(X-k)}$, may be obtained directly by substituting $X_i - k$ for X_i and $\mu - k$ for μ in Equation 5.2.1 and taking the square root, as follows:

$$\sigma_{(X-k)} = \sqrt{\frac{\sum_{i=1}^{N} [(X_i - k) - (\mu - k)]^2}{N}} \tag{5.8.11}$$

The balance of the proof will be left as an exercise for the reader.

NOTE 5.5: To prove (*Situation B*):

$$s_{(X+k)} = s \tag{5.3.4}$$

This proof is similar to *Note* 5.3. Given a sample of n scores (X_i), with mean $\bar{X}$ and standard deviation s, if a constant k is added to each score, the mean of the $X_i + k$ scores, $\bar{X}_{(X+k)}$, is $\bar{X} + k$ (Equation 4.3.1). The standard deviation of the $X_i + k$ scores may be obtained directly by substituting $X_i + k$ for X_i and $\bar{X} + k$ for $\bar{X}$ in Equation 5.2.3 and taking the square root, as follows:

$$s_{(X+k)} = \sqrt{\frac{\sum_{i=1}^{n} [(X_i + k) - (\bar{X} + k)]^2}{n - 1}} \tag{5.8.12}$$

The balance of the proof will be left as an exercise for the reader.

NOTE 5.6: To prove (*Situation B*):

$$s_{(X-k)} = s \tag{5.3.4}$$

This proof is similar to *Notes* 5.3, 5.4, and 5.5. Given a sample of n scores (X_i), with mean $\bar{X}$ and standard deviation s, a constant k is subtracted from each score to form the new scores $X_i - k$. The proof that the standard deviation of the new scores, $s_{(X-k)}$, is equal to s will be left as an exercise for the reader.

NOTE 5.7: To prove (*Situation C*):

$$\sigma_{gX} = g\sigma \tag{5.3.5}$$

Given a population of N scores (X_i), with mean μ and standard deviation σ, if each score is multiplied by a constant g, the mean of the gX_i scores, μ_{gX}, is $g\mu$ (Equation 4.3.4). The standard deviation of the gX_i scores, σ_{gX}, may be determined directly by substituting gX_i for X_i and $g\mu$ for μ in Equation 5.2.1 and taking the square root, as follows:

$$\sigma_{gX} = \sqrt{\frac{\sum_{i=1}^{N} (gX_i - g\mu)^2}{N}} \tag{5.8.13}$$

Factoring g from the numerator, we have

$$\sigma_{gX} = \sqrt{\frac{\sum_{i=1}^{N} g^2(X_i - \mu)^2}{N}} \tag{5.8.14}$$

Noting that g is a constant, apply Summation Rule 2 to obtain

$$\sigma_{gX} = \sqrt{\frac{g^2 \sum_{i=1}^{N}(X_i - \mu)^2}{N}}$$

$$= g\sqrt{\frac{\sum_{i=1}^{N} (X_i - \mu)^2}{N}}$$

$$= g\sqrt{\sigma^2}$$

$$= g\sigma \tag{5.8.15}$$

NOTE 5.8: To prove (*Situation C*):

$$\sigma_{X/g} = \frac{\sigma}{g} \tag{5.3.6}$$

This proof is similar to *Note* 5.7. Given a population of N scores (X_i), with mean μ and standard deviation σ. If each score is divided by a constant g, the mean of the X_i/g scores, $\mu_{X/g}$, is μ/g (Equation 4.3.5). The standard deviation of the X_i/g scores, $\sigma_{X/g}$, may be determined directly by substituting X_i/g for X_i and μ/g for μ in Equation 5.2.1 and taking the square root, as follows:

$$\sigma_{X/g} = \sqrt{\frac{\sum_{i=1}^{N}\left(\frac{X_i}{g} - \frac{\mu}{g}\right)^2}{N}} \tag{5.8.16}$$

The balance of the proof will be left as an exercise for the reader.

NOTE 5.9: To prove (*Situation C*):

$$s_{gX} = gs \tag{5.3.7}$$

This proof is similar to *Note* 5.7. Given a sample of n scores (X_i), with mean $\bar{X}$ and standard deviation s. If each score is multiplied by a constant g, the mean of the gX_i scores, $\bar{X}_{gX}$, is $g\bar{X}$ (Equation 4.3.4). The standard deviation of the gX_i scores, s_{gX}, may be determined directly by substituting gX_i for X_i and $g\bar{X}$ for $\bar{X}$ in Equation 5.2.3 and taking the square root, as follows:

$$s_{gX} = \sqrt{\frac{\sum_{i=1}^{n} (gX_i - g\bar{X})^2}{n - 1}} \tag{5.8.17}$$

The balance of the proof will be left as an exercise for the reader.

NOTE 5.10: To prove (*Situation C*):

$$s_{X/g} = \frac{s}{g} \tag{5.3.8}$$

This proof is similar to *Notes* 5.7, 5.8, and 5.9. Given a sample of n scores (X_i), with mean $\bar{X}$ and standard deviation s, each score is divided by a constant g to form the new scores X_i/g. The proof that the standard deviation of the new scores, $s_{X/g}$, is equal to s/g will be left as an exercise for the reader.

NOTE 5.11: To prove (*Situation D*):

$$\sigma = g\sigma_u \tag{5.3.12}$$

where

$$\sigma_u = \frac{1}{N}\sqrt{N \sum_{i=1}^{N} u_i^2 - \left(\sum_{i=1}^{N} u_i\right)^2} \tag{5.3.10}$$

and

$$u_i = \frac{X_i - k}{g} \tag{5.3.9}$$

Given a population of N scores (X_i), with mean μ and standard deviation σ, the relationship between μ and $\bar{u}$, the mean of the transformed u_i scores, may be expressed as

$$\mu = g\bar{u} + k \tag{4.3.9}$$

Solving Equation 5.3.9 for X_i, we obtain

$$X_i = gu_i + k \tag{5.8.18}$$

In Equation 5.2.1, substitute for X_i in accordance with Equation 5.8.18 and for μ in accordance with Equation 4.3.9. Then, taking the square root, we obtain

$$\sigma = \sqrt{\frac{\sum_{i=1}^{N} [(gu_i + k) - (g\bar{u} + k)]^2}{N}} \tag{5.8.19}$$

Removing the parentheses inside the brackets in the numerator, we obtain

$$\sigma = \sqrt{\frac{\sum_{i=1}^{N} (gu_i + k - g\bar{u} - k)^2}{N}}$$

$$= \sqrt{\frac{\sum_{i=1}^{N} (gu_i - g\bar{u})^2}{N}} \tag{5.8.20}$$

Factoring g from the numerator, we have

$$\sigma = \sqrt{\frac{\sum_{i=1}^{N} g^2(u_i - \bar{u})^2}{N}} \tag{5.8.21}$$

Noting that g is a constant, apply Summation Rule 2 to obtain

$$\sigma = \sqrt{\frac{g^2 \sum_{i=1}^{N}(u_i - \bar{u})^2}{N}}$$

$$= g\sqrt{\frac{\sum_{i=1}^{N} (u_i - \bar{u})^2}{N}} \tag{5.8.22}$$

The term inside the square root sign is σ_u^2, the definitional form of the variance of the u_i scores. (This expression for σ_u^2 may be obtained by substituting u_i for X_i and $\bar{u}$ for μ in Equation 5.2.1.) Then, substituting σ_u^2 for the term inside the square root sign, we obtain

$$\sigma = g\sqrt{\sigma_u^2}$$

$$= g\sigma_u \tag{5.8.23}$$

NOTE 5.12: To prove (*Situation D*):

$$s = gs_u \tag{5.3.13}$$

where

$$s_u = \sqrt{\frac{n \sum_{i=1}^{n} u_i^2 - \left(\sum_{i=1}^{n} u_i\right)^2}{n(n-1)}} \tag{5.3.11}$$

and

$$u_i = \frac{X_i - k}{g} \tag{5.3.9}$$

Given a sample of n scores (X_i), with mean $\bar{X}$ and standard deviation s. The relationship between $\bar{X}$ and $\bar{u}$, the mean of the transformed u_i scores, may be expressed as

$$\bar{X} = g\bar{u} + k \tag{4.3.9}$$

Solving Equation 5.3.9 for X_i, we obtain (as in *Note* 5.11)

$$X_i = gu_i + k \tag{5.8.18}$$

In Equation 5.2.3, substitute for X_i in accordance with Equation 5.8.18 and for $\bar{X}$ in accordance with Equation 4.3.9. Then, taking the square root, we obtain

$$s = \sqrt{\frac{\sum_{i=1}^{n} [(gu_i + k) - (g\bar{u} + k)]^2}{n-1}} \tag{5.8.24}$$

Removing the parentheses inside the brackets in the numerator, we obtain

$$s = \sqrt{\frac{\sum_{i=1}^{n} (gu_i + k - g\bar{u} - k)^2}{n-1}}$$

$$= \sqrt{\frac{\sum_{i=1}^{n} (gu_i - g\bar{u})^2}{n-1}}$$

$$= \sqrt{\frac{\sum_{i=1}^{n} g^2(u_i - \bar{u})^2}{n-1}} \tag{5.8.25}$$

Noting that g is a constant, apply Summation Rule 2 to obtain

$$s = \sqrt{\frac{g^2 \sum_{i=1}^{n}(u_i - \bar{u})^2}{n-1}}$$

$$= g\sqrt{\frac{\sum_{i=1}^{n} (u_i - \bar{u})^2}{n-1}} \tag{5.8.26}$$

The term inside the square root sign is s_u^2, the definitional form of the variance of the sample set of u_i scores. (This expression for s_u^2 may be obtained by substituting u_i for X_i and $\bar{u}$ for $\bar{X}$ in Equation 5.2.3.) Then, substituting s_u^2 for the term inside the square root sign, we obtain

$$\begin{aligned} s &= g\sqrt{s_u^2} \\ &= g s_u \end{aligned} \tag{5.8.27}$$

NOTE 5.13: To prove (Section 5.7): For standard scores z_i, the mean is equal to 0 and the standard deviation is equal to 1 where

$$\text{Population} \qquad z_i = \frac{X_i - \mu}{\sigma} \tag{5.7.1}$$

$$\text{Sample} \qquad z_i = \frac{X_i - \bar{X}}{s} \tag{5.7.2}$$

Considering the standard scores for a population first, we could determine the mean μ_z by substituting z_i for X_i in Equation 4.2.2 to obtain

$$\mu_z = \frac{\sum_{i=1}^{N} z_i}{N} \tag{5.8.28}$$

Now, in Equation 5.8.28, substitute for z_i in accordance with Equation 5.7.1 to obtain

$$\mu_z = \frac{\sum_{i=1}^{N} \left(\frac{X_i - \mu}{\sigma} \right)}{N} \tag{5.8.29}$$

Noting that μ and σ are constants, apply Summation Rules 2, 1, and 3 (in that order) to obtain

$$\begin{aligned} \mu_z &= \frac{\frac{1}{\sigma} \sum_{i=1}^{N} (X_i - \mu)}{N} \\ &= \frac{\frac{1}{\sigma} \left(\sum_{i=1}^{N} X_i - \sum_{i=1}^{N} \mu \right)}{N} \\ &= \frac{\frac{1}{\sigma} \left(\sum_{i=1}^{N} X_i - N\mu \right)}{N} \end{aligned} \tag{5.8.30}$$

Substituting $\Sigma X_i/N$ for μ, we obtain

$$\mu_z = \frac{\dfrac{1}{\sigma}\left(\sum_{i=1}^{N} X_i - N\dfrac{\sum_{i=1}^{N} X_i}{N}\right)}{N}$$

$$= \frac{\dfrac{1}{\sigma}\left(\sum_{i=1}^{N} X_i - \sum_{i=1}^{N} X_i\right)}{N}$$

$$= \frac{\dfrac{1}{\sigma}(0)}{N}$$

$$= 0 \tag{5.8.31}$$

In the same way, it can be proven that the mean, $\bar{X}_z$, for a sample set of standard scores z_i is equal to 0. This proof begins by substituting z_i for X_i in Equation 4.2.4 to obtain

$$\bar{X}_z = \frac{\sum_{i=1}^{n} z_i}{n} \tag{5.8.32}$$

Then, in the numerator, substitute for z_i in accordance with Equation 5.7.2. The balance of the proof will be left as an exercise for the reader.

Again considering the standard scores for a population, we could determine the standard deviation σ_z by substituting, in Equation 5.2.1, z_i for X_i and 0 for μ (since $\mu_z = 0$) and taking the square root. Making these substitutions, we obtain

$$\sigma_z = \sqrt{\frac{\sum_{i=1}^{N} (z_i - 0)^2}{N}}$$

$$= \sqrt{\frac{\sum_{i=1}^{N} z_i^{\,2}}{N}} \tag{5.8.33}$$

Now, in Equation 5.8.33, substitute for z_i in accordance with Equation 5.7.1 to obtain

$$\sigma_z = \sqrt{\frac{\sum_{i=1}^{N}\left(\dfrac{X_i - \mu}{\sigma}\right)^2}{N}} \tag{5.8.34}$$

Noting that σ is a constant, apply Summation Rule 2 to obtain

$$\sigma_z = \sqrt{\frac{\frac{1}{\sigma^2}\sum_{i=1}^{N}(X_i - \mu)^2}{N}}$$

$$= \frac{1}{\sigma}\sqrt{\frac{\sum_{i=1}^{N}(X_i - \mu)^2}{N}} \qquad (5.8.35)$$

Note that the term inside the square root sign is σ^2, the definitional form of the variance of the X_i scores (Equation 5.2.1). Substituting σ^2 for this term, we obtain

$$\sigma_z = \frac{1}{\sigma}\sqrt{\sigma^2}$$

$$= \frac{1}{\sigma}\sigma$$

$$= 1 \qquad (5.8.36)$$

In the same way, we can show that the standard deviation, s_z, for a sample set of standard scores z_i is equal to 1. This proof begins by substituting, in Equation 5.2.3, z_i for X_i and 0 for $\bar{X}$ (since $\bar{X}_z = 0$) and taking the square root. Making these substitutions, we obtain

$$s_z = \sqrt{\frac{\sum_{i=1}^{n}(z_i - 0)^2}{n - 1}}$$

$$= \sqrt{\frac{\sum_{i=1}^{n} z_i^2}{n - 1}} \qquad (5.8.37)$$

Now, in Equation 5.8.37, substitute for z_i in accordance with Equation 5.7.2. The balance of the proof will be left as an exercise for the reader.

NOTE 5.14: To prove (Section 5.7): For standard scores z'_i, the mean is equal to μ' (population) or $\bar{X}'$ (sample) and the standard deviation is equal to σ' (population) or s' (sample), where

Population $\quad z'_i = \frac{\sigma'}{\sigma}(X_i - \mu) + \mu' \qquad (5.7.3)$

Sample $\quad z'_i = \frac{s'}{s}(X_i - \bar{X}) + \bar{X}' \qquad (5.7.4)$

Let us first consider standard z'_i scores for a population. Given a population of N raw scores (X_i), with mean μ and standard deviation σ, it is desired to transform these raw scores to standard z'_i scores, with mean μ' and standard deviation σ'. Let us consider this transformation in three steps, as follows:

STEP 1: Using Equation 5.7.1, transform the raw scores to standard z_i scores, with zero mean and unit standard deviation.

STEP 2: Multiply each z_i score by σ' (a constant) to form the new scores $\sigma' z_i$. According to Equation 4.3.4, the mean of these new scores is equal to the constant σ' times the mean of the z_i scores (which is 0). Therefore, the mean of the $\sigma' z_i$ scores is 0. According to Equation 5.3.5, the standard deviation of the $\sigma' z_i$ scores is equal to the constant σ' times the standard deviation of the z_i scores (which is 1). Therefore, the standard deviation of the $\sigma' z_i$ scores is σ'.

STEP 3: Add μ' (a constant) to each $\sigma' z_i$ score to form the scores $\sigma' z_i + \mu'$. According to Equation 4.3.1, the mean of these scores is equal to the sum of the constant μ' plus the mean of the $\sigma' z_i$ scores (which is 0). Therefore, the mean of the $\sigma' z_i + \mu'$ scores is μ'. According to Equation 5.3.3, the standard deviation of the $\sigma' z_i + \mu'$ scores is equal to σ', the standard deviation of the $\sigma' z_i$ scores.

Therefore, we may write

$$z'_i = \sigma' z_i + \mu' \tag{5.8.38}$$

since the $\sigma' z_i + \mu'$ scores have the required mean μ' and standard deviation σ'. Substituting for z_i, according to Equation 5.7.1, we finally obtain

$$\begin{aligned} z'_i &= \sigma'\left(\frac{X_i - \mu}{\sigma}\right) + \mu' \\ &= \frac{\sigma'}{\sigma}(X_i - \mu) + \mu' \end{aligned} \tag{5.8.39}$$

For sample data, the proof that the z'_i scores (Equation 5.7.4) have a mean of $\bar{X}'$ and a standard deviation of s' can be developed in a similar manner. Given a sample of n raw scores (X_i), with mean $\bar{X}$ and standard deviation s, it is desired to transform these raw scores to standard z'_i scores, with mean $\bar{X}'$ and standard deviation s'. Consider this transformation in three steps, as follows:

STEP 1: Using Equation 5.7.2, transform the raw scores to standard z_i scores, with zero mean and unit standard deviation.

STEP 2: Multiply each z_i score by s' (a constant) to form the new scores $s'z_i$. It will be left to the reader to show that these new scores have a mean of 0 and a standard deviation of s'. (Follow the method of *Step* 2 for population data, presented previously.)

STEP 3: Add $\bar{X}'$ (a constant) to each $s'z_i$ score to form the scores $s'z_i + \bar{X}'$. It will be left to the reader to show that these scores have a mean of $\bar{X}'$ and a standard deviation of s'. (Follow the method of *Step* 3 for population data, presented previously.)

The balance of the proof is similar to the foregoing development for population data.

Part III
Foundation for Statistical Inference

6

PROBABILITY

6.1 INTRODUCTION

We have completed our study of the methods of descriptive statistics. It would seem logical now to continue with the presentation of introductory statistics by considering the methods of statistical inference. As noted previously (Chapter 2, Section 2.3), these are the methods applicable to sample data for the purpose of making inferences relating to the population from which the sample was selected. Actually, we have already begun to consider this area of statistical methods. It was pointed out in Chapters 4 and 5 that, although the methods presented are applicable to population data, they may be used for sample data as well, sometimes with slight modification. Unfortunately, however, it is not possible to progress very far in the study of inductive statistics without first studying elementary probability. The methods of statistical inference can only be presented and understood in terms of probability concepts and theory.

6.2 DEFINITION

The general notion of probability is not unfamiliar. We speak in terms of probabilities, perhaps more than we realize. For example, we often make statements such as, "I may miss the bus unless I hurry," "Joe will probably call me tomorrow," "Ted has some chance of winning the first prize," and "She is very likely to forget what I told her." The common element underlying these statements is a feeling of *less than complete assurance* or a feeling of *uncertainty*. That is, the *outcome* in each situation is uncertain.

This is so because *alternative possible outcomes* are recognized, each of which could materialize. For example, consider the statement, "Joe will probably call me tomorrow." What are the alternative possible outcomes to be considered? These depend on the specific circumstances involved. The call from Joe tomorrow may be considered important in itself so that the alternative outcomes are "Joe will call tomorrow" or "Joe will not call tomorrow." On the other hand, your only concern may be whether Joe will call today or tomorrow, with no doubt in your mind that he will call on one of these two days. Then, the alternatives become "Joe will call tomorrow" or "Joe will call today."

Another characteristic of statements like those just illustrated is the expression or implication of a *degree* of assurance. For example, "Ted has some chance of winning the first prize" expresses a *small* degree of assurance that Ted will win the first prize. On the other hand, "She is very likely to forget what I told her" expresses *considerable* assurance that she will forget. What is the basis for determining degree of assurance? Generally speaking, if one uses a method at all when making such statements, it is to base the degree of assurance on past experience, perhaps subconsciously. For example, if you feel that she will forget what you told her, it may be that she has forgotten what you have told her a number of times in the past. Or the small amount of attention she seemed to pay to what you said leads you to feel fairly certain that she will not remember, based on your experience with others who acted in a similar manner when you said something to them.

We have identified the following characteristics of the foregoing statements which are important from the point of view of probability: the existence of alternative possible outcomes, the uncertainty that a specified outcome will materialize, and the degree of assurance that the specified outcome will occur. Furthermore, the degree of assurance may be determined on the basis of experience. Generally speaking, probability deals with the degree of assurance (the chances or odds) that one of a set of alternative possible outcomes will occur. However, mathematical probability requires a more precise statement of the circumstances involved and of the degree of assurance relating to a specified outcome than is expressed in the foregoing statements. This will require the introduction of new concepts and terminology.

It is customary to present probability in terms of tossing coins, rolling dice or drawing cards from a deck, reflecting the early applications of probability methods to gambling problems. Today, of course, applications of probability theory are widespread throughout the areas of research and decision-making. However, it is still desirable to present probability theory in terms of gambling situations because it permits a simpler, more convenient type of presentation. The extension to other situations, such as sampling problems and statistical inference, is not difficult, as will be seen.

Let us consider two illustrative probability problems. What is the probability of obtaining the following:

1. A head, when a coin is tossed once?
2. A six of spades, when selecting a card from a well-shuffled deck of 52 playing cards?

In each problem, we can identify the *trial*, the *event*, and the *alternative possible outcomes*. In (1), the toss of a coin is the trial, head is the event, and the alternative possible outcomes are head and tail. In (2), selection of a card is the trial, 6 of spades is the event, and the 52 cards represent 52 alternative possible outcomes.

Let us generalize from these illustrations and formulate the definitions of these three important concepts. *A trial represents a circumstance which must lead to the occurrence of one of a set of alternative possible outcomes.* For example, the circumstance "toss of a coin" must lead to a head or a tail. *An event is the particular one of the alternative possible outcomes in which we happen to be interested.* This is the outcome which is specifically stated when a probability problem is raised. For example, we ask, "What is the probability of obtaining a head when tossing a coin once?" This identifies "head" as the event. *However, any one or more of the alternative possible outcomes may be referred to as events. The alternative possible outcomes refer to all the different ways in which a trial could result.* For example, toss of a coin could result in a head or a tail. Selection of a card from a well-shuffled deck of 52 cards could result in any one of the 52 cards being the card selected.

Mathematically, probability represents a proportion or relative frequency which specifies the degree of assurance that an event will occur. For example, suppose it is determined that an elementary school teacher has been absent because of illness 3% of the time during the last several school years. Therefore, on the average, we may expect that this teacher will be absent because of illness 3 out of 100 school days, if the past performance continues into the future. Based upon this teacher's record, we estimate that the probability is .03 that she will be absent because of illness during a school day. In other words, *the historical record provides a basis for estimating the degree of assurance (the probability) that a specified event will occur.* This example illustrates how the record of a single individual may be used to estimate a probability relating to this individual.

Let us consider a somewhat different type of situation. Suppose it is determined that 9% of the sophomores enrolled in a large university drop out before entering the senior year. This is based on, say, the experience of the university over a long period of years. Therefore, on the average, 9 out of 100 sophomores enrolled in this university may be expected to drop out before entering the senior year, if the historical pattern continues into the future. Based on this experience, we estimate that the probability is .09 that a sophomore enrolled at this university will drop out before entering the senior year. We are now ready to present a more formal definition of probability.

Probability (Definition 1). *If an event A occurs X times in n trials, the probability that A will occur in a given trial, denoted as P(A), is*

$$P(A) = \frac{X}{n}, \qquad \text{when} \quad n \text{ is infinitely large}$$

According to *Definition* 1, the probability of an event A is defined as a relative frequency or the proportion of times event A occurs in a series of *repeated trials*, where the number of repetitions of the trial is indefinitely (infinitely) large. This is another way of saying that the probability that event A will occur is defined as the relative frequency of occurrence *in the long run*. For example, the probability of a 4 when rolling a die (one of a pair of dice), denoted as $P(4)$, is defined as the proportion of times a 4 is obtained when the die is rolled an infinite number of times. Clearly, *the proportion or relative frequency for an infinitely large number of trials is a theoretical concept. This theoretical relative frequency, the relative frequency in the long run, can only be determined theoretically, or hypothesized.*

On the other hand, the theoretical relative frequency may be *estimated* experimentally. For example, $P(4)$ may be estimated by rolling the die a large number of times. A 4 will be obtained a certain number of times during the first few tosses of the die. Then, $P(4)$ may be estimated as the relative frequency computed by dividing the number of tosses for which the outcome was a 4 by the number of times the die was tossed. If the die is tossed a few more times, $P(4)$ can now be estimated as the number of times a 4 was obtained *in all tosses so far* divided by the total number of times the die was tossed. This provides a better estimate of $P(4)$ since it is based on a larger number of tosses. As the number of trials (tosses) is increased, $P(4)$ is estimated by dividing the cumulative number of times a 4 was obtained by the cumulative number of times the die was tossed. The larger the number of trials, the better the estimate of the relative frequency or the proportion of the times a 4 may be expected to occur *in the long run*.

We may distinguish between two types of probabilities, *a priori probability* and *empirical probability*. *A priori* probability is determined on a theoretical basis, whereas *empirical* probability refers to an estimated probability. For example, a die was rolled 504 times in order to estimate

$P(1, 2, \text{ or } 3)$, the probability of obtaining 1, 2, or 3 on a toss of the die. Table 6.2.1 presents the results of this experiment. Notice the change in the relative frequency of occurrence for the event 1, 2, or 3. When only 6 tosses of the die formed the basis for estimation, the relative frequency was .83. However, continued trials resulted in reducing this estimate until an apparent stabilization of the relative frequency to .48 was reached after 504 trials. On the basis of this experiment, we may estimate $P(1, 2, \text{ or } 3) = .48$. This is an *empirical* probability. On the other hand, we could

Table 6.2.1 RESULTS OF AN ACTUAL EXPERIMENT OF 504 ROLLS OF A DIE TO DETERMINE $P(1, 2, \text{ OR } 3)$

Cumulative Number of Tosses, n	Number of Times 1, 2, or 3 Was Obtained, X	Estimate of $P(1, 2, \text{ or } 3) = X/n$
6	5	.83
72	36	.50
144	74	.51
216	108	.50
288	147	.51
360	177	.49
432	209	.48
504	244	.48

reason that 1, 2, or 3 ought to come up just about as frequently as 4, 5, or 6 in the long run, or about half the time, so that we would expect $P(1, 2, \text{ or } 3) = \frac{1}{2}$ or .50. This is an *a priori* probability. It may be that the empirical probability (.48) would be modified by increasing the number of tosses and would approach .50 more closely.

Mathematically, since probability is defined as a relative frequency, the lowest possible value for any probability is 0 and the highest possible value is 1. This is expressed symbolically as

$$0 \leq P(A) \leq 1 \tag{6.2.1}$$

This expression states that "the probability an event A will occur can be equal to or greater than 0 or less than or equal to 1." $P(A) = 0$ indicates that the event A cannot occur, whereas $P(A) = 1$ indicates that it is certain that event A will occur. A set of alternative possible outcomes of a trial is called an *exhaustive* set if it includes *all* possible alternative outcomes. For example, in the toss of a coin, head and tail make up an exhaustive set of possible outcomes. In selecting a card from a well-shuffled deck of 52 cards, the 52 cards make up an exhaustive set, since these constitute the full set of alternative possible outcomes. If $P(\text{not } A)$ denotes "the probability of any one of the possible outcomes of a trial other than A," we may write

$$P(A) + P(\text{not } A) = 1 \tag{6.2.2}$$

This relationship is apparent when you think in terms of proportions instead of probabilities. Clearly, the proportion of times that an event A occurs plus the proportion of times this event does not occur is unity. Then, we may also write

$$P(\text{not } A) = 1 - P(A) \tag{6.2.3}$$

As an illustration, let event A refer to obtaining an even number (2, 4, or 6) when rolling a die once. Then, "not A" refers to obtaining a number which is not even (1, 3, or 5). Since we may expect to obtain an even number just about as often as an odd number, we may write

$$P(\text{even number}) = \tfrac{1}{2}$$

Then

$$P(\text{not an even number}) = 1 - P(\text{even number})$$
$$= 1 - \tfrac{1}{2} = \tfrac{1}{2}$$

When a coin is tossed once, only a head or a tail could occur, not both. When a die is rolled once, one and only one of the possible outcomes 1, 2, 3, 4, 5, or 6 could materialize. Events such as these are called *mutually exclusive* events. That is, *two or more events are mutually exclusive if one and only one can occur in a given trial.* When a card is selected from a well-shuffled deck of 52 cards, there are 52 mutually exclusive events. Since only one card is to be selected, the selection of any one of the 52 cards precludes selection of any of the other cards in the deck. Suppose an urn contains red-painted marbles, white-painted marbles, and some which are painted half red and half white. If the urn is thoroughly shaken and, while blindfolded, you select a marble, the events "selection of a marble with red paint" and "selection of a marble with white paint" are not mutually exclusive, since a marble could be selected with *both* red *and* white paint.

Two or more events are *equi-probable* if they are equally likely to occur. This is a condition which is often hypothesized or assumed rather than known. For example, when a die is rolled, the alternative outcomes 1, 2, 3, 4, 5, and 6 are usually assumed to be equi-probable events (to have equal probability), since one outcome is supposedly as likely to materialize as any of the others. This, of course, is not necessarily true. For example, it is not true if the die is loaded. Actually, it is true only for a die which is a perfectly formed cube and the material of which the die is made is perfectly homogeneous. If a deck of cards is not well-shuffled, it is less likely that the 52 cards represent 52 equi-probable outcomes when a card is to be selected, unless special precautions are taken so that the process of selecting a card gives each card an equal chance of being the one selected. In a well-shuffled deck, it is more likely that the 52 cards represent 52 equi-probable outcomes.

A set of alternative possible outcomes may be both mutually exclusive and equi-probable. For example, the possible outcomes head and tail when tossing a coin are both mutually exclusive and equi-probable. Similarly, the 52 possible outcomes when selecting a card from a well-shuffled deck are both mutually exclusive and equi-probable. These illustrations represent sets of alternative outcomes which are exhaustive as well as mutually exclusive and equi-probable.

We are now ready to present a second definition of probability which is not as generally applicable as *Definition* 1, but useful in a wide variety of situations.

Probability (Definition 2). *Given a trial with an exhaustive set of N alternative possible outcomes which are mutually exclusive and equi-probable, if X of these possible outcomes fall in the category A, then the probability that A will occur in a single trial is*

$$P(A) = \frac{X}{N} = \frac{\text{Number of possible outcomes in the category } A}{\text{Total number of possible alternative outcomes}}$$

Definition 2 defines probability of an event A as the proportion of an exhaustive set of possible outcomes which are in the A category. For example, what is the probability of picking a king or a queen when selecting a card, while blindfolded, from a well-shuffled deck of 52 cards? Since any one of the 52 cards in the deck has as much chance of being the card selected as any other card in the deck, the cards represent 52 equi-probable outcomes. Selection of one card precludes selection of any of the others, since only one card is to be selected. Hence, the 52 cards represent 52 mutually exclusive, as well as equi-probable, events. Event A in this illustration represents selection of a king or queen. Since there are 8 cards in the deck which are either a king or a queen, 8 of the 52 alternative possible outcomes are in the category A. Therefore, according to *Definition* 2, the probability that the card selected is a king or a queen may be determined as

$$P(\text{king or queen}) = \frac{X}{N} = \frac{8}{52} \quad \text{or} \quad \frac{2}{13}$$

As a second illustration, what is the probability that a red marble will be selected from an urn containing 5 red marbles and 10 blue marbles, if the selection is made while blindfolded and after the urn has been vigorously shaken? Since the urn contains 15 marbles, representing 15 mutually exclusive and equi-probable alternative outcomes, 5 of which are red, we may determine the probability of selecting a red marble, according to *Definition* 2, as

$$P(\text{red}) = \frac{5}{15} \text{ or } \frac{1}{3}$$

Although *Definition* 1 and *Definition* 2 both express probability as a proportion, they are conceptually different. In the case of *Definition* 2, we must determine the total number of mutually exclusive, equi-probable outcomes which can result from a trial and what proportion of these possible outcomes represent the event A. In the case of *Definition* 1, on the other hand, we are interested in the proportion of times the event A occurs in a long series of trials. For example, let us consider the urn containing 5 red and 10 blue marbles, previously mentioned. We observed that there were 15 mutually exclusive, equi-probable outcomes possible as a result of a trial (selection of a marble) and 5 of these fell in the category A (red marble). Therefore, according to *Definition* 2, we computed the probability of selecting a red marble, $P(\text{red})$, as $\frac{5}{15}$ or $\frac{1}{3}$. Suppose we want to determine this probability according to *Definition* 1 instead. How would we go about this?

According to *Definition* 1, $P(\text{red})$ represents the proportion of times a red marble is selected in a long series of trials. That is, a marble is selected from the urn (a trial) and the color is observed. Then, the marble is put back, the urn vigorously shaken and, while blindfolded, a marble is selected again (second trial) and the color noted. If such trials are carried out an infinite number of times, then the proportion of trials which result in a red marble is $P(\text{red})$. Of course, we cannot expect to carry out an infinite number of trials. Therefore, we may estimate $P(\text{red})$ based on a number of trials, using the method previously discussed (see Table 6.2.1). Or, we may determine this probability on some theoretical basis or on the basis of some hypothesis. For example, we may take into consideration the fact that $\frac{1}{3}$ of the marbles in the urn are red and set up the hypothesis that a red marble would be selected $\frac{1}{3}$ of the time in a long series of trials. On this basis, we would conclude that $P(\text{red}) = \frac{1}{3}$. Actually, this amounts to using *Definition* 2 to determine $P(\text{red})$. *When dealing with mutually exclusive and equi-probable alternative outcomes, the probability of an event A is identical whether determined according to Definition* 1 *or Definition* 2.

It is not always possible to determine probabilities by the use of *Definition* 2. In such cases, *Definition* 1 must be used. For example, suppose we know that a marble was removed from the urn mentioned above and we do not know whether it was a red or a blue marble. Assuming we are not permitted to count the marbles and determine how many are red and how many are blue, *Definition* 2 cannot be used to determine P(red). However, we may estimate this probability based upon a series of repeated trials, using *Definition* 1. Say, we wish to determine the probability of a 5 on the toss of a loaded die. We cannot assume that the alternative possible outcomes 1, 2, 3, 4, 5, and 6 are equi-probable, since the die is loaded. The required probability may be estimated according to *Definition* 1 by tossing the die a number of times and computing the proportion of times that a 5 is obtained. This proportion is an estimate of $P(5)$. Notice that *Definition* 1 uses n to denote the number of trials, since a finite number of trials, even if large, represents a sample of the unlimited number of trials when n becomes infinite. On the other hand, *Definition* 2 uses N to denote the number of possible outcomes in the exhaustive set, since this represents the *population* of all possible outcomes.

We will apply these definitions to determine probabilities for problems in the fields of psychology and education. Suppose a rat is introduced into a maze for the first time. This maze has 5 paths which the animal could take, only one of which leads to the food box. If it can be assumed that the entrances to the paths look identical to the rat, they represent 5 equi-probable alternatives facing the rat. If we are interested in which path is selected first, the 5 paths represent mutually exclusive possibilities. In this instance, the probability that the first path chosen by the rat leads to the food box is $\frac{1}{5}$ (or 1 chance in 5), according to *Definition* 2. However, it may be that the paths do not appear identical to the rat. For example, they are located differently in the maze. One entrance may be nearer to the rat when he is introduced into the maze, or the light may shine more brightly on one of the entrances, etc. It may not appear reasonable to assume that the choices facing the rat are equi-probable. In that event, the probability that the first path chosen by a rat will be the one leading to the food box would have to be determined experimentally, according to *Definition* 1, or hypothesized on some basis.

Experimental determination may be arrived at by selecting a group of rats, preferably a homogeneous group, and introducing them one at a time into the maze, under identical conditions. The proportion of the rats whose first choice is the path leading to the food box represents an estimate of the probability that this path will be the first one chosen by a rat when introduced into the maze for the first time. (We cannot estimate this probability by introducing the *same* rat into the maze again and again, since learning will take place during the successive trials.)

A teacher has a class of 10 girls and 15 boys and wishes to choose one of these students to represent the class on the student council. He writes the name of each student on a slip of paper, folds each slip in half, and places the folded slips into a box. After shaking the box vigorously, he asks a student to close his eyes and select one slip of paper from the box. The student whose name is on the slip selected will be chosen to represent the class. What is the probability that a boy will be chosen? Assuming the folded slips of paper are identical in every way, they represent an exhaustive set of mutually exclusive and equi-probable outcomes. Therefore, since there are 15 boys and 25 students in all, applying *Definition* 2, $P(\text{boy}) = \frac{15}{25} = \frac{3}{5}$ or .60. In other words, the probability is 3 chances in 5 or 60 chances in 100 that a boy will be selected.

A psychological testing service is considering purchase of a new type of test scoring machine and wishes to determine the probability that the machine will make an error in scoring a paper. The alternative possible outcomes when a paper is scored by the machine is "scored correctly" or "scored incorrectly." Clearly, these alternatives would not be expected to be equi-probable. Therefore, *Definition* 2 is not appropriate in this situation. In terms of *Definition* 1, the probability that a paper will be incorrectly scored is equal to the relative frequency of incorrectly scored papers over an infiintely long series of trials (the relative frequency in the long run). This probability may be estimated by scoring a large number of tests using the new machine and then reviewing each paper for scoring errors. The proportion of papers containing one or more scoring errors represents an estimate of the desired probability.

Definition 1 and *Definition* 2 are easy to apply directly in the simpler situations. However, in more involved situations, probabilities are more easily determined by the use of certain rules for combining probabilities. These rules are given in Section 6.4. In Section 6.3, a brief discussion of *permutations* and *combinations* is presented. This material will be useful in the development and application of the rules for combining probabilities and in later discussions.

PROBLEMS FOR PRACTICE AND REVIEW

1. If 8% of a certain strain of laboratory rats is known not to respond to a drug A, what is the probability that any particular rat of this strain will not respond to this drug? Which definition of probability did you use to arrive at your answer?

2. A bag contains 10 green chips, 5 white chips, and 20 orange chips. If you shake the bag vigorously and select a chip with your eyes closed, what is the probability that the chip selected will be (use *Definition* 2)

(a) orange?
(b) green or white? (*Hint:* Let X = number of green *and* white chips)
(c) blue?
(d) green, white, or orange?

3. Suppose you have a collection of dimes in your pocket issued in the following years: 2 in 1927, 1 in 1932, 1 in 1939, 6 in 1934, 7 in 1958, 1 in 1930, 1 in 1963, 3 in 1964, 5 in 1956, 3 in 1928, 2 in 1938, and 4 in 1943. If you shake your pocket vigorously and select one dime, what is the probability that the date it was issued is (use *Definition* 2)

(a) 1956?
(b) in the 1930's (*Hint:* Let X = number of coins dated in the 1930's)?
(c) before 1939?
(d) after 1956?
(e) in the 1920's or 1960's?
(f) between 1931 and 1944?

4. A class is made up of 6 boys (3 tall, 2 average height, 1 short) and 8 girls (3 tall, 3 average height, 2 short). Suppose the name of each pupil is written on a slip of paper and all the slips are placed in a box. After the box is shaken vigorously and, while the person is blindfolded, one slip is selected, what is the probability that the name on the slip is for

(a) a boy?
(b) a short girl?
(c) a tall boy?
(d) a pupil of average height?
(e) a short boy or a tall girl?
(f) not a short girl?
(g) not a pupil of average height?

5. The following information was obtained from a study of the records of a large high school for the last 15 years: on the average, 20% of the students obtained one F, 10% obtained two F's, 5% obtained three F's, and 1% obtained more than three F's. What is the probability that a student entering this high school will obtain (use *Definition* 1)

(a) two F's?
(b) no more than two F's? (*Hint:* X/n = proportion of students who obtained two F's or less)
(c) over two F's?
(d) no F's?

6. Two test forms (Form A and Form B) were prepared to determine whether married women who had withdrawn from the labor market for ten years or more are suitable for employment when they again attempt to obtain gainful employment. A sample of 300 women in this category were given both test forms and it was found that 110 failed both tests, 120 passed both tests, 30 passed Form A but not form B, and 40 passed Form B but not Form A. Based upon these sample results, what is the probability that a married woman in the category described will (use *Definition* 1)

(a) pass both tests? (*Hint:* X/n = proportion in the sample who passed both tests)
(b) pass Form A but not Form B?
(c) pass Form A?
(d) fail Form B?

7. If 3% of the time a student has been known to come to school late and 4% of the time he has been known to be absent, what is the probability that on the next school day (a) he will come to school early, (b) he will come to school?

6.3 PERMUTATIONS AND COMBINATIONS

Permutations relate to sequence. For example, we can place a red book and a white book on a shelf in the sequence red book—white book or white book—red book. Each sequence or arrangement is called a *permutation*. Let us analyze this situation to determine why two permutations are possible. Clearly, there are two ways of choosing the first book to place on the shelf (the red book or the white book). Then, for each of these ways, there is one way of choosing the second book, since only one book is left. Therefore, there are a total of (2)(1) = 2 permutations or orders of placing two different books on a shelf.

Suppose we have three books to arrange in some order on a shelf: a red book, a white book, and a green book. How many permutations are possible? Figure 6.3.1 analyzes this situation. For example, the first book to be placed on the shelf may be chosen in any one of three ways (red book, white book, or green book). For *each* of these ways, there are two ways of choosing the second book. As indicated in the figure, if the red book is chosen first, we may then choose between the white book and the green book for the second book to be placed on the shelf. If the white book is chosen first, then the second choice is between the red book and the green book, etc. Therefore, there are (3)(2) = 6 ways of choosing the first two books to place on a shelf. Finally, for *each* of these six ways of choosing the first two books, there is only one way to choose the third book, as shown in the figure. Therefore, the total number of ways to arrange three different books is (3)(2)(1) = 6 ways. Referring to Figure 6.3.1, we can easily identify the six permutations by following the arrows. The six arrangements are:

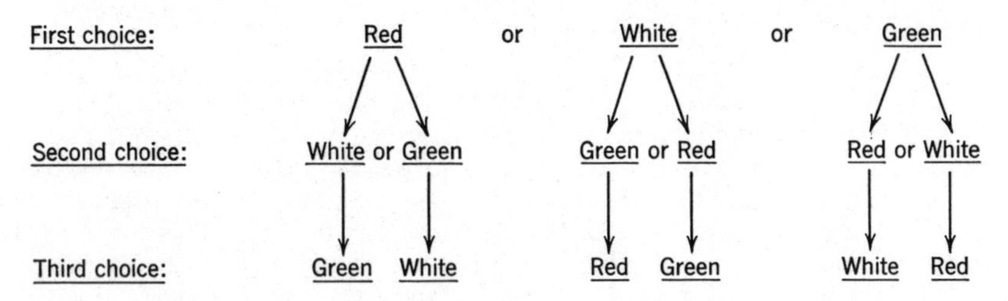

Fig. 6.3.1. Analysis of the number of permutations possible when arranging three books on a shelf: a red book, a white book, and a green book.

Red White Green	White Green Red	Green Red White
Red Green White	White Red Green	Green White Red

Clearly, the method for determining the number of possible permutations when arranging two different objects or three different objects is the same. In the case of two different objects, the number of possible permutations is (2)(1) = 2. In the case of three different objects, it is (3)(2)(1) = 6. Similarly, with four different objects, it is (4)(3)(2)(1) = 24. Let ${}_NP_N$ denote "the number of permutations of N different objects taken N at a time." That is, *all* N objects are used in each permutation. Then, in general, for a set of N different objects, the number of possible permutations may be determined as

$$ {}_NP_N = N(N-1)(N-2)\cdots(1) \tag{6.3.1}$$

Suppose a teacher wishes to seat five pupils in the five front seats in a classroom. This could be done in ${}_5P_5$ ways (the number of permutations of 5 pupils taken 5 at a time). We determine this, using Equation 6.3.1, as follows:

$$ {}_5P_5 = (5)(4)(3)(2)(1) = 120 \text{ ways}$$

The product (5)(4)(3)(2)(1) is called 5 *factorial* and is denoted by the symbol 5!. Then, 4! is read "4 factorial" and indicates the product (4)(3)(2)(1) and "3 factorial" or 3! indicates the product (3)(2)(1). In general, N factorial or $N!$ indicates the product $N(N-1)(N-2)\cdots(1)$. Note that $1! = 1$ and, by convention, $0! = 1$. Using the factorial notation, we may write Equation 6.3.1 as

$$ {}_NP_N = N! \tag{6.3.2}$$

Sometimes we are interested in the number of permutations possible when using only *some* of the objects in a set. For example, what is the number of possible permutations of 3 objects selected from a set of 5 different objects. Reasoning as before, there are 5 ways of choosing the first object, 4 ways of choosing the second object, and 3 ways of choosing the third object. Therefore, there are (5)(4)(3) = 60 ways of arranging 3 objects chosen from a set of 5 different objects. We use the symbol ${}_5P_3$ to denote "the number of possible permutations of 5 different objects taken 3 at a time." We may write

$$ {}_5P_3 = (5)(4)(3)$$

This may be written as

$$ {}_5P_3 = \frac{(5)(4)(3)(2)(1)}{(2)(1)} = \frac{5!}{2!} = \frac{5!}{(5-3)!}$$

Note that in the foregoing expression, the product (2)(1) appears in both the numerator and denominator, so that the value of ${}_5P_3$ is not affected. The last form in this equation expresses ${}_5P_3$ in terms of factorials using the total number of objects in the set (5) and the number included in each permutation (3). In general, then, we may determine the number of possible permutations of a set of N different objects taken X at a time as

$$_NP_X = \frac{N!}{(N - X)!} \tag{6.3.3}$$

Suppose two students are to be selected from a group of six to assist the teacher in a classroom presentation. In how many ways can two students out of six be selected so that the first one selected assists in the morning session and the second in the afternoon session? The number of permutations of six students taken two at a time is computed as (Equation 6.3.3.)

$$_6P_2 = \frac{6!}{(6 - 2)!} = \frac{6!}{4!} = \frac{(6)(5)(4)(3)(2)(1)}{(4)(3)(2)(1)} = (6)(5) = 30$$

It is not necessary to write out 6! and 4! in full to compute $_6P_2$. It follows, from the definition of factorials and as indicated above, that 4! divides into 6! leaving (6)(5) = 30. Therefore, we may write directly

$$_6P_2 = \frac{6!}{(6 - 2)!} = \frac{6!}{4!} = (6)(5) = 30$$

We may consider Equation 6.3.2 (and Equation 6.3.1) as a special case of Equation 6.3.3. That is, if $X = N$, Equation 6.3.3 becomes

$$_NP_N = \frac{N!}{(N - N)!} = \frac{N!}{0!} = N! \tag{6.3.4}$$

Very often the interest is in the number of *combinations* possible for a set of objects and not in the number of permutations. *A combination represents a collection of objects, without regard to order*. For example, a debating team is made up of three students: Joe, Ed, and Tom. If two of the three are to be called upon for rebuttal and it does not matter in which order they are called, there is no need to distinguish between, say, Joe, Ed and Ed, Joe. That is to say, the interest lies in the *combination* of team members to be called, not in the order in which they are called. The following three combinations of two team members out of the three are possible: Joe, Ed or Joe, Tom or Ed, Tom. Let us adopt the widely used symbol $\binom{3}{2}$ to denote "the number of possible combinations of 3 objects taken 2 at a time." Then, for the number of possible combinations of 3 students taken 2 at a time, we may write

$$\binom{3}{2} = 3$$

Of course, if we are interested in the number of possible permutations instead of combinations, we would have to take into account that *each* combination of two team members permits two permutations, since ${}_2P_2 = 2!$. For example, the combination Joe, Ed permits the two permutations Joe, Ed and Ed, Joe. Therefore, the number of possible permutations of 3 objects taken 2 at a time may be computed as

$${}_3P_2 = 2!\binom{3}{2}$$

Solving for $\binom{3}{2}$, we obtain

$$\binom{3}{2} = \frac{{}_3P_2}{2!}$$

In other words, we could compute the number of possible combinations using what we have already learned about permutations. That is, the number of *combinations* of 3 objects taken 2 at a time is equal to the number of *permutations* of 3 objects taken 2 at a time (${}_3P_2$) *divided by* $2!$. In general, the number of possible combinations of N objects taken X at a time, $\binom{N}{X}$, may be computed as

$$\binom{N}{X} = \frac{{}_NP_X}{X!} \tag{6.3.5}$$

Substituting for ${}_NP_X$, according to Equation 6.3.3, we obtain the very useful equation:

$$\binom{N}{X} = \frac{N!}{X!\,(N-X)!} \tag{6.3.6}$$

As an illustration, suppose it is desired to choose a committee of 5 from a class of 16 students. How many different committees of 5 students can be chosen? Since it does not matter in which order the 5 students are selected to serve on the committee, we are interested in the number of possible combinations of 16 students taken 5 at a time. Then, with $N = 16$ and $X = 5$, use Equation 6.3.6 to compute

$$\binom{16}{5} = \frac{16!}{5!\,(16-5)!} = \frac{16!}{5!\,11!} = 4368 \text{ combinations (committees)}$$

It is worthwhile to observe that each time we form a combination of 5 students out of 16, we leave aside 11 students who are not selected. Therefore, each time we form a combination, we are actually forming two combinations. One is the combination of 5 students to be on the committee and the other is the combination of 11 students who will not be on the committee. Therefore, it follows that the number of possible combinations of 5 students out of 16 is equal to the number of possible combinations of $16 - 5 = 11$ students out of 16. We may obtain this same result by writing $\binom{16}{16-5}$, the number of combinations of 16 students taken $16 - 5$ or 11 at a time, according to Equation 6.3.6. Using $N = 16$ and $X = 16 - 5$, we obtain

$$\binom{16}{16-5} = \binom{16}{11} = \frac{16!}{11!(16-11)!} = \frac{16!}{11!\,5!}$$

which is the same as $\binom{16}{5}$, shown previously. Generally, then, the number of possible combinations of N objects taken X at a time, $\binom{N}{X}$, is equal to the number of possible combinations of N objects taken $N - X$ at a time, $\binom{N}{N-X}$. Therefore, we may write

$$\binom{N}{N-X} = \binom{N}{X} \qquad (6.3.7)$$

PROBLEMS FOR PRACTICE AND REVIEW

1. A physics professor, in setting up a two-part experiment, has to choose between three different ways of setting up the first part and four different ways of setting up the second part. In how many ways can he set up his experiment, assuming all the different ways for each part are compatible with all the different ways for the other part?

2. In how many ways can you line up four different flags, if they must be arranged in a row?

3. Suppose an experimental psychologist has three different laboratory animals prepared for an experiment. In how many ways can he introduce them into a maze one at a time?

4. Five club members have been elected to a club directorate. In how many ways can they be assigned to five different committee chairmanships, if each may be assigned to only one post?

5. In how many ways can you place three out of five different pages into a loose-leaf binder, if it is important to take into account the sequence in which they are placed?

6. How many different three-digit numbers can be formed from the ten digits 0, 1, 2, . . . 9?

7. In how many ways can you arrange four books on a desk (lined up between a pair of book ends in a designated place on the desk), if you may choose from a collection of 50 different books?

8. How many combinations are possible of
(a) 8 objects taken 5 at a time?
(b) 8 objects taken 3 at a time?
(c) 9 objects taken 2 at a time?
(d) 9 objects taken 7 at a time?

9. In how many ways may three subjects be selected out of five, when there is no interest in the sequence of selection?

10. A loft is divided into seven offices and you are free to choose any four offices for your staff. In how may ways can you choose the four offices for your staff?

11. In how many ways can you set up a committee of five students out of a group of 13 students available to serve on this committee?

12. A psychologist has a pool of 12 different items to use in Part A of an aptitude test. If he is only interested in using six of these items and it does not matter in which order they are placed in the test, how many ways are there for him to select six out of this pool of items?

13. A principal has four mathematics teachers on his staff. He has funds to promote only two to a higher salary bracket. In how many ways can he choose two out of the four teachers for promotion?

14. The dean of a university has 15 invitations to speak for next month, but has the time to accept only three. In how many ways can he select three out of the 15?

15. A school teacher must choose six pupils (three girls and three boys) to represent the class at a school function. If the class is made up of eight girls and 10 boys, in how may ways can this teacher make his choice of the six pupils?

6.4 COMBINING PROBABILITIES

This section presents certain rules for combining probabilities which have been determined according to *Definition* 1 or *Definition* 2. These rules may be used to compute probabilities in the more involved situations.

Rule A: Addition rule for two events which are possible as a result of a trial. *Let A and B represent two of the possible outcomes of a trial. Then, P(A or B), the probability that A or B will occur, may be determined as*

$$P(A \text{ or } B) = P(A) + P(B) - P(A \text{ and } B)$$

This rule states that the probability that one of the events A or B will occur may be determined as the sum of $P(A)$, the probability that A will occur, and $P(B)$, the probability that B will occur, minus $P(A \text{ and } B)$, the probability that *both A and B* will occur. As an illustration, suppose a card is to be drawn from a well-shuffled deck of 52 playing cards. If you make the selection with your eyes closed, what is the probability that the card selected is an 8 or a red card? We know that there are four 8's and 26 red cards in the deck. However, two cards (the 8 of hearts and the 8 of diamonds) are *both* an 8 *and* red and, so, are included among the four 8's *as well as* among the 26 red cards. Therefore, the number of cards which are either 8 or red (or both) may be computed as $4 + 26 - 2 = 28$. In other words, 28 out of the 52 mutually exclusive and equi-probable possible outcomes when a card is selected represent cards which are 8 or red. Then, according to *Definition* 2, we may compute

$$\begin{aligned} P(8 \text{ or red}) &= \frac{28}{52} = \frac{4 + 26 - 2}{52} \\ &= \frac{4}{52} + \frac{26}{52} - \frac{2}{52} \\ &= P(8) + P(\text{red}) - P(8 \text{ and red}) \end{aligned}$$

Clearly, the proportion $\frac{4}{52}$, indicating that 4 cards out of the 52 are 8's, represents $P(8)$. The proportion $\frac{26}{52}$, indicating that 26 cards out of the 52 are red, represents $P(\text{red})$. Finally, the proportion $\frac{2}{52}$, indicating that 2 cards out of the 52 are *both* 8 *and* red, represents P (8 and red), the probability that the card selected is both 8 and red. It is apparent, then, that the reason for subtracting $P(8 \text{ and red})$ from the sum of $P(8)$ and $P(\text{red})$ is to correct for the *double counting* of the possible outcomes which are *both* 8 *and* red. As indicated in this illustration, $P(A \text{ or } B)$ determined according to *Rule A refers to the probability that either event A or event B will occur or that both will occur*. In other words, $P(A \text{ or } B)$ represents the probability that *at least A or B* will occur.

Let us apply *Rule A* to compute the probability in the following situation. Suppose a rat is introduced into a maze for the first time and that there are six equally attractive paths he could choose to take. Paths 1, 2, and 3 contain an electric shock device along the way, whereas paths 2 and 4 lead to the food box. The other paths, 5 and 6, lead to dead ends, with no shock as well as no food box. What is the probability that the first path chosen by the rat will either lead to the food box or contain a shock device? Since 2 paths lead to the food box, 3 paths lead to a shock device, and 1 path leads to both the food box and a shock device, using *Rule A*, we obtain

$$\begin{aligned} P(\text{food box or shock}) &= P(\text{food box}) + P(\text{shock}) \\ &\quad - P(\text{food box and shock}) \\ &= \tfrac{2}{6} + \tfrac{3}{6} - \tfrac{1}{6} = \tfrac{2}{3} \end{aligned}$$

Suppose the records of a high school show that 85% of the students pass science with the grade of C or better, 80% pass algebra with a C or better, and 70% of the students achieve a grade of C or better in both subjects. Then, we may compute the probability that a student will earn a grade of C or better in at least one of these subjects as

$$P\begin{pmatrix}\text{C or better}\\ \text{in science}\\ \text{or albegra}\end{pmatrix} = P\begin{pmatrix}\text{C or better}\\ \text{in science}\end{pmatrix} + P\begin{pmatrix}\text{C or better}\\ \text{in albegra}\end{pmatrix} - P\begin{pmatrix}\text{C or}\\ \text{better in}\\ \text{science and}\\ \text{algebra}\end{pmatrix}$$

$$= .85 + .80 - .70 = .95$$

Consider another type of situation. Suppose a fair die is rolled. What is the probability that it will result in a 3 or a 6? Applying *Rule A*, we have

$$P(3 \text{ or } 6) = P(3) + P(6) - P(3 \text{ and } 6)$$
$$= \tfrac{1}{6} + \tfrac{1}{6} - 0 = \tfrac{1}{3}$$

Since the events 3 and 6 are mutually exclusive, they cannot *both* occur in a single roll of a die. Therefore, $P(3 \text{ and } 6)$ must equal zero. This leads to a special addition rule for mutually exclusive events.

Rule B: Addition rule for mutually exclusive events. *If A and B are mutually exclusive events, then P(A or B), the probability that A or B will occur, may be determined as*

$$P(A \text{ or } B) = P(A) + P(B)$$

Rule B may be extended to include any number of mutually exclusive events. For example, in the case of three mutually exclusive events *A*, *B*, and *C*, we have

Rule B extended: If A, B, and C are mutually exclusive events, then P(A, B, or C), the probability that A, B, or C will occur, may be determined as

$$P(A, B, \text{ or } C) = P(A) + P(B) + P(C)$$

When a fair die is rolled, what is the probability of an even number? Since each of the three even numbers 2, 4, 6 are possible outcomes, we have a situation involving three mutually exclusive events. The required probability may be computed using *Rule B extended* as

$$P(2, 4, \text{ or } 6) = P(2) + P(4) + P(6)$$
$$= \tfrac{1}{6} + \tfrac{1}{6} + \tfrac{1}{6} = \tfrac{1}{2}$$

Extension of *Rule B* to more than three mutually exclusive events is apparent. The general addition rule, *Rule A*, also may be extended to include any number of events. However, it becomes rather involved. It is not appropriate to present this in an introductory statistics text.

The probability that two events, A and B, will *both* occur, $P(A \text{ and } B)$, noted in *Rule A*, is an illustration of a *joint probability. When two or more events are considered together, we may refer to these events as joint events or compound events.* For example, the occurrence of the two characteristics 8 and red, when selecting a card from a deck of 52 playing cards, represents a compound event made up of two simple events. On the other hand, occurrence of the three characteristics: a denomination less than 10, an even number, and red, when selecting a card, illustrates a compound event made up of three simple events. Such a compound event occurs if, say, the 2 of diamonds is selected.

The probability of occurrence of an event may be affected by the occurrence of another event. For example, suppose an urn contains 4 green marbles and 2 white marbles. The urn is well shaken and you select a marble, while blindfolded. After setting aside the marble selected, you wish to select a second marble. What is the probability that the second marble will be green? Clearly, this probability depends upon the outcome of the first selection. If the first marble selected is green, the probability of a green marble on the second draw is $\frac{3}{5}$, since only 3 green marbles are left and only 5 marbles remain in the urn. On the other hand, if the first marble selected is not green, then the probability of a green marble on the second draw is $\frac{4}{5}$, since 4 out of the 5 marbles remaining in the urn are green.

An event whose probability of occurrence is affected by the occurrence of another event is called a dependent event. The probability of a dependent event is called a conditional probability. We use the symbol $P(B \mid A)$ to denote "the conditional probability that the event B will occur, given that the event A has occurred." Referring to the foregoing illustration, P(green marble second | green marble first) represents the conditional probability of a green marble on the second selection, given that a green marble was selected the first time. P(green marble second | white marble first) represents the conditional probability of selecting a green marble, given that a white marble was selected first. We may read the symbol $P(B \mid A)$ briefly as "the probability of B, given A." Note that $P(B \mid A)$ is referred to as a *conditional probability* compared to $P(B)$ which may be referred to as an *unconditional probability*. We may now present the multiplication rule for probabilities.

Rule C: Multiplication rule for any two events. *If A and B are any two events, P(A and B), the probability that both A and B will occur may be determined as*

$$P(A \text{ and } B) = P(A) \cdot P(B \mid A)$$

According to this rule, the joint probability that two events will occur may be computed as the product of the *unconditional* probability that one of the two events will occur times the *conditional* probability that the other event will occur. Referring to the urn with 4 green marbles and 2 white marbles, mentioned previously, what is the probability of selecting 2 green marbles? The probability of a green marble on the first selection, P(green first), is $\frac{4}{6}$. The conditional probability of a green marble on the second selection, given that a green marble was selected the first time, P(green second | green first), is $\frac{3}{5}$. Therefore, applying *Rule C*, we compute the joint probability of obtaining 2 green marbles as

$$P(\text{green and green}) = P(\text{green first}) \cdot P(\text{green second} \mid \text{green first})$$
$$= \tfrac{4}{6} \cdot \tfrac{3}{5} = \tfrac{2}{5}$$

The probability is the same whether we select two marbles simultaneously or one at a time. However, in applying *Rule C, we always make the assumption that the selection is accomplished one at a time*. Then, in *Rule C*, event A refers to selection of the first marble and event B refers to selection of the second marble. When considering the selection of two green marbles, permutation is of no interest (since both marbles are green.) In many situations, however, permutation must be taken into account. For example, in the above illustration, what is the probability of selecting a green marble first and a white marble second? Then, event A refers to selection of a green marble and event B refers to selection of a white marble. We may compute the joint probability of selecting green–white, *in that order*, as

$$P(\text{green and white}) = P(\text{green}) \cdot P(\text{white} \mid \text{green})$$
$$= \tfrac{4}{6} \cdot \tfrac{2}{5} = \tfrac{4}{15}$$

On the other hand, what is the probability of selecting a green and a white marble, *without any concern as to the order in which selected*? In this case, remembering that *Rule C* is to be applied as if the marbles are selected one at a time, we must take into consideration the number of ways (permutations) in which the compound event (a green marble and a white marble) can occur. The number of permutations to be taken into consideration is ${}_2P_2 = 2!$ or 2. In other words, there are two ways of obtaining a green marble and a white marble (green–white or white–green). We have already determined that the joint probability of obtaining the sequence green–white, P(green and white), is $\frac{4}{15}$. Now, applying *Rule C*, we compute the joint probability of obtaining the white-green sequence, as

$$P(\text{white and green}) = P(\text{white}) \cdot P(\text{green} \mid \text{white})$$
$$= \tfrac{2}{6} \cdot \tfrac{4}{5} = \tfrac{4}{15}$$

Then, the compound event, obtaining a green marble and a white marble *in any order*, may materialize *either* as green–white *or* as white–green. These are mutually exclusive events, since, if one of these permutations materializes, the other cannot. Consequently, to determine the joint probability of a green marble and a white marble *in any order*, we must compute the probability of obtaining *either* the green–white sequence *or* the white–green sequence. That is, we must compute P(green and white or white and green) using *Rule B* for mutually exclusive events. Applying *Rule B*, we obtain

$$\begin{aligned} &P(\text{green and white or white and green}) \\ &\qquad = P(\text{green and white}) + P(\text{white and green}) \\ &\qquad = \tfrac{4}{15} + \tfrac{4}{15} = \tfrac{8}{15} \end{aligned}$$

It is important to determine whether permutation is involved when computing a joint probability, according to *Rule C*. Where permutation is to be taken into consideration and only a single specified permutation is involved, then the joint probability is computed for the specified permutation, using *Rule C*. However, if *two* permutations are involved, then the joint probability must be computed for *each* permutation (using *Rule C*) and *the two joint probabilities added* (according to *Rule B*), since the permutations represent mutually exclusive events.

Rule C also may be extended to cover situations involving more than two events. When two events are involved, the joint probability is determined as the product of the unconditional probability of one event and the conditional probability of the other. When more than two events are involved, the joint probability is determined as the product of the unconditional probability of one event and the conditional probability of each of the other events *determined successively*. More specifically, we have

Rule C extended: If A, B, and C are any three events, then P(A, B, and C), the probability that A, B, and C will occur, may be determined as

$$P(A, B, \text{and } C) = P(A) \cdot P(B \mid A) \cdot P(C \mid A, B)$$

The symbol $P(C \mid A, B)$ denotes "the conditional probability of event C, given that *both A and B* have occurred." We may read the symbol $P(C \mid A, B)$ briefly as "the probability of C, given that A and B have occurred." As an example, what is the probability of drawing all clubs when selecting 3 cards from a well-shuffled deck of 52 playing cards? The probability of a club on the first draw, P(club), is $\frac{13}{52}$. The conditional probability of a club on the second draw, given that the first card was a club, $P(\text{club} \mid \text{club})$, is $\frac{12}{51}$. Finally, the conditional probability of a club on the third draw, given that the first two cards were clubs, $P(\text{club} \mid \text{club, club})$, is $\frac{11}{50}$, since 11 out of the remaining 50 cards are clubs. Therefore, applying *Rule C extended*,

$$P(\text{club, club and club})$$
$$= P(\text{club}) \cdot P(\text{club} \mid \text{club}) \cdot P(\text{club} \mid \text{club, club})$$
$$= \frac{13}{52} \cdot \frac{12}{51} \cdot \frac{11}{50} = \frac{143}{11{,}050} \text{ or } .013$$

The previous illustration, of course, involved no consideration of permutation, since the 3 cards were all clubs. However, suppose we wish to determine the probability that the 3 cards selected are king, queen, ace, *in that order*. Applying *Rule C extended* to determine the probability of this particular permutation, we obtain

$$P(\text{king, queen, and ace}) = P(\text{king}) \cdot P(\text{queen} \mid \text{king}) \,.\, P(\text{ace} \mid \text{king, queen})$$
$$= \frac{4}{52} \cdot \frac{4}{51} \cdot \frac{4}{50} = \frac{8}{16{,}575} \text{ or } .00048$$

On the other hand, what is the probability of obtaining *either* of the two permutations king, queen, ace or king, ace, queen? We have already computed P(king, queen, and ace) and found it to be .00048 or 48 chances in 100,000. Then, for the second permutation, applying *Rule C extended*, we obtain

$$P(\text{king, ace, and queen}) = P(\text{king}) \cdot P(\text{ace} \mid \text{king}) \cdot P(\text{queen} \mid \text{king, ace})$$
$$= \tfrac{4}{52} \cdot \tfrac{4}{51} \cdot \tfrac{4}{50} = .00048$$

Using *Rule B*, the probability of obtaining *either* one *or* the other of the two mutually exclusive permutations is

$$P(\text{king, queen, and ace or king, ace, and queen})$$
$$= P(\text{king, queen, and ace}) + P(\text{king, ace, and queen})$$
$$= .00048 + .00048 = .00096$$

Suppose we ask: what is the probability of obtaining king, queen, ace *in any order*? In this case, we must take into consideration *all* possible permutations in which three such cards can be obtained. There are ${}_3P_3 = 3!$ or 6 mutually exclusive ways in which such a compound event could materialize. Then, the required probability is determined by first computing the joint probability for *each* of these 6 possible permutations. (This has already been done for two of these permutations.) Then, the probability of obtaining the desired set of 3 cards *in any order* is determined by *adding* the 6 joint probabilities, according to *Rule B extended.* A little reflection will convince the reader that the probability is the same for each permutation, so that the required probability is equal to (6)(.00048) or .00288.

Two events are independent if the occurrence or nonoccurrence of one has no effect whatsoever upon the occurrence or nonoccurrence of the other. For example, if two coins are tossed, the events "head on one coin" and "head on the other coin" are independent events. Clearly, the occurrence or nonoccurrence of a head on one coin has no effect whatsoever on the occurrence or nonoccurrence of a head on the other coin. And, if a coin is tossed twice, the events "head on the first toss" and "head on the second toss" are independent. On the other hand, if a coin is tossed once, the events "head" and "tail" are not independent. In this case, the occurrence of one of these events, say, tail, precludes the occurrence of the other event. Clearly, mutually exclusive events are not independent. When two cards are selected from a deck, events such as "ace on the first draw" and "king on the second draw" are independent *if the first card is replaced before the second card is selected.* No matter which card is selected first, the probability of a king on the second draw is $\frac{4}{52}$ *if the first card is returned to the deck and the cards thoroughly shuffled before the second card is selected.* As we have already seen, if the first card is *not* returned to the deck before the second draw, the outcome of the second selection is dependent upon which card was obtained on the first draw.

If two events are independent, the conditional probability must equal the unconditional probability for each of these events. For example, consider an urn containing red marbles and white marbles. Suppose two marbles are to be selected, one at a time, *with replacement.* That is, the first marble selected is replaced before the second marble is selected. What is the probability that the marbles selected are red and white, in that order? Clearly, these are independent events, since the occurrence or nonoccurrence of a red marble on the first draw has no effect whatsoever upon the occurrence or nonoccurrence of a white marble on the second draw. Consequently, in this case, $P(\text{white} \mid \text{red})$, the conditional probability of a white marble on the second draw given a red marble on the first draw, must be equal to $P(\text{white})$, the unconditional probability of a white marble, since the outcome of the first draw has no effect on the outcome of the second draw. This leads to the important relationships:

Rule D: If A and B are independent events, then

$$P(B \mid A) = P(B)$$

and

$$P(A \mid B) = P(A)$$

Actually, *Rule D* is often used as the definition of independent events. That is, if *Rule D* holds for two events A and B, then A and B are independent events. Such events are said to be *independent in the probability sense or statistically independent.*

We may restate the multiplication rule for probabilities, *Rule C*, in the case of independent events, as

Rule E: Multiplication rule for independent events. *If A and B are independent events, P(A and B), the probability that A and B will occur, may be determined as*

$$P(A \text{ and } B) = P(A) \cdot P(B)$$

This rule may be extended to include more than two independent events. For example:

Rule E extended: If A, B, and C are mutually independent events, then P(A, B, and C), the probability that all three events will occur, may be determined as

$$P(A, B, \text{ and } C) = P(A) \cdot P(B) \cdot P(C)$$

Extension of *Rule E* to more than three independent events is apparent. Note that in applying *Rule E* and *Rule E extended*, where different permutations are involved, these should be taken into account when computing probabilities, as discussed for *Rule C*. That is, the equations presented in *Rule E* and *Rule E extended* are for a *given* permutation of the events involved. Where permutation is a consideration, these rules should be applied to *each* permutation, in turn, as discussed in connection with *Rule C*.

Suppose a university plans to administer a three-part test to applicants for admission. Part 1 is to be machine scored, Part 2 is to be scored manually using a template, while Part 3 is of the essay type and is to be scored manually. It is known that the scoring machine produces incorrectly scored papers 3% of the time and that manual scoring using a template has been known to result in an incorrect score one time in a hundred, on the average. It is assumed that manual scoring of essay-type items never results in a scoring error. What is the probability that the composite score for a three-part test contains scoring errors for Part 1 and Part 2 and none for Part 3? Clearly the occurrence of scoring errors in the first two parts and the nonoccurrence of an error in the third part are independent events. The probability of a scoring error in Part 1, $P(\text{error 1})$, is .03; the probability of a scoring error in Part 2, $P(\text{error 2})$, is .01; while, the probability of a correct score for Part 3, $P(\text{correct 3})$, is 1.00 (certainty).

Then, applying *Rule E extended*, we obtain

$$P(\text{error 1, error 2, and correct 3})$$
$$= P(\text{error 1}) \cdot P(\text{error 2}) \cdot P(\text{correct 3})$$
$$= (.03)(.01)(1.00) = .0003$$

The reader will note that, in this situation, permutation is not involved.

Suppose a boys' club made up of 30 high school seniors wishes to distribute a silver pen, a silver pencil, and a set of books to the members. It is proposed to make the distribution as follows: The name of each club member will be written on a disc and the 30 discs will be put into a large bowl. Then, after the discs are thoroughly stirred in the bowl, the club president will select a disc while blindfolded. The member whose name appears on the disc will receive the silver pen. Then, the selected disc will be returned to the bowl, the discs thoroughly stirred, and the club treasurer will select a disc while blindfolded. The member whose name appears on the disc will receive the silver pencil. Then, the selected disc will be returned to the bowl, the discs thoroughly stirred, and the club secretary will select a disc while blindfolded. The member whose name appears on the disc will receive the set of books.

What is the probability that the president, the treasurer, and the secretary each receive one of the gifts? Since the discs were selected *with replacement*, selection of the president's name, the treasurer's name, and the secretary's name represent independent events. Since the order of selection determines the gift to be received, the permutation of the three names selected must be taken into account. For a given permutation, say, president, treasurer, secretary, the probability of the three names being selected may be determined according to *Rule E extended*, as follows (A denotes president's name, B denotes treasurer's name, and C denotes secretary's name):

$$P(A, B, \text{and } C) = P(A) \cdot P(B) \cdot P(C)$$
$$= \frac{1}{30} \cdot \frac{1}{30} \cdot \frac{1}{30} = \frac{1}{27{,}000}$$

Thus, the chances are 1 in 27,000 that the president will receive the first gift (silver pen), the treasurer will receive the second gift (silver pencil), and the secretary will receive the third gift (set of books). However, these three officers of the club may receive one of the three gifts in other sequences, so that we must take into consideration the ${}_3P_3(= 3!$ or $6)$ permutations possible. Since the probability of occurrence is the same for each permutation, we may compute the probability that these three officers will each receive a gift as $(6)(1/27{,}000) = 1/4500$ or .00022 (*Rule*

B extended). In other words, the chances are 22 in 100,000 that this compound event will occur.

Several examples now are presented which illustrate how the rules for combining probabilities may be used to determine probabilities in certain situations.

Example 1: In a class of 20 students in second-year statistics, 16 students *either* passed the first-year statistics course *or* passed a year course in calculus, or both. It is known that 9 students passed the year course in calculus, whereas 6 passed *both* the first-year statistics course *and* the year course in calculus. The instructor has a card for each student. If these cards are well shuffled and you select a card while blindfolded, what is the probability that you will select the card of a student who passed the first-year statistics course?

Solution: Let us use the following notation: A = student who passed first-year statistics; B = student who passed a year course in calculus.

We wish to determine the probability $P(A)$. Based on the given information, we know the following probabilities when selecting a card from the deck:

$$P(A \text{ or } B) = \tfrac{16}{20}$$
$$P(B) = \tfrac{9}{20}$$
$$P(A \text{ and } B) = \tfrac{6}{20}$$

Then, according to *Rule A*

$$P(A \text{ or } B) = P(A) + P(B) - P(A \text{ and } B)$$
$$\tfrac{16}{20} = P(A) + \tfrac{9}{20} - \tfrac{6}{20}$$

Solving for $P(A)$, we obtain

$$P(A) = \tfrac{16}{20} - \tfrac{9}{20} + \tfrac{6}{20} = \tfrac{13}{20}$$

Example 2: In a large city, the probability is .53 that the first born in a family will go to an out-of-town college and .19 that the first *and* second born children will go to an out-of-town college. What is the probability that the second born will go to an out-of-town college *if* the first born goes to an out-of-town college?

Solution: Let A = first born goes to out-of-town college
B = second born goes to out-of-town college

We wish to determine $P(B \mid A)$. The following probabilities are given:

$$P(A) = .53$$
$$P(A \text{ and } B) = .19$$

Then, according to *Rule C*

$$P(A \text{ and } B) = P(A) \cdot P(B \mid A)$$
$$.19 = .53 \cdot P(B \mid A)$$

Solving for $P(B \mid A)$, we obtain

$$P(B \mid A) = \frac{.19}{.53} = .35$$

Example 3: A study was made of on-the-job success of a large group of clerical workers who had taken an experimental clerical aptitude test. It was determined that the probability of passing the experimental test is .74; the probability of achieving on-the-job success is .66; and the probability of achieving on-the-job success, *if* a passing score was obtained on the experimental test, is .80. What is the probability of passing the experimental test *and* achieving on-the-job success? What is the probability of passing the test *or* achieving on-the-job success?

Solution: Let A = pass experimental aptitude test
B = achieve on-the-job success

We wish to determine

$$P(A \text{ and } B)$$
$$P(A \text{ or } B)$$

The following probabilities are given:

$$P(A) = .74$$
$$P(B) = .66$$
$$P(B \mid A) = .80$$

According to *Rule C*, we may write

$$P(A \text{ and } B) = P(A) \cdot P(B \mid A)$$
$$P(A \text{ and } B) = (.74)(.80) = .59$$

Then, according to *Rule A*, we have

$$P(A \text{ or } B) = P(A) + P(B) - P(A \text{ and } B)$$
$$P(A \text{ or } B) = .74 + .66 - .59 = .81$$

PROBLEMS FOR PRACTICE AND REVIEW

1. If you select a card from a well-shuffled deck of 52 playing cards while you are blindfolded, what is the probability that the card selected will be (a) red, (b) king or diamond, (c) jack or ace, (d) 6, 8, or 10, (e) queen or a spade?

2. A bag contains four green marbles, six white marbles and two marbles which are both white and green. If you shake the bag vigorously and select a marble with your eyes closed, what is the probability that the marble selected is (a) all white, (b) all white or all green, (c) white and green?

3. In a large population of scores, 63% are known to be above 100, 71% are for males over 21 years of age, and 59% are for males who are over 21 years of age *and* obtained a score above 100. If each score appears on a card and, after these cards are well shuffled, you select a card with your eyes closed, what is the probability that the card selected is for

(a) a male who is over 21 years of age and obtained a score above 100?
(b) a male over 21 years of age, or contains a score over 100?

4. A teacher maintains a card for each of the 15 students in his educational psychology class. He notes that seven of these students obtained over 90 on quiz 1, six obtained over 90 on quiz 2, and only three obtained over 90 in both quizzes. If you select a card from this set of class cards, after the cards are well shuffled and while you are blindfolded, what is the probability that you will select a card for a student who obtained over 90 on one or both of the two quizzes?

5. If the probability is .43 that a student enrolled in a certain college will major in business administration and .21 that this student will major in economics, what is the probability that a student enrolled in this college will major in business administration or economics?

6. If the probability is .18 that a laboratory animal will choose path A in a maze and .06 that he will choose path D, what is the probability that when such an animal is introduced into the maze he will choose either path A or D?

7. If the probability is .63 that a teenager will go to a dance, .31 that he will take out a girl on a date, and .09 that he will take out a girl on a date and go to a dance, what is the probability that he will either go to a dance or take a girl out on a date?

8. In a sample of 75 voters, 30 indicated that they favor candidate A, 13 favor candidate B, while the balance favors candidates C or D. If this sample is representative of the population, what is the probability that a voter will favor candidate A or candidate B?

9. If the probability is .04 that a subject will make at most a single error in performing a specified task, .17 that he will make two errors, and .32 that he will make three errors, what is the probability that a subject who is asked to perform this task will make (a) two or three errors, (b) less than three errors, (c) more than three errors?

10. A sample of 20 scores selected from a large population of scores showed that seven are in the 70's, eight are in the 80's, and three are in the 90's. Suppose that each score appears on a card and that the full set of cards fell on the floor and was widely scattered over the floor. Assuming that the sample of 20 scores is representative of the population, what is the probability that a card which happened to be picked up from the floor is not for a score in the 70–99 range?

11. A large, well-established research firm has determined that the probability is .43 that a professional job applicant will have little or no experience (under one year), .21 that he will have only a fair amount of experience (one or two years), and .29 that he will have three to five years of experience. What is the probability that the next professional job applicant for a position will have (a) at most five years of experience, (b) at least three years of experience, (c) over five years of experience?

12. If the probability is .15 that a marble selected from a bag will be blue and .29 that a number obtained when spinning a roulette wheel is ten or over, what is the probability that

(a) a marble selected from the bag is blue and the number obtained on the roulette wheel is ten or over?

(b) the marble selected is not blue and the number obtained is less than ten?

13. The probability that a particular rat, A, will select the path in a maze which leads to the food box is .47 and the probability that the psychologist in charge of the project will select this particular rat is .39. What is the probability that

(a) the psychologist will select rat A and the animal will select the path leading to the food box?

(b) the psychologist will select rat A but the animal will not select the path leading to the food box?

14. The probability that a student will pass a certain course is .11 and the probability that he will pass this course if he gives some time to study is .47. If the probability is .36 that he will give some time to study, what is the probability that he will give some time to study and pass the course?

15. A box contains five white balls, four yellow balls, six orange balls, and ten gray balls. If the box is vigorously shaken and two balls are selected while you are blindfolded, what is the probability that

(a) both balls are orange, if the balls are selected without replacement?
(b) both are yellow, if the balls are selected with replacement?
(c) the first is gray (not replaced) and the second is white?
(d) the first is orange (replaced) and the second is yellow?
(e) one is white and one is gray (without replacement)?
(f) one is yellow and one is orange (with replacement)?

16. Ten laboratory animals are alike in every way except in their response to tranquilizers A, B, and C. Five respond well only to tranquilizer A, three respond well only to B, and the remaining two respond well only to C. If the first two animals that happen to leave the cage when the door is opened are used in an experiment, what is the probability that

(a) the first to leave responds well to tranquilizer A and the second to C?
(b) both animals respond well to tranquilizer B?
(c) one responds well to A and one to B?
(d) the first responds well to A or C and the second to B?
(e) the first responds well to A and the second to A or B?

17. The probability is .24 that a mental patient will recover within a year, .58 that he will recover within a year if he is given psychotherapy, and .79 that psychotherapy will be available for this patient. What is the probability that

(a) this patient will be given psychotherapy and that he will recover within a year?
(b) this patient will recover within a year, if it is guaranteed that he will be given psychotherapy?

18. If, while blindfolded, you select three cards from a well-shuffled deck of playing cards (from which the aces, kings, queens, and jacks have been removed), what is the probability that you select
(a) first a 4, second a 3, third a 10, if selection is with replacement?
(b) first a 5 of spades, second a 9, third a 3 of diamonds, if selection is without replacement?
(c) three spades, if selection is with replacement?
(d) three 8's, if selection is without replacement?
(e) a 2, 6, and 8, if selection is without replacement?
(f) a 4, 10, and ace (selection without replacement)?

19. What is the probability that, in a well-shuffled deck of 52 playing cards, the top three cards are
(a) first the king of diamonds, second the 5 of spades, third the 2 of hearts?
(b) first a 10, second a queen, third the 4 of clubs?
(c) the 6 of clubs, the 3 of diamonds, and the ace of spades?
(d) a 5, an ace, and a queen?
(e) two red cards and a black card?
(f) all red cards?
(g) all 9's?
(h) first two cards queens and the third any card.

20. A teacher usually gives two midterm examinations and a final. If the probability is .14 that a student will fail the first midterm examination, .13 that he will fail the second midterm examination in the event he failed the first, and .23 that he will fail the final in the event he fails both midterm examinations, what is the probability that he will fail (a) both midterm examinations, (b) all three examinations?

21. The probability is .89 that a high school senior will have the funds to go to college next year, .93 that the college he prefers will accept him, and .58 that he will obtain all A's during the first school year. What is the probability that this high school senior will have the necessary funds, be accepted by the college he prefers, and obtain straight A's during the first school year?

22. A clinical psychologist is assigned three mental patients in a state hospital. These patients have similar emotional problems. If the probability is .29 that he will have success in treating patient A, .49 that the will have success with patient B if he succeeds with patient A, and .86 that he will have success with patient C if he succeeds with patients A and B, what is the probability that he will succeed with (a) patients A and B, (b) all three patients?

23. If the probability is .41 that a man or his wife will vote for candidate A, .38 that the man will vote for this candidate, and .29 that his wife will vote for the candidate, what is the probability that both the man and his wife will vote for candidate A? *Hint:* Use probability *Rule A.*

24. The probability is .77 that a student will fail French or chemistry, .24 that he will fail both of these subjects, and .48 that he will fail French. What is the probability that this student will fail chemistry?

25. A man prefers to walk to work. Often, he takes a bus when it rains. The probability is .51 that it will rain and he will take a bus to work, and .76 that it will rain. What is the probability that he will take a bus if it rains? *Hint:* Use probability *Rule C.*

26. Suppose A and B represent two tranquilizing drugs which are chemically related. If the probability is .56 that a subject will respond to A, .63 that he will respond to B, and .43 that he will respond to A or B, what is the probability that he will (*Hint:* Use probability *Rule A*, then *Rule C*) (a) respond to B, if he responds to A, (b) respond to A, if he responds to B?

27. It has been determined, on a tentative basis, that an outpatient with a certain emotional problem may be helped by drug therapy or psychotherapy or a combination of the two. Suppose the probability is .60 that he will be helped by psychotherapy, .18 that he will be helped by drug therapy, and .25 that he will be helped by drug therapy if psychotherapy is administered. What is the probability that the patient will be helped by (a) both drug therapy and psychotherapy, (b) drug therapy or psychotherapy?

6.5 PROBABILITY DISTRIBUTIONS

The idea of a *distribution* has already been introduced and discussed (Chapter 3, Section 3.6). The frequency distribution was discussed in considerable detail in Chapter 3. We are now ready to introduce another type of distribution which is of fundamental importance in statistical inference, the *probability distribution.*

Let us consider a specific situation. Suppose that, while blindfolded, we wish to select 4 cards from a well-shuffled deck of 52 playing cards, without replacement. Say, we are interested in the number of kings which will be included among the 4 cards selected. The minimum number of kings which could be included is 0 and the maximum is 4. Therefore, the number of kings possible in a set of 4 cards to be selected is a variable which may be denoted as X_i or, more simply, as X. The possible values for this variable are 0, 1, 2, 3, and 4. *It is our objective to determine the probability that X will take on each of its possible values.*

Let us begin by computing the probability that, when 4 cards are selected from a deck of 52 cards without replacement, X will have the value 2. In other words, what is the probability that 2 out of the 4 cards will be kings? Of course, such a compound event could occur in more than one way. For example, the first two cards selected could be kings (K) and the second two cards not kings (NK). The probability of such a compound event may be determined, according to *Rule C extended*, as follows:

$$P(K, K, NK, \text{and } NK) = \frac{4}{52} \cdot \frac{3}{51} \cdot \frac{48}{50} \cdot \frac{47}{49} = \frac{27{,}072}{6{,}497{,}400}$$

Another way in which such a compound event could occur is for the first and third cards selected to be kings and the second and fourth cards not kings. The probability of this occurring is the same as just computed. We may verify this by computing

$$P(K, NK, K, \text{and } NK) = \frac{4}{52} \cdot \frac{48}{51} \cdot \frac{3}{50} \cdot \frac{47}{49} = \frac{27{,}072}{6{,}497{,}400}$$

In general, the number of ways of obtaining 2 kings in 4 cards selected may be looked upon as the number of combinations possible of 4 objects taken 2 at a time or $\binom{4}{2}$. In other words, each possible combination of 2 cards out of 4 represents a possible pair of kings. According to Equation 6.3.6, we may compute

$$\binom{4}{2} = \frac{4!}{2!\,2!} = 6 \text{ possible combinations}$$

It is helpful to list these 6 possible combinations as follows:

Combination	First Card	Second Card	Third Card	Fourth Card
1	*K*	*K*	*NK*	*NK*
2	*K*	*NK*	*K*	*NK*
3	*K*	*NK*	*NK*	*K*
4	*NK*	*K*	*K*	*NK*
5	*NK*	*K*	*NK*	*K*
6	*NK*	*NK*	*K*	*K*

These 6 possible combinations represent mutually exclusive events and the probability that each of these events will occur is the same. Hence, according to *Rule B extended*, the probability of obtaining 2 kings when 4 cards are selected without replacement is computed as $\binom{4}{2}$ or 6 times the probability of obtaining any one of these combinations, such as $P(K, K, NK, \text{and } NK)$. In other words, the probability that $X = 2$, denoted as $P(X = 2)$, may be determined as

$$P(X = 2) = \binom{4}{2} P(K, K, NK, \text{and } NK)$$

Generally, then, *the probability that X will equal a given one of its possible values is determined by multiplying the number of possible combinations by the probability of obtaining one of these possible combinations.* Applying this procedure to determine the probability of obtaining each possible value of X, we obtain

$$P(X=0) = \binom{4}{0} P(NK, NK, NK, \text{ and } NK)$$

$$= (1)\left(\frac{48}{52} \cdot \frac{47}{51} \cdot \frac{46}{50} \cdot \frac{45}{49}\right) = .719$$

$$P(X=1) = \binom{4}{1} P(K, NK, NK, \text{ and } NK)$$

$$= (4)\left(\frac{4}{52} \cdot \frac{48}{51} \cdot \frac{47}{50} \cdot \frac{46}{49}\right) = .256$$

$$P(X=2) = \binom{4}{2} P(K, K, NK, \text{ and } NK)$$

$$= (6)\left(\frac{4}{52} \cdot \frac{3}{51} \cdot \frac{48}{50} \cdot \frac{47}{49}\right) = .025$$

$$P(X=3) = \binom{4}{3} P(K, K, K, \text{ and } NK)$$

$$= (4)\left(\frac{4}{52} \cdot \frac{3}{51} \cdot \frac{2}{50} \cdot \frac{48}{49}\right) = .001$$

$$P(X=4) = \binom{4}{4} P(K, K, K, \text{ and } K)$$

$$= (1)\left(\frac{4}{52} \cdot \frac{3}{51} \cdot \frac{2}{50} \cdot \frac{1}{49}\right) = .000004$$

Notice that the probability of selecting 4 cards with no kings, $P(X = 0)$, is computed by multiplying the number of combinations of 4 cards with 0 kings, $\binom{4}{0}$, by the probability of obtaining such a combination, $P(NK, NK, NK, \text{ and } NK)$. The probability of selecting 4 cards with 1 king, $P(X = 1)$, is computed by multiplying the number of combinations of 4 cards with 1 king, $\binom{4}{1}$, by the probability of obtaining such a combination, $P(K, NK, NK, \text{ and } NK)$, etc.

These computational results are summarized in Table 6.5.1 which presents the *probability distribution* for the variable X. Clearly, then, *a probability distribution shows the probability of obtaining each of the possible values of a variable.* A probability distribution may be used to answer many questions relating to the probability of obtaining a specified value of the variable, X. For example, what is the probability that, when 4 cards are selected without replacement from a deck of 52 cards, X will equal 3? Referring to Table 6.5.1, the answer is $P(X = 3) = .001$, or one chance in a thousand. What is the probability that X will be less than 2?

Table 6.5.1 PROBABILITY DISTRIBUTION: PROBABILITY OF OBTAINING X KINGS WHEN SELECTING FOUR CARDS FROM A DECK OF 52 PLAYING CARDS, WITHOUT REPLACEMENT

Number of Kings Included in 4 Cards Selected, X	$P(X =$ Specified Value)
0	.719
1	.256
2	.025
3	.001
4	.000004

Only two values of X are possible which are less than 2. These are 0 and 1. The probabilities that $X = 0$ and $X = 1$ are shown in Table 6.5.1. Since these are mutually exclusive events, the probability that $X < 2$ is computed as the sum of these two probabilities, according to *Rule B extended.* Therefore, $P(X < 2) = .719 + .256 = .975$, or 975 chances in a thousand. Clearly, the total of all the probabilities shown in the table must equal 1, except for possible rounding difference, since, when 4 cards are selected, it is a certainty that X must be equal to one of its possible values.

Let us consider a second illustration. Suppose it has been found by experience that 83% of the first-grade pupils in a certain community pass the reading-readiness test. What is the probability that, among the first 3 papers to be graded in a school year, a specified number will be passing papers? Let X denote the number of passing papers included in the set of 3. Then X may take on the values 0, 1, 2, or 3. We know from the given information that the probability that a first-grade pupil will pass the reading-readiness test, P(pass), is .83 and, so, the probability that he will fail, P(fail), is $1 - .83$ or .17. In this illustration, we are dealing with *independent events.* That is, whether a given pupil passes or fails has no effect on whether another pupil passes or fails. Therefore, following the general procedure in the first illustration, *the probability that X will be equal to a specified value may be determined by multiplying the pertinent number of possible combinations by the probability of obtaining one of these possible combinations* (according to *Rule E extended*). Applying this procedure, we obtain:

$$P(X = 0) = \binom{3}{0} P(\text{fail, fail, and fail})$$

$$= \binom{3}{0} P(\text{fail}) \cdot P(\text{fail}) \cdot P(\text{fail})$$

$$= (1)(.17)(.17)(.17) = (.17)^3 = .005$$

$$P(X = 1) = \binom{3}{1} P(\text{pass, fail, and fail})$$

$$= \binom{3}{1} P(\text{pass}) \cdot P(\text{fail}) \cdot P(\text{fail})$$

$$= (3)(.83)(.17)(.17) = (3)(.83)(.17)^2 = .072$$

$$P(X = 2) = \binom{3}{2} P(\text{pass, pass, and fail})$$

$$= \binom{3}{2} P(\text{pass}) \cdot P(\text{pass}) \cdot P(\text{fail})$$

$$= (3)(.83)(.83)(.17) = (3)(.83)^2(.17) = .351$$

$$P(X = 3) = \binom{3}{3} P(\text{pass, pass, and pass})$$

$$= \binom{3}{3} P(\text{pass}) \cdot P(\text{pass}) \cdot P(\text{pass})$$

$$= (1)(.83)(.83)(.83) = (.83)^3 = .572$$

These computational results are summarized in Table 6.5.2 which presents the probability distribution for the variable X. A most important characteristic of this probability distribution, not found in the distribution in Table 6.5.1, is that it deals with *independent events*. This is an illustration of the *binomial probability distribution* which has considerable importance as a theoretical distribution. More will be said about this in Chapter 8.

Table 6.5.2 PROBABILITY DISTRIBUTION: PROBABILITY OF OBTAINING *X* PASSING PAPERS WHEN GRADING THREE READING-READINESS EXAMINATION PAPERS FOR FIRST-GRADE PUPILS

Number of Passing Papers among 3 Papers Graded, X	$P(X = \text{Specified Value})$
0	.005
1	.072
2	.351
3	.572

PROBLEMS FOR PRACTICE AND REVIEW

1. If two cards are to be selected, while the person is blindfolded, from a well-shuffled deck of 52 playing cards, without replacement, determine the probability distribution of X, the number of red cards obtained.

2. The probability is .5 that a subject will improve in learning speed after undergoing a certain training program. If two subjects are put through this training program, determine the probability distribution for X, the number of subjects whose learning speed improves because of this program.

3. Determine the probability distribution for X, the number of tails obtained when six quarters are tossed simultaneously.

4. A test is made up of five multiple-choice items, with four choices per item. Assuming that you have absolutely no knowledge relating to the subject matter tested, so that each item is answered purely by guessing, determine the probability distribution for X, the number of correct responses.

*6.6 SETS: NOTATION AND OPERATIONS

The term *sets* is an abbreviation for *sets of points.* This is an abstract mathematical concept which has unlimited possibilities for application. *When applied to probability, we may conceptualize all possible outcomes of a trial as a set of points or a set.* As an illustration, consider the toss of a coin. The possible outcomes of a single toss of a coin are head and tail. We may think of each possible outcome as a point in one-dimensional space, as illustrated in Figure 6.6.1. The entire set of points is said to constitute the *universe set* or the *sample space.* In our illustration, the sample space is made up of only two points. Each point is referred to as an

* (This section may be omitted with no loss of continuity.)

element of the sample space or as a *sample point*. We will designate a set by an upper-case letter, such as S or A. That is, we may speak of the set of points in Figure 6.6.1 as set S.

Fig. 6.6.1. Set of points representing all possible outcomes of a single toss of a coin.

As a second illustration, Figure 6.6.2 presents the set of points which represents all possible outcomes of the toss of a single die. There are six possible alternative outcomes and, therefore, there are six points. Figure 6.6.3, which presents the set of points corresponding to *two tosses* of a die, illustrates a two-dimensional sample space, compared with Figures 6.6.1 and 6.6.2, which present one-dimensional sample spaces. The single point circled in Figure 6.6.3 represents the sample point (or element) corresponding to the possible outcome of 2 on the first toss and 5 on the second toss.

Typically, in probability, we are interested, not only in the total sample space (all possible alternative outcomes), but in *subsets* as well. *Any one or more points in a sample space make up a subset.* For example, the sample point 2, 5 in Figure 6.6.3 constitutes a subset of the total sample space. In this figure, we identify two additional subsets. The encircled column of points represents a subset of 6 points. Similarly, the subset of points corresponding to the possible outcomes of 4, 5, or 6 on the first toss of the die and 3 or 4 on the second toss, also is a subset made up of 6 sample points.

Fig. 6.6.2. Set of points representing all possible outcomes of a single toss of a die.

In Section 6.2 it was noted that any one or more of the alternative possible outcomes of a trial is called an *event*. A little reflection will convince the reader that a *subset of a sample space may be considered an event*. For example, the event "2 on the first toss and 5 on the second toss," when a die is tossed twice, is represented by the single point encircled in Figure 6.6.3. The event "4, 5, or 6 on the first toss and 3 or 4 on the second toss" is represented by the corresponding subset of 6 points encircled in Figure 6.6.3.

If a set contains no points, it is said to be an *empty set*. An empty set is often referred to as a *null set*. If A denotes a subset of a sample space and A' denotes the set of all points in the sample space *not included in the subset* A, then A' is the *complement* of A. For example, in Figure 6.6.3, denote the column of 6 points corresponding to the event "3 on the first toss and 1, 2, 3, 4, 5, or 6 on the second toss" as subset A. Then, the *complementary set*

A' is composed of the *balance of the points* in the sample space (the 36 − 6 = 30 points not in the encircled column).

Venn diagrams provide a convenient device for depicting sets and operations on sets. Figure 6.6.4 presents a Venn diagram where the rectangle represents the sample space and the circles represent specified events (subsets). As indicated in the figure, we denote the sample space as

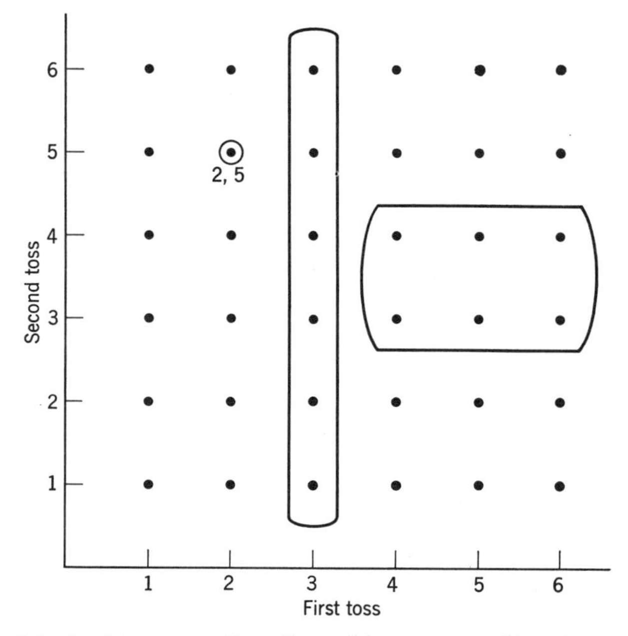

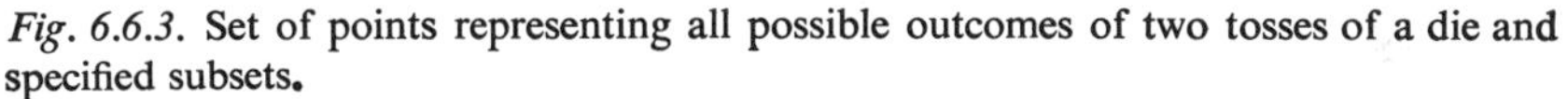

Fig. 6.6.3. Set of points representing all possible outcomes of two tosses of a die and specified subsets.

set *S* and the events as *A*, *B*, and *C*. Each event is a subset of *S*. It is useful to compare the Venn diagram in Figure 6.6.4 with the set in Figure 6.6.3. The full set of 36 points in Figure 6.6.3 corresponds to the area of the rectangle in Figure 6.6.4. Each represents all possible outcomes (the sample space). However, while Figure 6.6.3 represents a specific two-dimensional sample space, the Venn diagram is used in the most general way to denote "the sample space," no matter how many dimensions are involved or even when no specific problem is under consideration. Similarly, the three subsets identified in Figure 6.6.3 represent specific events. However, the subsets identified by circles in the Venn diagram are meant as general representations of events. It is not necessary to use circles. Any size or shape of space contained within the sample space may be used to denote an event. For example, we could denote an event by a square constructed within S or by a triangle, if so desired.

An important aspect of the events represented in a Venn diagram is *the way they relate to each other*. For example, events A and B in Figure 6.6.4 have *no points in common* (do not overlap). This indicates that these events cannot both occur in a single trial. That is, A and B are *mutually exclusive events*. On the other hand, events B and C do have points in common (the shaded area in the figure). A point contained in the common area between B and C denotes a possible outcome of *both* events B and C. Then, B and C do not represent mutually exclusive events.

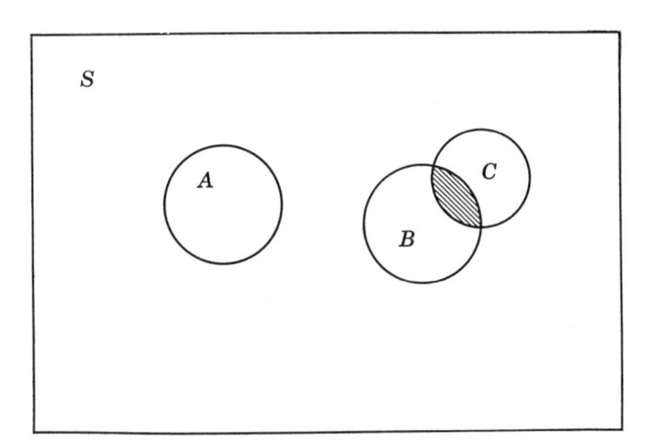

Fig. 6.6.4. Venn diagram depicting a sample space, S, and events (subsets) A, B, and C.

Following *Definition* 2, we may write the probability of event A (Figure 6.6.4), in terms of sets, as

$$P(A) = \frac{A}{S} \tag{6.6.1}$$

According to Equation 6.6.1, the probability that A will occur is equal to the proportion that the number of points (number of possible alternative outcomes) in subset A is of the total number of points (total number of possible alternative outcomes) in the sample space.

Equation 6.2.2, in Section 6.2, states that $P(A) + P(\text{not } A) = 1$. We may rewrite this in terms of sets as

$$P(A) + P(A') = 1 \tag{6.6.2}$$

where A' denotes the complementary set. In Figure 6.6.4, A' represents the entire sample space *outside of the subset* (circle) A.

We speak of the addition of sets as the *union* of the sets. The *union* of two sets, A and B, is usually written as $A \cup B$ and is made up of *all points which are contained in set A and set B*, including those points in *both A and B*, as well as those points in *only A* or *only B*. The Venn diagram in Figure 6.6.5, part A, presents events A and B in sample space S. $A \cup B$, read "the union of A and B," is made up of the *combined* set of points (combined area of the two circles) representing events A and B (the shaded area). If A and B are mutually exclusive events in a sample space, as depicted in Figure 6.6.5, part B, $A \cup B$ denotes the set made up of the points

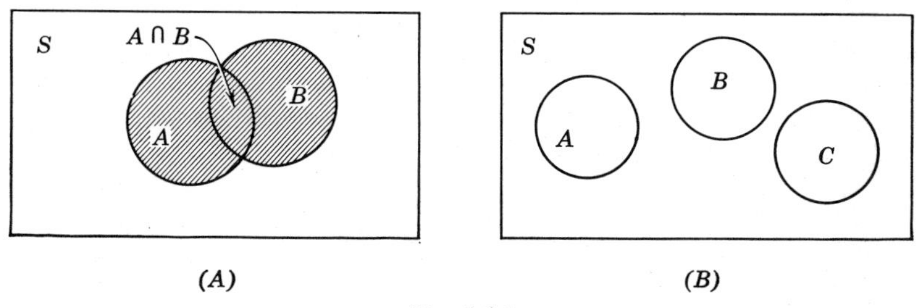

Fig. 6.6.5

contained in the area in subset A plus the points contained in the area in subset B. Similarly, if A, B, and C are mutually exclusive events, as shown in part B, $A \cup B \cup C$, read "the union of A, B, and C," denotes the set composed of the area in subset A, plus the area in subset B, plus the area in subset C. In the previous discussion in this chapter, we referred to $A \cup B$ as "A or B." These are alternative ways of saying the same thing.

We speak of the *intersection* of set A and set B to denote the set of points which are *common to both set A and set B*. We denote this set of common points by the symbol $A \cap B$, which is read "the intersection of A and B." Clearly, as indicated in Figure 6.6.5, part A, $A \cap B$ represents all possible alternative outcomes (points) which are in *both A and B*. Hence, $A \cap B$ represents the set of *compound events* "A and B." If A and B do not overlap (mutually exclusive events), as in Figure 6.6.5, part B, $A \cap B$ represents an empty set or the null set. Similarly, if A, B, and C are mutually exclusive events, the intersection of all three sets, $A \cap B \cap C$, is also a null set.

We are now able to restate the probability rules presented in Section 6.4 in terms of sets.

Rule A′: If A and B represent two events, each of which is possible as the result of a trial (two subsets in a sample space), then

$$P(A \cup B) = P(A) + P(B) - P(A \cap B)$$

The symbol $P(A \cup B)$ may be read as "the probability of the union of A and B" or as "the probability of A or B." The symbol $P(A \cap B)$ may be read as "the probability of the intersection of A and B" or as "the probability of A and B." Referring to Figure 6.6.5, part A, and equation 6.6.1, note that

$$P(A) = \frac{A}{S}$$

and

$$P(B) = \frac{B}{S}$$

Consequently, when we add $P(A) + P(B)$, as in *Rule A′*, we are counting the points in the set $A \cap B$ *twice* (since these points are in *both* sets *A and B*). Therefore, we subtract $P(A \cap B)$ to eliminate this double counting.

Rule B′: If A and B represent mutually exclusive events (two subsets in a sample space which do not overlap), then

$$P(A \cup B) = P(A) + P(B)$$

Rule B′ may be obtained from *Rule A′* by noting that for mutually exclusive events $P(A \cap B) = 0$.

Rule B′ extended: If A, B, and C represent mutually exclusive events (three subsets in a sample space which do not overlap), then

$$P(A \cup B \cup C) = P(A) + P(B) + P(C)$$

We may express the conditional probability $P(B \mid A)$ in set notation as

$$P(B \mid A) = \frac{P(A \cap B)}{P(A)} \tag{6.6.3}$$

In Equation 6.6.3, the events A and B belong to the same sample space S and $P(A) \neq 0$.

Rule C′: If A and B represent two events (two subsets in a sample space), then

$$P(A \cap B) = P(A) \cdot P(B \mid A)$$

Rule C′ follows immediately from Equation 6.6.3. The joint probability, $P(A \cap B)$, as expressed previously, implies the probability that first event A will occur and then event B will occur. We may express the probability that this compound event will occur in the reverse sequence as

$$P(B \cap A) = P(B) \cdot P(A \mid B)$$

Of course, $A \cap B$ and $B \cap A$ represent the same set. Reversing the order of writing A and B provides a convenient way of expressing the sequence of occurrence.

Figure 6.6.6 presents three intersecting subsets A, B, C, in a sample space S, representing events A, B, and C. The intersections, $A \cap B$, $B \cap C$, and $A \cap C$ are identified in the figure. $A \cap B \cap C$, the intersection of all *three* events, A, B, *and* C, also is identified (the shaded area). Clearly, $A \cap B \cap C$ is the set of points common to all three sets. Hence,

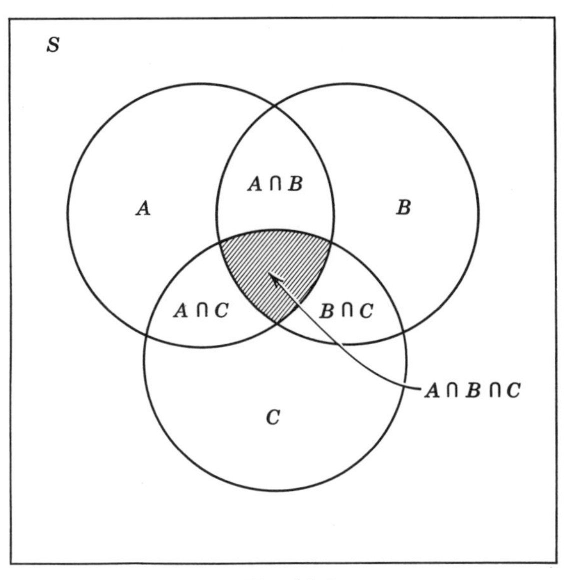

Fig. 6.6.6

$A \cap B \cap C$ represents the set of compound events "A, B, and C." We may express the conditional probability $P(C \mid A, B)$ in set notation as

$$P(C \mid A, B) = \frac{P(A \cap B \cap C)}{P(A \cap B)} \tag{6.6.4}$$

In Equation 6.6.4, events A, B, and C belong to the same sample space S and $P(A \cap B) \neq 0$.

Rule C′ extended: If A, B, and C represent three events (three subsets in a sample space), then

$$P(A \cap B \cap C) = P(A) \cdot P(B \mid A) \cdot P(C \mid A, B)$$

Rule C′ extended follows from Equations 6.6.3 and 6.6.4.

We know from *Rule D* that, for *independent events*, conditional probabilities are equal to the corresponding unconditional probabilities. For example, if A and B are independent events, $P(B \mid A) = P(B)$ and

$P(A \mid B) = P(A)$. We may then write *Rule E′* and *Rule E′ extended* based upon *Rule C′* and *Rule C′ extended*, respectively, as

Rule E′: If A and B are independent events, then

$$P(A \cap B) = P(A) \cdot P(B)$$

Rule E′ extended: If A, B, and C are independent events, then

$$P(A \cap B \cap C) = P(A) \cdot P(B) \cdot P(C)$$

7

RANDOM SAMPLING

7.1 INTRODUCTION

Reference has already been made to the fact that often it is found convenient or even necessary to investigate an area of interest based upon sample data rather than population data (Chapter 2, Section 2.3). Actually, only where the population to be studied is reasonably small and the required data easily obtainable at moderate cost should the collection and study of the full set of population data be considered. In all other situations, collection and study of sample data is more efficient and less expensive.

Suppose an English professor in a large university wants to know how many of the 60 students enrolled in the two sections of English 4 which he teaches plan to take English 5 next semester. Clearly, the practical thing for him to do is to ask each class to provide the required information by a show of hands. The population in this instance is small and the required information simple and easily obtainable. On the other hand, if he wishes to know how many of the sophomores enrolled in the university plan to take English 5 next semester, the project is of an altogether different nature. On the one hand, the population is considerably larger and, on the other hand, the information is more difficult to obtain, since the sophomores cannot be found collected in one or two places.

Suppose the dean in a university maintains a file card for each student enrolled showing certain biographical as well as scholastic information. Say, it is required to determine the proportion of the total enrollment coming from various foreign countries as indicated by the permanent home address appearing on the students' cards. If the total enrollment is small, say two or three hundred, collection of such information by studying the entire card file would not be a difficult matter. Even if the number of cards were larger, say, 500 or 1000, it may still be considered a reasonable task to collect the information for the entire population. However, at some point, say, if the file contains 2000 or more cards, it will no longer be convenient to collect data for the entire population. Furthermore, if it were required to collect more detailed and complicated data from each card, the maximum number of cards from which it would be convenient to study the entire population would be considerably smaller. For example, this would be true if it were required to collect data on month and year of birth, date of enrollment in the university, major field of study, scholastic average, and extra-curricula activity, as well as country of permanent residence.

Let us consider another type of situation. Suppose a firm of consultant psychologists has developed a new type of test to determine aptitude for selling life insurance. Before using this new test, it is necessary to try it out and determine its validity. This may involve administering the test to applicants and then, say, a year later, comparing the test scores with some measure of job success, such as the number of policies written. If, generally, it is found that high test scores were obtained by successful salesmen and low test scores were obtained by unsuccessful salesmen, the validity of the new test as a measure of aptitude for selling life insurance would be indicated. The population, in this situation, would be made up of all applicants for insurance-selling positions today and for some time in the future. Clearly, it would not be possible for the firm to try out the new test on the entire population. Even if the population were made up of applicants for, say, a five-year period, any extensive study of the validity of the new test, using the specified procedure, would be costly and impractical. Furthermore, the purpose of the test is to select salesmen for selling insurance. If the entire population for whom this test is meant is used to determine its validity, then there will be no need for the test whatsoever, since no part of the population will be left on whom to use it.

In many situations, including the illustrative situations just described, the only reasonable approach is to base the study upon sample data. If properly carried out, statistical investigations based upon sample data may be expected to provide useful and adequate information about the population. However, when we speak about sample data, we do not have in mind merely the use of some part of the population. That is, although any part of the full scope of data making up the population may be considered a sample, it is certainly not true that *any* sample provides a useful basis for determining the population characteristics.

For example, let us consider the illustrative situations described previously. If the English professor determines that 55% of the sophomores enrolled in his English classes intend to enroll in English 5 next semester, would he be justified in inferring that 55% of all the sophomores in the university intend to enroll in English 5? In other words, would you expect that the sophomores in this professor's English classes have the same intentions regarding enrollment in English 5 next semester as all the sophomores in the university?

Suppose the dean instructed his assistant to grab a handful of student file cards and determine the proportion of students in this sample who come from the various foreign countries. Suppose the dean also asked him to determine the proportion of these students in various other categories (by age, major field of study, etc.). Would it be reasonable to expect that the proportions so determined would hold for the entire population?

Finally, if the consultant psychologists decided to try out the new test on the applicants who happened to apply for insurance selling jobs in a local office of a single insurance firm during a single day, would it be reasonable to use the results obtained from such a sample to infer the validity of the test for all possible applicants for insurance sales work?

In summary, are the samples noted above *representative* of the population from which they were selected? This is the key consideration in sample selection. *A representative sample is one which reflects characteristics of the population from which it was selected, in true population proportion.* For example, if the proportion of sophomores in the professor's classes who intend to enroll in English 5 is equal to the proportion of all sophomores in the university who intend to enroll in English 5, then the sample would be a representative one. Similar considerations would also apply to the sample of students selected when the dean's assistant grabs a handful of cards, and the sample of applicants who are selected because they happened to apply for an insurance sales job on a certain day and in a particular local insurance office. Could samples selected by such procedures be representative samples?

A favorite method for selecting a representative sample, employed by those not trained in statistical methods, is to select a sample on a judgment basis. For example, suppose that, in the judgment of the English professor, a certain group of sophomores are representative of the population of sophomores with respect to intention to enroll in English 5, so that they may be considered to be an adequate sample for the purpose at hand. How can he know that this is a representative sample? If he knew enough of the intentions of all the sophomores in the university and of the sample of sophomores he selected to properly make such a judgment, then he would know enough about the intentions of the sophomores to make investigation of this matter entirely unnecessary. If he has any less information, his judgment in this matter cannot be considered reliable.

Actually, the only way in which one can *insure* the selection of a representative sample is to know the population thoroughly and hand-pick the particular items making up the sample. Clearly, in such a situation, complete knowledge of the population makes sampling or any kind of study wholly unnecessary. When less than perfect knowledge relating to a population is available and, in the usual situation, where only little is known about the population, *a representative sample can never be guaranteed.* However, where less than complete knowledge about a population is available, *if a sample is selected by the use of a random selection procedure, it is more likely that a representative sample will be obtained than if any other sample selection method is used. Such samples are called random samples.* When we speak of samples in this text, we will always mean *random samples.*

7.2 DEFINITION

It is not the particular items included in a sample which make it a random sample, *it is the method used in selection of the sample items.* For example, it is conceivable that the same set of scores may be selected as a sample from a population of scores on a judgment basis as when a random selection basis is used. However, when judgment is used in determining the particular items included in a sample, the result is a judgment sample. *Only with a random sample, a sample selected by a random selection procedure, may we apply the methods of inductive statistics to make inferences about a population on a probability basis.* We will discuss procedures for obtaining random samples by first considering sampling from a finite population and then from an infinite population. Furthermore, we will give separate consideration to sampling with replacement and sampling without replacement.

Generally speaking, sample selection procedures are easier to understand if we think in terms of sampling marbles from an urn. For example, suppose it is desired to select a sample of scores from a population of 500 clerical aptitude scores. Let us imagine that each score is printed on a marble and the 500 marbles are placed in an urn. Then, the problem becomes one of selecting a sample of marbles from the urn. Or, suppose it is desired to select a sample of subjects from a population of 200 employees in a firm. Then, let us imagine that the name of each employee is printed on a marble and the 200 marbles are placed in an urn. Again, the problem becomes one of selecting a sample of marbles from the urn.

When sampling without replacement from a finite population, a random sample is obtained if the items in the population have an equal probability of being selected on the first draw and, as items are selected, each remaining item in the population has an equal probability of being selected on succeeding draws. Let us see how such a *random selection procedure* is carried out. Suppose it is desired to select a random sample of 3 students without replacement from a population of 10 students. In order to simplify the discussion, say we print the initials of each student on a marble and place the 10 marbles in an urn. Then, we select 3 marbles as follows: Shake the urn vigorously and, while blindfolded, select a marble. Then, without replacing the selected marble, shake the urn vigorously again and, while blindfolded, select a second marble. Finally, without replacing the two marbles selected, repeat the procedure and select a third marble. The students whose initials appear on the 3 marbles selected constitute a random sample of size 3 selected from the population of 10 students without replacement. *Clearly, this selection procedure provides that the students in the population (or remaining in the population) have an equal probability of being selected.*

We may determine the probability that a given student (marble) will be selected in any draw, in the foregoing illustration, by use of *Definition* 2. For example, the probability is $\frac{1}{10}$ that any specified student will be selected on the first draw; $\frac{1}{9}$ that a second specified student will be selected on the second draw, when 9 students (marbles) remain in the population; and $\frac{1}{8}$ that a third specified student will be selected on the third draw, when only 8 students (marbles) remain in the population. Say, students A, B, and C are specified for the first, second, and third draws, respectively. Then, according to *Rule C extended*, which relates to conditional probabilities, the probability is $(\frac{1}{10})(\frac{1}{9})(\frac{1}{8}) = \frac{1}{720}$ that A will be selected on the first draw, B on the second draw, and C on the third draw. Suppose one of the marbles was glued to the side of the urn so that it had no chance at all of being selected. Then, the selection procedure just described cannot result in a random sample of 3 marbles out of the population of 10 marbles, since the 10 marbles did not have equal probabilities of being selected.

When sampling with replacement from a finite population of size N, a random sample of size n is obtained if, in each trial (draw), each item in the population has a probability of $1/N$ of being selected and the trials are independent. Let us consider an illustration to see how such a *random selection procedure* is carried out. Suppose we wish to select a random sample of $n = 2$ students out of a population of, say, $N = 5$ students. Again, let us write the initials of each student on a marble and place the 5 marbles in an urn. Then, select the sample as follows: First, shake the urn vigorously and, while blindfolded, select a marble. Note the initials on the marble selected. Then, *after replacing the marble*, shake the urn vigorously again and, while blindfolded, select a second marble from the urn. The two students whose initials appear on the selected marbles constitute a random sample. Of course, owing to the replacement procedure, it is possible for a student (a marble) to be selected twice. In such case, the random sample of two students is made up of a given student considered twice.

We may determine the probability that a specified student (marble) will be selected in any trial (draw) by use of *Definition* 2. For example, the probability is $\frac{1}{5}$ that a specified student will be selected in the first trial and, since the first marble selected is returned to the urn, the probability is also $\frac{1}{5}$ that a specified student will be selected in the second trial. Say, student A is specified for the first trial and student B for the second trial (where A and B may be the same student). Then, according to *Rule E*, which relates to independent events, the probability is $(\frac{1}{5})(\frac{1}{5}) = \frac{1}{25}$ that A will be selected in the first trial and B in the second trial. *Clearly, this selection procedure provides that each student in the population has an equal probability* ($1/N$ *or* $\frac{1}{5}$) *of being selected in each trial* (*draw*) *and the trials are independent* (*the outcome of one trial has no effect whatsoever upon the outcome of any other trial*).

Generally, samples are selected *without replacement*, so that no item can be selected more than once. However, it is worthwhile to know that samples selected *with replacement* may be used as a basis for estimating population characteristics. *When sampling with replacement, a finite population takes on some of the characteristics of an infinite population.* That is, it can never become exhausted and the population distribution never changes, no matter how many items are selected for the sample. Therefore, the concept of random sampling from an infinite population is very similar to random sampling with replacement from a finite population. An important difference is that we cannot specify that the probability of selection for each item in the population, in each trial, is $1/N$, as we did in random sampling with replacement from a finite population, since N is indefinitely (infinitely) large. When we speak of selecting a random sample from an infinite population, there is no need to specify whether selection is with or without replacement, since withdrawal of any number of items from the population has no effect on its distribution. *When sampling from an infinite population, a random sample of size n is obtained if the probabilities of selection are constant from trial to trial and the trials are independent.* Let us see what this means in terms of an illustration.

Imagine an infinite number of tosses of a fair die. This infinite series of trials (tosses) will generate an infinite population of 1's, 2's, 3's, 4's, 5's and 6's. Based on the *a priori* probability of $\frac{1}{6}$ for each of these six possible outcomes of a trial, we may state that this infinite (theoretical) population is composed of the values 1, 2, 3, 4, 5, and 6 in equal proportions. The values obtained in, say, five tosses of the die represent a random sample of size five from this infinite population, *since the probabilities of obtaining each of the six values* (1, 2, 3, 4, 5, *and* 6) *are constant from trial to trial and the trials are independent.* Clearly, the question of sampling with or without replacement is not appropriate in this sampling situation.

7.3 SAMPLE DESIGN AND SELECTION

A plan for collecting a sample is called a *sample design.* There are a variety of ways in which a sample could be designed. It is not appropriate in an introductory text to discuss sample designs in detail. However, it is worthwhile to mention and very briefly describe some of the simpler and frequently used types of sample designs.

The basic and simplest type of sample design is a *simple random sample* or, more briefly, a *random sample.* This involves selecting a specified number of items from the population under study, using one of the random selection procedures discussed in Section 7.2. For example, suppose it is desired to estimate the average salary paid to college teachers in a large university. Let us say the population is of size 800 and we wish to select a random sample of size 50 without replacement. A simple random sample may be obtained by writing each of the 800 names on a marble, placing the 800 marbles in an urn, and, then, having a blindfolded person select 50 marbles, one at a time, from the thoroughly mixed marbles. The 50 names so selected represent a random sample from the population of 800 teachers. Of course, the use of marbles in an urn would hardly seem to be a practical way to select a sample. Before presenting other types of sample designs, let us consider a more practical and frequently used method of selecting a random sample.

A more practical and often used method of selecting a random sample is to use a *table of random numbers* or, as it is also called, a *table of random digits.* Table B.1 in Appendix B presents such a table. *The digits in such a table are determined by some type of randomizing procedure which gives each of the* 10 *digits* (0, 1, 2, . . . , 9) *an equal chance of being selected.* For example, such a table could be constructed by using 10 marbles, each marble having printed on it one of the 10 digits. Then, these 10 marbles are placed in an urn, the urn is shaken vigorously and a marble is selected while blindfolded. The number printed on the selected marble becomes the first digit in such a table. The marble is returned to the urn and the procedure repeated. The number on the second marble selected becomes the second number entered in the table, etc. Actually, there are more sophisticated procedures which are used to produce such a table more conveniently. However, in any procedure used, the 10 digits 0, 1, 2, . . . , 9 have equal probability of selection. The 3500 random digits presented in Table B.1 are reproduced from page 1 of a publication which contains 105,000 random digits.

The first step in employing a table of random numbers to select a random sample is to identify each item in the population by a number. For example, in the illustration, there is a population of 800 teachers (or 800 salaries). Each teacher must be identified with a number from 001 to 800. Notice that we use 001, not merely 1. Since the highest number, 800, contains 3 digits, each number must be expressed in terms of 3 digits. Such identification may be accomplished in various ways. Suppose the bursar's office maintains a file containing a card for each teacher in the university, showing salary and other information. One way is to actually write the identifying number directly on each card in the bursar's file. Or we may agree that the cards, as they are filed in the cabinet, will be identified by the numbers 001 through 800 sequentially, without actually writing these numbers on the cards. Or, we could use lists of the teachers' names which happen to be available and agree that the numbers 001 through 800 are assigned to the names as they appear on the lists, with or without actually writing a number beside each name. *No matter which device is used, it is absolutely necessary that it be firmly decided, in advance, which number identifies which teacher.*

The next step is to decide at which point in the table of random numbers to begin and the method to be used in forming 3-digit numbers. Referring to Table B.1, notice that the digits are grouped into blocks of 5 rows and 5 columns. This is done for the convenience of the user. In the heading of the table, the numbers (1), (2), etc., identify groups of 5 columns each. The stub identifies the row or line number. We may identify the starting point in the table as: third column in group (4), line 7. Entering the table at the designated point, we find the digit 9. Then, we may decide to form 3-digit numbers by moving across line 7 toward the right, each set of 3 digits forming a 3-digit number. Moving toward the right, we form the numbers 994, 988, 723, etc. Or we may proceed as follows: choose the first 3-digit number as the digits in the third, fourth, and fifth columns in group (4), line 7. Using this procedure, the first number becomes 994. Then, moving down these 3 columns, read off 3-digit numbers. Succeeding numbers are 972, 281, 988, etc. It does not matter which method is chosen to enter the table and select the required numbers. *However, it is absolutely essential that the procedure be fully determined and rigidly specified before looking into the body of the random number table.* In this way, there will be no opportunity for the user to influence the particular numbers selected in any way.

Let us say the latter procedure is decided upon. Then, numbers are copied out of Table B.1 until 50 *acceptable* numbers are obtained. *Acceptable numbers are those which are consistent with the population and the sample design.* For example, the population has been identified with the number sequence 001 through 800. Therefore, any number read out of Table B.1 which exceeds 800 is not acceptable and should be ignored. The sample design specified sampling *without replacement*. Therefore, a number is acceptable only the *first* time it is selected. Even if it should come up again, it is to be included in the acceptable set of 50 numbers only once. Finally, the teachers (or their salaries) who have been assigned the 50 acceptable numbers make up the random sample required from the population of 800 teachers in the university.

The steps to be taken when using a table of random numbers may be summarized as follows:

1. Identify each item in the population by a number.
2. Decide on the point of entry into the table.
3. Decide on the method to be used to form numbers to correspond to the identifying numbers assigned in Step 1.
4. Copy a sufficient number of acceptable numbers.

The simple random design was called basic because all sample designs must include simple random sampling in one form or another. For example, consider the following frequently used sample design. Referring to our population of 800 college teachers, it could be decided to divide the population into relatively homogeneous groups. For example, we could set up the subpopulations: professors, assistant professors, etc. In this way, the salaries in each subpopulation will be considerably less variable than when all the salaries are included in a single group. A smaller sample is generally required when the variability is reduced (Chapter 9, Section 9.6). Therefore, establishing subpopulations or *strata*, as they are called, may result in a better sample design than a simple random sample, since the survey could then be carried out at less cost and in a shorter time.

If strata are set up, the sample design will then require that a simple random sample be selected from each *stratum* separately. Each stratum will be treated as a separate and independent population. The simple random sample for each stratum may be selected by the use of a table of random numbers, in the manner described previously. A sample design which specifies that the population is to be divided into strata and that a random sample is to be selected from each stratum is called a *stratified random sample*. The average salary paid to the college teachers in the total population is estimated on the basis of the data collected in the random samples from all the strata.

Another frequently used sample design is *cluster sampling*. Suppose the bursar's cards are filed in 10 drawers, the cards filed in each drawer being determined on an alphabetical basis, according to the teachers' surnames. The cards in each drawer may be called a *cluster* or group of cards. A *cluster sampling* design involves selecting a specified number of *clusters* (drawers) on a simple random selection basis and then basing the required estimate of average salary on the clusters of cards selected. A simple random sample of clusters may be obtained by assigning a number to each *cluster* and then employing a table of random numbers as previously described.

Another type of sample design often found convenient is a *systematic random sample*. Referring to the illustration, suppose we decide to select a *systematic random sample* of the population of 800 teachers. This could be accomplished quite easily by the use of the file of cards in the bursar's office, as follows: first, specify some interval, say, 10. Then, select a number within this interval (from 01 to 10) on a random selection basis. This may be accomplished by the use of a table of random numbers. After deciding how to enter the table and the procedure to follow to select 2-digit numbers, select the first acceptable 2-digit number read out of the table. Say the number selected is 07. Then, starting with the first card in the file, count until you reach the 7th card. This is the first card in the sample. Then, continue counting the cards sequentially, selecting every 10th card. That is, after selecting the 7th card, then select the 7 + 10 or 17th card, then the 17 + 10 or 27th card, etc. Continue this procedure until you have gone through all the teachers' cards in the file. The cards selected make up a *systematic random sample*.

The systematic sampling method may be used with a stratified sampling design. That is, after the strata have been designated, a systematic rather than a simple random sample is selected from each stratum. Such a sampling procedure is called a *stratified systematic random sample*.

Various sample designs have been presented as general background information for the reader. However, this text will be concerned only with simple random samples.

7.4 SAMPLING DISTRIBUTIONS

When a measure is computed based on population data, it is called a *parameter*. For example, the arithmetic mean, the median, the standard deviation, and the quartile deviation are illustrations of parameters, if computed on the basis of all the information in the population. However, if such a measure is computed on the basis of sample data, it is called a *statistic*. Clearly, *a parameter is a constant, since it is fixed for a population*. For example, there is only one value for μ and only one value for σ for a given population. On the other hand, *a statistic is a variable, since it may be expected to vary from sample to sample*. For example, the value obtained for $\bar{X}$ or s may be expected to vary from sample to sample. *The distribution of a statistic is called a sampling distribution. Such distributions are of cardinal importance in statistical inference. In fact, all statistical inferences are made on the basis of sampling distributions*. We will consider such distributions in greater detail in the following discussion.

Table 7.4.1 ALL POSSIBLE SAMPLES OF SIZE 2 SELECTED WITHOUT REPLACEMENT AND ALL POSSIBLE $\bar{X}$'s OBTAINABLE FROM THE POPULATION OF FIVE SCORES: 10, 20, 30, 40, 50

Scores in Sample	$\bar{X}$
10, 20	15
10, 30	20
10, 40	25
10, 50	30
20, 30	25
20, 40	30
20, 50	35
30, 40	35
30, 50	40
40, 50	45

Let us consider a simple population made up of the 5 scores 10, 20, 30, 40, and 50. The mean μ of this population is 30. Let us assume that we do not know the mean and wish to use $\bar{X}$ computed from sample data as an estimate. Say, $\bar{X}$ is to be computed from a random sample of size 2 selected without replacement. What are the different $\bar{X}$ values which can be obtained from this population? First, we need to determine the different samples of size 2 obtainable when sampling without replacement. The number of possible samples of size 2 (the number of combinations of 5 scores taken 2 at a time) may be computed as $\binom{5}{2} = 10$. Table 7.4.1 presents these 10 different combinations of scores in the first column. The second column shows the $\bar{X}$ computed from each of these possible samples.

These results are summarized in Table 7.4.2. The first column in Table 7.4.2 presents all the different values which could be obtained for $\bar{X}$ when selecting a random sample of size 2 without replacement from the population of 5 scores. The second column shows the frequency or the number of ways in which each possible $\bar{X}$ value could occur. For example, $\bar{X} = 15$ could occur in only one way. That is, the only time a sample mean of 15 could be obtained is when the random sample happens to be made up of the scores 10 and 20 as shown in Table 7.4.1. On the other hand, $\bar{X} = 25$

Table 7.4.2 SAMPLING DISTRIBUTION OF THE MEAN: PROBABILITY OF OBTAINING A SPECIFIED VALUE FOR $\bar{X}$, BASED ON DATA IN TABLE 7.4.1

$\bar{X}$	f	$P(\bar{X} = \text{specified value}) = \frac{f}{10}$
15	1	$\frac{1}{10}$
20	1	$\frac{1}{10}$
25	2	$\frac{2}{10}$
30	2	$\frac{2}{10}$
35	2	$\frac{2}{10}$
40	1	$\frac{1}{10}$
45	1	$\frac{1}{10}$
Total	10	1

could occur in two ways when the sample includes the scores 10 and 40 or 20 and 30.

It is interesting to observe from Table 7.4.2 that the mean ($\bar{X}$) of a random sample of size 2, which may be used as an estimate of μ, could vary from 15 to 45. Only 2 out of the 10 possible samples result in $\bar{X} = 30$, the true value of the parameter (μ). However, 6 out of the 10 possible samples result in $\bar{X}$ between 25 and 35, providing estimates of μ which are relatively close to the true parameter value. The last column in Table 7.4.2 presents the *relative frequencies* and *indicates the probability of obtaining each of the possible values of the variable* $\bar{X}$ when selecting a random sample of size 2 without replacement from the population of 5 scores. As defined and discussed in Chapter 6, Section 6.5, this is a *probability distribution. When the variable in a probability distribution is a statistic, the distribution is called a sampling distribution.*

The sampling distribution illustrated in Table 7.4.2 is the *sampling distribution of the mean*, since the variable is the sample mean $\bar{X}$. Based upon this distribution, we may make probability statements relating to the possible value of $\bar{X}$ computed on the basis of a random sample. For example, we may state that the probability is $\frac{2}{10}$ that a random sample of 2 scores selected without replacement from the population of 5 scores will result in a perfect estimate ($\bar{X} = 30$) of the parameter μ. We may denote this as $P(\bar{X} = 30) = \frac{2}{10}$. Or we may state that the probability is $\frac{2}{10} + \frac{2}{10} + \frac{2}{10} = \frac{6}{10}$ that $\bar{X}$ will have a value from 25 through 35 (according to probability *Rule B extended* for mutually exclusive events). We may denote this as $P(25 \leq \bar{X} \leq 35) = \frac{6}{10}$. Or we may state that the probability is $\frac{1}{10} + \frac{1}{10} = \frac{2}{10}$ that the sample mean $\bar{X}$ will exceed the parameter μ by 10 points or more (that is, it will equal 40 or 45). We may denote this probability as $P(\bar{X} - \mu \geq 10) = \frac{2}{10}$.

There is a sampling distribution for each statistic. For example, if the statistic we are dealing with is the sample mean $\bar{X}$, as in the foregoing illustration, we have the *sampling distribution of the mean.* If the statistic is the standard deviation s, we have the *sampling distribution of the standard deviation.* This may be constructed by computing s for each possible sample and then determining the relative frequencies as was done for $\bar{X}$ in Table 7.4.2. The relative frequencies represent the probabilities of obtaining specified values of the statistic.

It should be noted that *there is a different sampling distribution for a given statistic for each sample size.* For example, the sampling distribution of the mean presented in Table 7.4.2 is for samples of size 2. If another size sample is considered, say, a sample of size 3, we would have to determine all possible samples made up of 3 scores each, compute the mean for each possible sample, and then determine the relative frequencies as was done in Table 7.4.2.

A little reflection will indicate that *a sampling distribution is actually a population distribution.* That is, the sampling distribution specifies the probability of obtaining *any* of the possible values of a statistic. For example, in Table 7.4.2 *all* possible values of $\bar{X}$ are shown together with the associated probabilities. In other words, Table 7.4.2 presents the distribution of *a population of sample means.* Therefore, we should denote the mean and standard deviation of a sampling distribution by the use of symbols which we have reserved for populations. For example, we will use $\mu_{\bar{X}}$ and $\sigma_{\bar{X}}$ to denote the mean and standard deviation, respectively, for the sampling distribution of the mean. We will continue to use μ and σ to denote the corresponding measures for the population. Referring to the sampling distribution of the mean illustrated in Table 7.4.2, we may compute $\mu_{\bar{X}}$ based on the relative frequencies $P = f/10$, using Equation 4.3.12 (Chapter 4, Section 4.3). Note that in this equation, we must substitute $\bar{X}$ for X and P for p_i. (Actually, if we want to be more precise, we should write $\bar{X}_i$ instead of $\bar{X}$ and P_i instead of P.) Then, we obtain $\mu_{\bar{X}} = \Sigma \bar{X}P = 30$ (as shown in Table 7.4.3), indicating that $\mu_{\bar{X}} = \mu$, the population mean. This relationship between the mean of the sampling distribution of the mean and the population mean will be further considered in Chapter 8, Section 8.4.

We also may compute $\sigma_{\bar{X}}$ for the sampling distribution in Table 7.4.2 based on the relative frequencies P, using Equation 5.3.16 (Chapter 5,

Table 7.4.3 COMPUTATION OF THE MEAN AND THE STANDARD DEVIATION (STANDARD ERROR) FOR THE SAMPLING DISTRIBUTION PRESENTED IN TABLE 7.4.2

$\bar{X}$	P	$\bar{X}P$	$\bar{X}^2P$
15	$\frac{1}{10}$	1.5	22.5
20	$\frac{1}{10}$	2.0	40.0
25	$\frac{2}{10}$	5.0	125.0
30	$\frac{2}{10}$	6.0	180.0
35	$\frac{2}{10}$	7.0	245.0
40	$\frac{1}{10}$	4.0	160.0
45	$\frac{1}{10}$	4.5	202.5
	Total	30.0	975.0

Section 5.3). Using $\Sigma \bar{X}^2P = 975$ and $\Sigma \bar{X}P = 30$ (as shown in Table 7.4.3), we obtain

$$\sigma_{\bar{X}} = \sqrt{975 - (30)^2} = 8.7$$

The measure $\sigma_{\bar{X}}$ is of prime importance in the formulation of statistical inferences. (It is suggested that the reader review the interpretation of the standard deviation discussed in Chapter 5, Section 5.2.) The result $\sigma_{\bar{X}} = 8.7$ measures the extent to which sample means ($\bar{X}$'s) vary around their mean $\mu_{\bar{X}}$. Furthermore, since $\mu_{\bar{X}} = \mu$, $\sigma_{\bar{X}}$ is a measure of the extent to which sample means vary around the population mean. When a sample mean is used as an estimate of the population mean, we expect that this estimate will involve an element of error. The extent of error involved may be expected to vary from sample to sample. However, when taking into consideration all possible sample means which could result from a random selection procedure, $\sigma_{\bar{X}}$ is a measure of the extent of error to be expected, on the average. In other words, $\sigma_{\bar{X}}$ is a measure of the error to be expected due to random sampling (chance) when a sample mean is used as an estimate of the population mean. Consequently, $\sigma_{\bar{X}}$ is usually called the *standard error of the mean. Generally, the standard deviation of a sampling distribution is called a standard error.*

The concept of a sampling distribution has been developed and presented in terms of a very small population. Sampling from such a population is, of course, unrealistic. However, it offered a convenient basis for presenting and discussing a concept which is usually a difficult one for the introductory student. In the typical situation, we are concerned with sampling from large or very large populations—even from infinite populations. In such situations, it is impractical or impossible to list all possible samples. For example, say we are interested in samples of size 20 from a population of 800 scores. All possible samples of 20 scores out of 800, selected without replacement (all possible combinations of 800 scores taken 20 at a time), may be computed as $\binom{800}{20}$. This comes out to approximately 3724 followed by 35 zeros! On the other hand, if we sample from an infinite population, it is *impossible* to list all possible samples.

The concept of a sampling distribution is generally developed on the theoretical basis of repeated sampling from an indefinitely large (infinite) population. Let us use our imagination to construct the sampling distribution of the mean based on samples of size n selected from an infinite population of scores. Imagine that a random sample of n scores is selected and $\bar{X}$ computed. Then, a second sample of n scores is selected and, again, $\bar{X}$ is computed. Imagine that an infinite sequence of samples of n scores each are selected and, for each sample, $\bar{X}$ is computed. As a result, we have a collection of an infinite number of sample means. Now, let us imagine that we construct a table, similar to Table 7.4.2, presenting the different $\bar{X}$ values, the corresponding frequencies, and the corresponding probabilities (relative frequencies). We have now constructed, in our imagination, the *theoretical sampling distribution of the mean* based on sampling from an infinite population.

Fortunately, we do not have to go through the mental exercise just described to determine the theoretical sampling distribution for a statistic. More convenient methods have been developed for us by mathematical statisticians. These will be considered in Chapter 8, Section 8.4.

PROBLEMS FOR PRACTICE AND REVIEW

1. Determine the sampling distribution for the mean for samples selected from the following populations:

(a) Samples of $n = 2$ selected without replacement from the population 4, 8, 10, 12, 6.

(b) Samples of $n = 2$ selected with replacement from the population 21, 20, 22, 19.

2. For the following sets of data (populations), select a random sample (as indicated) by use of the table of random numbers (Table B.1) and estimate the population mean and standard deviation by computing $\bar{X}$ and s:

(a) Sample of $n = 5$ selected without replacement from the 53 research aptitude test scores in Problem 1 (following Section 3.4).

(b) Sample of $n = 10$ selected with replacement from the 70 error counts in Problem 3 (following Section 3.4).

(c) Sample of $n = 15$ selected without replacement from 113 spelling test scores in Problem 4 (following Section 3.4).

(d) Sample of $n = 20$ selected without replacement from 183 scores in Problem 5 (following Section 3.4).

(e) Sample of $n = 35$ selected without replacement from the 325 grades in Problem 6 (following Section 3.4).

(f) Sample of $n = 25$ selected without replacement from the 250 scores in Problem 7 (following Section 3.4).

State precisely the sample selection procedure used in (a) through (f).

8

THEORETICAL DISTRIBUTIONS

8.1 INTRODUCTION

Typically, when sample data are used to develop inferences about a population, we have only partial, often little, information relating to the population distribution. Certain theoretical distributions, developed on a mathematical basis, have been found widely useful as representative of population distributions encountered in practice. Two theoretical population distributions are presented in this chapter, the *normal distribution* and the *binomial population distribution.* In addition, *theoretical sampling distributions involving the normal and binomial distributions* are presented. The material in this chapter forms the basis for many of the applications of statistical inference presented in Parts IV and V of this text.

It has been observed in Chapter 1, Section 1.2, that the development of statistical methods involves an interlacing of concepts and methods developed throughout the text. The approach adopted by this text is to present concepts, to the extent appropriate, at the earliest possible point, in the hope that the resulting gradual method of development will be most helpful to the reader. This means that it will be necessary, from time to time, to refer to earlier sections of the text. For example, the idea of a distribution underlying a set of data was discussed and developed in Section 3.6 of Chapter 3, where the frequency distribution was presented. The concepts of discrete and continuous distributions were also introduced in Section 3.6. The reader should carefully review Section 3.6 before continuing with the present chapter.

8.2 NORMAL DISTRIBUTION

The most useful theoretical distribution in all of statistics is the *normal distribution*. Indeed, it is the single most important theoretical underpinning for the methods of inductive statistics. *The normal distribution, or the normal curve, as it is frequently called, represents a continuous distribution of an infinite population.* That is, the variable of the distribution X_i, or more simply X, is a continuous variable. As defined in Chapter 2, Section 2.4, a continuous variable is one which can take on any value between specified limits. In the case of the normal distribution, the limits of the variable X are $-$ infinity and $+$ infinity. In other words, X may take on any value. While it is not necessary for us to delve extensively into the mathematical properties of the normal curve, nevertheless, it is useful to note the equation of this distribution

$$Y = \frac{1}{\sqrt{2\pi}\sigma} e^{-\frac{1}{2}\left(\frac{X-\mu}{\sigma}\right)^2} \qquad (8.2.1)$$

where Y = height of the curve at a specified value of X
σ = standard deviation of the normal population
μ = mean of the normal population
$\pi = \frac{22}{7} = 3.1416$, a mathematically determined constant
$e = 2.7183$, a mathematically determined constant which is the base of the natural (Naperian) logarithms
X = a continuous variable

The normal distribution is a two-parameter distribution, the parameters being μ and σ. This means that specific values must be assigned to these two parameters before a specific normal curve can be identified. In other words, Equation 8.2.1 defines a *family* of normal curves, and each time values are specified for μ and σ, a particular normal distribution is identified. For example, let us specify $\mu = 100$ and $\sigma = 10$. The particular normal curve identified is presented in Figure 8.2.1, on the left. Note that the normal curve is perfectly symmetrical, with a centrally located peak. Therefore, the general appearance of the normal curve is like that of a bell or a hill. The mean, μ, is located at the center of the distribution, as indicated in the figure. Owing to the perfect symmetry of the distribution and the central peak, *the mean, median, and mode are all equal for a normal distribution.* Note that, as you move away from the center of the curve (the mean), the height of the curve is continuously reduced. At each end, the curve, as illustrated in the figure, is only barely above the horizontal axis. Actually, the normal distribution stretches out indefinitely in each direction, approaching but never touching the horizontal axis. This reflects

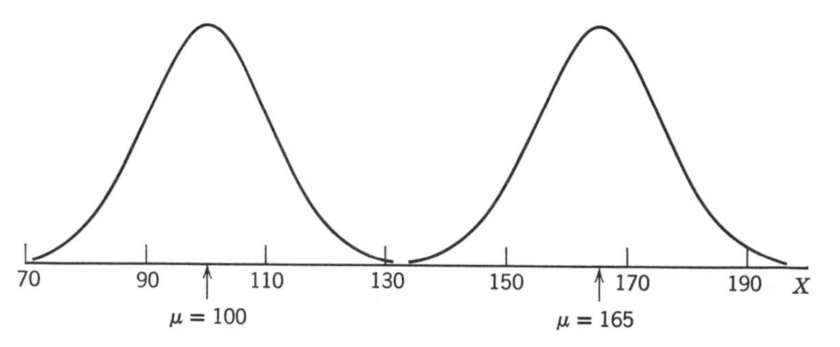

Fig. 8.2.1. Normal distributions with the same standard deviation and different means.

the fact that the limits of the variable X are $-$ infinity at the lower end and $+$ infinity at the upper end, as noted previously. Of course, it is not possible to show this in the figure.

How is the normal distribution affected if μ and σ are changed? Suppose, first, we specify that $\mu = 165$ instead of 100, while σ remains the same. The normal curve identified by these values for μ and σ is presented in Figure 8.2.1, on the right. Observe that the only effect on the distribution is to shift it to a higher position on the X scale. In all other respects, the two normal distributions are identical. Now, suppose the standard deviation changes. Figure 8.2.2 presents two normal distributions with the same mean but with different standard deviations. Note that the distribution with the larger σ has a greater spread or dispersion. Conversely, reducing the standard deviation results in a contraction of the central part of the

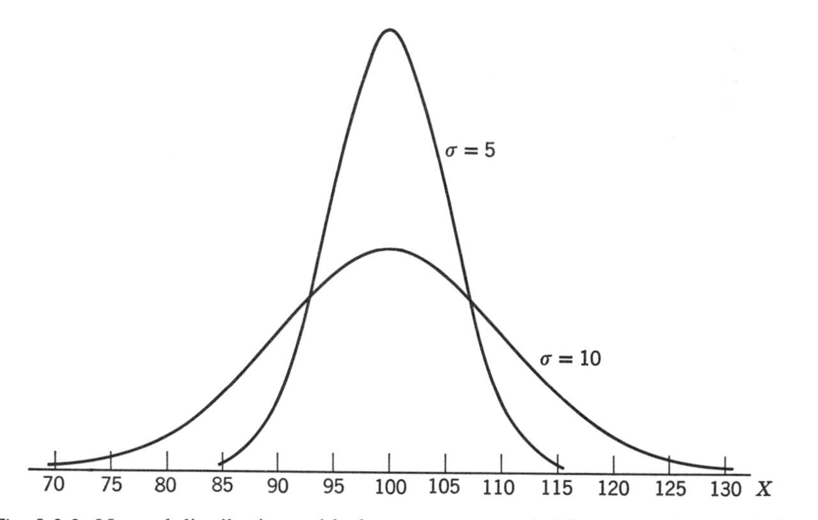

Fig. 8.2.2. Normal distributions with the same mean and different standard deviations.

distribution. In other words, the smaller the standard deviation, the greater is the concentration of the distribution around the mean. The effect of this increased concentration around the mean as σ is reduced is to increase the height of the curve in the central part of the distribution and reduce the height at the extremes, as indicated in Figure 8.2.2.

The most important use of the normal distribution in statistical inference is related to the area under the curve. It will be recalled from Chapter 3, Section 3.6, that the area under a continuous curve can be interpreted as a frequency or as a relative frequency. This interpretation results from the development of a continuous curve as a limiting form of the histogram, as presented in Section 3.6. Briefly, if you think of a histogram with class intervals becoming smaller and smaller, while the number of items included becomes greater and greater, you will eventually reach the theoretical continuous curve discussed in Section 3.6. The area under the smooth curve, as in the case of the area defined by the histogram, is equal to the total frequency or to the total of the relative frequencies, which is one. In the normal distribution, as expressed mathematically by Equation 8.2.1, the area under the curve is equal to one.

Of course, if the process explained in Section 3.6 is applied (theoretically) to a histogram, the resulting continuous distribution is not always a *normal* distribution. Only under certain mathematically defined conditions will the resulting continuous distribution have the properties of the normal curve. We will consider one such set of conditions in Section 8.7 of this chapter. However, it is not necessary for the student of introductory statistics to study the mathematical development of the normal curve. It is only necessary that he know the general properties of the normal distribution and how this theoretical curve is used in inductive statistics. It might be noted that Karl Friedrich Gauss was associated with the early development of the normal distribution, so that it is also referred to as the *Gaussian distribution*. It is also called the *normal curve of errors* because it has been found to approximate very closely the distribution of errors made when a given measurement procedure is repeated a large number of times. For example, if the length of a bar is measured, using the same yardstick, a large number of times, the distribution of these measurements around the mean will tend to be approximately normal. Finally, it should be noted that the term "normal" does not have any psychological connotation.

Observing Figure 8.2.2, the reader may well have wondered what it is about the two distributions (which look so different) that makes them both normal distributions. Actually, these are both normal distributions because *the distribution of the areas under the curves, when viewed on a comparable basis, are identical.* Referring to Figure 8.2.1, we observed that changing the mean has no effect whatsoever on the shape of the curve. The only effect is to change the location of the curve. In the one instance, the curve is located so that $\mu = 100$. In the other case, the curve is located so that $\mu = 165$. On the other hand, we observed from Figure 8.2.2 that changing the standard deviation has a decided effect on the shape of the distribution. Consequently, to achieve a comparable basis for comparing normal curves, we need to take the effect of the standard deviation into account. Let us pursue this by examining Figure 8.2.3.

Generally, our interest will be in the *standard normal distribution* expressed in standard z units. Figure 8.2.3 presents the *standard normal*

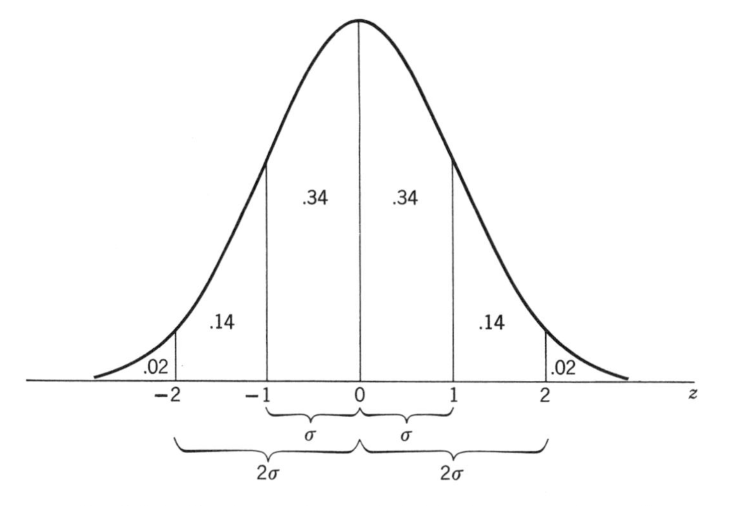

Fig. 8.2.3. The standard normal distribution ($\mu = 0$, $\sigma = 1$).

distribution. In this distribution, the variable X has been transformed to the variable z using Equation 5.7.1 (Chapter 5, Section 5.7). Briefly, according to Section 5.7, conversion to standard units (using Equation 5.7.1 for population data and Equation 5.7.2 for sample data) results in a distribution with mean equal to 0 and standard deviation equal to 1. Notice that the horizontal scale in Figure 8.2.3 is labeled z, not X, and the mean is at the point $z = 0$. Observe also the z values marked off on the horizontal scale. As discussed in Section 5.7, z values are in standard deviation units, so that the point marked off as $z = 1$ identifies a point on the horizontal scale which is 1 standard deviation *above* the mean. On the other hand, the point $z = -1$ identifies a point 1 standard deviation *below* the mean.

As indicated in Figure 8.2.3, .34 of the total area under the normal curve is contained between the mean and a point on the horizontal scale 1 standard deviation above the mean; .14 of the total area under the curve is contained between 1 standard deviation and 2 standard deviations above the mean (between $z = 1$ and $z = 2$); and .02 of the total area lies beyond a point 2 standard deviations above the mean (beyond $z = 2$). The proportion of the total area which lies below the mean is similarly distributed, as indicated in the figure.

It is the similarity in the distribution of the area under the curve when the distance from the mean is expressed in σ units, as in Figure 8.2.3, *which makes all normal distributions comparable.* For example, referring to the two distributions in Figure 8.2.2, the proportion of the total area under the curve between the mean and, say, $X = 105$ is less for the curve with $\sigma = 10$ than for the curve with $\sigma = 5$. Clearly, this is to be expected since a larger σ indicates a lesser concentration of the distribution around the mean, as previously noted. On the other hand, the proportion of the total area under the curve between the mean and any distance *expressed in σ units* is *identical* for both curves. For example, the proportion of the total area between the mean and 1σ above the mean is .34 for both normal distributions in Figure 8.2.2. In terms of the X variable, a distance of 1σ above the mean refers to the interval between $X = 100$ and $X = 105$ for the curve with $\sigma = 5$, and the interval between $X = 100$ and $X = 110$ for the curve with $\sigma = 10$. In terms of standard units, for both curves this interval is between $z = 0$ and $z = 1$. Similarly, the proportion of the total area under the curve between the mean and 2σ above the mean is .34 + .14 or .48 for both curves, as indicated in Figure 8.2.3 for the standard normal curve.

Information concerning the proportion of the area under the normal curve for specified intervals along the horizontal axis generally is required when the normal distribution is used in developing statistical inferences. In order to meet this need, tables of areas under the normal curve have been prepared and may be found in almost any text on statistical methods. These tables are based on the *standard normal curve*. Table B.2 in Appendix B is such a table. The shaded area under the normal curve at the head of the table indicates that the body of the table presents areas between the mean and specified z values. For example, suppose we wish to obtain the proportion of the area between the mean and $z = 1.00$ (one standard deviation above the mean). Look down the column headed "z" until you reach 1.0, then move across that row to the column headed ".00." The value .3413 which is obtained, corresponding to $z = 1.00$, is the proportion of the area under the normal curve between the mean and one standard deviation above the mean. This agrees with the .34 shown in Figure 8.2.3, after rounding to two decimals. Suppose we wish to determine the area between the mean and $z = 2.33$ (2.33 standard deviations above the mean). Look down the "z" column until you reach 2.3, then move across that row to the column headed ".03." The value .4901 in that position of the table, corresponding to $z = 2.33$, is the proportion of the area between $z = 0$ (the mean) and $z = 2.33$, as indicated in Figure 8.2.4, part *A*.

Table B.2 presents areas under the normal curve only for positive values of z. Clearly, this is all that is needed, since the curve is symmetrical about the mean. For example, what is the area under the curve between the mean and $z = -1.96$. Look in the table for the area corresponding to $z = 1.96$. We find .4750. Then, this is also the area corresponding to

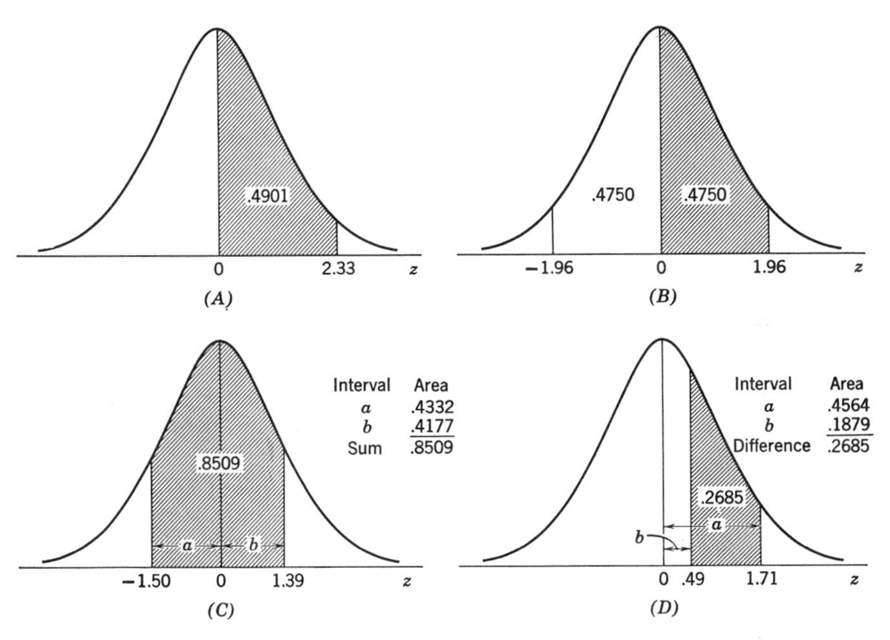

Fig. 8.2.4. Normal distribution: areas under the curve.

$z = -1.96$, since the area between the mean and $z = 1.96$ is *identically* equal to the area between the mean and -1.96. This is shown in Figure 8.2.4, part *B*.

Let us consider two more illustrations involving the use of Table B.2 to determine areas under the normal curve. Find the area between $z = -1.50$ and $z = 1.39$, as indicated by the shaded area in Figure 8.2.4, part *C*. Let us consider this area as made up of two sections. One section is the area between the mean and $z = -1.50$. This area is equal to .4332, as indicated in Table B.2. The second section is the area between the mean and $z = 1.39$. This area, according to Table B.2, is .4177. Finally, the area between $z = -1.50$ and $z = 1.39$ is determined as the *sum* of .4332 and .4177, or .8509. Now, what is the area between $z = .49$ and $z = 1.71$. Here, too, we must start out by first considering two areas. The first area to consider is between the mean and $z = 1.71$. This area is found to be .4564. The second area to consider is between the mean and $z = .49$. This area is .1879. Then, the area between $z = .49$ and $z = 1.71$ is determined by *subtracting the smaller area* (.1879) *from the larger area* (.4564) to obtain .2685, as indicated in Figure 8.2.4, part *D*.

Let us consider some illustrative problems in the fields of psychology and education. Suppose the scores (in seconds) on a typing speed test administered to all junior high school students in a large metropolitan area have a mean of 22.483 seconds and a standard deviation of 3.950

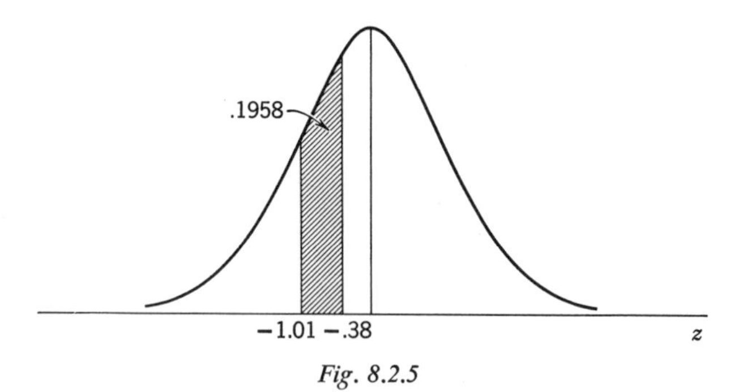

Fig. 8.2.5

seconds. Suppose it is known that these scores are distributed approximately like the normal curve. How can we estimate the percentage of the population of scores between 18.500 seconds and 21.000 seconds? Since the population of scores is approximately normal in distribution, we may refer to the table of normal curve areas, Table B.2, to determine the proportion of the scores included within the stated limits. However, Table B.2 refers to the *standard normal curve*. Therefore, we must transform the limits 18.500 and 21.000 to *standard units*. Using Equation 5.7.1 (for population data) from Chapter 5, Section 5.7, and noting that $\mu = 22.483$ and $\sigma = 3.950$, we compute

$$z_1 = \frac{18.500 - 22.483}{3.950} = -1.01$$

$$z_2 = \frac{21.000 - 22.483}{3.950} = -.38$$

It is suggested that a chart be sketched as a guide when determining areas under the normal curve. For example, Figure 8.2.5 presents the normal distribution with z_1 and z_2, as just computed, marked off. The area under the normal curve represents the population of scores. The shaded area in Figure 8.2.5, which is the area included between the limits expressed in standard units (z_1 and z_2), represents the proportion of the scores in the population between 18.500 and 21.000. Therefore, referring to Table B.2, the area between the mean and z_1 is found to be .3438, and between the mean and z_2 it is .1480. Then, subtracting the smaller area from the larger area, we obtain .1958. Consequently, we estimate that 19.58% of the scores in the population of typing speed test scores are between 18.500 and 21.000.

There is another interpretation of the area under a normal curve which is often made. Since the area corresponding to a specified interval along

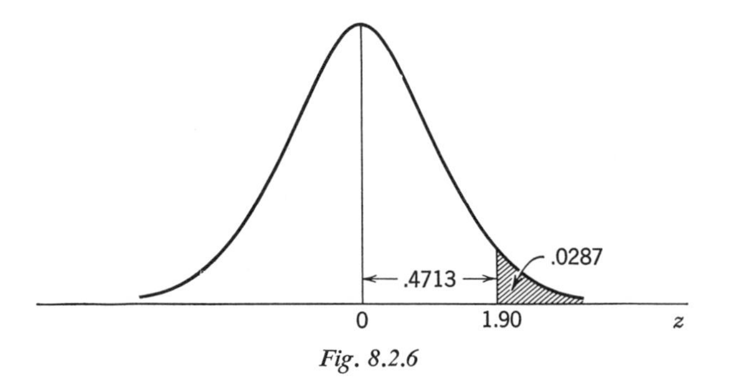

Fig. 8.2.6

the horizontal scale indicates a proportion or relative frequency, *it may also be interpreted as a probability. This is the principal use of the normal distribution in statistics.* Referring to the population of scores on a typing speed test just noted, we may state that the probability is .1958 (or about .20) that, if a score is selected at random from the population, it will have a value between 18.500 and 21.000. Now, let us find the probability that, if a score is selected at random from this population, it will be higher than 29.999. Transforming 29.999 to standard units, we obtain

$$z = \frac{29.999 - 22.483}{3.950} = 1.90$$

Figure 8.2.6 presents the standard normal curve with $z = 1.90$ marked off. The probability that the selected score is above 29.999 (which is, of course, the proportion of the population of scores higher than 29.999) is represented by the area under the curve above $z = 1.90$. This is the shaded portion of the area in Figure 8.2.6. Referring to Table B.2, we find that the area corresponding to $z = 1.90$ is .4713. This, of course, is the area between the mean ($z = 0$) and $z = 1.90$, as shown in the figure. Since the curve is perfectly symmetrical, half (.5000) of the total area under the curve lies on each side of the mean. Therefore, we may determine the area above $z = 1.90$ by subtracting the area between the mean and $z = 1.90$, .4713, from .5000 to obtain .0287. Hence, we may state that the probability is .0287, or about .03, that a score selected at random from the population of typing speed test scores will be above 29.999. Of course, we may also state that 2.87% of the scores in the population are above 29.999.

In the foregoing illustrations relating to the typing speed test scores, we were making the assumption that the scores are measured on a *continuous* scale. Such an assumption is necessary if we are to be able to represent a real population by the normal curve. It will be recalled that the variable of the normal curve is a continuous variable. Of course, all recorded

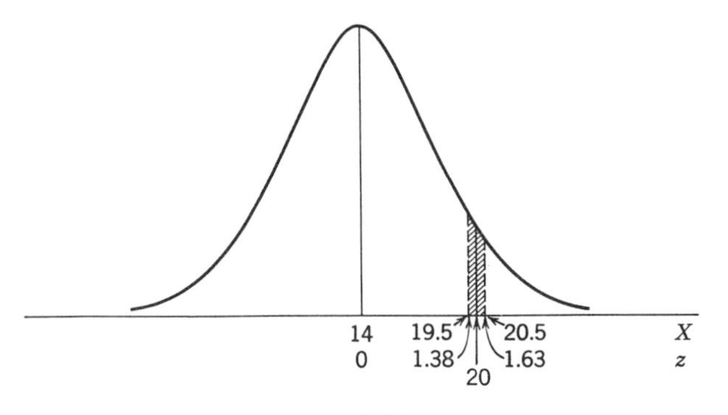

Fig. 8.2.7

variables are discrete, as discussed in Chapter 2, Section 2.4. However, it is not always reasonable to assume that the variable involved is continuous. For example, suppose it was determined for a very large population of college students that the mean number of times late to class during the previous school year was 14 times per student, with a standard deviation of four times per student. The variable in this illustration is the number of times late, which is clearly discrete, since it can only have the values 0, 1, 2, 3, etc. Let us assume that this variable is approximately normally distributed and let us use the normal curve to find the proportion of the college students who were late exactly 20 times. Figure 8.2.7 presents the normal curve, with the X variable (number of times late) shown along the horizontal axis and $X = 20$ and $\mu = 14$ marked off.

In order to be able to use the normal curve to determine the proportion of the population with $X = 20$, we must convert the discrete variable X to a continuous variable, as discussed in Chapter 3, Section 3.3. The relationship between discrete scores and continuous scores was presented in Figure 3.3.2 in Section 3.3. When converted, the *discrete score* 20 becomes the *continuous score interval* 19.5–20.5, as indicated by the shaded area in Figure 8.2.7. Using Equation 5.7.1, transform 19.5 to standard units to obtain $z_1 = 1.38$ and transform 20.5 to obtain $z_2 = 1.63$. These z values are shown in Figure 8.2.7 beneath the corresponding X-scale values. Referring to Table B.2, we find that the area between the mean and z_1 is .4162, and between the mean and z_2 it is .4484. Subtracting, we determine the area between z_1 and z_2 as .0322. Therefore, we may state that .0322 or 3.22% of the college students were late 20 times.

Suppose, in the foregoing illustration, we wish to determine the proportion of college students who were late between 10 and 18 times.

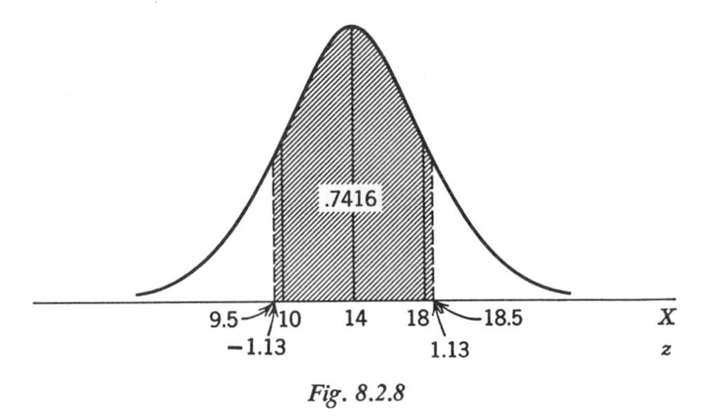

Fig. 8.2.8

Converting $X = 10$ and $X = 18$ to continuous scale values, we obtain the intervals 9.5–10.5 and 17.5–18.5, respectively. Then, the interval 10–18 becomes the continuous interval 9.5–18.5, as shown by the shaded area in Figure 8.2.8. We determine the area under the curve between the corresponding z values (-1.13 and 1.13, as indicated in the figure) to be .7416. Therefore, we may state that 74.16% of the college students were late between 10 and 18 times.

Of course, the probabilities and proportions determined in the foregoing illustrations are *estimated* values. This is to be expected, since the normal distribution, which refers to the distribution of a continuous variable for an infinite population, is a theoretical concept. Such a distribution can only approximate a real distribution, where the recorded variable is always discrete and the population, no matter how large, is never infinite.

Let us consider a final illustration which demonstrates another application of normal curve areas. Suppose a large population of social attitude scores has a mean of 118.35 and a standard deviation of 22.10. Assume the population distribution is approximately normal. Find the score below which 10% of the scores fall. In other words, find D_1, the first decile (see

Chapter 4, Section 4.7). Let us analyze this problem. Figure 8.2.9 presents a normal curve which represents the population of social attitude scores in standard units. The shaded portion of the area represents the lower 10% or .1000 of the area under the curve. Therefore, since the entire area to the left of the mean equals .5000, the area between the mean and the shaded portion under the curve is equal to .5000 − .1000 or .4000, as shown in Figure 8.2.9. Then, referring to Table B.2, look in the body of the table for

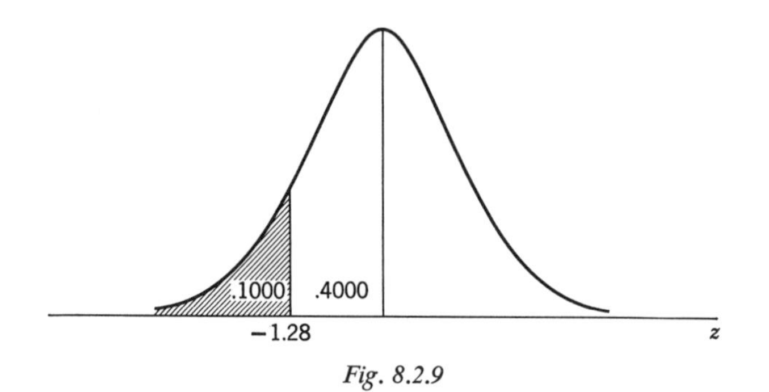

Fig. 8.2.9

a value as close to .4000 as you can find. The closest value is .3997 and the corresponding z is 1.28. However, since we are interested in the *lower* tail of the curve, for our problem the corresponding z is -1.28. Then, the area between the mean and $z = -1.28$ makes up about 40% (actually 39.97%) of the area under the curve, and the area to the left of $z = -1.28$ includes 10% of the total area. Therefore, $z = -1.28$ is the score we are looking for, since 10% of the population is below this value. However, z is in standard units and we wish to determine the score in terms of the original score variable (X). Using Equation 5.7.1 for z and substituting $z = -1.28$, $\mu = 118.35$, and $\sigma = 22.10$, we obtain

$$-1.28 = \frac{X - 118.35}{22.10}$$

Solving for X, we obtain $X = 90.06$. Hence, we may state that 10% of the social attitude scores are below 90.06.

8.3 FITTING A NORMAL CURVE

The distribution underlying a set of population data was discussed in Chapter 3, Section 3.6. It was noted that sometimes it is desired to approximate the population distribution by a smooth curve. Where data appear to be normally distributed, it may be desired to fit a normal curve to the data.

Table 8.3.1 FREQUENCY DISTRIBUTION OF SCORES ON A SCIENCE APTITUDE TEST FOR A POPULATION OF 1000 SUBJECTS

Discrete Class Limits	f_i	Continuous Class Limits
		99.5
100–109	3	
		109.5
110–119	17	
		119.5
120–129	40	
		129.5
130–139	100	
		139.5
140–149	230	
		149.5
150–159	230	
		159.5
160–169	220	
		169.5
170–179	95	
		179.5
180–189	45	
		189.5
190–199	19	
		199.5
200–209	1	
		209.5

This means specifying the particular normal curve which has the same mean and standard deviation as the set of data. Using this normal distribution, we may compute the theoretical class frequencies and compare them with the actual class frequencies. The following illustration will demonstrate this.

Table 8.3.1 presents a frequency distribution of scores obtained by a population of 1000 subjects on a science aptitude test. The histogram for this distribution is presented in Figure 8.3.1. The general form of the distribution appears to be similar to the normal distribution. Let us fit a normal curve to these data. First, computing the mean and standard deviation for this population, we determine that $\mu = 154.4$ and $\sigma = 16.3$.

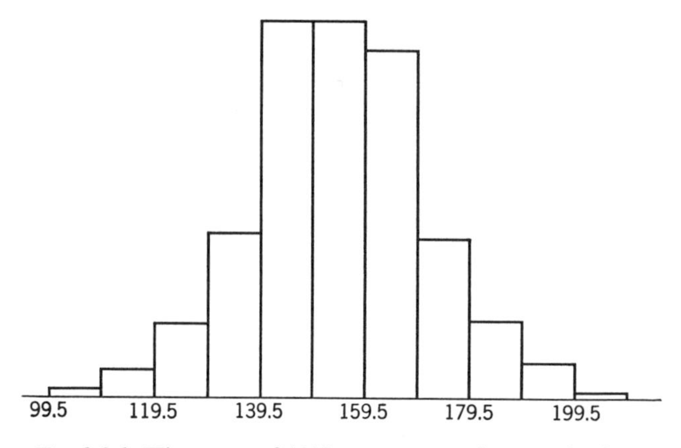

Fig. 8.3.1. Histogram of 1000 scores on a science aptitude test.

The normal curve appropriate for this set of scores has the same mean and the same standard deviation. Table 8.3.2 presents the computations required to determine the theoretical class frequencies. The first column presents the continuous class limits which are also shown in Table 8.3.1. The second column presents the z value corresponding to each continuous class limit. These are computed in the usual way, using Equation 5.7.1 from Chapter 5, Section 5.7. For example, for the first continuous class limit, 99.5, we compute

$$z_{99.5} = \frac{99.5 - 154.4}{16.3} = -3.37$$

Referring to Table B.2, determine the proportion of the area under the normal curve between the mean and each specified z value. This is shown in the third column of Table 8.3.2. Now, compute the values for the fourth column which show the proportion of the area under the curve

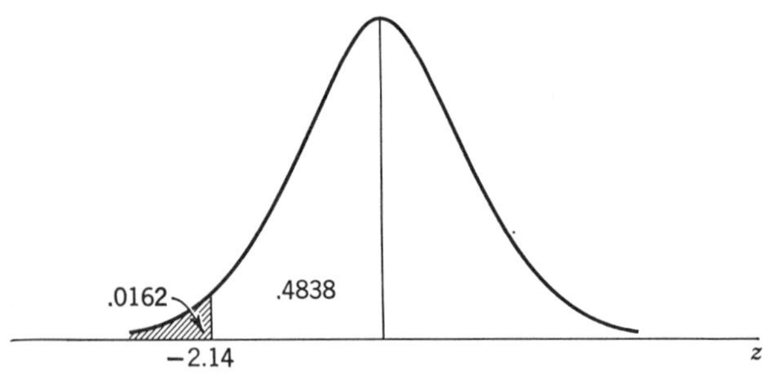

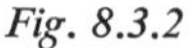

Fig. 8.3.2

Table 8.3.2 COMPUTATION OF THE THEORETICAL FREQUENCIES BASED ON THE NORMAL DISTRIBUTION: SCORES ON A SCIENCE APTITUDE TEST FOR 1000 SUBJECTS

		Normal Curve Area				
Continuous Class Limits	z	Between the Mean and z	Below z	Theoretical less than cum f	Class Frequencies Theoretical	Class Frequencies Actual
(1)	(2)	(3)	(4)	(5)	(6)	(7)
99.5	−3.37	.4996	.0004	0		
					3	3
109.5	−2.75	.4970	.0030	3		
					13	17
119.5	−2.14	.4838	.0162	16		
					47	40
129.5	−1.53	.4370	.0630	63		
					118	100
139.5	−.91	.3186	.1814	181		
					201	230
149.5	−.30	.1179	.3821	382		
					240	230
159.5	.31	.1217	.6217	622		
					202	220
169.5	.93	.3238	.8238	824		
					114	95
179.5	1.54	.4382	.9382	938		
					46	45
189.5	2.15	.4842	.9842	984		
					13	19
199.5	2.77	.4972	.9972	997		
					3	1
209.5	3.38	.4996	.9996	1000		

which lies *below* (to the left of) each specified z value. This is determined in the following way: Where z is *negative*, *subtract* the proportion in the third column from .5000; where z is *positive*, *add* .5000 to the proportion in the third column. For example, the third z value from the top in the second column of Table 8.3.2 is −2.14 and the area between this z value and the mean is .4838, as shown in the third column and also in Figure 8.3.2. Clearly, to determine the proportion of the area below $z = -2.14$ (the shaded area in the figure), we must *subtract* .4838 from .5000, since the area below the mean is .5000 of the total area under the curve. On the other hand, consider the second positive z value in the column, .93. The area between this z value and the mean is .3238, as shown in the adjacent column and also in Figure 8.3.3. Clearly, to determine the proportion of the area below $z = .93$ (the shaded area in the figure), we must *add* .5000 to .3238.

The column of normal curve areas below z (the fourth column in Table 8.3.2) indicates the proportion of the 1000 scores on the science aptitude test which are below z in value. For example, the second proportion in this column, .0030, indicates that (.0030)(1000), or 3 scores out of the population of 1000, are below the corresponding z value, -2.75. Furthermore, this z value corresponds to the continuous class limit 109.5. Therefore, we may state that 3 scores out of the 1000 are below 109.5. In the

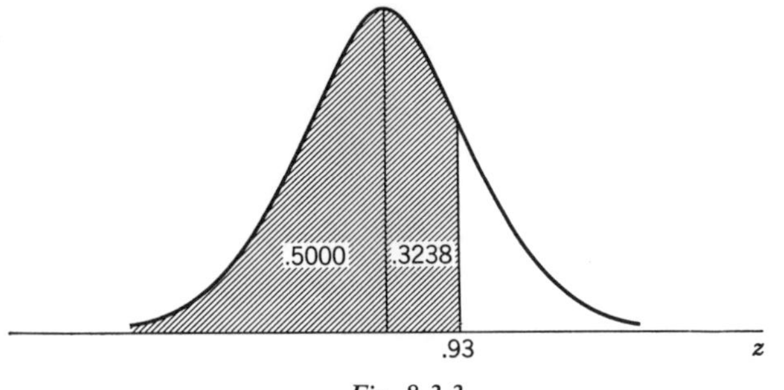

Fig. 8.3.3

same way, if we multiply each proportion in the fourth column by the total number of scores (1000), we obtain the number of scores in the population which have a lower value than the corresponding continuous class limit. For example, multiplying the third proportion in the column, .0162, by 1000, we obtain 16.2. Then, rounding this to 16, we may state that 16 scores out of the 1000 have a value lower than 119.5, the corresponding continuous class limit. These *theoretical less than cumulative frequencies* are presented in the fifth column of the table. (Less than cum f were discussed in Chapter 3, Section 3.3.) If we subtract the scores in successive pairs of these cum f, we obtain the *theoretical class frequencies*, as shown in the sixth column of the table. For example, the first pair of cumulative frequencies in the fifth column is 0 and 3. Then, $3 - 0 = 3$, which is the first theoretical class frequency shown in the sixth column. The second pair of cumulative frequencies is 3 and 16. Then, $16 - 3 = 13$, which is the second theoretical class frequency shown. Note that the theoretical class frequencies are written *between* the cumulative frequencies. This is the usual position for class frequencies, as discussed in Chapter 3, Section 3.3 and illustrated in the model frequency distribution in Table 3.3.1.

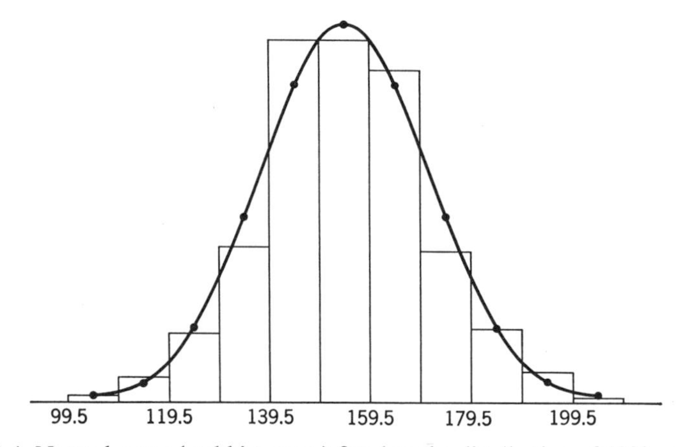

Fig. 8.3.4. Normal curve (and histogram) fitted to the distribution of 1000 scores on a science aptitude test.

The last column in Table 8.3.2 presents the actual class frequencies (copied from Table 8.3.1) for comparison with the theoretical class frequencies. It will be observed that they compare reasonably well, except in the central portion of the distribution. The relationship between the theoretical continuous distribution and the actual distribution of the population of 1000 science aptitude scores, as exhibited by the histogram, is better observed by inspecting Figure 8.3.4.

PROBLEMS FOR PRACTICE AND REVIEW

1. A very large population of scores on an essay-type language test is approximately normally distributed, with a mean of 107.42 and a standard deviation of 32.15. Assuming the scores represent a continuous scale, determine the percentage of the scores

(a) between 107.42 and 135.00.
(b) between 110.00 and 145.00.
(c) between 70.00 and 107.42.
(d) between 42.00 and 85.50.
(e) between 65.40 and 150.75.
(f) above 150.00.
(g) below 50.00.
(h) less than 60.00 or more than 100.00.

2. A large population of scores on a spatial perception test is approximately normally distributed with a mean of 78.64 and a standard deviation of 20.18. Assuming the scores are on a continuous scale, what is the probability that a score selected at random from this population will lie

(a) below 40?

(b) between 31 and 65?
(c) below 99?
(d) between 70 and 100?
(e) above 140?

3. The mean number of trials required per subject in a large school to accomplish a certain task was found to be 29.2, with a standard deviation of 6.7. If the variable "number of trials per subject" is considered discrete and is approximately normal in distribution, what is the probability that a randomly selected subject in the school required (a) 20 trials, (b) between 20 and 40 trials, (c) less than 20 trials?

4. The scores on a typing speed test for a large population of students are normally distributed with a mean of 26.76 minutes and a standard deviation of 6.03 minutes. Considering the score variable continuous, determine Q_1, Q_3, D_7, P_{28}.

5. The reaction time to a drug of a certain population of white rats is normally distributed with a mean of 27.6 seconds and a standard deviation of 6.2 seconds. Considering reaction time as a continuous variable

(a) Determine D_3, D_9, P_{47}, Q_3.

(b) Determine the reaction time for this population where 22% of the population of white rats have a greater reaction time.

(c) What is the probability that a rat selected at random from this population will have a reaction time to the drug (1) greater than 30 seconds, (2) less than 15 seconds, (3) between 15 and 20 seconds, (4) between 25 and 30 seconds?

6. The number of correct responses in a true-false answer test administered to a large population of junior high school pupils has a mean of 180.3 and a standard deviation of 46.9. If the variable "number of correct responses" is considered to be a discrete variable and the population distribution is approximately normal, what is the probability that a randomly selected junior high school pupil in this population will have a number of responses (a) equal to 100, (b) equal to 100 or less?

7. If a normally distributed population has a mean of 103.7 and a standard deviation of 16.9, what proportion of the population is

(a) equal to 140 or more?
(b) equal to 140 or less?
(c) equal to 83 or more?
(d) equal to 83 or less?
(e) between 70 and 80?
(f) between 140 and 150?

8. Fit a normal curve to the following distribution of 100 scores on an achievement test:

Scores	f_i
20–24	3
25–29	4
30–34	19
35–39	47
40–44	24
45–49	2
50–54	1

9. Fit a normal curve to the following distribution of 300 scores on an aptitude test:

Scores	f_i
140–149	3
150–159	47
160–169	95
170–179	107
180–189	42
190–199	6

8.4 SAMPLING DISTRIBUTIONS OF THE MEAN AND MEDIAN

In Chapter 7, Section 7.4, we introduced the concept of a sampling distribution and discussed its construction and interpretation. *Statistical inferences are essentially probability statements made on the basis of sampling distributions.* However, the sampling distributions used are constructed on the basis of sampling from theoretical (infinite) populations. Frequently used theoretical populations are the normal population, already discussed, and the binomial population, to be discussed in Section 8.5. Other theoretical populations also provide a basis for constructing sampling distributions.

Mathematical statisticians have developed *theoretical sampling models* by the application of probability theory to random sampling from infinite populations. Some of these models are presented in this section. Even though theoretical and based on sampling from infinite populations, these models are applicable to a wide variety of statistical problems encountered in the fields of psychology and education. Many of the applications of sampling theory in these fields are based on the assumption that the populations involved are infinite. Three sampling models are presented relating to measures of central tendency. Two present sampling distributions of the mean and one presents a sampling distribution for the median.

Model A: If samples of size n are selected from a normal population, with mean μ and standard deviation σ, *the sampling distribution of the mean is normal, with*

$$\textit{mean} \qquad \mu_{\bar{X}} = \mu \tag{8.4.1}$$

$$\textit{standard error of the mean} \qquad \sigma_{\bar{X}} = \frac{\sigma}{\sqrt{n}} \tag{8.4.2}$$

Suppose that a population of scores is normally distributed and that, for this population, $\mu = 160$ and $\sigma = 18$. Then, for random samples of a specified size, say, $n = 36$, the sampling distribution of the mean, according to *Model A*, is also normally distributed with mean $\mu_{\bar{X}}$ equal to 160 (the population mean) and standard error $\sigma_{\bar{X}}$ equal to $18/\sqrt{36}$ or 3. Clearly, in a problem involving sampling from a normal population, *Model A* provides considerable information concerning the sampling distribution of the mean. For example, what is the probability that a sample of size 36 selected from our illustrative population will have a mean greater than 165? Of course, the variable in the sampling distribution of the mean is $\bar{X}$. Since, according to *Model A*, the sampling distribution is

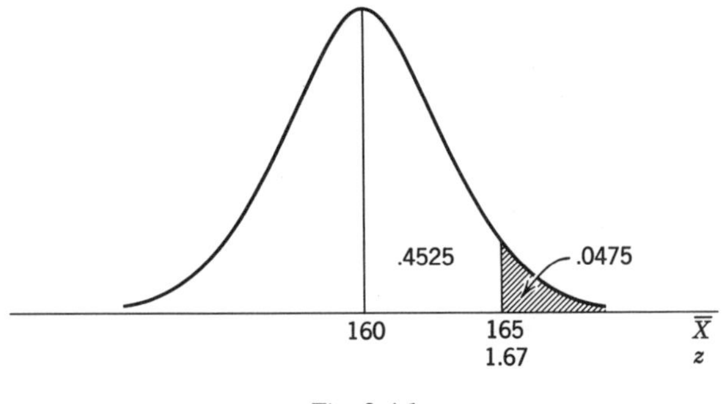

Fig. 8.4.1

distributed like the normal curve, this probability is represented by the area under the curve to the right of $\bar{X} = 165$, as indicated by the shaded area in Figure 8.4.1. We may refer to Table B.2 to determine this probability. First, of course, we must transform $\bar{X} = 165$ to standard units.

We compute standard units, generally, according to Equation 5.7.1 for population data and Equation 5.7.2 for sample data. However, we need to take into consideration that the variable we are now dealing with is $\bar{X}$, not X. Let us restate the transformation expressed in the equations for z, using words instead of symbols, as follows:

$$z = \frac{\begin{pmatrix}\text{specified value of}\\ \text{a variable}\end{pmatrix} - \begin{pmatrix}\text{mean of}\\ \text{the variable}\end{pmatrix}}{\begin{pmatrix}\text{standard deviation}\\ \text{of the variable}\end{pmatrix}} \tag{8.4.3}$$

Applying Equation 8.4.3 to the sampling distribution of the mean, where the variable is $\bar{X}$ and the standard deviation is called the standard error, we obtain

$$z = \frac{\bar{X} - \mu_{\bar{X}}}{\sigma_{\bar{X}}} = \frac{\bar{X} - \mu}{\sigma/\sqrt{n}} \tag{8.4.4}$$

Then, using Equation 8.4.4, with $\mu_{\bar{X}} = 160$ and $\sigma_{\bar{X}} = 3$, transform $\bar{X} = 165$ to standard units as follows:

$$z = \frac{165 - 160}{3} = 1.67$$

Referring to Table B.2, we determine the corresponding area as .4525. Subtracting from .5000, we obtain .0475 as the area above $\bar{X} = 165$ (shown in Figure 8.4.1). Therefore, the probability is .0475, or roughly 48 chances in 1000, that the mean of a random sample, with $n = 36$, selected from our illustrative population, will be greater than 165.

Let us identify several interesting and important aspects of *Model A*. First of all, the statistical theory underlying this model does not restrict the value of n, the sample size, in any way. Therefore, *Model A* holds for any size sample. This is not always true, as we will note in the case of the other two models presented in this section. Second, the mean of the sampling distribution of the mean, $\mu_{\bar{X}}$, is equal to the population mean, μ. We will observe a similar characteristic in other sampling models to be presented. We have already observed this relationship for the sampling distribution of the mean presented in Table 7.4.2 (Chapter 7, Section 7.4). Finally, Equation 8.4.2 indicates that $\sigma_{\bar{X}}$, the standard error of the mean, is *directly* proportional to σ, the population standard deviation, and *inversely* proportional to $\sqrt{n}$, the square root of the sample size. In other words, the larger σ, the larger $\sigma_{\bar{X}}$; whereas the larger n, the smaller $\sigma_{\bar{X}}$.

It is to be expected that the greater the variation in a population (σ large), the greater will be the variation among $\bar{X}$ values computed from samples selected from this population ($\sigma_{\bar{X}}$ large). Furthermore, the larger the sample, the greater is the amount of available information and the greater is our expectation that the sample mean will be a good estimate of the population mean. Recall (Chapter 7, Section 7.4) that $\sigma_{\bar{X}}$ measures the variation of sample means around the population mean. The smaller $\sigma_{\bar{X}}$, the more are sample means concentrated around the population mean. In other words, the smaller $\sigma_{\bar{X}}$, the more may we expect that a sample mean will be close to the population mean and the better estimate is $\bar{X}$ likely to be of the parameter μ.

Model A contains the restriction that the population from which samples are selected must be normal. This restriction may be relaxed somewhat so that the model also applies where sampling is from a population which very closely approximates the normal distribution. However, *Model B* provides a theoretical basis for the sampling distribution of the mean which is nearly completely free of this restriction.

Model B: If samples of size n, where n is large, are selected from an infinite population, with mean μ and standard deviation σ, *the sampling distribution of the mean is approximately normal, with*

$$\textit{mean} \qquad \mu_{\bar{X}} = \mu \tag{8.4.5}$$

$$\textit{standard error of the mean} \qquad \sigma_{\bar{X}} = \frac{\sigma}{\sqrt{n}} \tag{8.4.6}$$

Model B, which is based on the important mathematical theorem called the *Central Limit Theorem*, represents one of the most noteworthy models in statistical theory. Notice, in particular, that the population distribution is in no way specified in the model. In other words, if the conditions of the model are fulfilled, the sampling distribution of the mean is approximately normal *no matter what the shape of the population distribution* (within very wide limits). It is required that the population be infinite and the sample size large. The requirement of an infinite population, as already noted, is not a serious restriction. Another restriction of negligible importance is that σ must be finite. This is not a problem in psychology and education, since σ is usually finite in the problems encountered in practice. The requirement for a large sample is a more important restriction.

It is difficult to make any precise statement as to how large n must be to satisfy the requirements of *Model B*. The minimum sample size required is related to the distribution of the population. For example, if the population is normal, then the sample may be any size, no matter how small, since then *Model B* becomes *Model A*, where there is no restriction on sample size. On the other hand, if the population distribution is not normal, then the greater the difference between the population distribution and the normal distribution, the larger is the required minimum size. Following the general practice among statisticians, we will use the rule of thumb that the requirement of *Model B* relating to sample size is met if n is equal to 30 or more. *We will speak of samples with* $n \geq 30$ *as large samples and those with* $n < 30$ *as small samples.* The very general applicability of *Model B* to statistical problems encountered in practice is an important reason for the dominant position of the normal distribution in statistical theory.

The equation for the mean of the sampling distribution of the mean (Equation 8.4.5) and the standard error of the mean (Equation 8.4.6) are the same as for *Model A*. Similarly, transformation of $\bar{X}$ values to standard z units is accomplished by using Equation 8.4.4 in the same way as for *Model A*. For example, suppose we are planning to select a random sample of scores from a population with $\mu = 150$ and $\sigma = 25$. What is the probability that the sample mean will be less than 140, if a sample of size

50 is selected? This problem does not fit *Model A*, since it is not specified that the population is normal. However, we know from *Model B* that the sampling distribution of the mean for large samples is approximately normal. Therefore, the probability we are looking for is represented by the area under the normal curve below $\bar{X} = 140$. Transforming $\bar{X} = 140$ to standard units, using Equation 8.4.4, we obtain

$$z = \frac{140 - 150}{25/\sqrt{50}} = -2.83$$

Then, referring to Table B.2, the corresponding area under the normal curve is .4977, as shown in Figure 8.4.2. Subtracting from .5000, we obtain

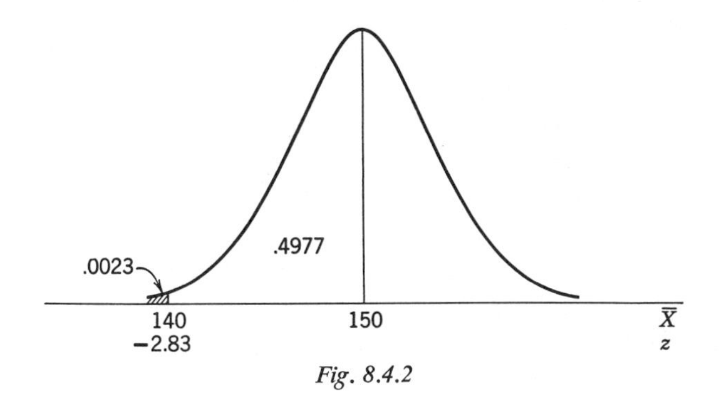

Fig. 8.4.2

.0023, which is the shaded area in the figure. Therefore, the probability is roughly .002, or 2 chances in 1000, that $\bar{X}$ computed from a sample of 50 scores selected from our illustrative population will be less than 140. In symbols, we may denote this probability as $P(\bar{X} < 140) = .002$. Clearly, considerable information relating to the sampling distribution of the mean is made available for sampling problems which meet the requirements of *Model B*.

Model C: If samples of size n, where n is large, are selected from a normal population, with mean (and median) μ and standard deviation σ, *the sampling distribution of the median is approximately normal, with*

$$\textit{mean} \qquad \mu_M = \mu \qquad (8.4.7)$$

$$\textit{standard error of the median} \qquad \sigma_M = 1.25\frac{\sigma}{\sqrt{n}} = 1.25\sigma_{\bar{X}} \qquad (8.4.8)$$

Notice that *Model C* is similar to *Model A* in that both relate to sampling from a normal population. However, *Model C* is applicable only when n

is large. In Chapter 4, Section 4.9, where the properties of the various averages were discussed, it was noted that an important reason for preferring the mean to the median is the tendency for sampling variability to be less for the mean. We may now be more precise as to this important advantage of the mean by referring to Equation 8.4.8. According to this equation, the variablility of sample medians is 25% greater than for sample means, as measured by their standard errors. This is the meaning of Equation 8.4.8 which states that σ_M is equal to $1.25\sigma_{\bar{X}}$.

An illustration will show what this means. Suppose we wish to select a random sample of 100 scores from a normally distributed population, with $\mu = 90$ and $\sigma = 15$. What is the probability that the sample median is no further than 2 points away from the population mean? In other words, what is the probability that the sample median is between 88 and 92? According to *Model C*, the sampling distribution of the median is approximately normal. Therefore, the probability we are looking for is represented by the area under the normal curve between $M = 88$ and $M = 92$. Referring to Equation 8.4.3 for z (in words), we may transform a sample median, M, to standard units according to the following equation:

$$z = \frac{M - \mu_M}{\sigma_M} = \frac{M - \mu}{1.25(\sigma/\sqrt{n})} \tag{8.4.9}$$

Then, transforming $M = 88$ and $M = 92$, we obtain

$$z_1 = \frac{88 - 90}{1.25(15/\sqrt{100})} = -1.07$$

$$z_2 = \frac{92 - 90}{1.25(15/\sqrt{100})} = 1.07$$

Referring to Table B.2, we find the corresponding area under the normal curve as .3577 (for both z values). The probability that the sample median will lie between 88 and 92 is then computed as the sum of these areas or .72 (rounded). Now, let us determine the probability that the sample mean will lie between 88 and 92. Transforming $\bar{X} = 88$ and $\bar{X} = 92$ to standard units, we obtain

$$z_1 = \frac{88 - 90}{15/\sqrt{100}} = -1.33$$

$$z_2 = \frac{92 - 90}{15/\sqrt{100}} = 1.33$$

Referring to Table B.2, the corresponding areas are .4082 (for both z values). Then, the probability that the sample mean will lie between 88 and

92 is .82 (rounded). Clearly, the probability is considerably greater that the sample mean will lie relatively close to the parameter μ than it is for the sample median.

PROBLEMS FOR PRACTICE AND REVIEW

1. A very large population of scores is normally distributed with a mean of 110 and a standard deviation of 20. If a sample of 16 scores is selected,

(a) what is the probability that the sample mean is (1) 100 or less, (2) between 100 and 120, (3) 120 or more?

(b) which sampling model did you use?

2. A large population of science aptitude scores is normally distributed with mean 76.34 and standard deviation 20.11.

(a) If a sample of 25 scores is selected, what is the probability that the sample mean is (1) between 70 and 80, (2) 85 or less?

(b) If a sample of 16 scores is selected, what is the probability that the sample mean is between 70 and 80?

(c) Which sampling model did you use?

3. A population of scores on accident-proneness is normally distributed with a mean of 134.03 and a standard deviation of 15.42.

(a) If a sample of 22 scores is selected, what is the probability that the sample mean is (1) between 125 and 145, (2) 130 or more?

(b) If a sample of 9 scores is selected, what is the probability that the sample mean is between 125 and 145?

4. A population of scores on anxiety neurosis is normally distributed with a mean of 47.13 and a standard deviation of 10.08. If a sample of 15 scores is selected, what is the probability that the sample mean is between 40 and 55?

5. A very large population of grades on ancient history has a mean of 63.72 and a standard deviation of 5.04. Assuming that the population distribution is normal, what is the probability that the mean of a sample of 15 grades selected from this population will lie between 60 and 65?

6. A very large population of scores on writing aptitude has a mean of 93.68 and a standard deviation of 17.44.

(a) What is the probability that the mean of a sample of 40 scores selected from this population will lie between 90 and 95?

(b) What is the probability that the sample mean will be equal to 90 or less?

(c) Which sampling model did you use?

7. In problem 6, what is the probability that the sample median will lie between 90 and 95? Indicate the sampling model appropriate.

8. In Problem 6, if a sample of 160 scores (instead of 40 scores) is selected, what is the probability that the sample mean will lie between 90 and 95?

9 In Problem 6, if $n = 160$ (instead of 40), what is the probability that the sample median will lie between 90 and 95?

10. If for a large population of scores $\mu = 124.6$ and $\sigma = 30.4$ and a sample ($n = 100$) is selected, what is the probability that $\bar{X}$ will (a) lie between 119.5 and 129.5, (b) equal 130 or more, (c) equal no more than 118?

11. In Problem 10,

(a) what is the probability that the median will lie between 119.5 and 129.5?

(b) what is the probability that the mean will lie between 119.5 and 129.5, if n is increased to 200?

8.5 BINOMIAL POPULATION

So far in this chapter we have considered only continuous populations, primarily the normal population. We now introduce a discrete population which has considerable importance in statistical theory and in applications to problems encountered in practice. Psychologists and educators often refer to such a population as a *dichotomous population.* Statisticians generally refer to it as the *binomial population.* We are referring *to a population where the items included are classified into one of two categories.* An example is a population of scores identified only as passing or failing. Or a population of students identified only as male or female. Or a population of white rats identified as "learning improved as a result of treatment" or "learning not improved as a result of treatment." Any population of items can be converted into a binomial population. This is true for any scale of measurement (nominal, ordinal, interval, ratio). For example, suppose we have a population of scholastic averages for seniors in a university. We can convert this into a binomial population in any number of ways. For example, we can identify each average only as to whether it is equal to three or more or, whether it is less than three. We may have a population of males classified into a number of occupational categories. We can convert this into a binomial population by, say, identifying each male as professional or not professional.

It is useful to assign the code 0 (zero) to each of the items in one category of a binomial population and the code 1 to each of the items in the other category. It is immaterial to which category each of these codes is assigned. It is advantageous, however, to assign the code 1 to the category of primary interest in an analysis. For example, we might be interested in studying the extent to which college freshmen have selected engineering as a major field of study. Our interest, then, is in whether a college freshman has selected engineering as his major field. Therefore, we can set up a binomial population by assigning the code 1 to freshmen who have selected engineering as the major field and the code 0 to all other freshmen. In other words, we set up a population of 1's and 0's. Actually, *statisticians often refer to a binomial population as a population of the* 1*'s and* 0*'s.*

Clearly, the binomial population distribution is made up of only two points. That is, the binomial variable X_i, or more simply X, is a discrete variable which can take on only two values, 0 and 1. The development of statistical theory relating to the binomial distribution and descriptive measures of a binomial population is based on the treatment of the codes 1 and 0 as if they are true item values or scores. Therefore, regardless of the scale of measurement of the original population data, after conversion to a binomial population, it is possible and meaningful to compute descriptive measures such as the mean and the standard deviation.

Suppose we are interested in the extent to which the 100 behavioral scientists attending a professional meeting were trained in eastern universities. That is, with respect to our interest, we view this group of be-

Table 8.5.1 BINOMIAL POPULATION DISTRIBUTION: BEHAVIORAL SCIENTISTS IN A GROUP WHO STUDIED IN EASTERN UNIVERSITIES (CODE 1) AND THOSE WHO STUDIED ELSEWHERE (CODE 0)

Code, X_i	f_i	$X_i f_i$	$X_i^2 f_i$
0	82	0	0
1	18	18	18
Total	100	18	18

havioral scientists as composed of two classes: those who were trained in eastern universities and those who were trained elsewhere. Table 8.5.1 presents this information, where the code 1 indicates "studied in eastern universities" and code 0 indicates "studied elsewhere." Table 8.5.1 represents a simple grouping table since it shows the number of items which have each of the possible values of the variable. We may compute the mean for this binomial population, using Equation 4.3.11 (Chapter 4, Section 4.3), as follows:

$$\mu = \frac{\sum X_i f_i}{N} = \frac{18}{100} = .18$$

Notice that the numerator 18 is actually f_1, the number in the population coded 1, and the denominator is equal to the total number in the population, $N = 100$. Therefore, *the mean μ computed for a binomial population expresses the proportion of the population in the category coded* 1. It is for this reason that it is most advantageous to assign the code 1 to the category of primary interest. For example, we may state, based on the computed value of μ, that .18 or 18% of the behavioral scientists at the meeting studied in eastern universities. Actually, *whenever we think in terms of a* *proportion, we are implying a binomial population.* For example, if we are interested in the proportion of women in a group, we are thinking in terms of dividing the group into two categories: women and others (which may include men and children). Or we may be interested in the proportion of scores in a population which are below 80. Then, we are thinking of the population as made up of scores identified only as "below 80" and "all other scores."

It is useful to identify the proportion of items in a binomial population which are in the category coded 1 by the symbol p. However, sometimes we may use μ. Based upon the foregoing discussion, we modify Equation 4.3.11 to show the equation for the *mean of a binomial population* as

$$\mu = \frac{f_1}{N} = p \tag{8.5.1}$$

In this equation, μ or p represents the mean of the binomial population or, what is the same thing, the proportion of items in the population assigned the code 1. The letter N denotes the population size and f_1 denotes the number of the N items which belong in the 1 category.

We may compute the standard deviation for the binomial population presented in Table 8.5.1, using Equation 5.3.14 (Chapter 5, Section 5.3), as follows:

$$\sigma = \frac{1}{N}\sqrt{N \sum X_i^2 f_i - \left(\sum X_i f_i\right)^2}$$

$$= \frac{1}{100}\sqrt{100(18) - (18)^2} = .38$$

The interpretation of σ is the same as in other situations previously discussed. That is, σ is a measure of the extent to which the 1's and 0's in the binomial population are dispersed around the mean p (or μ), on the average. (It is usually more difficult for the introductory student to grasp the interpretation of σ for the binomial population.) This is a highly important and frequently used measure of the binomial distribution. Equation 5.3.14 may be modified to arrive at the following far simpler equation for the *standard deviation of a binomial population:*

$$\sigma = \sqrt{p(1 - p)} \tag{8.5.2}$$

In this equation, p denotes the proportion of the items in the population which are in the category coded 1, and $1 - p$ denotes the proportion which are in the category coded 0. (*Note* 8.1 in Section 8.8 presents the proof for Equation 8.5.2.)

8.6 BINOMIAL PROBABILITY DISTRIBUTIONS

When sampling from a binomial population, we expect that the sample will include items from both categories. For example, suppose we sample from a population of students and our purpose is to determine the proportion of out-of-state students in the population. We assign the code 1 to each out-of-state student and the code 0 to each of the other students. We expect, of course, that a random sample will include both 1's and 0's. It is customary, when sampling from a binomial population, to call selection of an item coded 1 a "success" and selection of an item coded 0 a "failure." The type of question we will be concerned with in this section is directed toward the frequency (*number*) of successes obtained when selecting a sample. For example, what is the probability of obtaining 3 successes (out-of-state students) when selecting a sample of, say, 5 students? In the language of probability, we may consider the selection of a student as a trial. In these terms, we are interested in the probability of obtaining 3 successes in 5 trials. The *proportion* of successes obtained in n trials will also be considered. For example, what is the probability of obtaining .60 or 60% successes in 5 trials? Or what is the probability of obtaining .60 successes in a sample of 5? Of course, the term "success" as used here is not to be interpreted as necessarily having a favorable connotation.

Clearly, the *frequency* of successes and the *proportion* of successes in n trials are equivalent. That is, stating that we obtained 3 successes in 5 trials is equivalent to stating that we obtained .60 successes in 5 trials. We will denote the frequency of successes in a *sample* (n trials) by the symbol X and the proportion of successes in the *sample* as X/n. Then, the frequency of "failures" in n trials is $n - X$ and the proportion of "failures" may be denoted as $(n - X)/n$ or as $1 - (X/n)$. As in Section 8.5, we will denote the proportion of successes in the *population* (the proportion of 1's) as p. The parameter p has an alternative (equivalent) interpretation which we will often use. We will also interpret p as *the probability of a success in a single trial.* For example, let us say, in our illustrative population of students, that the proportion from out-of-state (category 1) is .40. Consequently, if we select a student at random from this population, the probability of a success (selecting an out-of-state student) is .40. In the same way, we may interpret $1 - p$ as the proportion of failures in the *population* or, alternatively, as *the probability of a failure in a single trial.*

In this section, two sampling distributions related to sampling from a binomial population will be presented. These are the *sampling distribution of a frequency*, where the variable is the statistic X, and the *sampling distribution of a proportion*, where the variable is the statistic X/n. Clearly, these are related sampling distributions. Not only are these distributions related, they are actually *identical*, except for the fact that they have different (but equivalent) variables. These sampling distributions are called *binomial probability distributions*. The statistical theory relating to the binomial probability distributions, which is treated in this section, involves sampling from an *infinite* binomial population.

Consider the population of outcomes from an infinite number of tosses of a fair die (a theoretical population). Suppose we are interested in the outcomes which are equal to 6, so that we are concerned with the infinite binomial population where the code 1 denotes the outcome 6 and the code 0 denotes any other outcome. The probability that a single trial (toss of the die) will result in a 6 (a success) is $\frac{1}{6}$. Also, p, the proportion of 1's in our binomial population, is $\frac{1}{6}$. Consider a sample of, say, 4 tosses of the die (4 trials). Let us discuss the sampling distribution of a frequency. Such a distribution shows the probability of obtaining each possible value of the statistic X, when taking into consideration all possible samples of a specified size.

Referring to our sample ($n = 4$) from the infinite binomial population, what are the possible values of the statistic X (the number of successes)? Clearly, X may have the values 0, 1, 2, 3, or 4. (That is, in 4 tosses of a die, we could obtain 0, 1, 2, 3, or 4 6's.) Then, the sampling distribution of a frequency in this instance will show the probability of obtaining $X = 0$, $X = 1, \ldots, X = 4$ in 4 trials. We will denote these probabilities as $P(X = 0)$, $P(X = 1)$, etc. Let us begin by considering the computation of $P(X = 2)$. In other words, what is the probability that 2 6's are obtained in 4 tosses of a die? Of course, we could obtain such a result in more than one way. For example, the first two tosses could result in a 6 (code 1) and the second two tosses in some other outcome (code 0). The probability of obtaining such a compound event may be computed according to probability *Rule E extended* for independent events, as follows (clearly, the trials are independent, since the outcome of one trial has no effect whatsoever upon the outcome of any other trial):

$$P(1, 1, 0, \text{ and } 0) = P(1) \cdot P(1) \cdot P(0) \cdot P(0)$$

Then, since the probability of a success, $P(1)$, is p and the probability of a failure, $P(0)$, is $1 - p$, we may write

$$\begin{aligned} P(1, 1, 0, \text{ and } 0) &= p \cdot p \cdot (1 - p) \cdot (1 - p) \\ &= p^2(1 - p)^2 \end{aligned}$$

Substituting $p = \frac{1}{6}$ and $(1 - p) = \frac{5}{6}$, we obtain

$$P(1, 1, 0, \text{ and } 0) = (\tfrac{1}{6})^2(\tfrac{5}{6})^2 = 25/1296$$

Another way of obtaining 2 6's in 4 trials is to obtain first a 6, then some other outcome, then a second 6, and then again some other outcome. The probability of this occurring is the same as just computed. *In general, the number of ways of obtaining* 2 6*'s in* 4 *tosses of a die may be looked upon as the number of combinations possible of* 4 *objects taken* 2 *at a time or* $\binom{4}{2}$. That is, each possible combination of 2 tosses out of the 4 represents a possible pair of 6's. Then, according to Equation 6.3.6 (Chapter 6, Section 6.3), we determine the number of possible combinations as

$$\binom{4}{2} = \frac{4!}{2!\,2!} = 6$$

We may list these 6 possible combinations of 2 successes (1's) and 4 failures (0's) as follows:

Combination	First Toss	Second Toss	Third Toss	Fourth Toss
1	1	1	0	0
2	1	0	1	0
3	1	0	0	1
4	0	1	1	0
5	0	1	0	1
6	0	0	1	1

These combinations represent 6 mutually exclusive events and the probability that each of these events will occur is the same. Therefore, according to probability *Rule B extended*, the probability of obtaining 2 successes (6's) in 4 trials may be computed as $\binom{4}{2} = 6$ times the probability of obtaining any one of these combinations. That is, we may write

$$P(X = 2) = \binom{4}{2} P(1, 1, 0, \text{ and } 0)$$

$$= \binom{4}{2} p^2(1 - p)^2$$

In general, then, *the probability that X will equal one of its possible values is determined by multiplying the number of possible combinations by the probability of obtaining one of these possible combinations.* Applying this procedure to determine the probability of obtaining each possible value of X, we obtain

$$P(X=0) = \binom{4}{0} P(0, 0, 0, \text{ and } 0)$$

$$= \binom{4}{0} P(0) \cdot P(0) \cdot P(0) \cdot P(0)$$

$$= \binom{4}{0} (1-p)^4 \tag{8.6.1}$$

$$P(X=1) = \binom{4}{1} P(1, 0, 0, \text{ and } 0)$$

$$= \binom{4}{1} P(1) \cdot P(0) \cdot P(0) \cdot P(0)$$

$$= \binom{4}{1} p(1-p)^3 \tag{8.6.2}$$

$$P(X=2) = \binom{4}{2} P(1, 1, 0, \text{ and } 0)$$

$$= \binom{4}{2} P(1) \cdot P(1) \cdot P(0) \cdot P(0)$$

$$= \binom{4}{2} p^2(1-p)^2 \tag{8.6.3}$$

$$P(X=3) = \binom{4}{3} P(1, 1, 1, \text{ and } 0)$$

$$= \binom{4}{3} P(1) \cdot P(1) \cdot P(1) \cdot P(0)$$

$$= \binom{4}{3} p^3(1-p) \tag{8·6.4}$$

$$P(X=4) = \binom{4}{4} P(1, 1, 1, \text{ and } 1)$$

$$= \binom{4}{4} P(1) \cdot P(1) \cdot P(1) \cdot P(1)$$

$$= \binom{4}{4} p^4 \tag{8.6.5}$$

Equations 8.6.1 through 8.6.5 were obtained by substituting p for $P(1)$ and $1 - p$ for $P(0)$. Now, substituting $p = \frac{1}{6}$ and $1 - p = \frac{5}{6}$, we obtain

$$P(X = 0) = \binom{4}{0}\left(\frac{5}{6}\right)^4 = .482$$

$$P(X = 1) = \binom{4}{1}\left(\frac{1}{6}\right)\left(\frac{5}{6}\right)^3 = .386$$

$$P(X = 2) = \binom{4}{2}\left(\frac{1}{6}\right)^2\left(\frac{5}{6}\right)^2 = .116$$

$$P(X = 3) = \binom{4}{3}\left(\frac{1}{6}\right)^3\left(\frac{5}{6}\right) = .015$$

$$P(X = 4) = \binom{4}{4}\left(\frac{1}{6}\right)^4 = .001$$

These results are summarized in Table 8.6.1, where *both* binomial probability distributions are presented. The first column, which presents X (the possible numbers of successes), and the last column, which presents $P(X)$ or the probability of obtaining each of the specified values of X, *make up the sampling distribution of a frequency*. The middle column presents the sample proportion of successes, X/n. These proportions are

Table 8.6.1 BINOMIAL PROBABILITY DISTRIBUTIONS: SUCCESSES IN A SAMPLE OF FOUR SELECTED FROM AN INFINITE BINOMIAL POPULATION WITH p = $\frac{1}{6}$

Number of Successes (6's) in a Sample of 4, X	Proportion of Successes (6's) in a Sample of 4, $\frac{X}{n}$	$P(X)$ or $P\left(\frac{X}{n}\right)$
0	0	.482
1	.25	.386
2	.50	.116
3	.75	.015
4	1.00	.001
	Total	1.000

obtained by dividing each of the possible values of X by the sample size $n = 4$. Therefore, the middle column presents all possible values of the sample proportion X/n. Clearly, the probabilities presented in the last column of the table are associated with the sample proportions (X/n), just as they are associated with the sample numbers of successes (X). For example, the probability that a sample of 4 will contain 3 successes, $P(X = 3)$, is .015. The probability that $\frac{3}{4}$ or .75 of the sample of 4 will represent successes, $P(X/n = .75)$, is also .015. Consequently, the middle

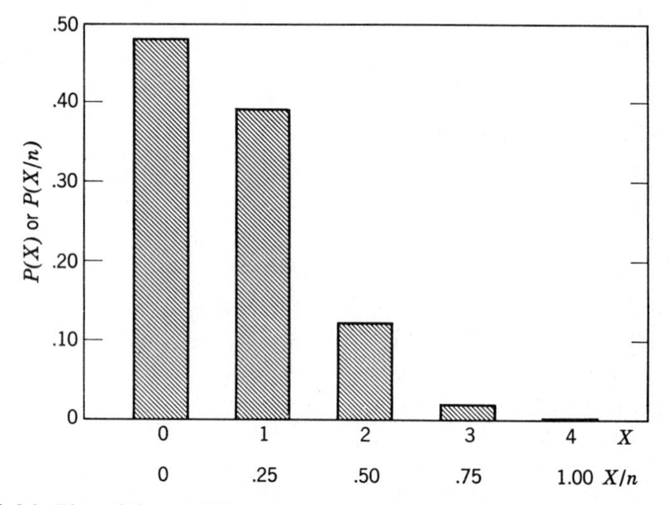

Fig. 8.6.1. Binomial probability distribution: Sampling distribution of a frequency (X) and sampling distribution of a proportion (X/n) for samples of $n = 4$ selected from an infinite binomial population with $p = \frac{1}{6}$ or .167.

column and the last column *make up the sampling distribution of a proportion.* Clearly, the two sampling distributions are identical. Figure 8.6.1 presents this common distribution. It will be observed that two horizontal scales are presented, an X scale and an X/n scale. Since these are both discrete variables, the appropriate graphic presentation is a bar chart.

The reader may have realized, as we developed the sampling distribution of a frequency, that we have gone through a similar development earlier. Much of what was just discussed repeats the presentation in Chapter 6, Section 6.5, where *probability distributions* were discussed. Actually, it was noted in that section that the *probability distribution* presented in Table 6.5.2 is a *binomial probability distribution.* We know now that it represents the *sampling distribution of a frequency*. In Table 6.5.2 we were dealing with samples of size 3 from a population of reading-readiness scores. It was carefully specified that we were dealing with *independent events.* We were interested in the number of passing scores, so that a passing score would be considered a success (coded 1). The possible values of X in that illustration were 0, 1, 2, or 3, which represented the possible number of successes (passing scores) in a sample of 3.

On the other hand, the first illustration in Section 6.5, resulting in the probability distribution presented in Table 6.5.1, is *not* a binomial probability distribution, *even though it involves sampling from a binomial population.* In that illustration we were concerned with samples of size 4 selected from a deck of 52 playing cards. Our interest then was in the number of kings included in a sample of 4 cards, so that the dichotomous population was made up of the two categories, kings and other cards (not kings). However, in this case, we were sampling *without replacement,* so that the probability of selecting a king in each of the 4 trials was not constant from trial to trial. That is, the probabilities for obtaining a king represented *conditional probabilities* and not probabilities of *independent events.* If we had sampled *with replacement,* the probability of obtaining a king would have been *constant* from trial to trial and *the trials would have been independent.* Then, the resulting probability distribution would have been a binomial probability distribution. In summary, *a binomial probability distribution results when samples are selected from a binomial population, the trials are independent, and the probability of success in a trial, p, is constant from trial to trial. The binomial population should be infinite; however, if finite, sampling should be with replacement.*

Let us again refer to Equations 8.6.1 through 8.6.5 and rewrite these equations as follows:

$$P(X = 0) = \binom{4}{0} p^0(1 - p)^4 \tag{8.6.1a}$$

$$P(X = 1) = \binom{4}{1} p^1(1 - p)^3 \tag{8.6.2a}$$

$$P(X = 2) = \binom{4}{2} p^2(1 - p)^2 \tag{8.6.3a}$$

$$P(X = 3) = \binom{4}{3} p^3(1 - p)^1 \tag{8.6.4a}$$

$$P(X = 4) = \binom{4}{4} p^4(1 - p)^0 \tag{8.6.5a}$$

Equation 8.6.1a is identical with Equation 8.6.1, except that it includes the factor p^0. However, $p^0 = 1$, since any term raised to the 0 power is equal to 1. Therefore, $P(X = 0)$ is the same whether expressed by one or the other of these equations. Equation 8.6.2a is identical with Equation 8.6.2. In Equation 8.6.2, the exponent to p is 1, just as in Equation 8.6.2a, even though it is not explicitly shown. For the same reason, Equations 8.6.4a and 8.6.4 are identical. Finally, since $(1 - p)^0 = 1$, $P(X = 4)$ is the same whether computed according to Equation 8.6.5a or Equation 8.6.5. In the rewritten equations, we can clearly observe that each equation is made up of *three* parts: a combinatorial term, a p term, and a $(1 - p)$ term. Certain additional features of these equations should also be noted. Observe that the combinatorial term bears a *definite* relationship to the corresponding X value. For example, for $P(X = 0)$, $\binom{4}{0}$ indicates the number of possible combinations of 4 objects (sample size) taken 0 at a time. For $P(X = 1)$, $\binom{4}{1}$ indicates the number of possible combinations of 4 objects (sample size) taken 1 at a time, etc. The exponent to p is *always* the value of X. For example, for $P(X = 3)$, we have p^3. The exponent to $(1 - p)$ is *always* $n - X$. For example, for $P(X = 3)$, the exponent to $(1 - p)$ is $4 - 3$, or 1. Based upon these relationships, we may write the *general term* for these equations as

$$P(X) = \binom{n}{X} p^X (1 - p)^{n-X} \tag{8.6.6}$$

Equation 8.6.6 *expresses the general term of the binomial probability distribution.* An explanation of each part of this expression follows:

X = A specified number of successes (items coded 1) which could be obtained in n trials (sample size).

$P(X)$ = The probability of obtaining X successes in n trials.

$\binom{n}{X}$ = The number of combinations of n trials with X successes, computed according to Equation 6.3.6. This is equal to *the number of ways in which X successes can occur in n trials.*

p = The probability of obtaining a success in a single trial.

p^X = The probability of obtaining X successes in one of the possible ways. Since we are dealing with *independent trials and constant probabilities from trial to trial*, we may obtain the probability of X successes, p^X, by application of probability *Rule E* or *Rule E extended*, as appropriate.

$(1 - p)$ = The probability of obtaining a failure in a single trial.

$n - X$ = The number of failures (items coded 0) which could be obtained in n trials.

$(1 - p)^{n-X}$ = The probability of obtaining $n - X$ failures. This is based upon probability *Rule E* or *Rule E extended*, as noted for p^X previously explained.

The general term of the binomial probability distribution, as expressed in Equation 8.6.6, *provides the basis for computing the probability that a random sample of size n, selected with constant probabilities from a binomial population, will contain X successes and n − X failures.* We are now ready to present a sampling model based on sampling from a binomial population.

Model D: If samples of size n (n trials) are selected from an infinite binomial population, where p (the probability of success in a given trial) is constant from trial to trial and the trials are independent:

1. *The sampling distribution of a frequency* (X, the number of successes in a sample) has

$$\textit{mean} \qquad \mu_X = np \tag{8.6.7}$$

$$\textit{standard error of a frequency} \qquad \sigma_X = \sqrt{np(1 - p)} \tag{8.6.8}$$

2. *The sampling distribution of a proportion* (X/n, the proportion of successes in a sample) has

$$\textit{mean} \qquad \mu_{X/n} = p \tag{8.6.9}$$

$$\textit{standard error of a proportion} \qquad \sigma_{X/n} = \sqrt{\frac{p(1 - p)}{n}} \tag{8.6.10}$$

Suppose we have a well-balanced roulette wheel containing the sequence of numbers from 1 through 50, so that, on the spin of the wheel, these numbers represent 50 equi-probable outcomes. Say we are interested in how many out of 5 spins of the wheel will result in a number higher than 30. Therefore, for this problem, we look upon the outcomes of spins of the wheel as forming a dichotomy. That is, we look upon the outcome of each spin as falling into the category "higher than 30," which we call "success" and to which we assign the code 1, or the category "30 or less," which we call "failure" and to which we assign the code 0. We consider a set of 5 spins of the wheel as a *sample* of all the spins possible for the life of the roulette wheel, an infinite number. The probability of success in a given trial, p, is computed as the number of possible outcomes in the "success" category (the 20 numbers which are over 30) divided by the total number of possible outcomes (50) of a spin. Therefore, $p = \frac{20}{50} = .4$. Using the general term of the binomial probability distribution (Equation 8.6.6), we can determine the probability of obtaining any possible number of successes. Substituting $n = 5$ (sample size), $p = .4$, and $1 - p = .6$ into

Equation 8.6.6, we obtain

$$P(X) = \binom{5}{X}(.4)^X(.6)^{5-X}$$

This represents the general term of the binomial probability distribution as it relates to the illustrative sampling problem. Using this general term, we can compute the probability of obtaining any specified value of X (number of successes). For example, let us compute the probability that a sample of 5 spins of the wheel will result in 3 successes (3 outcomes higher than 30). Substituting $X = 3$ into the foregoing general expression, we obtain

$$P(X = 3) = \binom{5}{3}(.4)^3(.6)^2$$

$$= (10)(.064)(.36) = .23$$

Therefore, the probability is .23 or 23 chances in 100 that 3 spins out of 5 will result in a number higher than 30. We may, similarly, determine the probability of obtaining any of the other possible values of X in 5 spins of the wheel. Clearly, application of Equation 8.6.6 to compute the probability for all possible values of X results in the *sampling distribution of a frequency*. According to *Model D*, we may compute the *mean* of this sampling distribution, using Equation 8.6.7. Substituting the appropriate values, we obtain

$$\mu_X = (5)(.4) = 2$$

Then, using Equation 8.6.8 and substituting the appropriate values, we obtain the *standard error of a frequency* as

$$\sigma_X = \sqrt{(5)(.4)(.6)} = \sqrt{1.20} = 1.1$$

What do these measures mean? Consider a very large (infinite) number of samples, where each sample is made up of 5 spins of the roulette wheel. The value of X (the number of successes obtained in a sample of 5 spins) may be expected to vary from sample to sample. In some samples, X will equal 0; in some samples, X will equal 1; etc. However, *on the average*, we may expect that X will equal 2. In other words, the mean of all the X values obtained is $\mu_X = 2$. Furthermore, the standard deviation of all the X values obtained in the infinite number of samples of 5 spins each is equal to $\sigma_X = 1.1$.

The different possible values of the *proportion* of successes in a sample of 5 spins (X/n) may be determined by dividing each possible value of X by $n = 5$. That is, the possible values of X/n are $\frac{0}{5} = 0$, $\frac{1}{5} = .2$, $\frac{2}{5} = .4$, etc. According to *Model D*, Equation 8.6.9, the *mean* of the *sampling distribution of a proportion*, $\mu_{X/n}$, is equal to the proportion of successes in the population (or the probability of success in a given trial), which in the illustration is $p = .4$. In other words, it may be expected that the mean of the X/n values obtained in a very large number of samples of 5 spins each will equal .4. The *standard error* of this sampling distribution may be determined by substituting appropriate values into Equation 8.6.10 to obtain

$$\sigma_{X/n} = \sqrt{\frac{(.4)(.6)}{5}} = \sqrt{.048} = .22$$

8.7 NORMAL APPROXIMATION TO THE BINOMIAL

Computation of the *exact* binomial probabilities, using Equation 8.6.6, becomes cumbersome and tedious as the sample size n becomes larger. For example, when sampling from a binomial population where the proportion of successes is .5, what is the probability that a sample of 100 will include .7 (or 70%) successes? The same problem could be stated in terms of obtaining 70 successes in a sample of 100. Following Equation 8.6.6, with $n = 100$, $X = 70$, and $p = .5$, this probability may be computed in the following way:

$$P(X = 70) = \binom{100}{70}(.5)^{70}(.5)^{30}$$

This is also the probability $P(X/n = .7)$. Clearly, this involves a considerable amount of computation. Usually, moreover, interest is not in the probability of obtaining a specified value of X, but in the probability that X will lie in some interval. For example, what is the probability that the sample of 100 in the foregoing illustration will include *at least* 70 successes (70 or more)? That is, determine $P(X \geq 70)$. This requires computing $P(X = 70), P(X = 71), P(X = 72), \ldots, P(X = 100)$ and then adding these probabilities (mutually exclusive events, probability *Rule B extended*), as follows:

$$\left.\begin{aligned} P(X = 70) &= \binom{100}{70}(.5)^{70}(.5)^{30} \\ P(X = 71) &= \binom{100}{71}(.5)^{71}(.5)^{29} \\ P(X = 72) &= \binom{100}{72}(.5)^{72}(.5)^{28} \\ &\cdots\cdots\cdots\cdots\cdots \\ &\cdots\cdots\cdots\cdots\cdots \\ &\cdots\cdots\cdots\cdots\cdots \\ P(X = 100) &= \binom{100}{100}(.5)^{100} \end{aligned}\right\} \quad \text{Sum} = P(X \geq 70)$$

Certainly, considerable effort is involved in carrying out the foregoing computations.

One alternative to performing such computations is to refer to the *Tables of the Binomial Probability Distribution* (Applied Mathematics Series 6) published by the U.S. National Bureau of Standards (1952). These tables present the *exact* binomial probabilities for values of n up to 49. Of greater interest to us is the fact that the *binomial probability distribution is closely approximated by the normal distribution when n is large.*

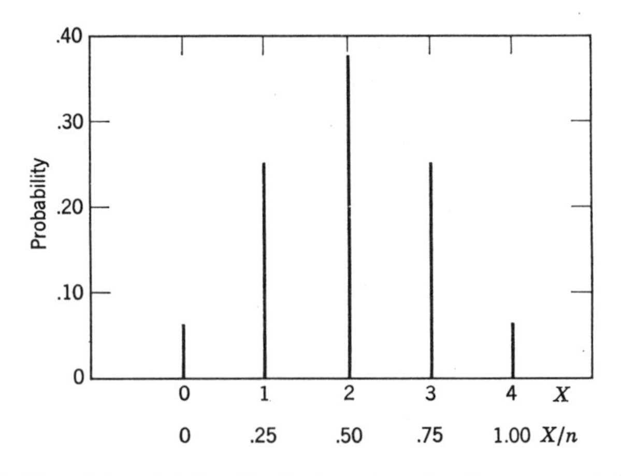

Fig. 8.7.1. Binomial probability distribution: Sampling from a population with $p = .5$ and $n = 4$.

This provides a very convenient basis for computing binomial probabilities. Reference to the general term of the binomial probability distribution (Equation 8.6.6) will indicate that this is a two-parameter distribution, the two parameters being n and p. In other words, a specific binomial probability distribution is identified when the sample size (n) and the proportion of successes in the population (p) are specified.

How well a binomial probability distribution is approximated by the normal curve depends on the particular values assigned to these parameters. For example, examine Figures 8.7.1 through 8.7.3. In these three figures, $p = .5$, whereas $n = 4$ in Figure 8.7.1, $n = 10$ in Figure 8.7.2, and $n = 20$ in Figure 8.7.3. In each case, it will be observed, the distribution is symmetrical around a central peak. This is always true for binomial probability distributions with $p = .5$. Furthermore, the distribution resembles the normal curve more closely as n increases. For small values of p, the distribution is markedly skewed. For example, examine Figures 8.7.4 through 8.7.7. In each case, $n = 20$. However, p varies from figure to figure. In

Figure 8.7.4, where $p = .04$, the distribution is a mirror image of the J-distribution, stretching out into a long thin tail to the right. The probabilities that $X = 5$ through $X = 20$ are so small that they do not show up in the figure. As p increases and approaches .5, the distribution approaches the symmetry observed in Figure 8.7.3, where $n = 20$ and $p = .5$.

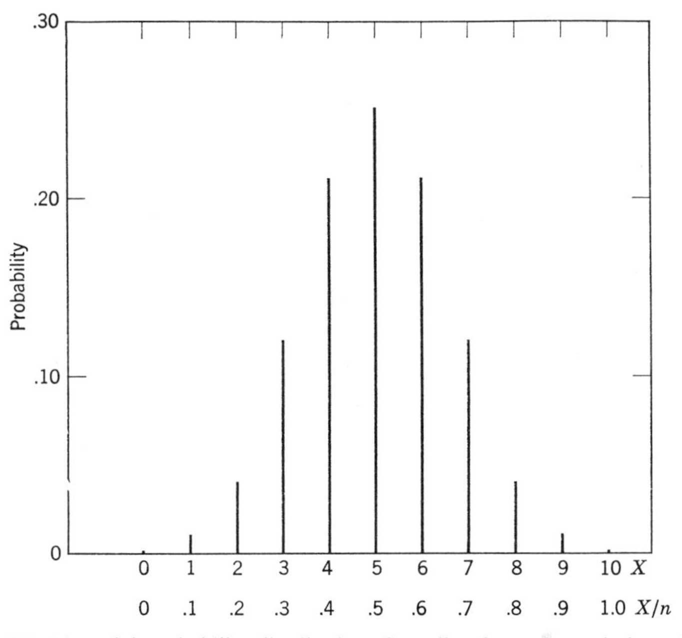

Fig. 8.7.2. Binomial probability distribution: Sampling from a population with $p = .5$ and $n = 10$.

In Figure 8.7.5 ($p = .05$) and in Figure 8.7.6 ($p = .1$), it can be observed that the distribution is approaching symmetry. Notice that there is still the long thin tail to the right (the probabilities for the higher values of X are too small to show up). The distribution in Figure 8.7.7, where $p = .2$, is very nearly symmetrical, except for the tail extending toward the right.

Clearly, when p or $1 - p$ is above .5, the other is below .5. Only when $p = .5$ are p and $1 - p$ equal, resulting in a symmetrical distribution. When $p = .5$ and n is large, the normal distribution very closely approximates the binomial probability distribution. As p moves away from .5 (above or below), the binomial probability distribution becomes skewed and the approximation becomes poorer, unless n is increased. This is shown in Figures 8.7.4 through 8.7.7 where p is below .5. It is equally true when p is above .5. Generally, then, n must be sufficiently large for the normal distribution to provide useful approximations to binomial probabilities. It is difficult to specify just how large a sample is required for this purpose because it depends on the value of p and on the degree of approximation required in a particular situation. As a rule of thumb, n should be 100 or more. However, if the population proportion p is far

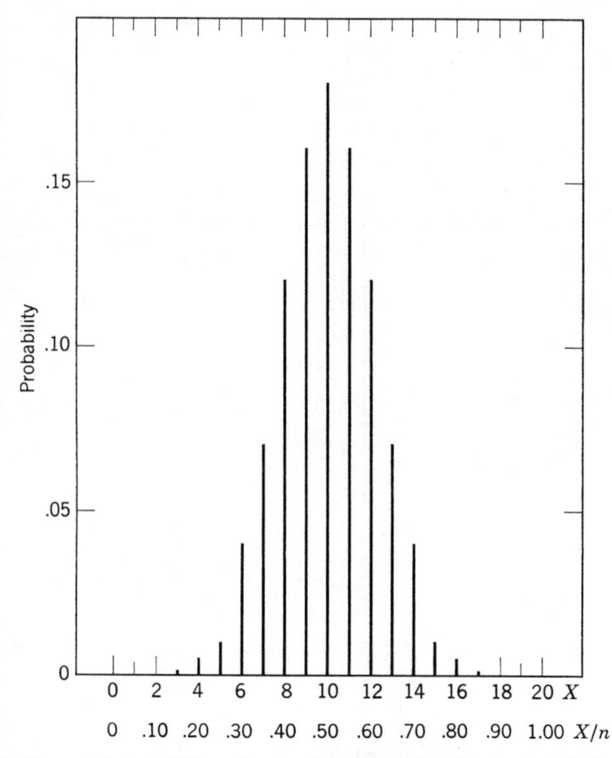

Fig. 8.7.3. Binomial probability distribution: Sampling from a population with $p = .5$ and $n = 20$.

from .5, say, if it is less than .3 or greater than .7, then, an n of 500 or more is preferable. In certain situations, the approximation may be considered to be satisfactory when p is not too close to 0 or 1 and when the following inequalities *both* hold:

$$np \geq 5 \tag{8.7.1}$$

and

$$n(1 - p) \geq 5 \tag{8.7.2}$$

These inequalities are presented only to provide a guide as to the minimum size sample to use for a specified value of p. However, it is recommended that considerably larger samples are to be preferred. In order to determine whether the normal approximation should be used at all, it is sufficient to make only one of the two comparisons shown in Equations 8.7.1 and 8.7.2. If p is less than $1 - p$, then make the comparison shown in Equation 8.7.1. On the other hand, if $1 - p$ is less than p, then make the comparison shown in Equation 8.7.2. For example, when sampling from

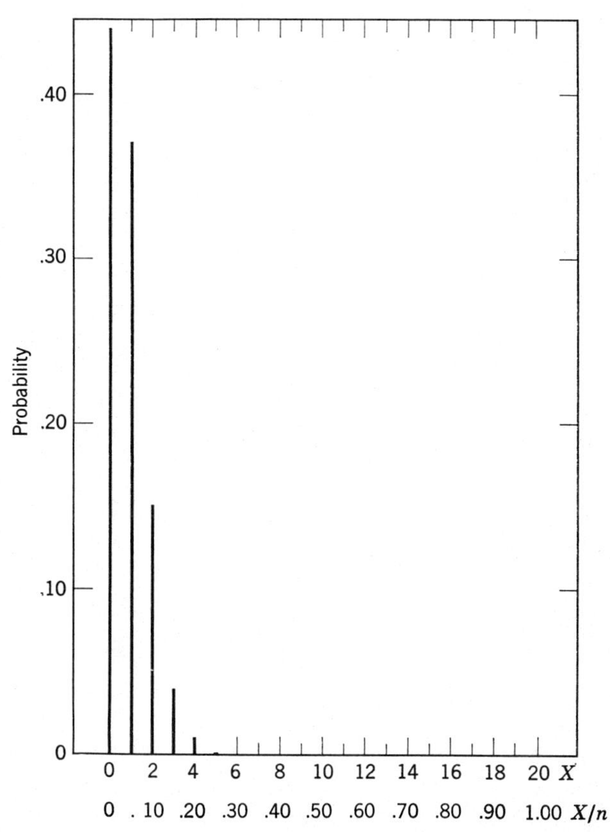

Fig. 8.7.4. Binomial probability distribution: Sampling from a population with $p = .04$ and $n = 20$.

a binomial population with $n = 60$ and $p = .1$, is it appropriate to use the normal approximation to the binomial probability distribution? Since $p = .1$ is less than $1 - p = .9$, compute (60)(.1), according to Equation 8.7.1, to obtain 6. Then, since this result is greater than 5, we conclude that the normal approximation is useful in this instance, in the minimum sense just explained. Clearly, there is no need to make the comparison shown in Equation 8.7.2, since we know that the product $(60)(.9) = 54$ must be larger than 6.

Table 8.7.1 presents the minimum size sample required for specified values of p (or $1 - p$, if this is smaller) so that the normal curve may be expected to approximate the binomial probability distribution reasonably well. This table was developed on the basis of the inequalities expressed in Equations 8.7.1 and 8.7.2. As indicated in the table, if $p = .5$, a sample as

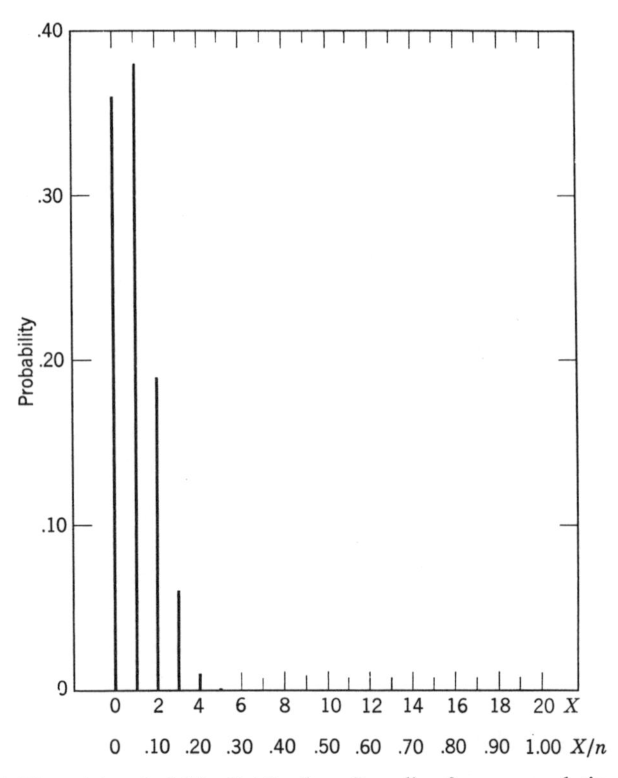

Fig. 8.7.5. Binomial probability distribution: Sampling from a population with $p = .05$ and $n = 20$.

small as 10 provides a reasonable estimate of binomial probabilities by the use of the normal approximation. However, as p (or $1 - p$) departs from .5, the minimum sample size required increases. For example, when $p = .25$, the minimum value of n is 20, whereas when $p = .05$, the minimum rises to 100. As p (or $1 - p$) approaches 0 (or 1.00), the minimum size sample required rises considerably. For example, when $p = .01$, n must be at least 500.

Let us make some comparisons of the (*exact*) binomial probabilities computed according to Equation 8.6.6, also using the normal curve

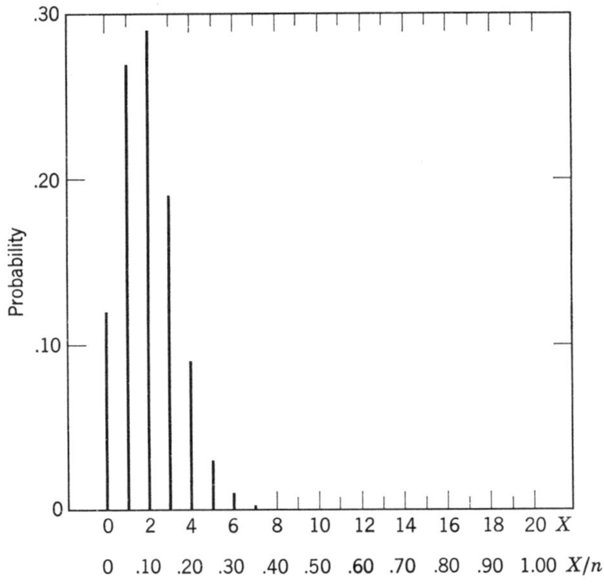

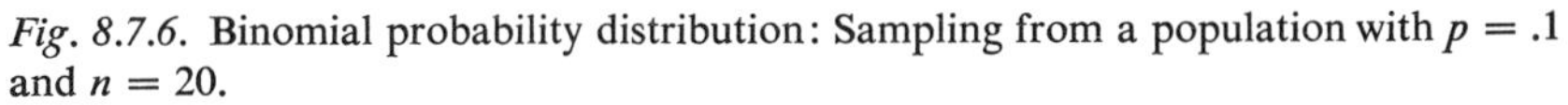

Fig. 8.7.6. Binomial probability distribution: Sampling from a population with $p = .1$ and $n = 20$.

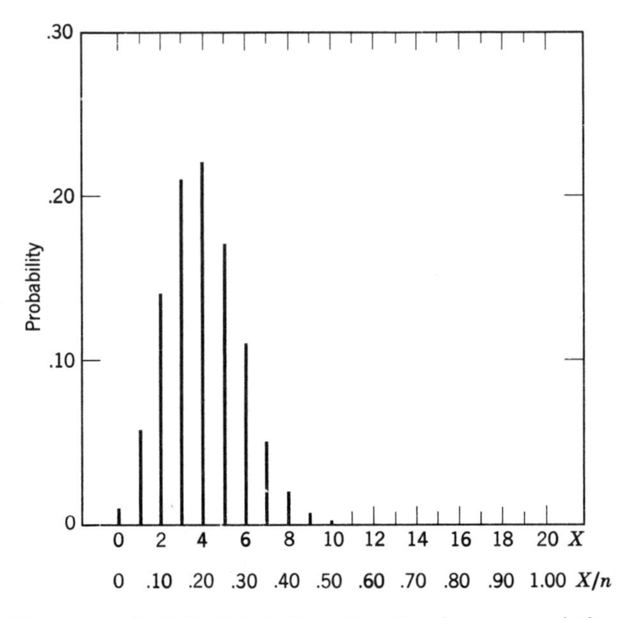

Fig. 8.7.7. Binomial probability distribution: Sampling from a population with $p = .2$ and $n = 20$.

Table 8.7.1 MINIMUM SAMPLE SIZE REQUIRED FOR THE NORMAL DISTRIBUTION TO PROVIDE A REASONABLE APPROXIMATION OF BINOMIAL PROBABILITIES

Smaller of p or $1 - p$	Minimum Sample Size, n
.50	10
.45	12
.40	13
.35	15
.30	17
.25	20
.20	25
.15	34
.10	50
.05	100
.04	125
.03	167
.02	250
.01	500

approximation. When sampling from a binomial population with $p = .5$, what is the probability that a sample of size 10 will contain 7 successes? Use of the normal approximation means to base the probability on the normal curve which has the same mean and standard deviation (standard error) as the binomial probability distribution which is being approximated. The mean and standard error of the sampling distribution of a frequency for samples selected from a binomial population with $p = .5$ and $n = 10$ (according to Equations 8.6.7 and 8.6.8) are

$$\mu_X = (10)(.5) = 5$$

$$\sigma_X = \sqrt{(10)(.5)(.5)} = 1.58$$

Then, the probability of 7 successes, $P(X = 7)$, may be estimated on the basis of the area under a normal curve with a mean of 5 and a standard deviation of 1.58. Since the variable X is discrete, to determine the probability that $X = 7$, we must find the area under the normal curve between $X = 6.5$ and $X = 7.5$, as shown in Figure 8.7.8. (The use of the normal curve to determine probabilities for discrete variables has been discussed in Section 8.2; see Figures 8.2.7 and 8.2.8.) Transformation of $X = 6.5$

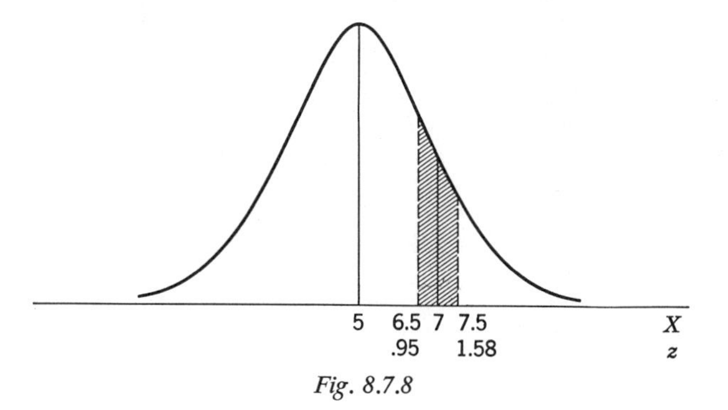

Fig. 8.7.8

and $X = 7.5$ to standard units is accomplished by expressing Equation 8.4.3 (Section 8.4) as follows:

$$z = \frac{X - \mu_X}{\sigma_X} = \frac{X - np}{\sqrt{np(1 - p)}} \tag{8.7.3}$$

(The second form of Equation 8.7.3 is obtained by substituting into the first form, according to Equations 8.6.7 and 8.6.8.) Then, we transform $X = 6.5$ and $X = 7.5$ to standard units as follows:

$$z_1 = \frac{6.5 - 5}{1.58} = .95$$

$$z_2 = \frac{7.5 - 5}{1.58} = 1.58$$

Referring to Table B.2, we determine the areas .3289 (corresponding to z_1) and .4429 (corresponding to z_2). Subtracting the smaller area from the larger, we obtain .1140 as the estimate of $P(X = 7)$. How does this compare with the exact probability determined according to Equation 8.6.6? Substituting $n = 10$, $p = .5$, and $X = 7$, we obtain

$$P(X = 7) = \binom{10}{7}(.5)^7(.5)^3 = .1172$$

Consequently, the estimated probability (.1140) is .0032 less than the exact probability. In some applications this may be considered to be an acceptable degree of approximation.

Suppose it is desired to compute the probability that the sample of 10 in the foregoing illustration will contain *at least* 7 successes, $P(X \geq 7)$? We may estimate this probability by determining the area in the upper tail of the normal curve, the area to the right of $X = 6.5$ or, in standard units (as determined previously), to the right of $z_1 = .95$. This is the shaded area in Figure 8.7.9. Subtracting the area from Table B.2 corresponding to this z value (.3289) from .5000, we obtain .1711 as the area in the upper tail. This represents the estimate of $P(X \geq 7)$. We may compute the exact probability that, in a sample of size 10, X is equal to 7 or more by computing the sum of the four probabilities $P(X = 7)$, $P(X = 8)$, $P(X = 9)$, and $P(X = 10)$. Each probability is computed according to

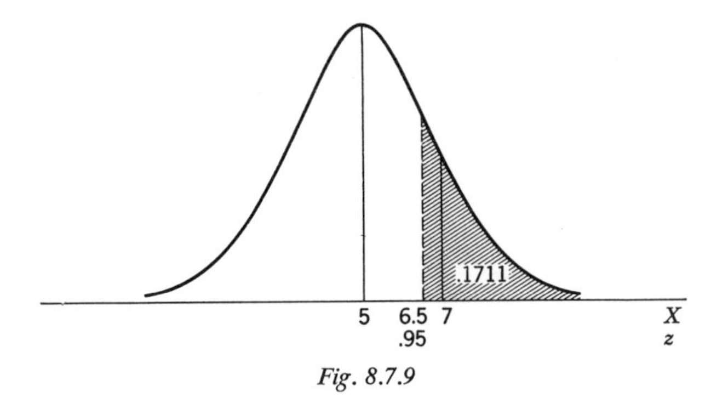

Fig. 8.7.9

Equation 8.6.6. Substituting into this equation $n = 10$, $p = .5$, and appropriate values for X, we obtain

$$\left.\begin{aligned} P(X = 7) &= \binom{10}{7}(.5)^7(.5)^3 \\ P(X = 8) &= \binom{10}{8}(.5)^8(.5)^2 \\ P(X = 9) &= \binom{10}{9}(.5)^9(.5) \\ P(X = 10) &= \binom{10}{10}(.5)^{10} \end{aligned}\right\} \begin{aligned} \text{Sum} &= P(X \geq 7) \\ &= .1719 \end{aligned}$$

Therefore, the estimated probability (.1711) is .0008 less than the exact probability (.1719).

Consider another illustration. When sampling from a binomial population with $p = .25$ and $n = 20$, what is the probability of obtaining a sample with *at least* 50% successes ($X/n \geq .50$)? First, we must identify the normal curve which will approximate the sampling distribution of a proportion for this illustration. That is, we must determine the mean and standard error of the sampling distribution by substituting $p = .25$ and $n = 20$ into Equations 8.6.9 and 8.6.10 to obtain

$$\mu_{X/n} = .25$$

$$\sigma_{X/n} = \sqrt{\frac{(.25)(.75)}{20}} = .097$$

Then, the probability of obtaining 50% successes or more in a sample of 20, $P(X/n \geq .50)$, may be estimated on the basis of the area under a normal curve with a mean of .25 and a standard deviation of .097. Of course, X/n is a discrete variable, just as X is a discrete variable, since the possible values of X/n are obtained by dividing the possible values of X by the constant n. Consequently, to use the normal curve approximation to compute the probability for a given value of X/n, say .50, we must determine the area under the normal curve in a continuous interval around .50, as we did in computing the probability for a given value of X. For example, for a sample of size 20, when $X/n = .50$ (or, more specifically, when $X/20 = .50$), $X = 10$. As we have seen, to determine $P(X = 10)$, we must find the area under the normal curve contained within the continuous interval $X = 9.5$ and $X = 10.5$. Let us write these limits, which define the continuous interval, as

$$X = 10 - .5 = 9.5$$

and

$$X = 10 + .5 = 10.5$$

Then, divide each of these X values by the sample size $n = 20$ to obtain

$$\frac{X}{n} = \frac{10}{20} - \frac{.5}{20} = \frac{9.5}{20} = .475$$

and

$$\frac{X}{n} = \frac{10}{20} + \frac{.5}{20} = \frac{10.5}{20} = .525$$

Therefore, to determine $P(X/n = .50)$, we must find the area under the appropriate normal curve between $X/n = .475$ and $X/n = .525$. In general, then, *to determine the probability that the sample proportion* (X/n) *takes on a specified value when a sample of size n is selected from a binomial population, we must find the area under the appropriate normal curve between*

$$\frac{X}{n} = \begin{pmatrix}\text{specified}\\ \text{sample}\\ \text{proportion}\end{pmatrix} - \frac{.5}{n} \tag{8.7.4}$$

and

$$\frac{X}{n} = \begin{pmatrix}\text{specified}\\ \text{sample}\\ \text{proportion}\end{pmatrix} + \frac{.5}{n} \tag{8.7.5}$$

Using Equations 8.7.4 and 8.7.5 we find that, to compute the probability that the sample proportion X/n equals .50 in a sample of size $n = 20$, we must determine the area under the normal curve between

$$\frac{X}{n} = .50 - \frac{.5}{20} = .475$$

and

$$\frac{X}{n} = .50 + \frac{.5}{20} = .525$$

These, of course, are the same values of X/n computed previously.

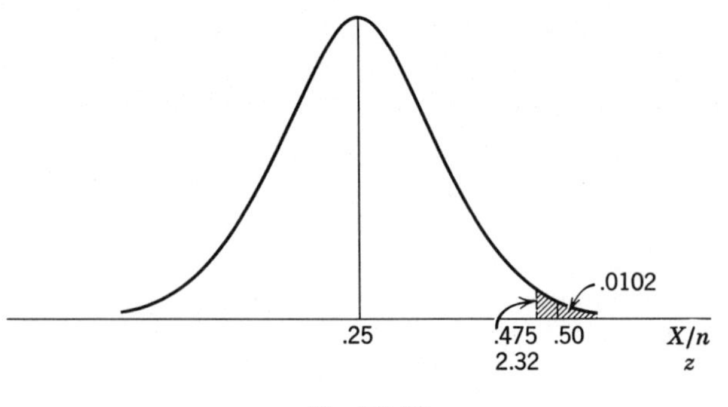

Fig. 8.7.10

Returning to the illustrative problem, we wish to determine $P(X/n \geq .50)$ when sampling from a binomial population with $p = .25$ and $n = 20$. This probability is represented by the area under the normal curve to the right of $X/n = .475$, as shown in Figure 8.7.10. Transformation of $X/n = .475$ to standard units is accomplished by expressing Equation 8.4.3 (Section 8.4) as follows:

$$z = \frac{\frac{X}{n} - \mu_{X/n}}{\sigma_{X/n}} = \frac{\frac{X}{n} - p}{\sqrt{\frac{p(1-p)}{n}}} \tag{8.7.6}$$

(The second form of Equation 8.7.6 is obtained by substituting into the first form, according to Equations 8.6.9 and 8.6.10.) Then, we transform $X/n = .475$ to standard units as follows:

$$z = \frac{.475 - .25}{.097} = 2.32$$

Referring to Table B.2, we determine the corresponding area as .4898. Subtracting this from .5000, we obtain .0102 as the estimated probability that the proportion of successes (X/n) in a sample of $n = 20$ selected from a binomial population with $p = .25$ will be at least .50.

The exact probability that the sample proportion will be equal to .50 or more may be computed by the use of Equation 8.6.6. However, the procedure required by this equation can only be applied to compute probabilities in terms of the *number* of successes in the sample (X), not in terms of the *sample proportion* (X/n). A sample proportion of .50, with $n = 20$, means $X = (.50)(20)$ or 10 successes. Therefore, $P(X/n \geq .50)$ is *identical* with $P(X \geq 10)$. We may compute this latter probability by successively applying Equation 8.6.6 to compute $P(X = 10)$, $P(X = 11)$, $P(X = 12), \ldots, P(X = 20)$. Then the sum of these probabilities is $P(X \geq 10)$. Following this approach, we may compute as follows (using $n = 20$ and $p = .25$):

$$\left.\begin{array}{l} P(X = 10) = \dbinom{20}{10}(.25)^{10}(.75)^{10} \\[2ex] P(X = 11) = \dbinom{20}{11}(.25)^{11}(.75)^{9} \\[2ex] P(X = 12) = \dbinom{20}{12}(.25)^{12}(.75)^{8} \\[2ex] \cdots\cdots\cdots\cdots\cdots\cdots \\ \cdots\cdots\cdots\cdots\cdots\cdots \\ \cdots\cdots\cdots\cdots\cdots\cdots \\[2ex] P(X = 20) = \dbinom{20}{20}(.25)^{20} \end{array}\right\} \quad \text{Sum} = P(X \geq 10)$$

Referring to the tables of binomial probabilities published by the National Bureau of Standards (noted previously), where exact probabilities are shown, we determine that $P(X \geq 10)$, also $P(X/n \geq .50)$, is .0139. This differs from the estimated probability (.0102) by .0037.

We are now ready to summarize the presentation in this section relating to the normal approximation to the binomial probability distributions by presenting *Model E.*

Model E: If samples of size n (sufficiently large) are selected with equal and independent probabilities from an infinite binomial population, where p (the proportion of successes in the population) is not very close to 0 or 1:

1. *The sampling distribution of a frequency* (X, the number of successes

in a sample) is approximately like the normal curve with

$$\textit{mean} \qquad \mu_X = np \tag{8.7.7}$$

$$\textit{standard error of a frequency} \qquad \sigma_X = \sqrt{np(1-p)} \tag{8.7.8}$$

2. *The sampling distribution of a proportion* (X/n, the proportion of successes in a sample) is approximately like the normal curve with

$$\textit{mean} \qquad \mu_{X/n} = p \tag{8.7.9}$$

$$\textit{standard error of a proportion} \qquad \sigma_{X/n} = \sqrt{\frac{p(1-p)}{n}} \tag{8.7.10}$$

Note that *Model E* specifies the conditions that the population proportion of successes, p, must not be very close to 0 or 1 and n must be sufficiently large (as discussed previously). The condition that samples of size n are selected *with equal and independent probabilities* is another way of expressing the condition in *Model D* that p is constant from trial to trial and the trials are independent. When these conditions are met, the binomial probability distributions (the *sampling distribution of a frequency* and the *sampling distribution of a proportion*) are approximately normal.

Suppose an indefinitely large (infinite) population of scores contains 8% failures. If we consider a failure as coded 1 (a success) and all other scores as coded 0, we may look upon this as a binomial population with $p = .08$. What is the probability that, in a sample of 1000 scores selected from this population, the sample proportion of successes will lie between .09 and .10? This sampling situation fits *Model E*, since we are sampling from an infinite binomial population and n is large. Then, since we are dealing with the statistic X/n, we may estimate the probability $P(.09 \leq X/n \leq .10)$ by determining the appropriate area under the normal curve with mean and standard deviation as follows (computed according to Equations 8.7.9 and 8.7.10, respectively, using $p = .08$ and $n = 1000$):

$$\mu_{X/n} = .08$$

$$\sigma_{X/n} = \sqrt{\frac{(.08)(.92)}{1000}} = .0086$$

The appropriate area under the normal curve for $X/n = .09$ to $X/n = .10$ is determined by the continuous interval defined by the following limits (using Equation 8.7.4 to obtain the *lower* limit corresponding to $X/n = .09$ and Equation 8.7.5 to obtain the *upper* limit corresponding to $X/n = .10$), as shown in Figure 8.7.11

$$\frac{X}{n} = .09 - \frac{.5}{1000} = .0895$$

$$\frac{X}{n} = .10 + \frac{.5}{1000} = .1005$$

Transforming these limits to standard units (Equation 8.7.6), we obtain

$$z_1 = \frac{.0895 - .08}{.0086} = 1.10$$

$$z_2 = \frac{.1005 - .08}{.0086} = 2.38$$

Referring to Table B.2, the corresponding areas are .3643 (for z_1) and .4913 (for z_2). Subtracting the smaller area from the larger, we obtain .1270.

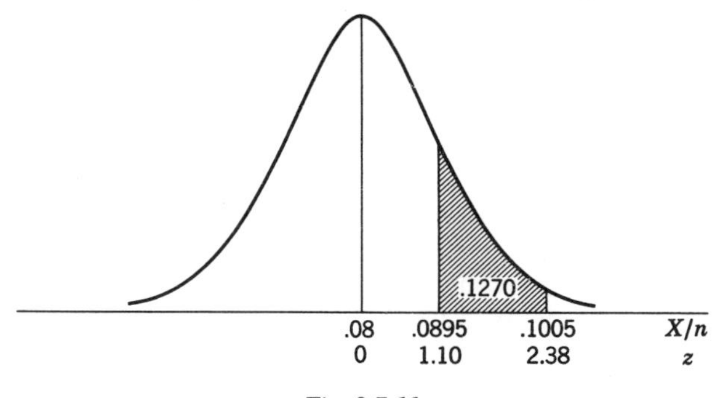

Fig. 8.7.11

Therefore, we estimate that $P(.09 \leq X/n \leq .10)$, the probability that the sample proportion of successes (failing scores) will lie between .09 and .10, is .127 or about 127 chances in 1000.

PROBLEMS FOR PRACTICE AND REVIEW

1. In a population of 650 mental patients, 295 were judged to be improved as the result of a new program of psychotherapy. If patients judged to be improved are coded 1 and the others are coded 0,

(a) compute the mean and standard deviation for the resulting binomial population.

(b) compute the mean and standard error for the sampling distribution of a frequency for samples of size 10.

(c) compute the mean and standard error for the sampling distribution of a proportion for samples of size 10.

2. In Problem 1
(a) what is the probability of 2 successes in a sample of size 3?
(b) what is the probability of no successes in a sample of size 4?

3. It was found that 90 out of a population of 300 subjects showed no response to an experimental tranquilizer. If subjects showing no respose are coded 1 and the others are coded 0,
(a) compute the mean and standard deviation for the resulting binomial population.
(b) compute the mean and standard error for the sampling distribution of a frequency for samples with $n = 25$.
(c) compute the mean and standard error for the sampling distribution of a proportion for samples with $n = 25$.

4. If a sample of size 8 is selected from the binomial population in Problem 3, what is the probability of obtaining (a) 3 successes, (b) 5 successes, (c) 3 or 5 successes, (d) 25% successes, (e) 50% successes?

5. In a study, it was found that ten out of a population of 50 middle-aged male subjects did not respond to hypnosis. If subjects who did not respond are coded 1 and the others are coded 0,
(a) compute the mean and standard deviation for the resulting binomial population.
(b) compute the mean and standard error for the sampling distribution of a frequency for samples with $n = 8$.
(c) compute the mean and standard error for the sampling distribution of a proportion for samples with $n = 8$.
(d) what is the probability of a success in a single trial (in the random selection of a single subject) for this binomial population?

6. For the binomial population in Problem 5,
(a) what is the probability of obtaining 4 successes in a sample of 10?
(b) what is the probability of obtaining 7 successes in a sample of 10?
(c) what is the probability of obtaining $\frac{1}{3}$ successes in a sample of 6?
(d) what is the probability of obtaining $\frac{1}{2}$ successes in a sample of 6?

7. Given a binomial population with $p = .2$,
(a) determine the complete sampling distribution of X (the number of successes) for samples of size 4.
(b) based upon the sampling distribution computed in (a), what is the probability that X will be (1) no higher than 1, (2) 2 or more, (3) 1 or 2?

8. Given a binomial population with $p = .6$, determine the complete sampling distribution of X/n (the proportion of successes) for samples of size 5.

9. In a large university, 50% of the students are known to major in the social sciences. Using the normal curve approximation, determine the probability that, in a sample of 150 students from this university,
(a) 60% are social science majors.
(b) 40% are social science majors.
(c) over 60% are social science majors.
(d) between 40 % and 60% are social science majors.

10. In Problem 9, using the normal curve approximation, what is the probability that the number of social science majors in the sample of 150 students equals (a) 78, (b) between 65 and 70, (c) 86 or more?

11. The records show that 17% of the outpatients in a clinic for emotional disorders have been treated in this clinic for two years or more. Using the normal curve approximation, what is the probability that a sample of 420 outpatients from this clinic will include

(a) no more than 57 patients who have been treated for two years or more?
(b) no fewer than 81 patients who have been treated for two years or more?

12. A study showed that 32% of the membership of a professional association are psychologists or educators. What is the probability that a sample of 250 members of this association will include

(a) 72 who are psychologists or educators?
(b) between 65 and 90 who are psychologists or educators?

13. In Problem 11, what is the probability that in the sample of 420 patients

(a) 15% or less have been treated for two years or more?
(b) between 15% and 20% have been treated for two years or more?

14. A survey indicated that 25% of the voters in a large city are opposed to the establishment of a municipal college. What is the probability that in a sample of 1000 voters, those opposed to the establishment of such a college will amount to (a) 27% or more, (b) 22% or less?

15. In Problem 14, what is the probability that a sample of 1000 voters will include

(a) 280 or more who oppose the municipal college?
(b) 230 or less who oppose the municipal college?

8.8 SAMPLING MODELS AND STATISTICAL INFERENCE

We have considered, so far, five statistical sampling models. *Models A* and *B* relate to the sampling distribution of the mean, *Model C* relates to the sampling distribution of the median, and *Models D* and *E* relate to the two (equivalent) binomial probability distributions, the sampling distribution of a frequency and the sampling distribution of a proportion. These five models are applicable to a wide area of statistical problems encountered in practice. Additional models will be presented from time to time, as needed. Let us now consider the characteristics of these models and say something, in a general way, about their applicability to problems arising in practice.

The sampling models define theoretical situations. In each instance, we assume repeated sampling from an infinite (theoretical) population. In *Models A* and *C*, the normal population is specified; in *Model B* it is only specified that the population must be infinite (also, σ must be finite); and *Models D* and *E* apply to a binomial population. In each model, we assume simple random sampling. The sample size n specified in a model represents the outcome of n *independent* trials with probabilities constant from trial to trial. This is a consequence of sampling from an infinite population, as explained in Chapter 7, Section 7.2. Sample size requirements vary among the models. Only for *Models A* and *D* is n permitted to have any value. *Models B* and *C* require that we have n large. We have defined $n \geq 30$ as a large sample which fulfills the requirements of these two models. In the binomial sampling model, *Model E*, the sample size required depends upon the value of p (the proportion of successes in the population).

Finally, each model describes a sampling distribution which is a consequence of repeated sampling from the specified population. In each model, except *Model D*, the sampling distribution is described as normal or approximately normal. This is of considerable importance because it provides a good deal of information relating to a sampling distribution. Each model provides equations to compute the mean and standard error of the sampling distribution. In summary, then, *each model describes a sampling distribution based on simple random sampling from an infinite population.* Although all five models are applicable to problems met in practice, we will be particularly concerned with *Models B* and *E*. These are, by far, the most useful ones. *Model A* is also useful. However, the requirement that the population distribution must be normal is a restrictive requirement. We will say very little about *Models C* and *D*. *Model C* was included to present the reader with a model relating to a measure of central tendency other than the mean. In addition, it provided the opportunity to show that the standard error of the mean is considerably smaller than the standard error of the median, an important advantage of the mean over the median. *Model D* is of limited use, since computation of binomial probabilities is cumbersome when carried out according to Equation 8.6.6, except when n is small. However, *Model D* provided a convenient step toward development of *Model E*.

Inductive statistics provide methods for making statistical inferences about a population based on sample data, and for evaluating the risks involved. *The sampling distribution provides the conceptual basis for development of the methods of inductive statistics.* Herein lies the importance of sampling models. Application of the methods of inductive statistics requires a knowledge of the population distribution from which a sample is selected and description of the sampling distribution for the statistic involved. Typically, we select only one sample and, using the data contained in this sample, prepare and evaluate estimates relating to the population. Typically, only partial information is available concerning the population and very little relating to the sampling distribution. *The usual procedure is to relate the problem at hand to an appropriate theoretical sampling model,* thus making available the full scope of information contained in the model pertaining to the population and, in particular, to the sampling distribution. It is clear, however, that no problem in statistical inference encountered in practice can *precisely* fit any of the theoretical models.

Therefore, we must consider how theoretical models can be used to solve statistical problems.

Generally, we will be concerned with statistical problems involving means and proportions. For example, we may wish to estimate the mean score obtained by high school juniors on a personality test based on a sample of scores and to measure the reliability of the estimate. Or, a psychologist may wish to estimate the mean reaction time of middle-aged men to a certain stimulus based on a sample and to measure the reliability of the estimate. In a wide area of such problems, it is appropriate to conceptualize the problem in terms of *Model B*. On the other hand, we may wish to estimate the proportion of junior high school students whose parents both have college degrees, basing the estimate and a measure of its reliability on sample data. In statistical problems involving proportions, it is appropriate to conceptualize the problem in terms of *Model E*. However, the method used in conceptualizing a statistical problem in terms of a sampling model depends upon the type of sampling situation involved. This will be considered further in subsequent chapters.

8.9 ALGEBRAIC NOTE

NOTE 8.1: To prove (Section 8.5):

$$\sigma = \sqrt{p(1 - p)} \qquad (8.5.2)$$

The standard deviation σ for a simple grouping table is determined as (Chapter 5, Section 5.3)

$$\sigma = \frac{1}{N}\sqrt{N \sum X_i^2 f_i - (\sum X_i f_i)^2} \qquad (5.3.14)$$

The two summations, $\Sigma X_i^2 f_i$ and $\Sigma X_i f_i$ are both equal to f_1, the number of items in the population which are in the category coded 1. (This can be seen readily by referring to Table 8.5.1 and observing the columns headed $\Sigma X_i^2 f_i$ and $\Sigma X_i f_i$. In each case, the column total is 18, the number of items in the population in the category coded 1.) Substituting f_1 for $\Sigma X_i^2 f_i$ and $\Sigma X_i f_i$ in Equation 5.3.14, we obtain

$$\sigma = \frac{1}{N}\sqrt{N f_1 - (f_1)^2} \qquad (8.8.1)$$

Now, place $1/N$ inside the square root sign, where it becomes $1/N^2$, to obtain

$$\sigma = \sqrt{\frac{N f_1 - (f_1)^2}{N^2}} \qquad (8.8.2)$$

Then,

$$\sigma = \sqrt{\frac{f_1}{N} - \left(\frac{f_1}{N}\right)^2} \tag{8.8.3}$$

Substituting $p = f_1/N$, according to Equation 8.5.1, we obtain

$$\sigma = \sqrt{p - p^2} \tag{8.8.4}$$

Finally, factoring out p,

$$\sigma = \sqrt{p(1 - p)} \tag{8.8.5}$$

Part IV
Applications of Statistical Inference

9

ESTIMATION AND CONFIDENCE INTERVALS

9.1 POINT AND INTERVAL ESTIMATES

Problems relating to estimation of population parameters make up a very important area of statistics. This will be the first area we will study which requires application of the methods of inductive statistics. We will concern ourselves with estimation of means and proportions based upon data collected by simple random sampling of a population.

An estimate of a parameter may be one of two types, a *point estimate* or an *interval estimate*. Usually, both types are determined when an estimate is required. For example, suppose a research psychologist wishes to determine the mean time required by first-year trade school students to perform a complicated task after undergoing a specified type of instruction. He selects a random sample of, say, 65 first-year trade school students and determines that the mean time required for this sample group of students is 37.4 minutes. He then estimates that the mean time required for all first-year trade school students in the population is 37.4 minutes. In other words, he uses the sample mean $\bar{X}$ as an estimate of the population mean μ. This is a *point estimate*. Clearly, *a point estimate represents a single value, a point on a scale of values*. In general, then, *the mean computed from a random sample* $\bar{X}$ *represents a point estimate of the population mean* μ.

Of course, it is not likely that a sample mean will *exactly* equal the mean of the population from which the sample was selected. Actually, as we have seen, there is a full distribution of sample means which are possible when random samples are selected from a population. This is what we have called the *sampling distribution of the mean.* Therefore, when a point estimate is prepared, it is customary to accompany the estimate with some kind of measure to indicate how good an estimate it is. For example, the psychologist in the illustration might have stated that, based upon the sample data, he estimates the population mean μ to be 37.4 ± 3.9 (minutes). In other words, he estimates that $\mu = 37.4$ minutes, but that it could be as much as 3.9 minutes more or less. That is, μ could be as low as $37.4 - 3.9 = 33.5$ minutes or as high as $37.4 + 3.9 = 41.3$ minutes.

He could also have stated this by saying that he estimates the population mean as 37.4 minutes, but that it could be equal to some value in the interval 33.5 minutes to 41.3 minutes. However, while an interval estimate (such as 33.5 to 41.3 minutes) certainly provides a "safer" estimate of μ than a point estimate (such as 37.4 minutes), how confident are we that the stated interval really includes the population mean? For example, the psychologist might have stated that he is 95% confident that the interval 33.5 to 41.3 minutes includes the population mean μ. Such a statement provides a considerable amount of information relating to the population parameter being estimated and to the reliability of the estimate. We call such a statement an *interval estimate*. That is, *an interval estimate specifies an interval (a range of values) wherein, with a stated degree of confidence, it is claimed that the parameter being estimated lies.*

Point and interval estimates also may be computed for a population proportion. For example, it is determined from a sample of 150 secondary school teachers that 11% have education beyond the master's degree. We use the sample proportion $X/n = .11$ as an estimate of the population proportion p. That is, *the sample proportion X/n provides a point estimate of the population proportion p.* An interval estimate would state that we are, say, 95% confident that the interval $.11 \pm .04$ includes the population proportion. Or that the interval .07 to .15 includes p. *An interval estimate is determined on a probability basis, taking into account the sampling distribution of the statistic used as the point estimate.* For example, the sample mean $\bar{X}$ is used as a point estimate of μ and the sampling distribution of the mean $\bar{X}$ is used to compute an interval estimate for μ. Similarly, the sample proportion X/n is used as a point estimate of p and the sampling distribution of a proportion X/n is used to compute an interval estimate for p. *An interval estimate, as just described, is called a confidence interval.*

The theoretical basis of confidence intervals, construction of such intervals, and the interpretation of the degree of confidence expressed (such as 95% confident) will be presented in the following sections. However, this presentation will treat different types of sampling situations separately. Section 9.2 will treat *large samples* ($n \geq 30$) selected from *very large populations*, whereas Section 9.3 will treat *small samples* ($n < 30$) selected from *very large populations.* Both sections will discuss confidence intervals for the *mean.* Section 9.4 will deal with confidence intervals for *population proportions.* Section 9.5 will discuss confidence intervals computed on the basis of sampling from *finite populations* which are not very large. Finally, in Section 9.6 we will consider *how large a sample* should be selected to provide a useful and acceptable estimate of a population mean or proportion.

9.2 MEANS: LARGE SAMPLES

Typically, samples are selected from finite populations without replacement. However, under certain circumstances, such sampling situations may be conceptualized in terms of sampling from an infinite population. For example, suppose a random sample of 100 scores is to be selected, without replacement, from a population of 5000 scores in order to estimate the population mean. On the first trial, when 1 score is to be selected from the 5000 scores, the probability is $1/5000 = .0002$ that a given score will be the one selected. On the second trial, when 1 score is to be selected from the remaining 4999 scores, the probability is $1/4999$ that one of the remaining scores will be selected. This probability is only negligibly different from .0002. Even when the last sample score is to be selected (the 100th score), the probability is $1/4901 = .000204$ that a given one of the 4901 remaining scores will be the one selected. Clearly, the probability of a score being selected is very nearly constant from trial to trial. This reflects the fact that the sample size (100) represents a very small percentage of the population size (5000). For the same reason, removal of sample scores has only a negligible effect upon the distribution of scores in the population. Hence, the trials may be considered to be independent.

As discussed in Chapter 7, Section 7.2, random sampling from an infinite population implies independent trials and constant probability of selection from trial to trial. These two conditions of sampling are closely approximated when sampling without replacement from a very large finite population, if the sample represents a negligible proportion of the population. *When the sample size n is less than 5% of the population size N, the sample may be considered as making up a negligible part of the population.* That is, $n/N < .05$. The ratio n/N is called the *sampling ratio.*

If we accept the sampling situation described above as approximating sampling from an infinite population and, furthermore, if we restrict ourselves to large samples ($n \geq 30$), then this sampling situation fits *Model B* (Chapter 8, Section 8.4). This is an important advantage, since

Model B provides considerable information relating to the sampling distribution of the mean. According to *Model B*, the sampling distribution of the mean is approximately normal, with mean μ (population mean) and standard error $\sigma_{\bar{X}} = \sigma/\sqrt{n}$ (σ is the population standard deviation). Figure 9.2.1 presents this distribution. Any value of $\bar{X}$ along the horizontal scale in the figure represents a possible sample mean. When it is desired to estimate a population mean, only a single sample is selected and the $\bar{X}$ computed from this sample is used as the point estimate of μ. However, there is no way of knowing which one of the possible $\bar{X}$ values is represented

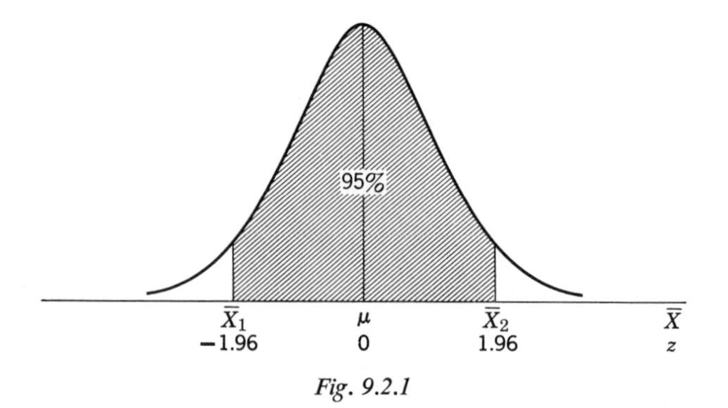

Fig. 9.2.1

by the sample mean computed. If it happens to be an $\bar{X}$ value far in the lower tail of the sampling distribution, it represents an unlucky underestimate. If, on the other hand, it happens to be an $\bar{X}$ value far in the upper tail, it represents an unlucky overestimate. Fortunately, however, most of the $\bar{X}$ values obtainable from random sampling are concentrated around the mean μ, as indicated by the central peak in the sampling distribution.

Two of the possible sample means obtainable, $\bar{X}_1$ and $\bar{X}_2$, are shown in Figure 9.2.1 These $\bar{X}$ values were selected so that the corresponding z values are -1.96 and 1.96, respectively. We may determine, by reference to Table B.2, that 95% of the area under the normal curve is contained in the interval between $z = -1.96$ and $z = 1.96$. In other words, $\bar{X}_1$ and $\bar{X}_2$ are limits which define an interval wherein 95% of the possible sample means lie. We may also state that the probability is .95 that the mean of a random sample will lie in this interval. Then, in general, expressing the mean of a sample in standard units, according to Equation 8.4.4 (Chapter 8, Section 8.4), and also expressing the limits $\bar{X}_1$ and $\bar{X}_2$ in standard units, we may write

$$P\left(-1.96 < \frac{\bar{X} - \mu}{\sigma_{\bar{X}}} < 1.96\right) = .95 \qquad (9.2.1)$$

Equation 9.2.1 states in symbols exactly what has already been said in words. That is, the probability is .95 that a sample mean $\bar{X}$ [in standard units $(\bar{X} - \mu)/\sigma_{\bar{X}}$] will lie between $\bar{X}_1$ and $\bar{X}_2$ (or, in standard units, between -1.96 and 1.96).

When a random sample is selected from a population in order to estimate the population mean μ, not only is μ unknown but usually the population standard deviation σ is also unknown. Therefore, in such a situation, we cannot compute the standard error of the mean, $\sigma_{\bar{X}} = \sigma/\sqrt{n}$. We, then, must *estimate* $\sigma_{\bar{X}}$ by computing

$$s_{\bar{X}} = \frac{s}{\sqrt{n}} \tag{9.2.2}$$

where s is the standard deviation computed from the sample data. We call $s_{\bar{X}}$ the *estimated standard error of the mean.* Substituting $s_{\bar{X}}$ for $\sigma_{\bar{X}}$ in Equation 9.2.1, we obtain

$$P\left(-1.96 < \frac{\bar{X} - \mu}{s_{\bar{X}}} < 1.96\right) = .95 \tag{9.2.3}$$

The probability expressed in Equation 9.2.1 continues to hold when we substitute $s_{\bar{X}}$ for $\sigma_{\bar{X}}$ in Equation 9.2.3 *because we are dealing with a large sample* ($n \geq 30$).

Now, let us consider the term inside the parentheses in Equation 9.2.3

$$-1.96 < \frac{\bar{X} - \mu}{s_{\bar{X}}} < 1.96 \tag{9.2.4}$$

Multiplying through by $s_{\bar{X}}$, we obtain

$$-1.96s_{\bar{X}} < \bar{X} - \mu < 1.96s_{\bar{X}} \tag{9.2.5}$$

Then, subtracting $\bar{X}$, we obtain

$$-\bar{X} - 1.96s_{\bar{X}} < -\mu < -\bar{X} + 1.96s_{\bar{X}} \tag{9.2.6}$$

Multiplying through by -1 (which requires that we *reverse* the inequality signs) we obtain

$$\bar{X} + 1.96s_{\bar{X}} > \mu > \bar{X} - 1.96s_{\bar{X}} \tag{9.2.7}$$

Finally, reversing the sequence of terms (merely for convenience), we obtain

$$\bar{X} - 1.96s_{\bar{X}} < \mu < \bar{X} + 1.96s_{\bar{X}} \tag{9.2.8}$$

Equation 9.2.8 represents a modified version of Equation 9.2.4, which was removed from the parentheses in Equation 9.2.3. Returning Equation 9.2.8 to the parentheses, we obtain

$$P(\bar{X} - 1.96s_{\bar{X}} < \mu < \bar{X} + 1.96s_{\bar{X}}) = .95 \tag{9.2.9}$$

What does Equation 9.2.9 say? This equation states that the probability is .95 that the two variable limits $\bar{X} - 1.96s_{\bar{X}}$ and $\bar{X} + 1.96s_{\bar{X}}$ will include the population mean μ. More specifically, if we think in terms of *repeated sampling* from a population, we may then visualize such an interval computed from *each* sample. Then, according to Equation 9.2.9, 95% of such intervals computed for all possible samples of a given size will include μ. We may state also that *the probability is .95 that, if such an interval is computed from a random sample, it will include the mean* μ. Such an interval is called a *confidence interval.* The probability attached to this interval is called a *confidence coefficient*. The limits are called *confidence limits.* More specifically, the *lower confidence limit* (LL) is

$$LL = \bar{X} - 1.96s_{\bar{X}} \tag{9.2.10}$$

and the *upper confidence limit* (UL) is

$$UL = \bar{X} + 1.96s_{\bar{X}} \tag{9.2.11}$$

If we express $s_{\bar{X}}$ according to Equation 9.2.2, we may write the lower and upper confidence limits as

$$LL = \bar{X} - 1.96\frac{s}{\sqrt{n}} \tag{9.2.12}$$

$$UL = \bar{X} + 1.96\frac{s}{\sqrt{n}} \tag{9.2.13}$$

It may be convenient to express a confidence interval more compactly as

$$\bar{X} \pm 1.96s_{\bar{X}} \tag{9.2.14}$$

or as

$$\bar{X} \pm 1.96\frac{s}{\sqrt{n}} \tag{9.2.15}$$

Considering the fact that 95% of the intervals so constructed include μ (based upon the notion of *repeated sampling* from a population), a feeling of confidence is provided that the interval determined from a *particular* random sample will contain the population mean. *Therefore, to express the degree of confidence that* μ *is included, we speak of a particular interval constructed, as just discussed, as a* .95 *confidence interval.* As a consequence, of course, 5% of all the intervals which could be constructed will *not* include μ. In other words, a .95 confidence interval implies a 5% risk that μ will not be included.

Suppose a sample of 144 scores is selected from a population of scores on a new aptitude test administered to all high school students in the country. Construct a .95 confidence interval for the population mean, if it is determined that the sample mean $\bar{X}$ is 148 and the sample standard deviation s is 28. Applying Equations 9.2.12 and 9.2.13, we compute

$$LL = 148 - 1.96\frac{28}{\sqrt{144}} = 148 - 4.57 = 143.43$$

$$UL = 148 + 1.96\frac{28}{\sqrt{144}} = 148 + 4.57 = 152.57$$

We may state that we are 95% confident that the interval 143.43 to 152.57 includes the population mean score. We may also present this confidence interval as 148 $\pm$ 4.57. When written in this form, we exhibit the point estimate (148) as well as provide a measure, at the .95 level of confidence, of the maximum extent to which this point estimate may be in error (4.57). *We may state, at the .95 level of confidence, that* $1.96(s/\sqrt{n})$ *(from Equations* 9.2.12 *and* 9.2.13) *represents the maximum amount by which* $\bar{X}$ *could be in error when it it is used as an estimate of* μ.

We have been talking about .95 confidence intervals. However, confidence intervals may be constructed at any desired level of confidence. Our confidence limit equations, such as Equations 9.2.12 and 9.2.13, include the constant 1.96. It will be recalled that we used $z = -1.96$ and $z = 1.96$ in Figure 9.2.1, so that the area between these two limits makes up 95% of the area under the curve. *If we want to construct, say, a* 98% *confidence interval, we would have to find* z *values which include* 98% *of the area under the curve. Such values are* $z = -2.33$ *and* $z = 2.33$. *Therefore, if we substitute* 2.33 for 1.96 *in Equations* 9.2.12 *and* 9.2.13, *we could construct* 98% *confidence intervals.* In all other respects, we carry out the computations as before.

Suppose a sample of 100 scores is selected from a very large population of scores, and $\bar{X} = 83.84$ and $s = 12.00$. Construct a .98 confidence interval for the population mean. Applying Equations 9.2.12 and 9.2.13, with 2.33 substituted for 1.96, we obtain

$$LL = 83.84 - 2.33\frac{12.00}{\sqrt{100}} = 83.84 - 2.80 = 81.04$$

$$UL = 83.84 + 2.33\frac{12.00}{\sqrt{100}} = 83.84 + 2.80 = 86.64$$

Therefore, the .98 confidence interval for the mean is 81.04 to 86.64 or, 83.84 $\pm$ 2.80. We may also state, at the .98 level of confidence, that if 83.84 is used as an estimate of μ, the maximum error we could make is 2.80. *Clearly, then, to construct a confidence interval at any desired level of confidence, we must substitute the appropriate* z *value for* 1.96 *in Equations*

9.2.12 *and* 9.2.13. We may express these equations more generally by substituting z for 1.96 into these equations to obtain

$$LL = \overline{X} - z\frac{s}{\sqrt{n}} \tag{9.2.16}$$

$$UL = \overline{X} + z\frac{s}{\sqrt{n}} \tag{9.2.17}$$

We may also rewrite Equations 9.2.10 and 9.2.11 by substituting z for 1.96 to obtain

$$LL = \overline{X} - zs_{\overline{X}} \tag{9.2.18}$$

$$UL = \overline{X} + zs_{\overline{X}} \tag{9.2.19}$$

Finally, we may make a similar substitution and rewrite the more compact Equations 9.2.14 and 9.2.15 to read

$$\overline{X} \pm zs_{\overline{X}} \tag{9.2.20}$$

and

$$\overline{X} \pm z\frac{s}{\sqrt{n}} \tag{9.2.21}$$

Together, the width of a confidence interval and the confidence coefficient provide a measure of how good an estimate we have. For example, a confidence interval such as 135 ± 10 at the .95 level of confidence is not nearly as good an estimate of μ as the same confidence interval at the .99 level of confidence. Clearly, the chances are 5 in 100 that an interval at the .95 level does not include μ, whereas the chances are only 1 in 100 that the interval at the .99 level does not include μ. Or, looking at it the other way, we feel quite comfortable about an interval when we know that 95 out of 100 intervals constructed in the same manner (based upon a large number of random samples of the same size) will include the population mean. On the other hand, we feel considerably safer about an interval when we know that 99 out of 100 intervals constructed in the same manner will include μ. In the latter instance, with a .99 level of confidence, we are nearly certain that a computed interval contains μ. The interval 135 ± 5 represents a much better estimate of μ than 135 ± 10, if both are at the same level of confidence. Say, they are both at the .95 level of confidence. In the former instance, we are 95% confident that the maximum error is 5 points, whereas in the latter case, we are 95% confident that the maximum error is 10 points.

No doubt, it has occurred to the reader that confidence intervals at the 1.00 level of confidence would be preferable, since then we would be *certain* that the stated interval includes the population mean. Unfortunately, when sample data are used to estimate unknown population parameters, we can never be certain of any estimate or any interval. Two exceptions come to mind. One is the trivial interval "– infinity to + infinity," which is always true, but which provides no useful information whatsoever. Say, if we know that the scores in a population could not be lower than 0 nor higher than 100, the confidence interval for the mean "0 to 100" is equally worthless.

The higher the level of confidence, the greater will be the z value to be entered into the various equations for the confidence interval. For example, for a .95 confidence interval we must use $z = 1.96$; for a .98 confidence interval we must use $z = 2.33$; and, for a .99 confidence interval we must use $z = 2.58$. Clearly, the greater the value of z, the wider the resulting confidence interval and the more vague and less informative is the confidence interval. On the other hand, while an interval with a lower level of confidence is narrower than one constructed at a higher level of confidence based upon the same sample data, it provides less assurance that the interval contains the population mean. The most frequently used confidence level is .95. However, the .98 and .99 confidence levels are frequently used.

An interval which has purposely been constructed at a lower level of confidence, in order to produce a narrower interval and therefore make the estimate look better, is deceptive. It is good practice to decide *beforehand* what level of confidence to use, taking into consideration the problem at hand, and not to depart from this decision when constructing the confidence interval. Referring to the equations presented for the confidence interval, say, Equation 9.2.21, we note that the sample size n appears in the denominator of the expression $z(s/\sqrt{n})$. This is the expression for the maximum error expected at a specified level of confidence. It is this expression which determines the width of the confidence interval. Hence, the larger the sample size, the smaller is the maximum expected error and the narrower is the resulting confidence interval for any specified level of confidence. Consequently, *a narrower confidence interval at any desired level of confidence may be obtained by increasing the sample size.*

A final word of caution. After a confidence interval has been constructed, say, at the .95 level of confidence, it is *absolutely incorrect* to state that the probability is .95 that the population mean is contained in the *particular* interval constructed. Such a statement implies that the population mean is a variable, which, of course, is pure nonsense. *It is the confidence interval which is the variable. This probability relates to the procedure used in constructing the confidence interval. It is this procedure, coupled with the concept of repeated sampling, which provides a variable confidence interval.* In other words, if we select samples of a given size again and again from the same population (assumed to be infinite) and construct a confidence interval based on each sample, say, at the .95 level of confidence, we may expect that 95% of the intervals so constructed will contain the population mean and 5% will not. Hence, the probability .95 applies to the procedure for constructing confidence intervals based on random samples, which tends to produce intervals including the population mean 95% of the time.

Summary: This section presents a method for constructing confidence intervals for a population mean to be used where the following conditions are met:

1. Population very large.
2. Large sample ($n \geq 30$).
3. $n/N < .05$.

PROBLEMS FOR PRACTICE AND REVIEW

1. A sample of 130 teenage boys obtained a mean score of 94.61 on an emotional maturity test, with a standard deviation of 18.52. Construct a .95 confidence interval for the mean score in the population.

2. In Problem 1, construct a .99 confidence interval.

3. In Problem 1, assume $n = 520$.

4. A sample of 75 mental patients in the private hospitals of a certain region show a mean hospital stay of 23.1 months, with a standard deviation of 6.8 months. Construct a .98 confidence interval for the mean number of months of hospital stay for all the patients in these hospitals.

5. In Problem 4, construct the confidence interval at the .95 level of confidence.

6. In Problem 4, suppose the standard deviation is 3.4 months. Construct a .95 confidence interval.

7. A sample of 200 college freshmen obtained a mean score of 108.9 on a science aptitude test, with a standard deviation of 21.5. Construct a confidence interval for the mean score at the .98 level of confidence.

8. In Problem 7, assume $n = 50$.

9. In Problem 7, if $\bar{X}$ is used as a point estimate of μ, what is the maximum error expected at the .98 level of confidence?

9.3 MEANS: SMALL SAMPLES

In this section we will consider situations involving selection of small samples ($n < 30$) from very large populations. In such situations, the sample size, of necessity, makes up a negligible part of the population. Therefore, the relationship $n/N < .05$ clearly holds. As a result, we may conceptualize such a sampling situation in terms of sampling from an infinite population, as we did in the case of large samples in Section 9.2. However, we cannot use *Model B* as the theoretical model, since this model relates only to large samples. However, if we restrict ourselves to samples selected from populations which are approximately normally distributed, we may use *Model A* to fit this sampling situation, since *Model A* has no sample size restriction.

We know that, for sampling situations which fit *Model A*, the sampling distribution of the mean is like the normal distribution, with mean μ (population mean) and standard error $\sigma_{\bar{X}} = \sigma/\sqrt{n}$ (σ is the population standard deviation). Following Equation 9.2.1 in Section 9.2, we could set up the equation

$$P\left(-1.96 < \frac{\bar{X} - \mu}{\sigma_{\bar{X}}} < 1.96\right) = .95 \qquad (9.3.1)$$

As before, this equation states that the probability is .95 that a sample mean expressed in standard units will lie between the z values -1.96 and 1.96. However, the similarity ends here. That is, *if we substitute* $s_{\bar{X}}$ *for* $\sigma_{\bar{X}}$ *in Equation* 9.3.1 *as was done in Equation* 9.2.3, *we cannot claim that the probability expressed in Equation* 9.3.1 *still holds.* It will be recalled that the probability expressed in Equation 9.2.1 holds in Equation 9.2.3 *because we were dealing with large samples.* If $\bar{X}$ is normally distributed, as it is in *Model A*, then, in terms of standard units $(\bar{X} - \mu)/\sigma_{\bar{X}}$ it is also normally distributed. However, when $s_{\bar{X}}$ is substituted for $\sigma_{\bar{X}}$, the resulting variable $(\bar{X} - \mu)/s_{\bar{X}}$ may be considered to be normally distributed *only when dealing with large samples.* Mathematical statisticains have shown that, when dealing with small samples, this variable has a distribution which differs significantly from the normal distribution. Moreover, the smaller the sample, the greater is the difference. The distribution of this variable is like the *t distribution* or Student's *t*. This was originally developed by W. S. Gosset who published his findings under the pen-name "Student." It is general practice to reserve the symbol z for $(\bar{X} - \mu)/s_{\bar{X}}$ for use with large samples and to use t to denote this variable for use with small samples, as follows:

$$t = \frac{\bar{X} - \mu}{s_{\bar{X}}} \qquad (9.3.2)$$

Figure 9.3.1 presents a diagrammatic comparison of the t distribution and the normal distribution. Notice that both distributions are perfectly symmetrical around $\mu(= 0)$, which denotes the mean of each distribution, and each has a central peak. The t distribution is not as high as the normal distribution in the central portion, but it is higher in the tails. This means, of course, that the t distribution is more spread out than the normal distribution. In other words, a smaller proportion of the area under the curve is concentrated around the mean for the t distribution than for the normal distribution and a larger proportion of this area is in the tails. *Consequently, if the limits $-z$ and z shown in Figure* 9.3.1 *identify an interval containing a specified proportion of the total area under the normal curve, the corresponding t limits must be further in the tails of the t distribution to mark off an interval containing an equal proportion of the total area under the t distribution curve.* This relationship between the z limits for the normal

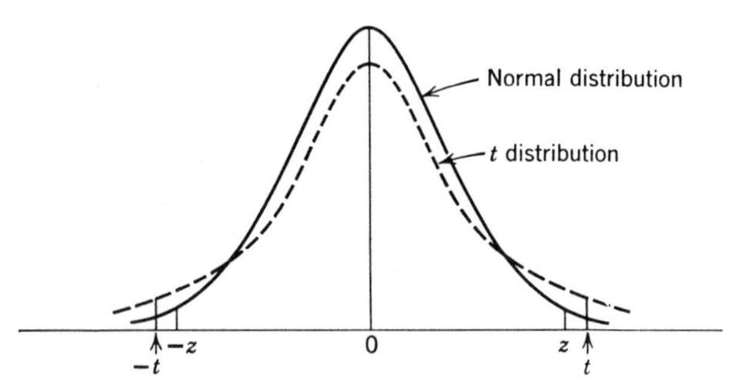

Fig. 9.3.1. Diagrammatic comparison of the t distribution and the normal distribution.

distribution and the t limits for the t distribution is presented in Figure 9.3.1.

Actually, there are many t distributions. A particular t distribution is identified by the number of *degrees of freedom* (usually abbreviated df) involved in a problem. *When constructing confidence intervals for the mean, $df = n - 1$.* That is, the number of degrees of freedom is one less than the sample size. Generally, degrees of freedom relate to the "freedom to vary" in a set of data. For example, we know from Equation 4.9.1 that the sum of the deviations around the mean is zero. Therefore, if we know only that a set of data is made up of 4 scores, with a mean of 120, we have the freedom to select 3 scores in any way we please, but the fourth is then rigidly determined. For example, we may specify the deviations from the mean for 3 scores as 8, −10, and 12. These 3 deviations add to 10; then, the fourth deviation *must* be −10, so that the 4 deviations will add to zero. Applying these deviations to the mean of 120, we obtain a possible set of 4 scores as 128, 110, 132, and 110. In the sense just described, a sample of size 4 provides 4 − 1 or 3 degrees of freedom. We will encounter other types of problems involving the t distribution where df are determined in a different way. In each such situation, the method for determining df will be indicated.

Table 9.3.1 presents comparative data showing t values for various df and corresponding z values. For example, consider the first row in the table. The z value shown in this row, Column (4), is 1.96. If we assume that this is the z value (positive and negative) in Figure 9.3.1, then the area under the normal curve contained between the z limits -1.96 and 1.96 is .95, as shown in Table 9.3.1, first row, Column (3). Of course, with an interval defined by these limits, the area in both tails is $1.00 - .95 = .05$, half of this (.025) in each tail. The areas in the tails corresponding to .95 between the limits are shown in the first row, Columns (1) and (2), of the

Table 9.3.1 COMPARATIVE z AND t VALUES FOR SPECIFIED AREAS UNDER THE NORMAL AND t DISTRIBUTIONS, RESPECTIVELY

Area in Tail		Area Between Limits	z	t for Specified Degrees of Freedom			
One	Both			120	60	30	10
(1)	(2)	(3)	(4)	(5)	(6)	(7)	(8)
.025	.05	.95	1.96	1.98	2.00	2.04	2.23
.01	.02	.98	2.33	2.36	2.39	2.46	2.76
.005	.01	.99	2.58	2.62	2.66	2.75	3.17

Source: Table III of Fisher and Yates, *Statistical Tables for Biological, Agricultural and Medical Research*, Oliver & Boyd Ltd., Edinburgh, by permission of the authors and publishers.

table. We may note from Column (5) that, for 120 df, the corresponding t value which defines an interval cutting off an area of .025 in each tail of the t distribution (.05 in both tails) is 1.98. In other words, if the z limits are -1.96 and 1.96 in Figure 9.3.1, the corresponding t limits for 120 df are -1.98 and 1.98. In this instance, the difference is not appreciable. However, we note from Table 9.3.1, Columns (6), (7), and (8), that this t value increases to 2.00 for 60 df, 2.04 for 30 df, and 2.23 for 10 df. Clearly, the t limits shown in Figure 9.3.1 move further and further into the tails as the number of degrees of freedom is reduced. For example, for 10 df, the t limits are -2.23 and 2.23, which are quite different from the corresponding z limits of -1.96 and 1.96. In other words, as the sample size (and df) is *increased*, the t distribution becomes more like the normal distribution. For large samples, the differences between the two distributions may be ignored for many purposes. The other data in Table 9.3.1 show a similar relationship between the t values and z values.

Since t values depend on the number of degrees of freedom, it is convenient to present only such t values as may be required, in place of a complete t table for each specified number of degrees of freedom. Such data are presented in Appendix *B*, Table B.3. The first column lists df, the number of degrees of freedom, which runs from 1 through 29. The symbol ∞ denotes an *infinite* number of degrees of freedom. The other columns are headed by numbers which specify the area in *both tails* of the t distribution combined. These areas represent probabilities, as in the case of the normal distribution. The first probability (or area) column is .5. This means that the t values shown in this column cut off, *in both tails combined*, .5 of the area under the t distribution curve. For example, for 15 df, the t value in this column is .691. Then, if $-t = -.691$ and $t = .691$ in the figure at the head of Table B.3, the total area in both tails (the shaded areas) is .5 of the total area under the curve. Each tail (each shaded area) contains $\frac{1}{2}$ of .5, or .25 of the total area. Referring to the probability column headed .05, we note that for, say, 10 df, the t value in the table is 2.228. Therefore, if $-t = -2.228$ and $t = 2.228$, the area is .05 in both tails combined and .025 in each tail. We observed this when we discussed the first row of Table 9.3.1, where 2.228 was rounded to 2.23.

It has already been noted that, as df (or sample size) becomes larger, the t distribution becomes more and more like the normal distribution. In the limiting case, with an infinite number of df, the two distributions coincide. Consequently, in the bottom row of Table B.3, where df $= \infty$, the t values are identically the same as the corresponding z values. For example, for .05 of the total area in both tails, or .025 in each tail, the t value is 1.96 for df $= \infty$. Similarly, in a normal distribution, for the limits corresponding to 1.96 ($-z = -1.96$ and $z = 1.96$), the same proportion of the total area under the curve is cut off in each tail. This may be determined from Table B.2. It is also shown in the first row of Table 9.3.1.

Returning to Equation 9.3.1, we may take into account that substituting $s_{\bar{X}}$ for $\sigma_{\bar{X}}$ results in the variable $(\bar{X} - \mu)/s_{\bar{X}}$, which has the t distribution, by writing

$$P\left(-t_{.05} < \frac{\bar{X} - \mu}{s_{\bar{X}}} < t_{.05}\right) = .95 \tag{9.3.3}$$

The symbol $t_{.05}$ denotes a t value such that, for a stated number of degrees of freedom, the limits $-t_{.05}$ and $t_{.05}$ cut off in both tails .05 of the total area under the curve, or .025 in each tail. Clearly, these are the t values in Table B.3, column headed .05. According to Equation 9.3.3, the probability is .95 that the mean $\bar{X}$, expressed in standard units as $(\bar{X} - \mu)/s_{\bar{X}}$, will lie in the interval defined by the limits $-t_{.05}$ and $t_{.05}$, for df $= n - 1$. Equation 9.3.3 corresponds to Equation 9.2.3 presented in Section 9.2 for large samples. Following the same approach used to arrive at Equation 9.2.9 in the previous section, we obtain

$$P(\bar{X} - t_{.05}s_{\bar{X}} < \mu < \bar{X} + t_{.05}s_{\bar{X}}) = .95 \tag{9.3.4}$$

Then, we may write lower and upper confidence limits as

$$LL = \bar{X} - t_{.05}s_{\bar{X}} \tag{9.3.5}$$

$$UL = \bar{X} + t_{.05}s_{\bar{X}} \tag{9.3.6}$$

The foregoing pair of equations are to be used to construct .95 confidence intervals, since the symbol $t_{.05}$ denotes t limits which cut off .05 of the area under the t distribution in both tails combined. We may write equations for confidence limits applicable to any level of confidence as

$$LL = \bar{X} - ts_{\bar{X}} \tag{9.3.7}$$

$$UL = \bar{X} + ts_{\bar{X}} \tag{9.3.8}$$

We use the symbol t generally to denote a t value for any specified number of degrees of freedom and any desired level of confidence. Substituting $s_{\bar{X}} = s/\sqrt{n}$, we obtain

$$LL = \bar{X} - t\frac{s}{\sqrt{n}} \tag{9.3.9}$$

$$UL = \bar{X} + t\frac{s}{\sqrt{n}} \tag{9.3.10}$$

Finally, we may write these equations more compactly as

$$\bar{X} \pm ts_{\bar{X}} \tag{9.3.11}$$

or

$$\bar{X} \pm t\frac{s}{\sqrt{n}} \tag{9.3.12}$$

Suppose a sample of 16 scores is selected from a very large population which is normally distributed. We determine that $\bar{X} = 101.3$ and $s = 18.8$. We may construct a .98 confidence interval for the mean as follows: since the sample size is less than 30, we must use Equations 9.3.9 and 9.3.10. We determine df $= 16 - 1 = 15$. Then, for a .98 confidence interval, we must refer to the column headed .02 in Table B.3, since $1 - .98 = .02$. The required t value is 2.602. Finally, making the proper substitutions into Equations 9.3.9 and 9.3.10, we obtain

$$LL = 101.3 - (2.602)\frac{18.8}{\sqrt{16}} = 89.1$$

$$UL = 101.3 + (2.602)\frac{18.8}{\sqrt{16}} = 113.5$$

The desired .98 confidence interval for the mean is, then, 89.1 — 113.5.

Summary: This section presents a method for constructing confidence intervals for a population mean to be used where the following conditions are met:

1. The population is very large and distributed approximately like the normal curve
2. The sample size is small ($n < 30$)

PROBLEMS FOR PRACTICE AND REVIEW

1. A sample of 20 junior high school girls obtained a mean score of 124.6 on a memory test, with a standard deviation of 31.8. Construct a .95 confidence interval for the population mean score.

2. In Problem 1, construct the confidence interval at the .99 level of confidence.

3. In Problem 1, assume $n = 40$.

4. A sample of 15 patients in a large state mental hospital obtained a mean score of 27.1 on a picture test, with a standard deviation of 9.6. Construct a .98 confidence interval for the population mean.

5. In Problem 4, assume $n = 30$.

6. A sample of 25 trade school students required a mean of 16.4 minutes to perform a specified task, with a standard deviation of 4.7 minutes. Construct a .98 confidence interval for the mean time required for the population of trade school students.

7. In Problem 6, construct the confidence interval at the .95 level of confidence.

8. In Problem 6, if $\bar{X}$ is used as a point estimate of μ, what is the maximum error expected at the .98 level of confidence?

9. A sample of 22 adults in an adult education program have a mean age of 30.23 years, with a standard deviation of 5.62 years. Construct a .95 confidence interval for the population mean age.

10. In Problem 9, if $\bar{X} = 30.23$ is used as a point estimate of μ, what is the maximum error at the .95 level of confidence?

9.4 PROPORTIONS

Estimation of population proportions is a type of problem which is frequently encountered. For example, a university may need to estimate the proportion of entering freshmen with an IQ above a certain level, in order to evaluate the caliber of students being attracted. A psychologist may be carrying out a study for insurance companies where it is required to determine the proportion who are accident-prone in various population categories. A social psychologist may wish to estimate the proportion of college seniors who have deep-seated feelings of hostility toward certain groups.

In this section we will consider construction of confidence intervals for proportions based on samples selected from very large populations. We will restrict our consideration to situations where $n/N < .05$ so that we may conceptualize the sampling situation in terms of sampling from an infinite population. If we further restrict ourselves to populations where the proportion p is not too close to 0 or 1, then *Model E* provides a suitable theoretical description of the type of sampling situations under consideration. It may appear to the reader that the various restrictions noted considerably reduce the usefulness of the method to be presented. However, this is not so. Many estimation problems relating to proportions encountered in practice fall within the scope of sampling situations as defined.

According to *Model E*, the sampling distribution of a proportion X/n is approximately normal, with mean $\mu_{X/n} = p$ (the population proportion) and standard error $\sigma_{X/n} = \sqrt{p(1-p)/n}$. Therefore, we may set up an equation for the sample proportion X/n, similar to Equation 9.2.1, as follows:

$$P\left(-1.96 < \frac{\dfrac{X}{n} - \mu_{X/n}}{\sigma_{X/n}} < 1.96\right) = .95 \tag{9.4.1}$$

This equation states that the probability is .95 that a sample proportion expressed in standard units will lie between the limits $z = -1.96$ and $z = 1.96$. Substituting p for $\mu_{X/n}$, we may rewrite this equation as

$$P\left(-1.96 < \frac{\dfrac{X}{n} - p}{\sigma_{X/n}} < 1.96\right) = .95 \tag{9.4.2}$$

When a sample is selected from a population in order to estimate a population proportion p, the value of this parameter, of course, is unknown. In such situations, we cannot compute $\sigma_{X/n}$. Therefore, we must *estimate* $\sigma_{X/n}$ by computing

$$s_{X/n} = \sqrt{\frac{\dfrac{X}{n}\left(1 - \dfrac{X}{n}\right)}{n}} \tag{9.4.3}$$

We call $s_{X/n}$ the *estimated standard error of a proportion*. Substituting $s_{X/n}$ for $\sigma_{X/n}$ in Equation 9.4.2, we obtain

$$P\left(-1.96 < \frac{\dfrac{X}{n} - p}{s_{X/n}} < 1.96\right) = .95 \tag{9.4.4}$$

The probability expressed in Equation 9.4.2 continues to hold to an acceptable approximation in Equation 9.4.4 *only when the sample size is sufficiently large*. The sample size required is the same as discussed in connection with *Model E* (Chapter 8, Section 8.7). As then noted, the sample should be of *size* 100 *or more. However, if the population proportion is considered to be far from* .5, *say, it is thought to be less than* .3 *or greater than* .7, *then, a sample of size* 500 *or more is preferable.*

Following the same approach used to arrive at Equation 9.2.9, we obtain (based upon Equation 9.4.4)

$$P\left(\frac{X}{n} - 1.96s_{X/n} < p < \frac{X}{n} + 1.96s_{X/n}\right) = .95 \qquad (9.4.5)$$

Then, we may write lower and upper confidence limits as

$$LL = \frac{X}{n} - 1.96s_{X/n} \qquad (9.4.6)$$

$$UL = \frac{X}{n} + 1.96s_{X/n} \qquad (9.4.7)$$

This pair of equations is to be used to construct .95 confidence intervals for a population proportion, since z limits of -1.96 and 1.96 are used. We may write more general equations for confidence intervals for any level of confidence as

$$LL = \frac{X}{n} - zs_{X/n} \qquad (9.4.8)$$

$$UL = \frac{X}{n} + zs_{X/n} \qquad (9.4.9)$$

We could set up an alternative set of equations by substituting for $s_{X/n}$ in the foregoing equations, according to Equation 9.4.3. However, this would result in a very complicated looking pair of equations. It is better, when computing confidence limits for a population proportion, to compute $s_{X/n}$ according to Equation 9.4.3; then use this result and compute the confidence limits according to Equations 9.4.8 and 9.4.9. We may write the equations for confidence limits more compactly as

$$\frac{X}{n} \pm zs_{X/n} \qquad (9.4.10)$$

Suppose that a sample of 500 scores selected from a very large population includes 45 failures. Construct a .99 confidence interval for the proportion of failures in the population. We determine a point estimate for p by computing $X/n = \frac{45}{500} = .09$. Using Equation 9.4.3, we compute the estimated standard error of a proportion as

$$s_{X/n} = \sqrt{\frac{.09(1 - .09)}{500}} = .013$$

Finally, using Equations 9.4.8 and 9.4.9 and noting that $z = 2.58$ provides limits (-2.58 and 2.58) which include 99% of the area under the normal curve, we obtain

$$LL = .09 - 2.58(.013) = .09 - .034 = .056$$

$$UL = .09 + 2.58(.013) = .09 + .034 = .124$$

Therefore, we may state that the interval .056 to .124 contains the population proportion at the .99 level of confidence (nearly certainty). Also, if .09 is used as a point estimate of the population proportion of failures, .034 represents the maximum error we could make at the .99 level of confidence.

Summary: This section presents a method for constructing confidence intervals for a population proportion to be used where the following conditions are met:

1. Population very large.
2. $n/N < .05$.
3. p not too close to 0 or 1.
4. Sample size sufficiently large ($n \geq 100$; see foregoing discussion).

PROBLEMS FOR PRACTICE AND REVIEW

1. A survey of college faculty members showed that 27 out of 150 college teachers obtained graduate training in the college in which they are teaching. What would you estimate as the proportion of college teachers who obtained graduate training in the college in which they are teaching?

2. In Problem 1, construct a .95 confidence interval for the population proportion.

3. In Problem 1, what would you say is the maximum error expected at the .95 level of confidence, if the sample proportion is used as an estimate of the proportion in the population?

4. A sample of 430 college seniors showed that 152 are education majors. Construct a .98 confidence interval for the proportion of college seniors who are education majors.

5. A survey of 850 high school teachers indicated that 102 favored the teaching of elementary statistics in secondary schools. Construct a .99 confidence interval for the proportion of high school teachers who are in favor of this.

6. In Problem 5, if the sample proportion is used as a point estimate of the population proportion, what is the maximum error expected at the .99 confidence level?

7. If 133 out of 325 laboratory rats succeed in finding the food box within a specified time, when introduced into a newly constructed maze for the first time, construct a .95 confidence interval for the population proportion of laboratory rats who may be expected to do the same.

8. In a large city, a sample of 250 housewives showed that 194 scored high on an anxiety scale. Construct a .95 confidence interval for the proportion of housewives in the city who would be expected to score high on the anxiety scale.

9.5 FINITE POPULATIONS

When sampling from a very large population, it is more likely that the sampling ratio n/N will be negligible than when samples are drawn from smaller populations. We have been considering a sampling ratio which is less than .05 as negligible. This is a somewhat arbitrary, but generally accepted practice among statisticians. *When the sampling ratio is appreciable, say, .05 or more, we must take into account the effects of sampling without replacement from a finite population.* In such a sampling situation, we cannot ignore the changes which occur in the population distribution as items are removed from the population during the sample selection process. As an illustration, suppose a random sample of 100 scores is to be selected (without replacement) from a population of 500 scores. When the first score is to be drawn from the population, the probability is $\frac{1}{500} = .0020$ that a specified score will be selected. However, after 99 scores have been removed from the population, the probability is $\frac{1}{401} = .0025$ that a specified one of the remaining 401 scores will be selected.

The effect of sampling without replacement from a finite population is to reduce the standard error of a statistic compared with the standard error of the statistic if the sampling were with replacement from the same population or from an infinite population. For example, we have studied the sampling distribution for three statistics: the mean $\overline{X}$, the sample proportion X/n, and the sample number of successes X when sampling from a binomial population. We have described each of these distributions, based upon sampling from an infinite population, by stating the equations for the mean and the standard error. When sampling without replacement from a finite population, the mean of each of these sampling distributions is the same as already presented. However, the equations for the standard error must be adjusted by multiplying by a *finite population correction* factor (often abbreviated as fpc), as follows:

$$\text{\textit{Finite population correction} factor for the standard error of a statistic} = \sqrt{\frac{N-n}{N-1}} \qquad (9.5.1)$$

Applying the fpc from Equation 9.5.1, we may write the following equations for the standard errors to be used when *sampling without replacement from a finite population:*

$$\sigma_{\bar{X}} = \frac{\sigma}{\sqrt{n}}\sqrt{\frac{N-n}{N-1}} \qquad (9.5.2)$$

$$\sigma_{X/n} = \sqrt{\frac{p(1-p)}{n}}\sqrt{\frac{N-n}{N-1}} \qquad (9.5.3)$$

$$\sigma_X = \sqrt{np(1-p)}\sqrt{\frac{N-n}{N-1}} \qquad (9.5.4)$$

These equations are identical with the corresponding equations previously presented (Equations 8.4.2, 8.6.10, and 8.6.8), except for multiplication by the fpc. The corresponding *estimated* standard errors may be written, similarly, as

$$s_{\bar{X}} = \frac{s}{\sqrt{n}}\sqrt{\frac{N-n}{N-1}} \qquad (9.5.5)$$

$$s_{X/n} = \sqrt{\frac{\frac{X}{n}\left(1-\frac{X}{n}\right)}{n}}\sqrt{\frac{N-n}{N-1}} \qquad (9.5.6)$$

$$s_X = \sqrt{n\left(\frac{X}{n}\right)\left(1-\frac{X}{n}\right)}\sqrt{\frac{N-n}{N-1}} \qquad (9.5.7)$$

Since, typically, samples are greater than 1, the numerator of the fpc will be smaller than the denominator, as can be seen from Equation 9.5.1. Consequently, this correction factor will be less than 1. The larger the sample size n relative to the population size N, the smaller is the fpc. For example, for a sample of 10,000 scores selected from a population of 88,000 scores, we may compute the fpc as

$$\sqrt{\frac{88{,}000 - 10{,}000}{88{,}000 - 1}} = .94$$

On the other hand, for a sample of only 2500 scores selected from the same population, the fpc is

$$\sqrt{\frac{88{,}000 - 2500}{88{,}000 - 1}} = .99$$

Clearly, when n is small relative to N, the fpc is so close to 1 that it is not worthwhile to compute it. Of course, when n is small relative to N, the sampling ratio n/N is small. Hence, *when the sampling ratio is small, we may neglect the fpc when computing standard errors.* In other words, the use of Equations 9.5.2, 9.5.3, and 9.5.4 for computation of standard errors is *always* correct when sampling without replacement from a finite population. This is true whether the population is very large, large, or small, and no matter what the sample size. It is also true whether the sampling ratio is large or small. However, when the sampling ratio is small, say, less than .05, multiplication by the fpc (as required by these equations) is hardly different from multiplying by 1, so that we may just as well omit this factor from the equations. In other words, in such instances, standard errors may be computed using the previous equations not involving the fpc (Equations 8.4.2, 8.6.10, and 8.6.8).

On the other hand, when the sampling ratio is not small ($n/N \geq .05$), it is better to use the standard error equations which include the fpc for computation of standard errors (Equations 9.5.2, 9.5.3, and 9.5.4 or, the corresponding equations for the estimated standard errors). For example, suppose a sample of 250 college graduates out of a population of 1000 achieved a mean score of 82.30 on a test which measures on-the-job success, with a standard deviation of 14.10. Construct a .98 confidence interval for the mean test score for the population. Since we are dealing with a large sample, Equations 9.2.18 and 9.2.19 are to be used to construct the lower and upper confidence limits, respectively. However, since the sampling ratio is 250/1000 or .25, the finite population correction factor cannot be ignored. Therefore, we compute the estimated standard error of the mean using Equation 9.5.5 as

$$s_{\bar{X}} = \frac{14.10}{\sqrt{250}} \sqrt{\frac{1000 - 250}{1000 - 1}} = .67$$

Then, using $z = 2.33$ for .98 confidence limits, we obtain

$$LL = 82.30 - 2.33(.67) = 82.30 - 1.56 = 80.74$$
$$UL = 82.30 + 2.33(.67) = 82.30 + 1.56 = 83.86$$

Therefore, we may state that we are 98% confident that the interval 80.74–83.86 includes the population mean score. In other words, if we use

82.30 as a point estimate of the population mean, the maximum error is 1.56 at the .98 level of confidence.

It should be noted that, even if the sampling ratio is equal to or greater than .05, it is "safe" to construct a confidence interval without taking into account the fpc. For example, in the foregoing illustration, we could compute $s_{\bar{X}}$ according to Equation 9.2.2 to obtain

$$s_{\bar{X}} = \frac{14.10}{\sqrt{250}} = .89$$

Then, we obtain confidence limits as

$$LL = 82.30 - 2.33(.89) = 82.30 - 2.07 = 80.23$$

$$UL = 82.30 + 2.33(.89) = 82.30 + 2.07 = 84.37$$

Clearly, if we are 98% confident that the interval 80.74–83.86 contains the population mean (as before), we are *at least* 98% confident that the *wider* interval 80.23–84.37 contains this parameter. However, the wider the interval, the less useful it is. Therefore, it is advisable to take the fpc into account where the sampling ratio is not negligible ($n/N \geq .05$).

PROBLEMS FOR PRACTICE AND REVIEW

1. A sample of 25 subjects, out of a population of 250, obtained a mean score of 147.3 on an aptitude test, with a standard deviation of 21.6. Compute
(a) the sampling ratio.
(b) the finite population correction factor.
(c) the standard error of the mean.
(d) the confidence interval for the population mean on the aptitude test at the .98 level of confidence.

2. A sample of 250 subjects was selected from a population of 1500. It was found that 95 out of this sample showed no response to a new drug which was administered orally. Compute
(a) the sampling ratio.
(b) the finite population correction factor.
(c) the standard error of a proportion.
(d) the confidence interval for the population proportion expected to show no response to oral administration of the drug, at the .95 level of confidence.

9.6 SAMPLE SIZE

A good deal has been said about the use of sample data. It has, no doubt, occurred to the reader that, in any sampling situation, a decision must be made as to *how large* a sample is needed. Determination of sample size is often complicated, since many factors must be taken into consideration, including the costs involved. However, we have developed sufficient statistical theory to permit a general discussion of this subject and to present certain procedures for estimating sample size.

When a sample is to be selected, we must first determine the purpose for which the sample is to be used. The size of sample to be selected depends upon whether the sample data are to be used for estimation of a population mean, a population proportion, or for some other purpose. We know that an estimate based upon sample data is not likely to be *exactly* equal to the parameter estimated. Consequently, the size of sample depends, as well, upon "how good" an estimate is required. "How good" means *how much error is acceptable* when a point estimate is used to represent a population parameter and *how much confidence is required* that the maximum error does not exceed the amount stated. We will develop procedures to determine sample size when the objective is to estimate a population mean or a population proportion.

Since the size of sample to be selected depends upon the *maximum error acceptable* for a given sampling situation at a *specific level of confidence*, it is appropriate to turn to the equations for confidence intervals as a basis for developing sample size equations. We know from Section 9.2, Equation 9.2.21, that the maximum error to be expected at a stated level of confidence, when $\bar{X}$ is used as a point estimate of the population mean μ, is

$$m = z\frac{s}{\sqrt{n}} \tag{9.6.1}$$

where m denotes the maximum error expected. Let us rewrite this equation, using σ in place of s, to obtain

$$m = z\frac{\sigma}{\sqrt{n}} \tag{9.6.2}$$

Solving Equation 9.6.2 for the sample size n, we obtain

$$n = \left(\frac{z\sigma}{m}\right)^2 \tag{9.6.3}$$

Equation 9.6.3 provides a convenient basis for estimating sample size when the sample is to be used to estimate a population mean.

Suppose it is desired to select a sample in order to estimate the mean score obtained by engineering students in a tactual perception test. It is specified that the mean score is to be estimated so that we are 95% confident that the estimate is off by no more than 2 points. Therefore, we may use Equation 9.6.3 with $m = 2$ (the maximum error specified) and $z = 1.96$ (reflecting the 95% confidence level required). What should we use for σ?

This, of course, represents the unknown standard deviation of the population of tactual perception test scores. It is not necessary to know the precise value of σ in order to use equation 9.6.3 to estimate the sample size n. Often, a fair estimate of σ will be available from other information. For example, the standard deviation of actual perception test scores may be known for a similar population, such as for a previous class of engineering students. If no information is available, it may be necessary to collect data from a small pilot sample in order to obtain an estimate of σ. Let us suppose that it is known from previous years that σ is about 18. Then, entering the appropriate values into equation 9.6.3, we estimate the required sample size as

$$n = \left(\frac{(1.96)(18)}{2}\right)^2 = 311.17$$

Fractional results should always be rounded up to provide a small additional margin of protection. Therefore, we estimate that a sample of 312 scores should be selected.

Let us consider a second illustration. How large a sample is required to estimate the mean summertime earnings of college freshmen, if it is specified that the estimate is not to be off by more than $30 at the .98 level of confidence? Suppose it is estimated from past information that the standard deviation of summertime earnings for college freshmen is approximately $55. Then, entering Equation 9.6.3 with $m = 30$, $z = 2.33$, and $\sigma = 55$, we obtain

$$n = \left(\frac{(2.33)(55)}{30}\right)^2 = 18.23$$

Therefore, we estimate that the summertime earnings of 19 college freshmen should be collected for the sample. However, this is a small sample, so that the use of z in Equation 9.6.3 is not appropriate. We may develop an equation for sample size appropriate for small samples by expressing the maximum error to be expected, according to Equation 9.3.12 (Section 9.3) as follows:

$$m = t\frac{s}{\sqrt{n}} \tag{9.6.4}$$

Solving Equation 9.6.4 for n, we obtain

$$n = \left(\frac{ts}{m}\right)^2 \tag{9.6.5}$$

Equation 9.6.5 may be used to *improve* the estimate of sample size when Equation 9.6.3 indicates that a small sample is to be used to estimate a population mean. In the foregoing example, we estimated, according to

Equation 9.6.3, that a sample of size 19 is needed. Since $n = 19$ represents a small sample, we consider this to be a *first approximation* and use Equation 9.6.5 to improve the estimate of sample size. This equation requires that we refer to the t distribution with $n - 1 = 19 - 1$ or 18 df. Then, for the .98 level of confidence (.02 in both tails), $t = 2.552$. Substituting this t value into Equation 9.6.5 and using $m = 30$ and $s = 55$, we obtain

$$n = \left(\frac{(2.552)(55)}{30}\right)^2 = 21.90$$

Therefore, we estimate that the summertime earnings of 22 college freshmen should be collected to estimate the mean summertime earnings for the population.

When X/n is used as a point estimate of a population proportion p, we know from Section 9.4, Equation 9.4.10 that the maximum error to be expected at a stated level of confidence is

$$m = zs_{X/n} \tag{9.6.6}$$

where m denotes the maximum error expected, as before. Rewriting this equation, using $\sigma_{X/n}$ instead of $s_{X/n}$, we obtain

$$m = z\sigma_{X/n} \tag{9.6.7}$$

Noting that $\sigma_{X/n} = \sqrt{p(1 - p)/n}$, we obtain after substitution

$$m = z\sqrt{\frac{p(1 - p)}{n}} \tag{9.6.8}$$

Solving Equation 9.6.8 for n, we obtain

$$n = p(1 - p)\left(\frac{z}{m}\right)^2 \tag{9.6.9}$$

Equation 9.6.9 provides a convenient basis for estimating sample size when the sample is to be used to estimate a population proportion. The problem in this instance is to obtain an estimate of p to enter into this equation. A fair estimate of the population proportion may be available from past studies or, if no information is available, a small pilot sample may be collected to provide a basis for estimating p. There is another approach which may be taken. Notice that $p(1 - p)$ appears in Equation 9.6.9 as a multiplier. Therefore, if a *maximum value* for $p(1 - p)$ is used, a *maximum estimate* of the sample size required for a given sampling situation will be obtained. It can easily be verified that when $p = \frac{1}{2}$, the product $p(1 - p)$ is at its maximum. That is $\frac{1}{2}(1 - \frac{1}{2}) = \frac{1}{4}$ is the *highest* value that this product can have. (The reader may wish to try various alternative values of

p to verify this). Therefore, substituting $\frac{1}{4}$ for $p(1 - p)$, we may rewrite Equation 9.6.9 as

$$n \leq \frac{1}{4}\left(\frac{z}{m}\right)^2 \quad (9.6.10)$$

or

$$n \leq \left(\frac{z}{2m}\right)^2 \quad (9.6.11)$$

Equation 9.6.11 may be more convenient to use. Suppose a sample is to be collected to estimate the proportion of teachers who are serving on a temporary basis. It is specified that an estimate is desired which does not differ from the population proportion by more than .05 at the .99 level of confidence. If no information is available to provide a fair estimate of p, we may use Equation 9.6.11, with $z = 2.58$ and $m = .05$, to obtain

$$n \leq \left(\frac{2.58}{(2)(.05)}\right)^2 = 665.64$$

Therefore, rounding up, we estimate that a sample of 666 teachers *at most* is required. On the other hand, if we determine from previous information that the proportion of teachers serving on a temporary basis is about .30, then using Equation 9.6.9, with $p = .30$, $z = 2.58$, and $m = .05$, we obtain

$$n = .30(1 - .30)\left(\frac{2.58}{.05}\right)^2 = 559.14$$

Therefore, if information is available on which to base a fair estimate of p, we may find that a smaller sample is adequate to produce the desired estimate. In the foregoing illustration, the estimated value of p leads to an estimated sample of 560 teachers, compared to 666 when the maximum sample size was determined.

It should be noted that, if it is intended to construct a confidence interval for a population proportion as discussed in Section 9.4, the sample size must meet the requirements as noted in that section. Therefore, if the use of Equation 9.6.9 or Equation 9.6.11 leads to a sample size which is smaller than required, it will be necessary to increase the size of sample selected to meet those requirements.

PROBLEMS FOR PRACTICE AND REVIEW

1. A survey of college-trained men over 40 is being planned to estimate the mean score of this population on a reading speed test. How large a sample is required, if it is specified that the estimate of μ should not be off by more than

3 points at the .95 level of confidence? It is assumed, based upon previous experience, that $\sigma = 25$.

2. How large a sample of college seniors should be selected to estimate the mean amount of summertime earnings of college seniors, within 50 cents, at the .95 level of confidence? Assume $\sigma = 5$ dollars.

3. How large a sample of scores should be selected from a very large population to estimate the mean within 5 points at the .95 level of confidence? It is estimated that $\sigma = 10$.

4. It is desired to estimate the proportion of married men in a large city who consider themselves to be happily married. How large a sample is required, if it is specified that the estimate should not be off by more than .01 at the .95 level of confidence?

5. How large a sample should be selected from the adult residents in a large city to determine the proportion who oppose a new bond issue to finance school construction? Assume it is desired to produce an estimate which will be off by no more than .05 at the .98 level of confidence.

6. In a very large community, about 25% of the high school seniors usually apply for college scholarships. If it is desired to estimate the proportion of seniors currently enrolled in the high schools of this community who plan to apply for college scholarships, how large a sample of seniors should be selected for interviewing to produce an estimate which is off by no more than .03 at the 98 level of confidence?

10

TESTS OF HYPOTHESES: AN AREA OF DECISION MAKING

10.1 INTRODUCTION

In Chapter 9 we encountered the application of inductive statistics for the first time. The use of *sampling models* as the *theoretical foundation* upon which statistical inferences are based was presented and discussed in considerable detail. It was indicated how *sampling distributions are used to formulate statistical inferences and how the risks involved are measured in terms of probability*. In this chapter, another application of the methods of inductive statistics will be examined. This is an area of *statistical decision making* called *tests of hypotheses*. Here, too, as in all applications of inductive statistics, sampling models provide the theoretical foundation for making statistical inferences. As in Chapter 9, statistical inferences will be made on the basis of appropriate sampling distributions and probability will be used to express the risks involved. The use of sampling distributions in this chapter may appear to be a little more complicated at first. However, by carefully studying the text and working out the various practice problems, the reader will soon find the material quite manageable.

A vital and demanding duty of administrators and others in the fields of psychology and education, as well as in all areas of business and professional activity, is *decision making*. Generally, this requires consideration and evaluation of myriad facts and opinions. For example, the administrator of a university or the superintendent of a city school system may have to decide whether to replace a presently used teaching method with a new approach, or whether to replace present equipment with something new and presumably better. The qualities of the present teaching method and of the new approach must be carefully studied; similarly, the old and the new equipment must be studied. The advantages and disadvantages of the old and the new must be compared. Decisions are nearly always made on the basis of limited information. For example, although there may be adequate understanding as to the merits and deficiencies of the presently used teaching method and present equipment, this is not generally true for the new method of teaching and the new piece of equipment. Some study and, perhaps, testing of the new method and the new equipment are required to permit an evaluation of the new versus the old. However, typically, study and testing provide only limited information. Consequently, *decision making is frequently performed under conditions of uncertainty.* There is always the *risk* that, from time to time, unwise decisions will be made and, perhaps, financial loss incurred. Moreover, decision making often cannot be avoided because, even when ignored, the negative action amounts to a positive decision to do nothing. However, whether negative or positive, *decision making entails risk that an incorrect decision will be made.*

We will be concerned with certain types of decision-making problems where the methods of statistical inference can offer assistance in the decision-making process. This is the area of statistical inference generally referred to as *testing hypotheses* or *tests of significance.* Let us consider some illustrative problems of the types which we will study.

The principal of a large high school observes that the general average of student performance has been lower during the last two semesters than during previous semesters. He is aware that there has been a larger-than-usual turnover of teachers in the school during this period. Generally, the new teachers are fairly experienced, but many are married women who have not been teaching for several years. During this period, there also has been a substantial turnover in the families living in the community served by the school. The principal needs to know whether the lower scholastic performance of the student body reflects the turnover of the faculty, or a change in the average scholastic ability of students entering the school. If the former, the problem may be expected to clear up as the newly hired teachers continue teaching in the school. However, if the latter possibility is true, then the principal will need to make appropriate adjustment in the methods of teaching and even in the curricula.

How will the principal decide what to do? He knows that he must take into consideration the student population for some years ahead, as well as the present student enrollment, since he must develop intermediate-range, if not long-range, plans. He decides to select a random sample of students, both from the first-year students currently enrolled in the high school and those presently attending classes in the eighth and ninth grades in the junior high schools in the area. Such a sample will represent the population of new students presently enrolled in the high school and the potential enrollment for the near future. The principal knows, from information collected over the years, that the mean score of first-year students entering the high school has been about 100 on a certain scholastic aptitude test. He reasons that, if the sample indicates that the mean score on this test is about 100 for the population, he need not worry. In such an event, the problem should clear itself up. On the other hand, if the population mean appears to be below 100, then he will examine the situation further and determine how to adjust the educational program of the school. (It is assumed, for simplicity, that the scholastic aptitude test is appropriate for both first-year high school students and eighth and ninth grade junior high school students.)

Let us reflect upon the principal's problem. *We know that the sample mean $\bar{X}$ could vary very considerably, no matter what the value of the population mean μ.* That is to say, even if the population mean is 100, a particular sample selected from the population could result in an $\bar{X}$ value considerably different. Suppose $\bar{X} = 95$, should the principal conclude that μ is quite likely 100? Suppose $\bar{X} = 90$, what should the principal conclude? If $\bar{X}$ turns out to be 85, is this sufficiently different from 100 for the principal to decide that μ is less than 100, *even though such an $\bar{X}$ value could result from a sample selected from a population with $\mu = 100$?* We will be concerned with such problems.

As a second illustration, consider the problem of a psychological research laboratory. The chief psychologist of the laboratory is considering the replacement of a special testing machine with a new model put out by the same manufacturer. The model presently being used is satisfactory, although it has not lived up to many of the claims made for it by the manufacturer. This machine is a very sensitive piece of equipment which jams very frequently. Although it is a simple matter to restart the machine after jamming, requiring merely the depressing of a lever, it is considered to be a nuisance. The new model, it is claimed by the manufacturer, may be expected to jam only 15% of the time, representing an important improvement over the older model. However, in view of the past experience with this manufacturer, the chief psychologist is not sure that he can rely upon the claims of the manufacturer.

He decides to test the manufacturer's claim by making 500 trials of the machine. The proportion of times that the machine jams during this sample of 500 trials will be used to evaluate the performance of the machine. Clearly, as in the case of the sample mean $\bar{X}$ noted previously, *we must take into account the sampling distribution of a statistic.* In this instance, we must consider the sampling distribution of the sample proportion X/n. That is, *even if the population proportion of trials (over the life of the machine) which result in a jam of the machine, p, is actually* .15, *the sample proportion, X/n, may be quite different.* This is another illustration of the problems we will consider.

Consider a final illustration. Suppose it is desired to evaluate whether there is a difference in the ability to learn mathematics between male and female undergraduate college students. A mathematics aptitude test is administered to a random sample of male undergraduates and to a random sample of female undergraduates. Comparison of the mean test scores for the two samples will be used to evaluate the difference between the two population means. In this illustration, the statistic "difference between two sample means" is used to evaluate the parameter "difference between two population means." However, *even if the population mean for male undergraduates is identical with the population mean for female undergraduates, we know that the difference between two particular sample means could be substantial.* Hence, here too *we face the problem of deciding how to interpret findings based upon sample data.* In other words, in each of these illustrations *a decision must be made based upon limited information, accompanied by the risk that an incorrect decision may be made.*

10.2 FORMULATING THE PROBLEM

The reader may well wonder why we speak about testing hypotheses if our interest is in decision making. Referring to the three illustrations just presented, it will be noted that, in each case, the decision-making problem was recast in terms of a *measurable characteristic.* For example, in the first illustration, the principal recast his problem relating to the generally lower average performance of the student body in terms of the population mean on a scholastic aptitude test (a measurable characteristic). In the second illustration, the chief psychologist recast his problem as to whether the new model should be purchased in terms of the proportion of times the machine may be expected to jam (a measurable characteristic). In the third illustration, the problem relating to the difference in the ability to learn mathematics between male and female college students was recast in terms of the difference in the mean score on a test between the population of scores for male students and the population of scores for female students (a measurable characteristic). It will now be shown that *statistical decision making involves testing of an appropriate hypothesis relating to the measurable characteristic.*

In general, decision making on a statistical basis requires careful appraisal of a problem and reformulation so that the problem can be handled statistically. The general features of such a reformulation of a problem are outlined in Figure 10.2.1. Let us examine the process of reformulation of a decision-making problem by reference to a specific problem and to Figure 10.2.1. This process requires a *precise* statement of

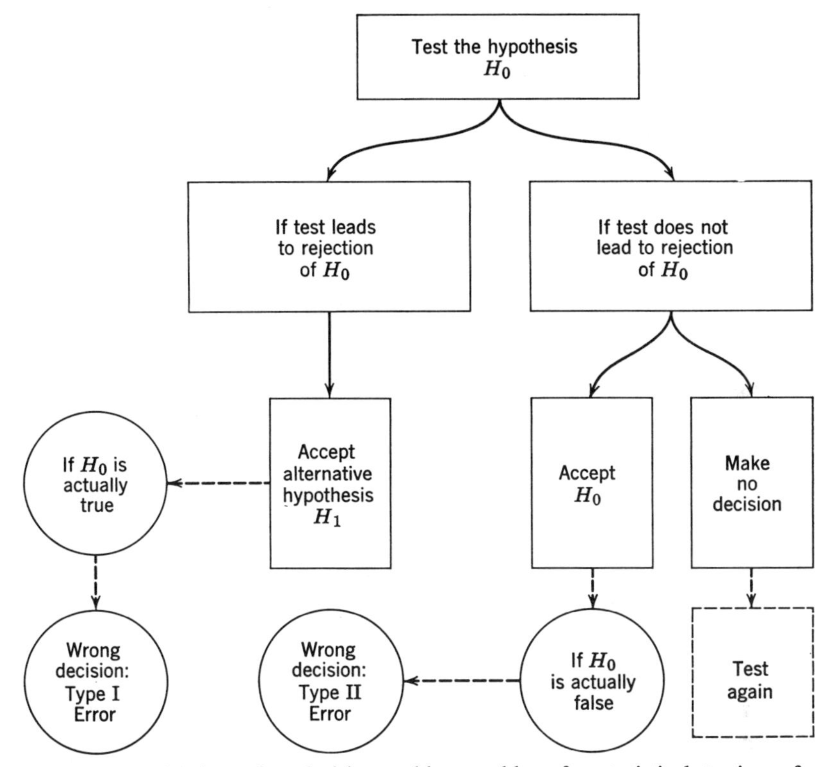

Fig. 10.2.1. Evaluation of a decision-making problem for statistical testing of an appropriate hypothesis.

the problem, including the *alternative decisions* which could be made. Let us consider the problem of the chief psychologist, noted previously, who needs to decide whether or not to purchase the new machine. In the form "to purchase or not to purchase," the problem cannot be handled statistically. However, when the problem is more precisely formulated so that the question relates to the proportion of the trials of the machine that may be expected to result in a jam, we have a specific instead of a general problem. In this form, the problem can be handled statistically. We think in terms of all possible trials of the machine during its expected lifetime as a population of trials. Then, the proportion of trials resulting in a jam of the machine represents a *parameter* of this population. Determination of the *population parameter pertinent to a decision-making problem* is the first step in formulating the problem for the application of statistical methods.

The second step is to set up an *appropriate hypothesis to be tested.* The appropriateness of a hypothesis is determined by the various considerations involved in a decision-making problem and by the requirements of statistical methodology. In the illustration, the important considerations relate to the proportion of times the machine may be expected to jam. Is this proportion actually .15 as claimed by the manufacturer or is it *greater than* .15? Application of statistical methods requires that any hypothesis set up for testing must be *specific*. That is, if the hypothesis set up is that the population proportion, denoted by p, is greater than .15, this is not specific, since *any* value of p which is greater than .15 satisfies this hypothesis. On the other hand, the hypothesis that $p = .15$ *is* specific. One and only one value of p satisfies this hypothesis. Then, this is an appropriate hypothesis to be tested. In other words, the chief psychologist will hypothesize that the claim of the manufacturer is true. This does not mean, necessarily, that he actually *believes* it is true. It only means that this is the hypothesis he will test.

Clearly, we obtain a *specific* hypothesis, appropriate for testing, if we hypothesize that there is *no difference* between the true value of p and the value claimed by the manufacturer. Such a hypothesis is called a *null hypothesis*. It is a hypothesis of *no difference* in the sense just described. Therefore, for the illustrative problem we set up the *null hypothesis:* $p = .15$. We will denote the *hypothesis to be tested* by the symbol H_0. It is customary to write $H_0 : p = .15$, to be read as "the hypothesis to be tested is $p = .15$."

In Section 10.3, a procedure will be discussed for testing H_0. As a result of testing, a decision will be made concerning this hypothesis. That is, it will be decided either to *reject* H_0 or *not to reject* H_0. These alternatives are presented in Figure 10.2.1, where two arrows lead from the single block in the first row to the two blocks in the second row. As the next step in problem formulation, we must set up an appropriate *alternative hypothesis* which will be accepted in the event that H_0 is *rejected.* Clearly, the chief psychologist's concern in testing the hypothesis H_0 is that it may be false. That is, p may be greater than .15 and, therefore, he will not feel inclined to purchase the new machine. (He is not concerned with the possibility that the machine will jam *less than* 15% of the time, since there is no doubt that the manufacturer is making the best claim he can for his product.) Consequently, in this illustration, the appropriate alternative hypothesis, which we will denote as H_1, is that p is greater than .15. We may write this hypothesis symbolically as $H_1 : p > .15$, to be read "the alternative hypothesis is p is greater than .15." That is, if the statistical test of the hypothesis H_0 leads to *rejection*, the alternative hypothesis H_1 will be accepted. In other words, if the test procedure leads the chief psychologist to reject the hypothesis that the machine will jam 15% of the time, he can only conclude that it will jam more often. Acceptance of H_1 as a consequence of rejection of H_0 is shown in Figure 10.2.1 by the arrow which leads to the box "accept alternative hypothesis H_1."

The reader may be wondering why the alternatives resulting from the test of H_0 are *reject* H_0 or *do not reject* H_0. Why not have the alternatives *reject* H_0 or *accept* H_0? In other words, why do we consider *do not reject* H_0 as an alternative instead of *accept* H_0? These may appear to the reader to be saying the same thing. Actually, this is not so. We will observe in the discussion of the statistical test of H_0 to be described in Section 10.3 that sample data will be evaluated and a decision made on the basis of these data whether or not to reject H_0. If this test does not lead to rejection of H_0, there is always the possibility that we have a "*chance result*." That is, there is always the possibility that H_0 is actually false, but, owing to the vagaries of random sampling, the test erroneously did not lead to rejection.

Although we speak *in general* of not rejecting H_0, *in any particular test we must decide what our course of action will be*. That is, we must decide specifically what to do if the statistical test does not lead to rejection of H_0. As indicated in Figure 10.2.1, we must decide whether we will "*accept* H_0" if the test does not lead us to reject it, or whether to "*make no decision*" *at present*. If the decision is to accept the null hypothesis H_0, then our course of action is indicated. For example, in the illustration, if the statistical test fails to reject the hypothesis that $p = .15$, the chief psychologist would then decide to accept this hypothesis and purchase the new model. On the other hand, it may be decided to make no decision at present, since the chief psychologist may want to feel safer that acceptance of H_0 (and purchasing the machine) is a correct decision. In this instance, he could proceed to carry out a second test before deciding to accept H_0. For example, the chief psychologist may feel that the present model is performing quite satisfactorily and before he decides to make a heavy financial outlay to purchase the new model he wants to feel very certain that the money will be well spent.

In the usual situation, if H_0 is not rejected, it is accepted. This is the more convenient approach since it leads to completion of the decision-making process. That is, it is usually desired to reach a conclusion rather than allow the problem to remain undecided. However, in certain situations, as just noted, it is necessary to proceed with caution. In such situations, if H_0 is not rejected, it is not accepted either. No decision is made and further testing is carried out. This is indicated in Figure 10.2.1 by the arrow drawn with a dashed line leading to a block bordered with a dashed line. Sometimes, in a research project, it may be appropriate to make no decision, in the event H_0 is not rejected, and not to pursue the matter by further testing. Therefore, a dashed line is used to enclose this block to indicate that sometimes further testing is not performed.

So far we have shown in the discussion, and as portrayed in Figure 10.2.1, that one of three possible *decision routes* may be taken in a decision-making problem, as follows:

1. Test the hypothesis H_0. If H_0 is rejected, accept the alternative hypothesis H_1.
2. Test the hypothesis H_0. If H_0 is not rejected, accept this hypothesis.
3. Test the hypothesis H_0. If H_0 is not rejected, make no decision. Further testing may follow.

It should be emphasized that *the two hypotheses H_0 and H_1 are determined on the basis of the circumstances involved in the decision-making problem itself.* So far, the requirements of statistical theory are that H_0, the hypothesis to be tested, is *specific* and that it is a *null hypothesis*. Furthermore, at an early stage of planning of the statistical test, it must be decided whether the foregoing decision routes 1 and 2 or 1 and 3 will be incorporated in the formulation of the problem, one of which will be indicated as the route to follow to arrive at a decision. *The choice of routes* 1 *and* 2 *or* 1 *and* 3 *is based upon the circumstances relating to the problem at hand.*

Clearly, whichever pair of decision routes is chosen, there is the possibility of *error*. The possibility of error has been alluded to at various points during the foregoing discussion. Of course, any time a decision is made, there exists the possibility that it is an incorrect decision. Examining the three possible decision routes just listed, only in route 3 is no decision made. However, route 1 leads to the decision to accept the alternative hypothesis H_1. This could be an erroneous decision. Route 2 leads to the decision to accept the hypothesis being tested, H_0. This also could be an erroneous decision. Hence, two types of error are possible when a test is conducted. If H_0 is actually true but the test procedure leads to rejection of this hypothesis and acceptance of H_1, we call this a *Type* I *error*. On the other hand, if H_0 is actually false but the test procedure does not lead to rejection of this hypothesis and it is accepted, we call this a *Type* II *error*. Consequently, *a Type* I *error is made when the hypothesis being tested is true and it is rejected. A Type* II *error is made when the hypothesis being tested is false and it is accepted.* Note that, if the formulation of the problem specifies that routes 1 and 2 will be used to *arrive at a solution, either a Type* I *or a Type* II *error is possible.* On the other hand, if routes 1 and 3 are specified as the basis for decision, then *only a Type* I *error is possible.* The circles in Figure 10.2.1 present the Type I and Type II error possibilities as just discussed.

We may summarize the steps involved in the procedure for formulating a decision-making problem so that it is suitable for statistical evaluation, as follows:

1. Specify the *parameter* pertinent to the problem (the *test parameter*).
2. Set up the *hypothesis to be tested* (H_0).
3. Set up an *alternative hypothesis* (H_1) to be *accepted*, in the event H_0 is *rejected.*
4. Specify whether H_0 will be *accepted* or whether *no decision* will be made, in the event H_0 is *not rejected.*
5. Specify the *level of significance* at which the test should be conducted. This step is part of the required formulation of the problem. However, it has not yet been discussed. We will consider this aspect of problem formulation in Section 10.3.

Applying these steps to the problem facing the chief psychologist, as discussed previously, we have

1. Test parameter: p, the proportion of times the new model may be expected to jam.
2. $H_0{:}p = .15$.
3. $H_1{:}p > .15$.
4. If H_0 is not rejected, accept it.
5. This step will be discussed in Section 10.3.

10.3 CONSTRUCTING THE DECISION MODEL

Statistical decision making may be looked upon as a *three-phase procedure*, as follows:

A. *Appraisal and reformulation of the decision-making problem* to put the problem into a form suitable for the application of statistical methods.

B. *Construction of a decision model* which takes into account the various aspects of the decision-making problem developed in phase A and which specifies *precisely* how a decision is to be made. The decision model is constructed on the basis of appropriate statistical theory.

C. *Evaluation of sample data* in terms of the decision model constructed in phase B and the reaching of a decision via an appropriate decision route as developed in phase A.

Phase A has already been discussed in Section 10.2. It appears that in this phase statistical theory is involved only in the way in which we determine the hypothesis to be tested. Otherwise, phase A appears to require only a careful, precise reformulation of the decision-making problem. Actually, although not apparent, the *manner* in which a decision-making problem is to be reformulated, as previously discussed, has been determined on the basis of considerations relating to statistical methodology. Consequently, reformulation in the manner required permits the application of the inductive methods of statistics to a decision-making problem. On the other hand, in the other two phases (B and C), the use of statistical methods will be apparent. Actually, we ought to indicate an *additional phase* between B and C. This is the phase of sample data collection. However, for the sake of simplicity, we are assuming that sample data are collected and available for evaluation and decision making when we are ready to carry out the steps of phase C.

Generally speaking, construction of a decision model involves determination of the statistic to be used for the test (the *test statistic*) and specification of the *sampling distribution of the test statistic*. Then, the sampling distribution is used to construct a *decision rule* which specifies when H_0, the hypothesis being tested, is to be rejected, and when it is not to be rejected. Description of a sampling distribution requires adequate knowledge of the population from which a sample is selected. As discussed in Chapter 8, Section 8.8, only limited information is available, as a rule, concerning a population. Consequently, we must rely upon a suitable *theoretical sampling model* to provide us with a description of the sampling distribution of the test statistic. We have studied five such sampling models in Chapter 8: *Models A, B, C, D, and E.* We will use these models, as appropriate, for constructing decision models, and additional sampling models will be introduced as needed.

The reader should not be confused by the two types of models. A *sampling model*, as we have already studied, provides a description of a sampling distribution based upon sampling from a theoretical population. Such theoretical models are required since, in sampling situations encountered in practice, only limited information is available relating to the population sampled. Therefore, only from the sampling model can a useful description of the sampling distribution be obtained. A *decision model*, on the other hand, uses the sampling distribution to provide a basis for rejecting or not rejecting the hypothesis being tested.

Determination of the statistic to be used for a test is usually a simple matter. For example, in the problem facing the chief psychologist, discussed previously, the test parameter is p, the proportion of trials in the population which results in a jam of the machine. Then, the test statistic is X/n, the proportion of trials in a sample which results in a jam of the machine. In other decision-making problems which we will discuss, the test parameter will be the population mean μ. In such problems, the test statistic will be $\bar{X}$, the sample mean. Clearly, the test statistic in each instance is the statistic which is used as the estimate of the parameter. The test statistic to be used for each type of decision-making problem which we will study will be specifically indicated. Stating the *test statistic to be used* represents the first step in constructing a decision model.

The second step involves specifying the *sampling distribution of the test statistic.* Let us consider this for the chief psychologist's problem, which involves the population proportion p as the test parameter. In problems involving a population proportion, we will restrict our consideration to problems which meet the following conditions:

1. Population is very large.
2. $n/N < .05$.
3. p is not too close to 0 or 1.
4. Sample size is sufficiently large ($n \geq 100$).

It will be observed that these are the same conditions we applied to problems involving construction of confidence intervals for a population proportion (Chapter 9, Section 9.4). The sampling model applicable to such problems is *Model E.* According to this model, the sampling distribution of a proportion X/n is approximately normal, with mean $\mu_{X/n} = p$ (the population proportion) and standard error $\sigma_{X/n} = \sqrt{p(1 - p)/n}$. This is the specification of the sampling distribution of the test statistic X/n.

The third step in constructing a decision model is to specify the *variable to be used for testing* (the *test variable*). This is usually a simple matter. For example, the foregoing sampling distribution is approximately normal. In dealing with a normal curve, it is customary to use standard z units. There fore, *when the sampling distribution of the test statistic may be represented by a normal curve, the test variable is always z.* This will be true for many of the decision-making problems with which we will be concerned. In other problems, the test variable will be t, already encountered in Chapter 9.

The final step in constructing a decision model is to determine a *decision rule which indicates precisely how to decide whether to reject or not to reject H_0, the hypothesis being tested.* It is easiest to understand this step if we think in terms of a specific example. Let us consider the chief psychologist's problem. Recall that he has decided to make 500 trials of the new model and note the proportion of this sample of 500 trials which results in a jam of the machine. The sample proportion X/n is the test statistic and the population proportion of jams, p, is the test parameter. We have already determined that the sampling distribution of the test statistic X/n is approximately normal. Figure 10.3.1 presents this sampling distribution, *assuming that H_0 is true* ($p = .15$).

Recall that interpretation of sample results presents a knotty problem to the chief psychologist. Even if the manufacturer's claim is correct, so that $p = .15$, *how can he decide this based upon sample results*? For example, as indicated by the sampling distribution in Figure 10.3.1, many different sample proportions are possible, even if p is actually equal to .15. Taking into account the alternative hypothesis, $H_1 : p > .15$, the concern of the chief psychologist is that p may be greater than .15. If X/n turns out to be just a little greater than .15, it would appear safe to accept the hypothesis that $p = .15$. However, if X/n turns out to be considerably greater than .15,

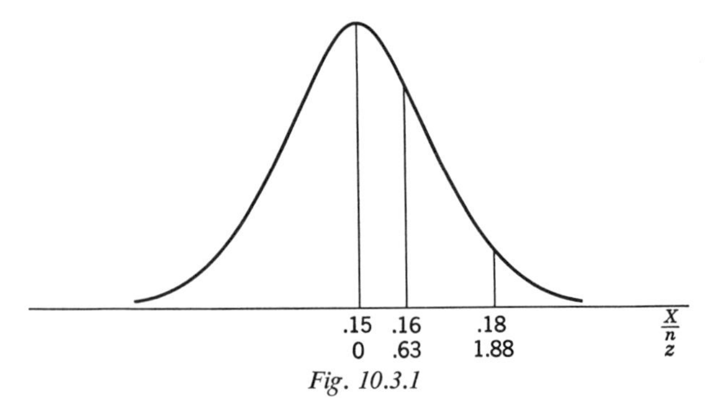

Fig. 10.3.1

this would be strong indication against the manufacturer's claim. *How much greater* than .15 must the sample proportion be for the chief psychologist to feel that he ought to reject the manufacturer's claim? Clearly, this is a matter of how much *risk* he is willing to take that such a decision might be wrong.

Suppose the chief psychologist sets up a rule that he will reject the manufacturer's claim that $p = .15$ if the sample proportion of trials resulting in a jam X/n is greater than, say, .16. How much risk is he taking that he will make an incorrect decision if he is led to reject the claim? We may determine this risk by computing the probability that a proportion X/n computed from a random sample will be greater than .16 *if, in the population, p is actually* .15. Since the sampling distribution of X/n is approximately normal (Figure 10.3.1), we convert $X/n = .16$ to z so that we may refer to the normal curve table, Table B.2, to determine this probability. Using Equation 8.7.6 and remembering that we are considering a sample of $n = 500$ trials of the new model and that $p = .15$ we compute

$$z = \frac{.16 - .15}{\sqrt{\dfrac{.15(1 - .15)}{500}}} = .63$$

Then, we determine that, for $z = .63$, .26 of the total area under the curve lies in the upper tail of the sampling distribution (to the right of $z = .63$ in Figure 10.3.1). Recall that the sampling distribution in Figure 10.3.1 is based on sampling from a population with $p = .15$. Consequently, we may state that in sampling from such a population, the probability is .26 that a sample proportion will exceed .16. In other words, if the manufacturer's claim is true, but the chief psychologist follows his rule to reject this claim if the sample proportion X/n is greater than .16, then the probability is .26 that he will be led to reject this claim, thus making an incorrect decision. Such a decision error (to reject the hypothesis that $p = .15$ when it is true) is what we have called a Type I error. Then, .26 represents the *probability of committing a Type I error. This probability is a measure of the risk which the chief psychologist takes of making an incorrect decision* if he follows his rule to reject the hypothesis that $p = .15$ if the sample proportion exceeds .16.

A probability of .26 indicates that an X/n value higher than .16 may be expected to occur quite frequently when based upon a sample of 500 trials where the actual population proportion p is .15 (26 times in 100 samples of 500 trials each, on the averge). Clearly, this is too high a risk of error for the chief psychologist to take. Suppose he changes his rule and selects .18 to determine whether he will accept the manufacturer's claim (H_0:$p = .15$) or reject it. More specifically, suppose he states that he will reject H_0 if the sample proportion X/n turns out to be greater than .18; otherwise, he will accept it. What is his risk of a wrong decision under this rule if p should actually equal .15? Converting $X/n = .18$ to z units, we obtain

$$z = \frac{.18 - .15}{\sqrt{\dfrac{.15(1 - .15)}{500}}} = 1.88$$

We determine that, for $z = 1.88$, only .03 of the total area under the curve is in the upper tail (the area to the left of $z = 1.88$ in Figure 10.3.1). Therefore, we may state that the probability is .03 that a proportion computed from a random sample of 500 trials of the new model will exceed .18, if the true proportion of jams in the population is .15. In other words, if the manufacturer's claim is true, but the chief psychologist follows his rule to reject this claim if the sample proportion X/n is greater than .18, then the probability is only .03 that he will commit a Type I error. This does not appear to be too great a risk for the chief psychologist to take. Hence, he may announce a *decision rule* as follows: *If the sample proportion is equal to* .18 *or less, accept* H_0 *(the hypothesis that the manufacturer's claim is true). If the sample proportion is greater than* .18, *reject* H_0 *and accept the alternative hypothesis* H_1 *(that* p *is greater than* .15).

In the usual situation, a decision rule is determined by *first* specifying the amount of risk that is considered acceptable that a Type I error will occur. For example, suppose the chief psychologist states that he is willing to accept a risk of 5 in 100 that an error will be made if he rejects the null hypothesis H_0. That is, he is willing to accept a probability of .05 that a Type I error will occur. Then, following the reasoning used above to measure the risk of a wrong decision, let us find a z value which cuts off .05 in the upper tail of the area under the sampling distribution of a proportion X/n (which, as we have noted before, is approximately normal). Such a z value may be found by looking in the table of the normal curve (Table B.2) for a z value such that .50 − .05 or .45 of the area under the curve is contained between the mean ($z = 0$) and the desired z value. We find that $z = 1.64$ satisfies this requirement. Then, .05 of the total area is in the upper tail, as indicated in Figure 10.3.2. We are interested in the *upper* tail, rather than the *lower* tail, *in view of the formulation of the alternative hypothesis* ($H_1 : p > .15$) which indicates that, if the null hypothesis ($H_0 : p = .15$) should be rejected, the chief psychologist will conclude that p is *greater than* .15. Using Equation 8.7.6 and entering 1.64 for z, .15 for p (or $\mu_{X/n}$), and 500 for n (in the denominator), we obtain

$$16.4 = \frac{X/n - .15}{\sqrt{\dfrac{.15(1 - .15)}{500}}}$$

Solving for X/n, we obtain $X/n = .176$, as indicated in Figure 10.3.2. Therefore, *if the true value of p is* .15, then the probability is .05 that the proportion X/n computed from a random sample will exceed a z value of 1.64 or the corresponding X/n value of .176. Consequently, if the chief psychologist wishes to restrict his risk of committing a Type I error to no greater than 5 chances in 100, he could do so by agreeing to a *decision rule* as follows: *If X/n computed from the sample turns out to be equal to* .176 *or less, accept* H_0 *(that the manufacturer's claim is true). If X/n exceeds* .176, *reject* H_0 *and accept* H_1 *(that p is greater than* .15). *It is customary to express a decision rule in terms of the test variable z instead of the test statistic X/n, as follows: If z computed from sample data turns out to be equal to or less than* 1.64, *accept* H_0. *If z exceeds* 1.64, *reject* H_0 *and accept* H_1. In this text, the latter procedure will be followed.

The Greek letter α (*alpha*) is used to denote the probability of committing a Type I error. In the illustration, $\alpha = .05$, as indicated in Figure 10.3.2. Notice, as shown in Figure 10.3.2, that an ordinate constructed at the point $z = 1.64$ divides the sampling distribution into two parts or regions, a *region of rejection* (also called *the critical region*) and a *region of acceptance*. The region of rejection is determined by α, the probability of committing a Type I error. In the illustration, if the z value determined from the sample data exceeds 1.64, it falls into the region of rejection, leading to rejection of the hypothesis being tested (H_0) and acceptance of H_1. On the other hand, if the z value is equal to or less than 1.64, it falls into the region of acceptance, leading to acceptance of H_0. Of course, in a given problem, if the decision rule specifies that no decision will be made at present if H_0 is not rejected, the region of acceptance becomes the *region of no decision*. The probability of committing a Type I error, α, is also called

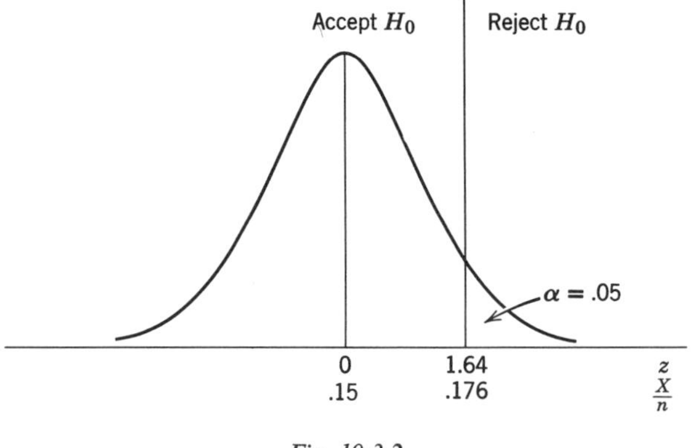

Fig. 10.3.2

the *level of significance* of a test. In Section 10.2, it was noted that step 5 in formulating the decision problem is to specify the *level of significance* of the test. It was noted that completion of this step for the chief psychologist's problem had to be postponed until this concept was explained. This step may now be completed by stating that the test will be conducted at the .05 level of significance.

Very frequently, .05 is chosen as the level of significance at which a test is conducted. However, any level of significance desired could be used. In the usual situation, a level of significance higher than .05 is hardly ever used, since it permits too high a risk (probability) that a Type I error will be made. On the other hand, a lower level of significance is often used where a .05 probability of a Type I error is considered too high. In such cases, $\alpha = .02$ or $\alpha = .01$ is often used.

We may summarize the steps involved in constructing a decision model, as follows:

1. Specify the *statistic to be used for the test* (the *test statistic*).
2. Determine the *sampling distribution of the test statistic*. This involves

specifying the theoretical sampling model appropriate to the problem.

3. Specify the *variable to be used in the test* (the *test variable*) and present the computational equation.

4. State the *decision rule* in terms of the *test variable*. This involves precise determination of the *region of rejection* (taking into account the alternative hypothesis, H_1, and the level of significance of the test) and the *region of acceptance or no decision*, as required by the decision route specified in step 4 of phase A. This decision rule may be expressed in written or in chart form (as in Figure 10.3.2). (It is a good idea for the beginner to do both.)

Applying these steps to the problem facing the chief psychologist, as discussed previously, we have the following:

1. Test statistic: X/n, the proportion of trials resulting in a jam in a sample of 500 trials.

2. Sampling model appropriate: *Model E*. Sampling distribution of X/n is approximately normal, with mean $\mu_{X/n} = p$ and standard error

$$\sigma_{X/n} = \sqrt{\frac{p(1-p)}{n}}$$

3. Test variable:

$$z = \frac{X/n - p}{\sqrt{\frac{p(1-p)}{n}}}$$

4. Decision rule: If $z > 1.64$, reject H_0 and accept H_1. Otherwise, accept H_0 (expressed also in Figure 10.3.2).

10.4 EVALUATING THE SAMPLE DATA

Phases A and B of the statistical decision-making procedure provide the planning and preparation required for evaluating the sample data and reaching a decision. Suppose the chief psychologist asks his assistant to perform 500 trials of the new model and finds that 92 out of the sample of 500 trials resulted in a jam of the machine. Then, the sample proportion of trials resulting in a jam is computed as $X/n = 92/500 = .184$. *How should he use this information to arrive at a decision* as to whether or not to purchase the new model? He notes that the decision rule stated in step 4 of the decision model (constructed in Section 10.3) instructs him to reject H_0 ($p = .15$) and accept H_1 ($p > .15$) if a random sample results in a z (test variable) greater than 1.64. Otherwise, he is to accept H_0. Therefore, using the equation for z from step 3 of the decision model, he computes

$$z = \frac{.184 - .15}{\sqrt{\dfrac{.15(1 - .15)}{500}}} = 2.13$$

Referring to the decision rule, he notes that $z = 2.13$ falls in the region of rejection, as indicated in Figure 10.4.1. Therefore, following the decision rule, he rejects H_0 and accepts H_1, indicating his conclusion that p is

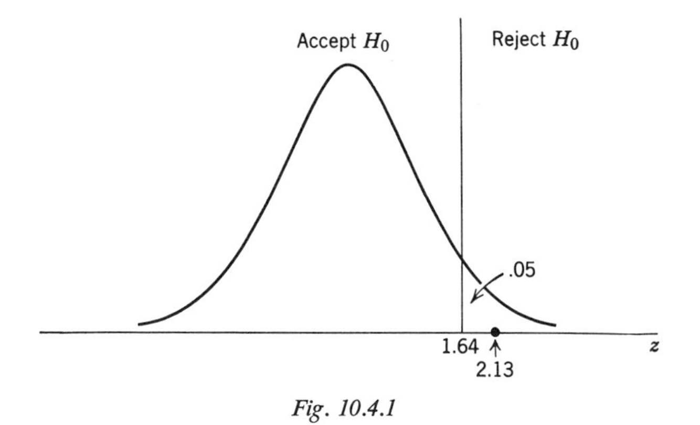

Fig. 10.4.1

greater than .15. Consequently, he makes the decision not to purchase the new model.

It is important to understand what it means to *reject the null hypothesis* which states that $p = .15$. *It does not mean that we have proven that p does not equal* .15. It only means that it has been agreed to reject the hypothesis that $p = .15$ if a sample proportion X/n exceeds a value of .176 (corresponding to $z = 1.64$), since it is *very improbable* ($\alpha = .05$) that such a sample proportion could come from a population where p is equal to .15. However, it is *not impossible* and the chief psychologist is taking a *risk* of $\alpha = .05$ that he has made an *incorrect decision* (Type I error).

Evaluation of the sample data (phase C) is a relatively simple operation involving the following steps:

1. Compute the *test statistic* based upon the sample data.
2. Convert the test statistic to the *test variable*, using the computational equation in phase B, step 3.
3. Evaluate the test variable according to the *decision rule* formulated in phase B, step 4.
4. Make the decision.

We will apply these steps to the chief psychologist's problem:

1. Test statistic: $X/n = 92/500 = .184$
2. Test variable: $z = \dfrac{.184 - .15}{\sqrt{\dfrac{.15(1 - .15)}{500}}} = 2.13$
3. $z = 2.13$ falls in the region of rejection. Therefore, reject H_0 and accept H_1.
4. Decision: Do not purchase the new model.

10.5 DECISION RISKS

We have observed that decision making involves the risk of committing one of *two types of errors*, a *Type I error* and a *Type II error*. This has been noted in Section 10.2 and presented in Figure 10.2.1. Let us repeat the definitions given in Section 10.2.

Type I error: The error committed when the hypothesis being tested (H_0) is *true* and it is *rejected.*

Type II error: The error committed when the hypothesis being tested (H_0) is *false* and it is *accepted.*

These two types of errors, sometimes called *error of the first kind* (Type 1) and *error of the second kind* (Type II), constitute *the risks of decision making*. The degree of risk involved in a decision making problem is measured in terms of probability. We have already noted that the Greek letter α is used to denote the probability of committing a Type I error. The Greek letter β (beta) is used to denote the probability of committing a Type II error. So far, we have discussed Type I errors and have shown how a predetermined and acceptable amount of risk that a Type I error will be made can be incorporated into the decision model (step 4 of phase B). What about Type II errors? Why have we not incorporated an acceptable degree of risk that such an error will be made? We will consider Type II errors further in this section and show how the two types of errors relate to each other.

Let us examine the concept of the *alternative hypothesis* H_1. In the illustrative problem relating to the chief psychologist, we have set up the hypothesis $H_1{:}p > .15$ as an alternative to the hypothesis being tested, $H_0{:}p = .15$. This alternative hypothesis, clearly, is not a *specific alternative*. Consider the specific alternative hypothesis $H_1{:}p = .21$. In other words, suppose that the decision-making procedure is altered so that we test the hypothesis $H_0{:}p = .15$ against the *specific alternative* $H_1{:}p = .21$, instead of against the more general alternative $H_1{:}p > .15$. *Only in such a situation,* *where we test H_0 against a specific alternative, are we able to determine β, the probability of committing a Type II error.*

So far, as in Figure 10.3.2, we have considered the sampling distribution of X/n *on the assumption that H_0 is true*, so that we used $\mu_{X/n} = p = .15$. We will now assume that the specific alternative $H_1: p = .21$ is true and construct the sampling distribution as presented in Figure 10.5.1. Note that, in Figure 10.3.2, the mean of the sampling distribution is $z = 0$ or $X/n = .15$, whereas in Figure 10.5.1 the mean is $z = 0$ or $X/n = .21$. Note further that, in Figure 10.3.2, the division between the regions of

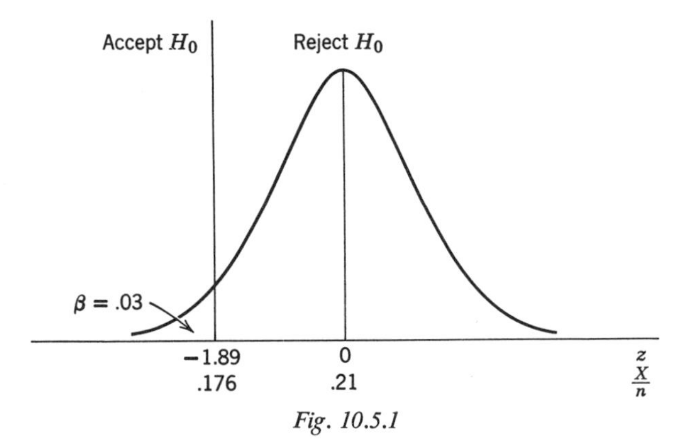

Fig. 10.5.1

acceptance and rejection is at $z = 1.64$ or $X/n = .176$. The same point, $X/n = .176$, is located in Figure 10.5.1; however, the corresponding z value is different because these two figures present *different* sampling distributions of the statistic X/n (different normal curves). The z value corresponding to $X/n = .176$, for Figure 10.5.1, is computed as follows (using the equation in step 3 of the decision model, phase B):

$$z = \frac{.176 - .21}{\sqrt{\frac{.21(1 - .21)}{500}}} = -1.89$$

This value, $z = -1.89$, is also shown in Figure 10.5.1, as are the regions of acceptance and rejection (as in Figure 10.3.2). We may determine, by the use of the normal curve table, Table B.2, that .03 of the total area under the sampling distribution curve is the *lower* tail (to the left of $p = .176$ or $z = -1.89$), as indicated in Figure 10.5.1. How can we interpret this?

Figure 10.5.1 presents the sampling distribution of X/n based upon sampling from a population *where the proportion p is equal to* .21. The area to the left of $X/n = .176$ indicates that the probability is .03 that X/n computed from a random sample *selected from such a population* will be equal to .176 or less. That is to say, the probability is .03 that X/n computed from such a sample will fall in the region of acceptance. In other words, the probability is .03 that the hypothesis $p = .15$ will be accepted, *if the true proportion of times the machine will jam, p, is actually equal to* .21. Clearly, this would be an erroneous decision, a Type II error. Hence, if $p = .21$, β, the probability of a Type II error, is equal to .03.

Let us place the sampling distribution of Figure 10.3.2 on the X/n scale in Figure 10.5.2, with the mean at .15. Now, place the sampling distribution of Figure 10.5.1 on this scale, with the mean at .21. Finally, construct

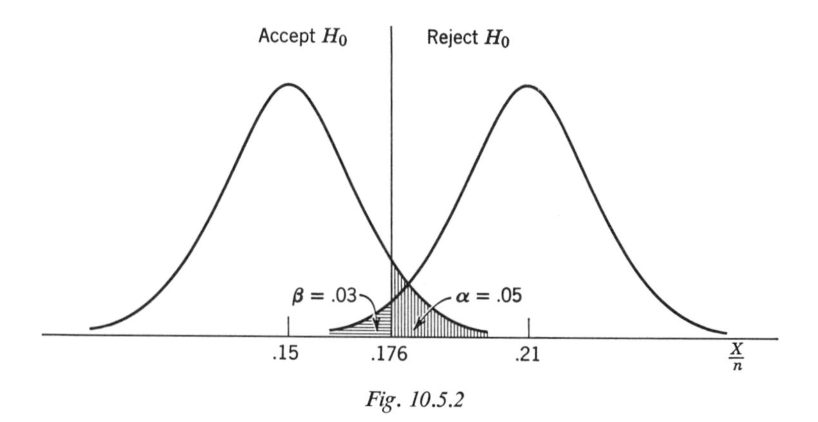

Fig. 10.5.2

an ordinate at the point $X/n = .176$, with the regions of acceptance and rejection identified. Now, with the two sampling distributions placed side-by-side, we can observe the relationship between the probability of a Type I error α and the probability of a Type II error β. These probabilities are indicated in the figure. Note that the area in the *upper* tail of the distribution with mean .15 (based upon the null hypothesis H_0) is equal to $\alpha = .05$ and that this lies in the region of rejection. On the other hand, the area in the *lower* tail of the distribution with mean .21 based upon the *specific* alternative hypothesis H_1 is equal to $\beta = .03$ and this lies in the region of acceptance.

We may move the vertical line (ordinate) in Figure 10.5.2 up or down the scale of X/n values. Then, the regions of rejection and acceptance will change and so will the values of α and β. For example, if this line is moved *up* the scale (*above* $X/n = .176$) then α becomes *smaller* and β becomes *larger*. In other words, if we *reduce* the probability (risk) of committing a Type I error α, we *increase* the probability (risk) of committing a Type II error β. Conversely, if we move this line *down* the scale (*below* $X/n = .176$), then α becomes *larger* and β becomes *smaller*. In other words, if we *increase* the probability of committing a Type I error α, we *reduce* the probability of committing a Type II error β.

Clearly, then, it is *not possible* to construct a test which will minimize the risk of committing *both* errors. The usual practice is to predetermine α at a level acceptable to the decision maker and accept the β level which results. Furthermore, the hypothesis to be tested H_0 is always *specific*, so that a predetermined α can be built into the decision model. This is the reason for testing the null hypothesis, which is always a *specific* hypothesis. In the foregoing illustration, we tested $H_0{:}p = .15$ which, clearly, is specific. On the other hand, how can we set up a specific alternative hypothesis? Should we hypothesize that if p is not equal to .15, it is equal to the specific value .21, as in the foregoing illustration? Or should we use $p = .18$ as the alternative? Usually, we have no basis for choosing a *specific* alternative and must be content with a general alternative, such as $H_1{:}p > .15$. However, we cannot determine the probability of a Type II error unless the alternative is *specific*, as already noted.

10.6 ONE-TAIL VERSUS TWO-TAIL TESTS

We will once again refer to the decision-making problem of the chief psychologist. Recall that he is interested in purchasing the new model only if it is at least as good as claimed by the manufacturer, that is, if p, the proportion of trials which could be expected to jam, is no greater than .15. Clearly, the new model would be even more attractive to the chief psychologist if p were *less than* .15. However, it is not to be expected that the manufacturer will understate the desirable qualities of his product. Quite the contrary, the only concern of the chief psychologist is that p may be *greater than* .15. Consequently, his problem is to decide whether $p = .15$ or whether $p > .15$. Accordingly, in phase A he set up $p = .15$ as the hypothesis to be tested and $p > .15$ as the alternative hypothesis. It should be clear that *both* hypotheses, H_0 and H_1, are logical consequences of the decision-making problem. The null hypothesis, H_0 is always a *specific* hypothesis, *so that we know what to expect if it is true*. In other words, this hypothesis must be *specific* so that we can specify the pertinent sampling distribution and determine the regions of rejection and acceptance (or the region of no decision). For example, we were able to specify the pertinent sampling distribution for the chief psychologist's problem, as presented in Figure 10.3.2, only because the hypothesis to be tested, $H_0{:}p = .15$, is specific. This specific hypothesis led to the sampling distribution of X/n with mean $\mu_{X/n} = p = .15$ and standard error,

$$\sigma_{X/n} = \sqrt{\frac{p(1-p)}{n}} = \sqrt{\frac{.15(1-.15)}{500}} = .016$$

The alternative hypothesis, $H_1{:}p > .15$, on the other hand, is *not* a specific hypothesis. This was discussed in Section 10.5 where it was noted that information is not available to provide a basis for a specific alternative hypothesis. However, the formulation of the alternative hypothesis may vary as to type. For example, in the illustrative problem, the alternative hypothesis $H_1{:}p > .15$, is called a *one-sided alternative* because it specifies alternative values of p which are only on *one side* of $p = .15$. That is, it specifies only those p values which are greater than .15. A one-sided alternative always leads to a test where the region of rejection lies entirely in one

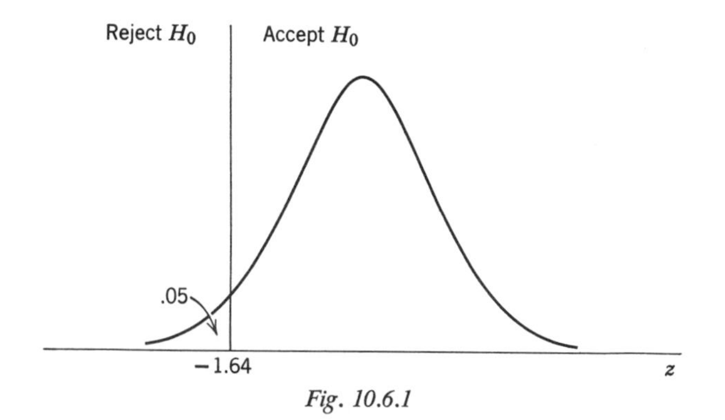

Fig. 10.6.1

tail of the sampling distribution. For example, in Figure 10.3.2 the region of rejection is in the upper tail of the distribution. Such a test is called a *one-tail test. Clearly, a one-sided alternative always leads to a one-tail test.*

The one-sided alternative shown in the chief psychologist's problem leads to a one-tail test involving the *upper tail* of the sampling distribution. In some problems, a one-sided alternative may lead to a one-tail test involving the *lower tail* of the distribution. For example, look at the illustration relating to the new model from the point of view of the manufacturer. Suppose his engineer tells him that, in his opinion, $p = .15$. However, the manufacturer feels very strongly that his engineer is being overly conservative and that p is actually less than .15. Say, the manufacturer decides to run a test by making a number of trials of the new model. His decision-making problem is to decide whether $p = .15$ or whether $p < .15$. He will set up the null hypothesis that the value of p is no different than claimed by his engineer. In other words, for him we have $H_0{:}p = .15$, the same as for the chief psychologist. However, his alternative hypothesis will be different. Clearly, for the manufacturer, the logical alternative is $H_1{:}p < .15$. This is a one-sided alternative which leads to a one-tail test involving the *lower tail.* This is shown in Figure 10.6.1, assuming that the manufacturer chooses to conduct his test at the .05 level of significance.

Finally, it should be noted that not all alternative hypotheses are one-sided. For example, let us view the manufacturer's problem a little differently. Suppose that he has every confidence in his engineer. However, it is his policy to try to substantiate a claim before using it in advertising. Assume that the manufacturer has no basis for doubting the engineer's claim that $p = .15$ and is interested only in testing whether $p = .15$ or whether $p \neq .15$ (p is not equal to .15). Here, too, he will test the null hypothesis that p is as claimed by the engineer, $H_0 : p = .15$. However, now, he sets up the alternative hypothesis $H_1 : p \neq .15$. This is a *two-sided*

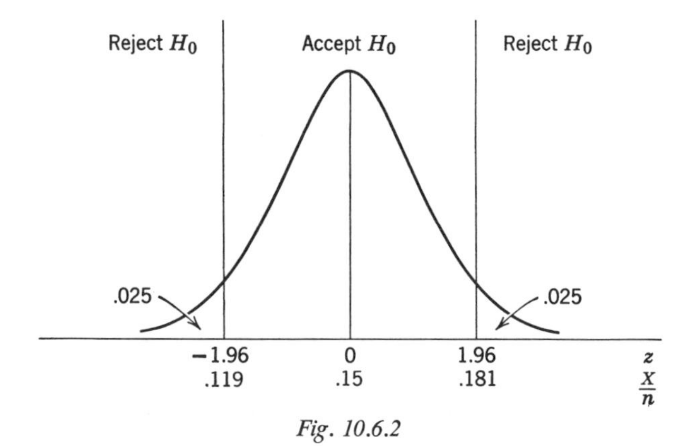

Fig. 10.6.2

alternative, since it specifies alternative values of p which are on *both sides* of $p = .15$. That is, $p \neq .15$ indicates that p could be either less than or greater than .15.

A two-sided alternative leads to a two-tail test. This is shown in Figure 10.6.2, assuming that the manufacturer conducts his test at the .05 level of significance. Notice that the region of rejection appears in *both* tails of the sampling distribution for a two-tail test. The z values which determine the two parts of the region of rejection are selected so that the areas in the tails are *equal* and *together* make up .05 ($= \alpha$) of the total area under the curve. Therefore, since $\frac{1}{2}(.05) = .025$, we need to determine a z value which cuts off .025 of the total area in the upper tail of the curve. Using Table B.2, we determine that $z = 1.96$ is such a z value. Then, $z = -1.96$ is the z value which cuts off an equal area (.025) in the lower tail. These z values are shown in Figure 10.6.2. The two-tail test, where the region of rejection appears in both tails, indicates that if the sample proportion X/n is sufficiently different from .15 so that it falls in either tail, the hypothesis being tested H_0 will be rejected. Let us convert the z values -1.96 and 1.96 to the corresponding X/n values. Using Equation 8.7.6 and entering -1.96 for z, .15 for p (or $\mu_{X/n}$), and (assuming that the manufacturer plans to use a sample of 500 trials of the new model) substituting 500 for n (in the denominator), we obtain

$$-1.96 = \frac{X/n - .15}{\sqrt{\dfrac{.15(1 - .15)}{500}}}$$

Solving for X/n, we obtain .119. Then, using Equation 8.7.6 again and entering the same values as before, but substituting 1.96 for z, we obtain

$$1.96 = \frac{X/n - .15}{\sqrt{\dfrac{.15(1 - .15)}{500}}}$$

Solving for X/n, we obtain .181. These two X/n values are shown in Figure 10.6.2. Now, we may state more specifically that, if X/n computed from a sample of 500 trials is less than .119 or more than .181, the null hypothesis H_0 will be rejected.

Clearly, proper selection of the alternative hypothesis in a decision-making problem is of considerable importance. The level of significance of a test (α) determines the *size* of the region of rejection. However, as indicated in the foregoing discussion, the alternative hypothesis determines *where the region of rejection will be located* in the sampling distribution. In subsequent chapters, examples will be presented illustrating statistical decision-making problems involving various types of alternative hypotheses.

10.7 SUMMARY NOTE

A summary of the steps involved in the three-phase procedure to be used in statistical decision making follows:

A. Formulate the Problem

1. Specify the *test parameter.*
2. State the *hypothesis to be tested* (H_0).
3. Set up an *alternative hypothesis* (H_1) to be accepted in the event H_0 is rejected.
4. Specify whether H_0 will be *accepted* or whether *no decision will be made*, in the event H_0 is *not rejected.*
5. Specify α, the *level of significance* of the test.

B. Construct the Decision Model

1. Specify the *test statistic.*
2. Determine the *sampling distribution of the test statistic* by specifying the theoretical sampling model which is appropriate.
3. Specify the *test variable* and the computational equation.

4. State the *decision rule* in terms of the test variable, defining the *region of rejection* on the one hand, and the *region of acceptance or of no decision* on the other. (This may be presented in chart form.)

C. Evaluate the Sample Data

1. Compute the *test statistic* based upon the sample data.
2. Compute the *test variable* based upon the test statistic (from the preceding step 1) using the computational equation in phase B, step 3.
3. Evaluate the *test variable* according to the *decision rule* (phase B, step 4).
4. Make the decision.

Clearly, phase A requires a systematic evaluation of a decision-making problem. This is a valuable analytical tool for management as well as research workers, since it leads to a specific, clear-cut statement of the various important aspects of a problem. Phase B, on the other hand, is the statistical planning phase which leads to the formulation of a *decision rule.* The decision rule states precisely how a decision will be made based upon the formulation of the problem in phase A. It is important to complete phases A and B *before* the sample data are examined. This is necessary to prevent the sample findings from influencing the development of phases A and B. For example, as previously noted, the level of significance at which it is decided to conduct a test and the way in which the alternative hypothesis is formulated determine the size and location of the region of rejection. After observing the sample data, it may be quite easy to adjust α or the way in which H_1 is formulated to lead to a desired decision. Such a test is statistically worthless, as well as fraudulent.

In the following chapters, we will apply this three-phase procedure to different types of decision-making problems. The uniform manner in which this procedure is applied will become apparent. This should lead to a better understanding of the role of statistical methods in the decision-making process.

PROBLEMS FOR PRACTICE AND REVIEW

Chapters 11 and 12 present the application of the three-phase decision-making procedure to a variety of problems involving different parameters and sampling models. For each type of decision-making problem, illustrations are presented showing how the three-phase statistical procedure is used. Practice and review problems are not presented in this chapter, but appear in Chapters 11 and 12.

11

STATISTICAL DECISION MAKING: SINGLE-SAMPLE TESTS

11.1 PROPORTIONS

The chief psychologist's problem, presented and discussed in Chapter 10, illustrates decision-making problems where the test statistic involved is a *proportion.* In this section, further illustrations of decision-making problems of this type will be presented and in each case the three-phase procedure for statistical decision making presented in the previous chapter will be applied. As noted in Section 10.3, we will be concerned with decision-making problems involving proportions which meet the following criteria (so that *Model E* is the appropriate sampling model): (1) the population is very large; (2) the sampling ratio n/N is less than .05; (3) the population proportion p is not too close to 0 or 1; and, (4) the sample size n is sufficiently large ($n \geq 100$).

Suppose the superintendent of schools in a large midwestern city is considering the use of a newly devised science achievement test for high school seniors in the school system. The chief of the high school division of the school system, who supervised construction of this test, assured the superintendent that the test was constructed so that 60% of the population of high school seniors may be expected to obtain scores within the interval 70–85. The superintendent would not consider authorizing the use of this test unless he felt sufficiently confident that 60% of the population could be expected to score within the interval specified by his division chief. Therefore, he instructs his assistant to try out this test on a random sample of 100 high school seniors in the school system and to evaluate whether 60% of the population of scores may be expected to fall within the 70–85 interval. Furthermore, he informs his assistant that he must make a decision either way very soon and that he is willing to take a chance of no more than 2 in a 100 that, if he decides *not* to authorize the use of this test, he will be making an incorrect decision (by deciding that the population proportion of scores which may be expected to fall within the 70–85 interval is not .60). We will apply the three-phase decision-making procedure to this problem.

A. Formulation of the Problem

1. Test parameter: p, the proportion of the population of scores falling within the interval 70–85.

2. $H_0: p = .60$. This is the null hypothesis that there is no difference between the true value of p and the value of .60 claimed by the chief of the high school division.

3. $H_1: p \neq .60$. This is the appropriate alternative (two-sided), since the superintendent is concerned only whether $p = .60$ or $p \neq .60$. He has no preconceived idea as to whether p is greater than or less than .60, in the event that p is not equal to .60.

4. If H_0 is not rejected, it will be accepted (since the superintendent wishes to make a decision either way).

5. $\alpha = .02$. This was determined by the superintendent. (Although this should always be an administrative determination, the statistician is often called upon to assist in deciding on the level of significance at which a test is to be conducted.)

B. Construction of the Decision Model

1. Test statistic: X/n, the proportion of scores in the sample of 100 falling in the 70–85 interval.

2. Sampling *Model E* is appropriate. Therefore, the sampling distribution of X/n is approximately normal, with $\mu_{X/n} = p$ and

$$\sigma_{X/n} = \sqrt{\frac{p(1-p)}{n}}$$

3. Test variable:

$$z = \frac{X/n - p}{\sqrt{\dfrac{p(1-p)}{n}}} = \frac{X/n - .60}{.049}$$

We substituted $p = .60$ and $n = 100$ into the foregoing equation for z on the assumption that H_0 is true. This will facilitate the computation required for phase C, step 2.

4. If $z < -2.33$ or $z > 2.33$, reject H_0 and accept H_1. Otherwise, accept H_0 (see Figure 11.1.1).

C. Evaluation of the Sample Data

Suppose that 69 out of the 100 scores in the sample fall within the interval 70–85.

1. Test statistic: $X/n = 69/100 = .69$
2. Test variable: $z = (.69 - .60)/.049 = 1.84$
3. $z = 1.84$ falls in the region of acceptance. Therefore, accept H_0.
4. The superintendent decides to authorize the use of the new test for high school seniors in the school system.

A coding clerk in a university laboratory approached his supervisor for a raise in salary, claiming that his work was far more accurate than the

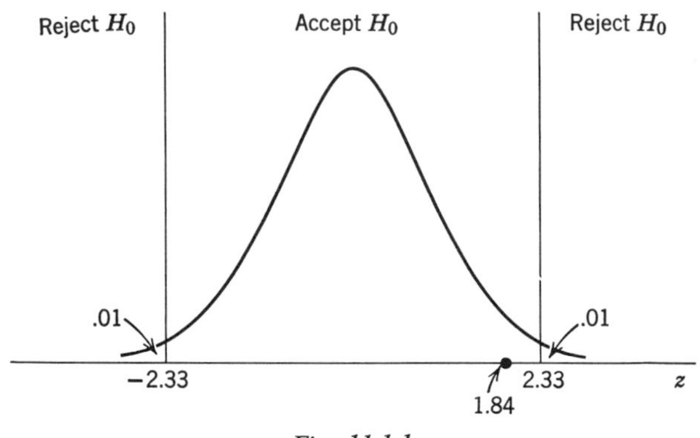

Fig. 11.1.1

work of the others. The supervisor stated that he would consider the matter and let him know. The supervisor is concerned that, if he raised this clerk's salary, there would be complaints from the others unless there is clear evidence that he is more accurate in his work. The supervisor decides that he will select a random sample of 600 codes from this employee's work during the previous week. He knows that the error rate for coding averages about 5%. He is willing to take only a small risk, say 1 chance in a 100, that he will make a mistake if he decides that this clerk's error rate is less than the average .05. However, he plans not to use this test to decide that this clerk *is* average in his error rate. That is, if this test does not indicate that the clerk is more accurate than the average, he will review this clerk's production for an additional week or so before making his decision. We will apply the three-phase decision-making procedure to this supervisor's problem.

A. Formulation of the Problem

1. Test parameter: p, the proportion of codes in error (the error rate) taking into consideration the clerk's coding over a long period of time (the population of codes prepared by this clerk).

2. $H_0: p = .05$. This is the null hypothesis that there is no difference between the clerk's error rate and the average error rate of .05.

3. $H_1: p < .05$. This is the appropriate alternative (one-sided), since the supervisor is interested in determining whether the clerk is average or better than average (lower error rate) in coding accuracy. The question as to whether this clerk is less accurate (higher error rate) is not pertinent to this investigation.

4. If H_0 is not rejected, no decision will be made (until the supervisor has studied the matter further).

5. $\alpha = .01$ (the level of significance of the test determined by the supervisor to insure a small risk of a Type I error).

B. Construction of the Decision Model

1. Test statistic: X/n, the proportion of errors in the sample of 600 codes.

2. Sampling *Model E* is appropriate. Therefore, the sampling distribution of X/n is approximately normal, with

$$\mu_{X/n} = p \quad \text{and} \quad \sigma_{X/n} = \sqrt{\frac{p(1-p)}{n}}$$

3. Test variable:

$$z = \frac{X/n - p}{\sqrt{\dfrac{p(1-p)}{n}}} = \frac{X/n - .05}{.009}$$

The more specific equation for z (the second form) is computed by substituting $p = .05$ on the assumption that H_0 is true.

4. If $z < -2.33$, reject H_0 and accept H_1. Otherwise, make no decision at present (see Figure 11.1.2).

C. Evaluation of the Sample Data

Suppose that the sample of 600 codes included 16 which were in error.

1. Test statistic: $X/n = 16/600 = .027$
2. Test variable: $z = (.027 - .05)/.009 = -2.56$
3. $z = -2.56$ falls in the region of rejection. Therefore, reject H_0 and accept H_1.
4. The supervisor decides to raise the clerk's salary.

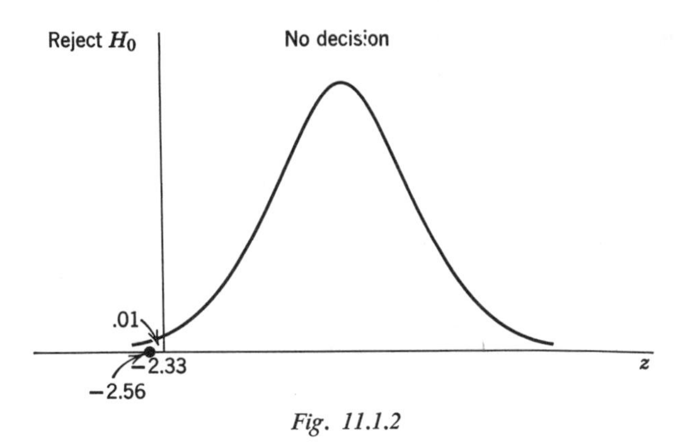

Fig. 11.1.2

11.2 MEANS: LARGE SAMPLES

In this section, we will consider a different type of decision-making problem. We will examine problems where the test statistic involved is the sample mean $\bar{X}$. We will restrict our consideration to problems which meet the following conditions:

1. Population is very large.
2. Large sample ($n \geq 30$).
3. $n/N < .05$.

It will be noted that these are the same conditions we applied to problems involving construction of confidence intervals for a population mean based upon data in a large sample (Chapter 9, Section 9.2). The sampling model applicable to such problems is *Model B*. In such problems, it will be recalled, the sampling distribution of the mean is approximately normal, with mean $\mu_{\bar{X}} = \mu$ (population mean) and the estimated standard error $s_{\bar{X}} = s/\sqrt{n}$. Let us consider some decision-making problems involving means and where a decision is based upon a large sample.

An experimental psychologist is interested in using a drug to slow down the speed of reaction of laboratory rats to an electric shock stimulus. The literature accompanying the new drug states that it will reduce such reaction time to an average (mean) of 35 seconds. If this claim is true, the psychologist would like to use the drug for his next project which requires the use of a large number of rats over a three-year period. However, he wishes to verify the claim of the manufacturer before deciding on the use of the drug. For this purpose, he asks his supplier to send him a sample of 50 rats of the particular strain he plans to use in his experiment. He plans to administer the drug to this sample and to use the data obtained to evaluate the claim of the drug manufacturer. He is willing to take a risk of 5 chances in 100 that he will decide *not* to use the drug if, in fact, the manufacturer's claim is true. Let us apply the three-phase decision-making procedure to this problem.

A. Formulation of the Problem

1. Test parameter: μ, the mean reaction time after drug administration for the population of the particular strain of laboratory rats which the psychologist plans to use in his project.

2. $H_0: \mu = 35$ seconds. This is the null hypothesis that there is no difference between the true mean reaction time, after drug administration, and 35 seconds as claimed by the manufacturer.

3. $H_1: \mu \neq 35$ seconds. This is the appropriate alternative (two-sided), since the psychologist has no preconceived idea as to whether μ is greater than or less than 35 seconds, in the event that it is not equal to 35 seconds. His only concern is whether or not he can accept the claim that $\mu = 35$ seconds.

4. If H_0 is not rejected, it will be accepted (since he must decide whether or not to use the drug.)

5. $\alpha = .05$. This is the amount of risk the psychologist is willing to take that a Type I error will be committed (the level of significance of the test).

B. Construction of the Decision Model

1. Test statistic: $\bar{X}$, the mean reaction time computed for the sample of 50 rats.

2. Sampling *Model B* is appropriate. Therefore, the sampling distribution of $\bar{X}$ is approximately normal, with $\mu_{\bar{X}} = \mu$ and $s_{\bar{X}} = s/\sqrt{n}$.

3. Test variable: $$z = \frac{\bar{X} - \mu}{s/\sqrt{n}} = \frac{\bar{X} - 35}{s/\sqrt{50}}$$

The equation for z is the same as Equation 8.4.4, with the *estimated* standard error $s_{\bar{X}} = s/\sqrt{n}$ substituted for the true standard error $\sigma_{\bar{X}} = \sigma/\sqrt{n}$. It is convenient to substitute $n = 50$ and $\mu = 35$ (on the assumption that H_0 is true) in order to facilitate the computation required for phase C, step 2.

4. If $z < -1.96$ or $z > 1.96$, reject H_0 and accept H_1. Otherwise, accept H_0 (see Figure 11.2.1).

C. Evaluation of the Sample Data

Suppose that the mean reaction time for the sample of 50 rats is 36.42 seconds, with a standard deviation of 6.30 seconds.

1. Test statistic: $\bar{X} = 36.42$ seconds
2. Test variable: $z = \dfrac{36.42 - 35}{6.30/\sqrt{50}} = 1.60$
3. $z = 1.60$ falls in the region of acceptance. Therefore, accept H_0.
4. The psychologist decides to use the drug for his next project.

A psychological testing service has prepared a social adjustment test which it claims is appropriate for sixth-grade pupils in a large eastern city, even though it is quite lengthy. The testing service claims that, on the

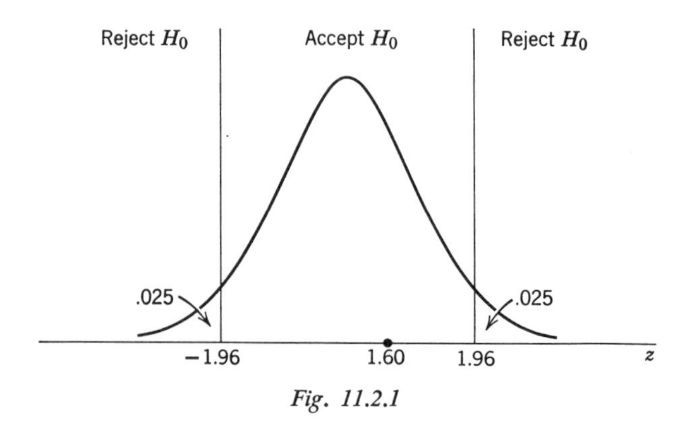

Fig. 11.2.1

average, it may be expected that 40 out of the 50 items will be attempted by the sixth graders in that city's school system. The superintendent of schools in that city is interested in using this test in the elementary schools if he can feel assured that, on the average, *no fewer than* 40 items may be expected to be attempted by the sixth-grade pupils in the school system. He asks the head of the elementary school department to try out this test on a random sample of 100 sixth graders in the school system. He advises the department head that he does not wish to take too great a risk, say, not more than 2 chances in 100, that he will decide *against* using the test, if, in fact, it fulfills the claim of the testing service. On the other hand, if the sample results do not seem to indicate that this claim is false, he will be in no hurry to decide in favor of the test, either. He will probably decide to try it out on a second sample of sixth graders before authorizing its use throughout the school system. We will apply the three-phase procedure to this problem.

A. Formulation of the Problem

1. Test parameter: μ, the mean number of items attempted for the population of sixth graders in the school system.

2. $H_0: \mu = 40$ items attempted. This is the null hypothesis that there is no difference between the true mean number of items attempted and 40 items, as claimed by the testing service.

3. $H_1: \mu < 40$ items. This is the appropriate alternative, since the superintendent needs to decide whether he may expect that the mean number of items which will be attempted by the sixth graders is 40 or whether it is less than 40. He is not concerned about the possibility that it might be greater than 40, since he has indicated that he is interested in

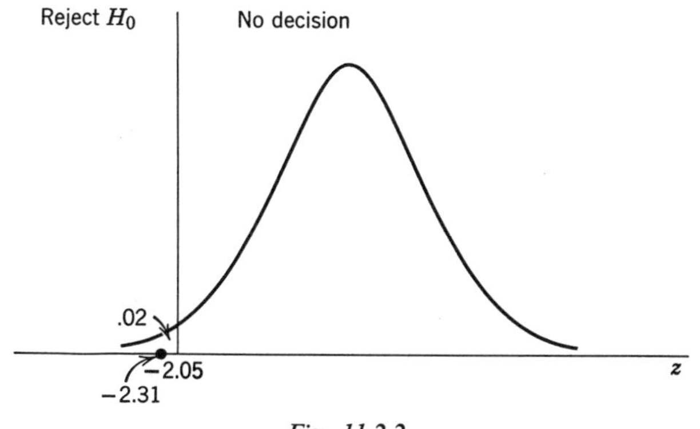

Fig. 11.2.2

adopting this test if the mean number attempted may be expected to be *at least* 40.

4. If H_0 is not rejected, no decision will be made. (The superintendent may try the test on another sample of sixth graders.)

5. $\alpha = .02$

B. Construction of the Decision Model

1. Test statistic: $\bar{X}$, the mean number of items attempted for the sample of 100 sixth graders.

2. Sampling *Model B* is appropriate. Therefore, the sampling distribution of $\bar{X}$ is approximately normal, with $\mu_{\bar{X}} = \mu$ and $s_{\bar{X}} = s/\sqrt{n}$.

3. Test variable: $z = \dfrac{\bar{X} - \mu}{s/\sqrt{n}} = \dfrac{\bar{X} - 40}{s/\sqrt{100}}$

We substituted $\mu = 40$ (on the assumption that H_0 is true) and $n = 100$.

4. If $z < -2.05$, reject H_0 and accept H_1. Otherwise, make no decision at present (see Figure 11.2.2).

C. Evaluation of the Sample Data

Suppose that the sample test performance for the 100 sixth graders shows a mean of 38.55 items attempted and a standard deviation of 6.3 items.

1. Test statistic: $\bar{X} = 38.55$ items
2. Test variable: $z = \dfrac{38.55 - 40}{6.3/\sqrt{100}} = -2.31$
3. $z = -2.31$ falls in the region of rejection. Therefore, reject H_0 and accept H_1.
4. The superintendent decides not to authorize the use of this test.

11.3 MEANS: SMALL SAMPLES

In this section we will consider decision-making problems where the test statistic involved is the sample mean $\bar{X}$ and the sample selected is small ($n < 30$). We will consider only those problems involving sampling from a very large population which is approximately normal in its distribution. These are the same conditions specified for construction of confidence intervals for a population mean based upon a small sample (Chapter 9, Section 9.3). The sampling model appropriate for such problems is *Model A*. However, in the typical sampling situation, we must use s as an estimate of σ and $s_{\bar{X}}$ as an estimate of $\sigma_{\bar{X}}$. The sampling distribution of the mean $\bar{X}$ is approximately normal, according to *Model A*. As noted in Section 9.3, when $\bar{X}$ is transformed to standard units $(\bar{X} - \mu)/s_{\bar{X}}$, using $s_{\bar{X}}$ instead of $\sigma_{\bar{X}}$, the resulting variable is no longer approximately normal. This variable is distributed like the t distribution, as explained in Section 9.3. Accordingly, let us set up *Model F* as follows:

Model F: If samples of size n are selected from a normal population with mean μ and estimated standard deviation s (computed from the sample), the sampling distribution of the statistic

$$\frac{\bar{X} - \mu}{s_{\bar{X}}} = \frac{\bar{X} - \mu}{s/\sqrt{n}}$$

is like the t distribution, with $n - 1$ degrees of freedom.

Note that *Model F*, like *Model A*, contains the restriction that the population from which samples are selected must be normal. This restriction, as in *Model A*, may be relaxed somewhat so that the model also applies where samples are selected from a population which very closely approximates the normal distribution. Furthermore, *Model F*, like *Model A*, applies for any sample size n. However, for large samples (where the number of degress of freedom $n - 1$ is large) the t distribution is so similar to the normal distribution that the distribution of the statistic $(\bar{X} - \mu)/s_{\bar{X}}$ may be considered approximately normal. Our interest in the use of *Model F* is for small size samples ($n < 30$). We will consider some illustrative decision-making problems involving small samples, where *Model F* is the appropriate sampling model.

The business manager in a large university knows that, as a rule, the average amount of tuition unpaid averages \$250 at midsemester. However, he has the feeling that this semester payment has been slower than usual. If this is true, he will have to prepare a letter to send to the slow-paying students. However, since it requires a good deal of work to review all the student accounts to find those which are falling behind in payments, he would like to determine whether this is necessary. If the average amount due is \$250 (or less), then review of the student accounts would not be necessary. He decides to select a random sample of 25 student accounts and test, at the .05 level of significance, whether the mean unpaid tuition for all student accounts is \$250 (or less).

A. Formulation of the Problem

1. Test parameter: μ, the mean unpaid balance in the population of all student accounts.

2. $H_0: \mu = \$250$. Even though the business manager is interested in determining whether the mean is \$250 *or less*, we must formulate a *specific* hypothesis to be tested.

3. $H_1: \mu > \$250$. This is the appropriate alternative, since the business manager is concerned that, if μ is not \$250 (or less), it is greater than \$250.

4. If H_0 is not rejected, it will be accepted.

5. $\alpha = .05$.

B. Construction of the Decision Model

1. Test statistic: $\bar{X}$, the mean unpaid balance outstanding for the sample of 25 student accounts.

2. Sampling *Model F* is appropriate (assuming that the distribution of student account balances in the population is closely approximated by the normal curve). The sampling distribution pertinent to this problem is like the t distribution, with $n - 1 = 25 - 1$, or 24 df.

3. Test variable: $t = \dfrac{\bar{X} - \mu}{s/\sqrt{n}} = \dfrac{\bar{X} - 250}{s/\sqrt{25}}$

4. If $t > 1.711$, reject H_0 and accept H_1. Otherwise, accept H_0. This t value was determined by referring to Table B.3 and finding the t value for 24 df in the column corresponding to the probability .1. Recall that Table B.3 presents t values which cut off a specified area in *both tails of the*

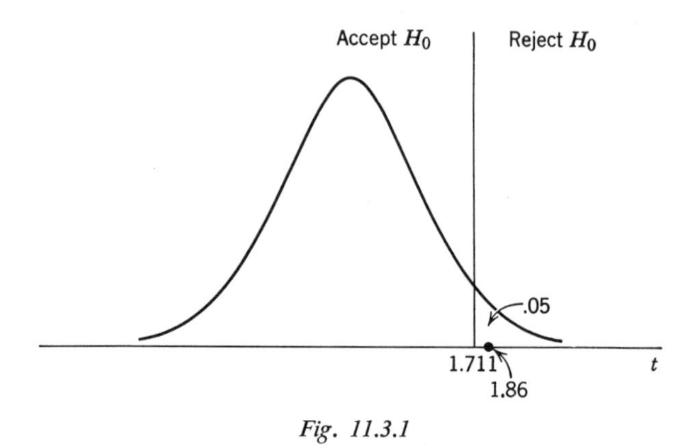

Fig. 11.3.1

distribution combined. Therefore, $\alpha = .05$ for a one-sided alternative indicates .05 in one tail and .1 in both tails (see Figure 11.3.1).

C. Evaluation of the Sample Data

Suppose the sample of 25 student accounts shows a mean unpaid balance of \$263.10 and a standard deviation of \$35.25.

1. Test statistic: $\bar{X} = \$263.10$

2. Test variable: $t = \dfrac{263.10 - 250}{35.25/\sqrt{25}} = 1.86$

3. $t = 1.86$ falls in the region of rejection. Therefore, reject H_0 and accept H_1.

4. The business manager decides to review the student accounts and send a letter to slow-paying students.

The principal of a large high school noted that during the last few months there has been an unusually rapid turnover in the families living in the community served by the school. He is concerned that, if the scholastic ability of the new students to enter the school should be much lower than the ability of the students previously enrolled, he would have to make appropriate changes in the study programs offered. He decides to look into this problem by administering a scholastic aptitude test to a random sample of 22 of the junior high school students in the community who represent the major source of enrollment for the high school. He knows that the mean score on this test has been about 125 for students entering the high school. If he can accept the hypothesis that the mean is at least 125 for the junior high school population in the community, at the .05 level of significance, he will not make any changes in the study programs. Suppose that the sample of 22 scores on the scholastic aptitude test showed a mean of 121.3 and a standard deviation of 12.7. What should the principal decide to do?

A. Formulation of the Problem

1. Test parameter: μ, the mean score on the scholastic aptitude test for the population of junior high school students.
2. $H_0: \mu = 125$. This is the *specific* hypothesis to be tested.
3. $H_1: \mu < 125$.
4. If H_0 is not rejected, it will be accepted.
5. $\alpha = .05$.

B. Construction of the Decision Model

1. Test statistic: $\bar{X}$, the mean test score for the sample of 22 junior high school students.
2. Sampling *Model F* is appropriate (assuming that the test scores for the population are approximately normal in distribution). The sampling distribution pertinent to this problem is like the t distribution, with 21 df.
3. Test variable: $t = \dfrac{\bar{X} - \mu}{s/\sqrt{n}} = \dfrac{\bar{X} - 125}{s/\sqrt{22}}$
4. If $t < -1.721$, reject H_0 and accept H_1. Otherwise, accept H_0. ($t = -1.721$ was determined by referring to Table B.3 and finding the t value corresponding to 21 df in the column for probability .1) See Figure 11.3.2.

C. Evaluation of the Sample Data

1. Test statistic: $\bar{X} = 121.3$
2. Test variable: $t = \dfrac{121.3 - 125}{12.7/\sqrt{22}} = -1.37$

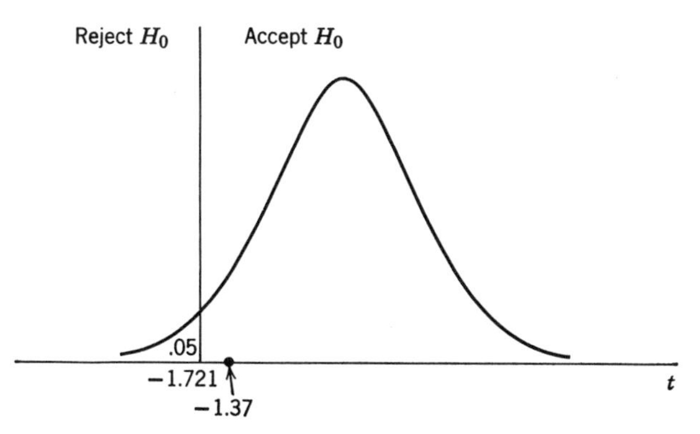

Fig. 11.3.2

3. $t = -1.37$ falls in the region of acceptance. Therefore, accept H_0.

4. The principal decides not to make any changes in the study programs of the high school.

PROBLEMS FOR PRACTICE AND REVIEW

For each of the following problems, complete each step in the three-phase decision-making procedure.

1. In the experience of the elementary schools in a large city, 3% of the pupils fail to be promoted at the end of the school year. If it is found that this percentage has changed (either way), the school programs and teaching methods will be reviewed and adjustments will be made, as appropriate. However, it is desired to take a risk of no more than 2 chances in 100 that it will be incorrectly concluded that the percentage of pupils failing to be promoted has changed. A sample of the records of the city's schools showed that 13 out of 250 pupils failed to be promoted last year. Based on this sample, what decision should be made?

2. In Problem 1, what decision should be made if the level of significance is .05 instead of .02?

3. In Problem 1, what decision should be made if a sample of the records for 125 pupils showed that 5 failed to be promoted. Use the .05 level of significance.

4. A textbook publisher suggested to the superintendent of a large elementary school system that he consider replacing the first-grade reader now being used with a newly published reader. According to the publisher, a well-known educational research specialist is of the opinion that 30% of the first-graders enrolled in the school system will score over 120 on a certain reading achievement test if the new reader is adopted. This is of great interest to the superintendent. He decides to try out the new reader on a sample of 150 first-graders and is willing to take a risk of 5 in 100 that he will be making an incorrect decision if he decides not to purchase the new readers. Assume it is found that 30 out of the 150 first-graders score over 120 on the reading achievement test after using the new reader. Should the superintendent decide to purchase the new reader?

5. In Problem 4, determine the probability of committing a Type II error (β) for the specific alternative hypothesis (a) $p = .20$, (b) $p = .10$.

6. A psychiatric clinic is considering the use of various new medications for drug therapy. The literature accompanying one of the drugs being considered claims that it may be expected to lead to marked improvement in 60% of the patients during the first three months of use for certain mental disorders. The director of the clinic decides to try this new medication on a sample of 100 patients who were diagnosed as having one of the specified mental disorders. If 55 out of the 100 patients show marked improvement, should the director accept the claim that the drug is (at least) 60% effective during the first three months of use? Conduct this test at the .01 level of significance.

7. In Problem 6, determine the probability of committing a Type II error (β) for the specific alternative (a) $p = .50$, (b) $p = .45$.

8. In Problem 6, assume it is the manufacturer of the drug who is conducting the test and that he wishes to decide whether or not to use .60 as the proportion who will obtain marked improvement. He uses a two-sided alternative hypothesis and the .10 level of significance.

9. In a large state college, the experience has been that .73 of the entering freshmen pass the reading comprehension test. It is desired to test, at the .02 level of significance, whether this proportion has changed (either way). What would you conclude if a sample of 300 entering freshmen included 237 who passed this test?

10. In Problem 9, conduct the test, at the same level of significance, if the purpose was to determine whether higher quality freshmen have been enrolling in the college.

11. A resident psychologist in a large hospital proposed a new form of psychotherapy for a certain type of mental disorder, claiming that, on the average, a patient will be ready for outpatient treatment in ten weeks. It was decided to test this claim on a sample of 35 patients, taking a risk of 2 chances in 100 that the claim will be rejected if it is true. However, if the claim is not rejected, it will not be accepted for general use until it is further tested and evaluated. What decision should be made if the mean time required for the 35 patients to be ready for outpatient treatment is found to be 12.19 weeks, with a standard deviation of 7.24 weeks?

12. In Problem 11, conduct the test using the .05 level of significance.

13. In Problem 11, assume that a sample of 80 patients were used in the test, resulting in $\bar{X} = 12.19$ weeks and $s = 7.24$ weeks. Conduct this test at the .02 level of significance.

14. A psychometrician has constructed a mechanical skill test suitable for junior high school students in the larger cities. It has been constructed to produce a population mean of 150, as claimed by the psychometrician. In order to test whether this is a valid claim, the mechanical skill test was administered to a sample of 350 junior high school students, resulting in a mean of 153.01 and a standard deviation of 23.31 for the sample set of scores. Using the .01 level of significance, would you reject the claim that $\mu = 150$?

15. In Problem 14, conduct the test assuming that it is strongly suspected that $u > 150$.

16. A physical education teacher claims that he can train high school seniors to perform a stunt on the horizontal bar in a mean time of 425 seconds. Suppose it is suspected that the teacher is over-stating the mean time required and that for a sample of 35 seniors it was found that the mean time required was 416.18 seconds, with a standard deviation of 19.42 seconds. Using these sample results, test the claim of the teacher using the .05 level of significance.

17. In Problem 16, suppose it is not suspected that the teacher's claim represents an over-statement. Test this claim, using a two-sided alternative. Use the sample information and level of significance as before.

18. A psychologist claimed that a reading comprehension test for high school seniors which he recently constructed was designed so that $\mu = 125$. A sample of 25 high school seniors was given this test in order to test this claim (with no preconceived idea as to whether μ is above or below 125, in the event it did not equal 125). Test this claim at the .01 level of significance, if the sample mean was found to be 111.28 and the standard deviation 22.13.

19. A university file clerk's salary level requires that a minimum of 160 documents per day be classified, coded and filed. A sample of 15 days showed that this clerk handled a mean of 156.4 documents in the required manner, with a standard deviation of 9.9 documents. Would you conclude, at the .005 level of significance, that this clerk was at least meeting the minimum productivity requirement for the salary level?

20. It was claimed that, on the average, a rat would require 15 trials before locating the food box in a certain maze. A sample of 22 rats required a mean of 13.7 trials, with a standard deviation of 3.4 trials. Would you conclude, at the .01 level of significance, that it is easier for a rat to find the food box than claimed?

12

STATISTICAL DECISION MAKING: TWO-SAMPLE TESTS

12.1 INTRODUCTION

The problems in statistical decision making so far presented involved tests of hypotheses based upon a *single sample*. In each instance, *a kind of standard or a reference value for a particular parameter* was expressed in the hypothesis to be tested. After formulating the problem and constructing the decision model, a random sample was selected to test this standard or reference value. In many decision-making problems, however, the interest is in a *comparison* rather than a *standard*. For example, a teacher may want to compare the effectiveness of two teaching methods in order to decide which one to use. A psychologist may want to compare two aptitude tests in order to decide which is more suitable for a given purpose. An educational research worker may want to compare the learning ability of men and women in order to establish a study program. In such problems, *the hypothesis to be tested is, typically, that the value for a specified parameter is identical for the populations involved, or that the difference between them is equal to zero.* The alternative hypothesis is usually that the difference between the parameters is *not* equal to zero.

After formulating the problem and constructing the decision model, a random sample is selected from *each population* in order to test the specified hypothesis. For example, to test whether men and women college students have equal aptitude for studying foreign languages, we would set up the hypothesis that the mean score on a specified aptitude test is identical for the two populations, or that the *difference between the means is equal to zero.* Two random samples would be selected, one of the male college students and one of the female college students. The three-phase decision-making procedure is used to arrive at a decision.

In Sections 12.2 through 12.5 we will consider tests which involve two *independent samples. Two samples are independent if the selection of scores for either sample has no effect whatsoever upon the selection of scores for the other.* The two samples of college students noted previously are independent samples if each is selected as a random sample from its population. On the other hand, if the samples of male and female college students are selected in such a way that each member of the female sample is a sister of a member of the male sample, then these are not independent samples; they are *dependent samples.* A test for dependent samples will be presented in Section 12.6.

The illustration relating to the two samples of college students involves two populations, one sample selected from each. In some problems, the fact that two populations are involved is not as apparent. For example, suppose the objective of a study project is to decide which of two teaching methods is more suitable for teaching history in the junior high schools in a certain city. Two samples are selected from the junior high school population in the city and the two teaching methods tried out, one on each sample. Then the same achievement test is administered to both samples of students and the results compared. Although the junior high school students make up a single population of *students*, this study project is actually concerned with *two populations of scores.* One is the score population which *would be obtained* if all the junior high school students in the city were taught by one of the methods and then took the test. The other is the score population which *would be obtained* if all these students were taught, instead, by the other method and then given the test. However, although these are *nonexistent* populations, the alternatives involved in the decision-making problem (choosing between the two teaching methods) are conceptualized in terms of these two populations.

In some decision-making problems the objective of the testing procedure is to decide whether two samples could come from a *single* population. For example, we may have two samples of machine-scored test papers and it may be necessary to decide whether they could both have been scored on the same scoring machine. In such problems, statistical decision making involves conceptualizing the problem in terms of two populations of machine-scored papers, on the assumption that two machines, not one, were used. One population represents all papers to be scored during the lifetime of one of these machines. The other represents all papers to be scored during the lifetime of the other machine. The hypothesis to be tested would state that a specified parameter has the identical value for both populations, or that *the difference between them is equal to zero*, which is to be expected if these populations are, in fact, one and the same population. In the illustration, the pertinent parameter may be the proportion of scores incorrectly determined by the machine. Then, the hypothesis to be tested is that the *difference in this proportion for the two populations is equal to zero.*

It should be noted that the three-phase decision-making procedure we have studied is not only applicable to problems requiring "action" decisions. For example, it may be desired to investigate whether men and women are equally accident-prone. This may only be a research inquiry, possibly for publication in a professional journal, and not intended to lead to a particular "action" decision, such as instituting special safety measures. Of course, others may use these research findings as a basis for decision making where specific actions are to be taken.

In this chapter, we will consider decision-making problems involving two-sample decision models, where the test parameter is either the difference between population proportions or the difference between population means.

12.2 PROPORTIONS

In decision-making problems involving the comparison of proportions, we will use p_1 to denote a proportion for population 1 and p_2 to denote the corresponding proportion for population 2. We will use n_1 to designate the size of sample selected from population 1 and n_2 to designate the size of sample selected from population 2. We will be concerned with *independent samples*. That is, each of the samples n_1 and n_2 is selected on a random selection basis from its population *independently* of the other sample.

As an illustration, suppose a traffic-safety committee in a large city claims that men and women are not equally accident-prone. Although it is left an open question as to which sex is more accident-prone, it is argued by the committee that traffic-safety problems should be studied separately for men and women. It is proposed that a sample of men and a sample of women be selected from the residents of the city aged 16 and above and an accident-prone measurement test be administered to each sample. The proportion failing the test in each sample (scoring below 90) will represent an estimate of the proportion of each sex in the city who are accident-prone. In this illustration, let the population of male residents aged 16 and above represent population 1 and the proportion of this population who are accident-prone be denoted as p_1. Then, population 2 will represent the population of female residents in the city aged 16 and above and p_2 will denote the proportion of this population who are accident-prone. The test parameter in such problems is $p_1 - p_2$. This difference will be positive if the male population is more accident-prone than the female population (p_1 larger than p_2) and it will be negative if the reverse is true (p_1 smaller than p_2). On the other hand, if the men and women in the city are equally accident-prone, this difference will be equal to zero.

The test statistic in such problems is the *difference between the sample proportions*, $X_1/n_1 - X_2/n_2$. In our illustration, n_1 represents the number of men selected for the sample of male residents, n_2 represents the number of women selected for the sample of female residents, X_1 denotes the number of men in the sample who are judged to be accident-prone (failed the test), and X_2 denotes the number of women in the sample who are judged to be accident-prone. *In order to carry out a statistical test of a hypothesis concerning the difference between two population proportions, we must know something about the sampling distribution of the difference between sample proportions*, $X_1/n_1 - X_2/n_2$. We have encountered sampling distributions in previous chapters (for example, Chapter 8). However, in each instance we have considered the sampling distribution of a statistic based upon sampling from a *single* population. Now, we must consider the sampling distribution of a statistic based upon sampling from *two* populations. This is a little more difficult to visualize, at first; however, conceptually, it is no different.

Consider two infinite populations, population 1 and population 2, and samples n_1 and n_2 selected from these populations. We compute the proportions X_1/n_1 and X_2/n_2 for these samples, respectively, and then we compute the statistic $X_1/n_1 - X_2/n_2$. Each sample is selected on a random selection basis from its population so that, taking into account the concept of repeated sampling, the sample proportions X_1/n_1 and X_2/n_2 are variables, which is true for any statistic. Consequently, the difference statistic $X_1/n_1 - X_2/n_2$ may be expected to vary between *pairs of samples* n_1 and n_2. Let us use our imagination to develop the sampling distribution of the *difference between sample proportions* X_1/n_1 and X_2/n_2. Imagine that a random sample of size n_1 is selected from population 1, X_1 of these n_1 items are found to be in the category of interest (say, accident-prone) and the proportion X_1/n_1 is computed. Then, a random sample of size n_2 is selected from population 2, X_2 of the n_2 items are found to be in the category of interest and the proportion X_2/n_2 is computed. Then, the difference $X_1/n_1 - X_2/n_2$ is determined.

Now, imagine that a *second* sample n_1 is selected from population 1, X_1 is determined for this sample and X_1/n_1 is computed. Likewise, a *second* sample n_2 is selected from population 2, X_2 is determined for this sample and X_2/n_2 is computed. Then, the difference $X_1/n_1 - X_2/n_2$ is determined for this *second pair of samples*. Now, imagine that this process is carried out an infinite number of times. Each time the sample proportions X_1/n_1 and X_2/n_2 are computed and the difference $X_1/n_1 - X_2/n_2$ determined. As a result, we have an infinite number of differences between sample proportions. Now, imagine that we construct a table, similar to Table 7.4.2 (Chapter 7, Section 7.4), presenting the different values obtained for $X_1/n_1 - X_2/n_2$, the corresponding frequencies, and the corresponding probabilities (relative frequencies). We have now constructed, in our imagination, the *theoretical sampling distribution of the difference between sample proportions, based upon independent samples selected from two infinite populations. Model G*, which follows, describes this sampling distribution. (At this point, it is good idea to review Section 7.4.)

Model G: Let population 1 and population 2 represent infinite populations, with p_1 and p_2 the proportion of items in a category of interest in each population, respectively; n_1 and n_2 (each sufficiently large) represent independent random samples selected from population 1 and population 2, respectively. Then, if X_1 of the n_1 items and X_2 of the n_2 items represent the number of sample items in the category of interest, the sampling distribution of the difference between sample proportions, $X_1/n_1 - X_2/n_2$, is approximately normal, with

$$\textit{mean: } \mu_{(X_1/n_1 - X_2/n_2)} = p_1 - p_2 \qquad (12.2.1)$$

standard error of the difference between proportions:

$$\sigma_{(X_1/n_1 - X_2/n_2)} = \sqrt{\frac{p_1(1-p_1)}{n_1} + \frac{p_2(1-p_2)}{n_2}} \qquad (12.2.2)$$

Model G is applicable to problems which satisfy the following conditions for *each* population and for *each* sample: (1) the population is very large; (2) the sampling ratio n/N is less than .05; (3) the population proportion is not too close to 0 or 1; and (4) the sample is sufficiently large ($n \geq 100$). These are familiar conditions. These conditions were specified previously when dealing with proportions. For example, these conditions were specified for decision-making problems relating to proportions in Chapter 11, Section 11.1.

Let us suppose that the traffic-safety committee in our illustration decides to select a sample of 350 men (n_1) and 300 women (n_2). It is decided to test the claim of the committee that men and women are not equally accident-prone by administering the accident-prone measurement test to these samples. The .05 level of significance is to be used. Let us apply the three-phase decision-making procedure to this problem.

A. Formulation of the Problem

1. Test parameter: $p_1 - p_2$, the difference between the proportions in population 1 and population 2 who are accident-prone.
2. $H_0: p_1 - p_2 = 0$. This is the null hypothesis that there is no difference between p_1 and p_2. It may appear strange that the hypothesis to be tested is that p_1 and p_2 are equal (so that $p_1 - p_2 = 0$), even though the traffic-safety committee claims that these proportions are *not* equal. However, it should be noted that the null hypothesis (as just expressed) is *specific*. The hypothesis $p_1 - p_2 \neq 0$ cannot be tested by our procedure, *since it is not specific*.
3. $H_1: p_1 - p_2 \neq 0$. This is the appropriate alternative (two-sided), since the committee has left it an open question as to which sex is more accident-prone in the event that they are not equally accident-prone.
4. If H_0 is not rejected, it will be accepted.
5. $\alpha = .05$

B. Construction of the Decision Model

1. Test statistic: $X_1/n_1 - X_2/n_2$, the difference between the proportion of accident-prone members in each sample (as determined by the test).
2. Sampling *Model G* is appropriate. Therefore, the sampling distribution of $X_1/n_1 - X_2/n_2$ is approximately normal, with mean and standard error as in *Model G*, Equations 12.2.1 and 12.2.2, respectively.

Before continuing with the development of phase B, let us consider the mean of the sampling distribution of $X_1/n_1 - X_2/n_2$ (Equation 12.2.1) and the standard error (Equation 12.2.2). Construction of the decision model, phase B, is carried out on the assumption that the hypothesis being tested (H_0) is true. Consequently, under this assumption p_1 and p_2 are equal, so that the mean of the sampling distribution, as expressed by Equation 12.2.1, becomes

$$\mu_{(X_1/n_1 - X_2/n_2)} = p_1 - p_2 = 0 \tag{12.2.3}$$

Furthermore, if we use p to represent both p_1 and p_2 (since they are assumed to be equal), we may rewrite Equation 12.2.2 as

$$\sigma_{(X_1/n_1 - X_2/n_2)} = \sqrt{\frac{p(1-p)}{n_1} + \frac{p(1-p)}{n_2}}$$

$$= \sqrt{p(1-p)\left(\frac{1}{n_1} + \frac{1}{n_2}\right)} \tag{12.2.4}$$

Of course, in a given problem, we do not know p_1, p_2, or p. We estimate p_1 and p_2 by the sample proportions X_1/n_1 and X_2/n_2, respectively. In order to estimate the common value p, assuming p_1 and p_2 are equal, we *pool* the information obtained in both samples and estimate p by computing X/n as

$$\frac{X}{n} = \frac{X_1 + X_2}{n_1 + n_2} \tag{12.2.5}$$

Then, we compute the *estimated* standard error of the difference between proportions by substituting X/n for p in Equation 12.2.4 to obtain

$$s_{(X_1/n_1 - X_2/n_2)} = \sqrt{\frac{X}{n}\left(1 - \frac{X}{n}\right)\left(\frac{1}{n_1} + \frac{1}{n_2}\right)} \tag{12.2.6}$$

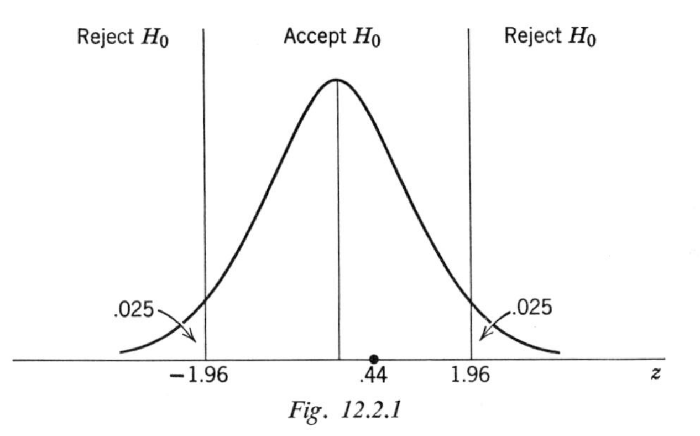

Fig. 12.2.1

Let us now continue with phase B of the decision-making procedure.

3. Test variable: $$z = \frac{\left(\dfrac{X_1}{n_1} - \dfrac{X_2}{n_2}\right) - (p_1 - p_2)}{s_{(X_1/n_1 - X_2/n_2)}} = \frac{X_1/n_1 - X_2/n_2}{s_{(X_1/n_1 - X_2/n_2)}}$$

The second form for z is obtained by recognizing that $p_1 - p_2 = 0$, on the assumption that H_0 is true (Equation 12.2.3). See Equation 12.2.6 for $s_{(X_1/n_1 - X_2/n_2)}$.

4. If $z < -1.96$ or $z > 1.96$, reject H_0 and accept H_1. Otherwise, accept H_0 (see Figure 12.2.1).

C. Evaluation of the Sample Data

Suppose that 52 out of the sample of 350 male residents were judged to be accident-prone (failed the test), whereas 41 out of the sample of 300 female residents were judged to be accident-prone.

1. Test statistics: $\dfrac{X_1}{n_1} = \dfrac{52}{350} = .149$

$$\frac{X_2}{n_2} = \frac{41}{300} = .137$$

$$\frac{X}{n} = \frac{52 + 41}{350 + 300} = \frac{93}{650} = .143$$

2. Test variable: $z = \dfrac{.149 - .137}{\sqrt{.143(1 - .143)\left(\dfrac{1}{350} + \dfrac{1}{300}\right)}} = .44$

3. $z = .44$ falls in the region of acceptance. Therefore, accept H_0.

4. The traffic-safety committee decides to drop its claim that men and women are not equally accident-prone.

In problems involving the comparison of population proportions, or other parameters, the objective is often to test whether observed sample differences are *statistically significant.* That is, the objective is to test the null hypothesis that the parameter in question (say, the population proportion) is equal for two populations. However, if H_0 is not rejected, it is not accepted either. Such *tests of significance* of the difference between parameters based upon sample data are frequently used in the analysis of research findings.

PROBLEMS FOR PRACTICE AND REVIEW

1. A sample of 200 local residents enrolled in a large university showed that 18 failed one or more subjects compared with 21 out of 240 out-of-state residents enrolled at the school who failed one or more subjects. Would you conclude, at the .01 level of significance, that there is no difference in the proportion who fail one or more subjects between local and out-of-state residents?

2. In a sample of 450 men aged 21 and over, 132 indicated a feeling of prejudice toward minority groups. In a sample of 300 women aged 21 and over, 122 indicated such a feeling of prejudice. Would you conclude, at the .02 level of significance, that men and women aged 21 and over exhibit an equal amount of prejudice toward minority groups?

3. In a psychiatric clinic, 235 patients out of a sample of 360 showed improvement after psychotherapy compared to 239 patients out of a sample of 410 who showed improvement after shock therapy. Would you conclude, at the .05 level of significance, that the proportion of patients who can profit from each of these types of therapy is the same?

4. In Problem 3, suppose it is believed that psychotherapy is the more effective form of treatment. Using a one-sided alternative and the .05 level of significance, would you conclude that psychotherapy is the more effective form of treatment?

5. A sample of 150 undergraduate students showed that 63 scored over 130 on a social adjustment inventory, Form A, whereas, 56 out of a sample of 145 undergraduates scored over 130 on Form B of this test. Would you conclude that the proportion scoring over 130 is the same for Forms A and B in the population? Use the .05 level of significance.

6. If in Problem 5, it is actually believed that Form A scores will tend to have a larger proportion over 130 than Form B scores, conduct the test using an appropriate one-sided alternative.

12.3 MEANS: LARGE SAMPLES

In two-sample decision-making problems involving the comparison of means, we will use μ_1 and σ_1 to denote the mean and standard deviation, respectively, for population 1, and μ_2 and σ_2 to denote the corresponding parameters for population 2. As before, we will use n_1 and n_2 to designate the samples selected from population 1 and population 2, respectively. We will use $\bar{X}_1$ and s_1 to denote the mean and standard deviation for sample n_1, and $\bar{X}_2$ and s_2 to denote the corresponding statistics for sample n_2. In this section, we will consider only *independent samples.* The test statistic in such problems is *the difference between the sample means,* $\bar{X}_1 - \bar{X}_2$. In order to be able to carry out a statistical test of a hypothesis relating to the statistic $\bar{X}_1 - \bar{X}_2$, we must say something about the sampling distribution of this statistic.

Conceptually, the sampling distribution of $\bar{X}_1 - \bar{X}_2$ is similar to the sampling distribution of the difference between two sample proportions, discussed in Section 12.2. Imagine that a sample of size n_1 is selected from population 1 (infinite) and that $\bar{X}_1$ is computed for this sample. Then, imagine that a sample of size n_2 is selected from population 2 (infinite) and $\bar{X}_2$ is computed. Then, compute the difference $\bar{X}_1 - \bar{X}_2$. Now, imagine that a *second* pair of samples are selected, n_1 from population 1 and n_2 from population 2, $\bar{X}_1$ and $\bar{X}_2$ computed, as well as the difference $\bar{X}_1 - \bar{X}_2$. Now, imagine that this process is carried out an infinite number of times. Each time, $\bar{X}_1$ and $\bar{X}_2$, as well as $\bar{X}_1 - \bar{X}_2$, are computed. As a result, we have an infinite number of differences $\bar{X}_1 - \bar{X}_2$. Now, imagine that we construct a table, similar to Table 7.4.2, presenting the different values obtained for $\bar{X}_1 - \bar{X}_2$, the corresponding frequencies, and the corresponding probabilities. We have now constructed, in our imagination, the *theoretical sampling distribution of the difference between sample means,* based upon *independent samples* selected from *two* infinite populations. *Model H* describes this sampling distribution.

Model H: Let population 1 and population 2 represent infinite populations, with μ_1, σ_1, and μ_2, σ_2 the corresponding means and standard deviations; n_1 and n_2 represent large, independent, random samples selected from population 1 and population 2, respectively. Denote the mean as $\bar{X}_1$ for sample n_1 and as $\bar{X}_2$ for sample n_2. Then, the sampling distribution of the difference between sample means $\bar{X}_1 - \bar{X}_2$ is approximately normal, with

mean:

$$\mu_{(\bar{X}_1-\bar{X}_2)} = \mu_1 - \mu_2 \tag{12.3.1}$$

standard error of the difference between means:

$$\sigma_{(\bar{X}_1-\bar{X}_2)} = \sqrt{\sigma_{\bar{X}_1}^2 + \sigma_{\bar{X}_2}^2}$$

$$= \sqrt{\frac{\sigma_1^2}{n_1} + \frac{\sigma_2^2}{n_2}} \tag{12.3.2}$$

Model H is applicable to problems which satisfy the following conditions for *each* population and *each* sample: (1) the population is very large; (2) sample size is equal to 30 or more; and (3) the sampling ratio n/N is less than .05. These are the same restrictions applied to decision-making problems involving the mean computed from a large sample in Chapter 11, Section 11.2.

As an illustration, suppose that it is desired to test whether a tranquilizing drug has any effect on the ability of men 60 years of age and over to perform a certain task. Suppose a research clinic administers this medication to a random sample of 75 subjects and a placebo (saline solution) to a random sample of 80 subjects. The first sample ($n_1 = 75$) is designated the experimental sample, and the second sample ($n_2 = 80$) is designated the control sample. The subjects in each sample are asked to perform the required task and a record is kept of the number of errors made by each subject. It is desired to test whether there is a significant difference in the mean number of errors made by each sample at the .01 level of significance. It is *not* intended to conclude, based upon this test, that the drug has no effect upon the ability to perform the task.

A. Formulation of the Problem

1. Test parameter: $\mu_1 - \mu_2$, the difference between the mean number of errors in population 1 (the error counts per man aged 60 and over, assuming that the task was attempted by these men after the drug was administered) and population 2 (the error counts per man aged 60 and over, assuming that the task was attempted by these men after the placebo was administered).

2. $H_0: \mu_1 - \mu_2 = 0$

3. $H_1: \mu_1 - \mu_2 \neq 0$. This is the usual alternative when two parameters are compared.

4. If H_0 is not rejected, it will not be accepted either (since it is not intended to conclude, based upon this test, that the drug has no effect).

5. $\alpha = .01$.

B. Construction of the Decision Model

1. Test statistic: $\bar{X}_1 - \bar{X}_2$, the difference between the mean number of errors in the two samples.

2. Sampling *Model H* is appropriate. Therefore, the sampling distribution of $\bar{X}_1 - \bar{X}_2$ is approximately normal, with mean and standard error as in *Model H*, Equations 12.3.1 and 12.3.2.

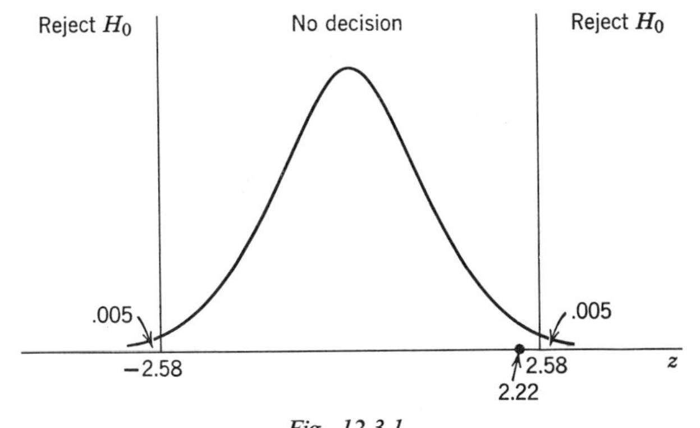

Fig. 12.3.1

3. Test variable: $$z = \frac{(\bar{X}_1 - \bar{X}_2) - (\mu_1 - \mu_2)}{s_{(\bar{X}_1 - \bar{X}_2)}}$$

$$= \frac{\bar{X}_1 - \bar{X}_2}{\sqrt{\dfrac{s_1^2}{n_1} + \dfrac{s_2^2}{n_2}}}$$

The second form is obtained by recognizing that $\mu_1 - \mu_2 = 0$, on the assumption that H_0 is true. Also, we have substituted the *estimated* standard error $s_{(\bar{X}_1 - \bar{X}_2)}$ for the standard error $\sigma_{(\bar{X}_1 - \bar{X}_2)}$.

4. If $z < -2.58$ or $z > 2.58$, reject H_0 and accept H_1. Otherwise, make no decision (see Figure 12.3.1).

C. Evaluation of the Sample Data

Suppose the experimental sample ($n_1 = 75$) showed a mean of 21.6 errors, with a standard deviation of 8.9, whereas the control sample ($n_2 = 80$) showed a mean of 18.2 errors, with a standard deviation of 10.1.

1. Test statistic: $\bar{X}_1 - \bar{X}_2 = 21.6 - 18.2 = 3.4$

2. Test variable: $z = \dfrac{21.6 - 18.2}{\sqrt{(8.9)^2/75 + (10.1)^2/80}} = 2.22$

3. $z = 2.22$ falls in the region of no decision.

4. No conclusion is drawn with respect to the effect of the drug on the ability of men aged 60 and over to perform a certain task.

PROBLEMS FOR PRACTICE AND REVIEW

1. A sample of 45 social science majors obtained a mean score of 132.16 on a vocabulary recall test, with a standard deviation of 28.71. A sample of 54 business administration majors obtained a mean of 120.98, with a standard deviation of 30.47, on the same test. Would you conclude, at the .05 level of significance, that the mean score on the vocabulary recall test is the same for the population of social science majors and the population of business administration majors?

2. The number of letters opened, stamped and sorted was recorded for a sample of 75 hours for clerk A and for a sample of 64 hours for clerk B. Based on these sample data, it was found that clerk A processed a mean of 63.2 letters per hour, with a standard deviation of 16.3, whereas clerk B processed a mean of 69.6 letters per hour, with a standard deviation of 18.4. Would you conclude that the mean number of letters per hour processed by these clerks is the same? Use the .02 level of significance.

3. In Problem 2, assume that clerk B is paid more than clerk A, and it is expected that this clerk will process more letters per hour. Using the .02 level of significance and the appropriate one-sided alternative, would you conclude that clerk B processes a higher mean number of letters per hour than clerk A?

4. In order to evaluate the relative difficulty of performing a certain task by two different methods, two samples of subjects were selected and each method tried. A sample of 110 subjects required a mean of 12.64 minutes per subject to perform the task using method 1, with a standard deviation of 3.96 minutes. A sample of 146 subjects required a mean of 13.72 minutes per subject using method 2, with a standard deviation of 4.54 minutes. Would you conclude, at the .01 level of significance, that the mean time per subject required to perform the task is the same for both methods?

5. A sample of 420 subjects was asked to draw a line of a specified length, from left to right, while blindfolded. The mean length of line drawn was 28.61 inches, with a standard deviation of 9.18 inches. A second sample, made up of 365 subjects, also blindfolded, was asked to draw a line of the same specified length, but from right to left. The mean length of line drawn was 27.14 inches, with a standard deviation of 12.21 inches. Would you conclude, at the .05 level of significance, that the mean length of line drawn is the same whether drawn from left to right or from right to left?

6. A sample of 40 typists was asked to type a portion of printed copy on Brand A typewriters, and a sample of 38 typists was asked to type from the same copy on Brand B typewriters which have a slightly different keyboard. The first sample noted made a mean of 17.5 errors, with a standard deviation of 4.1 errors. The other sample made a mean of 16.2 errors, with a standard deviation of 5.3 errors. Would you conclude, at the .01 level of significance, that the mean number of errors made when using either brand of typewriter is the same?

12.4 MEANS: SMALL SAMPLES

Statistical tests relating to decision-making problems involving the comparison of means based upon small-sample data are similar to tests explained when large-sample data are used. However, the statistical theory used in developing the appropriate sampling model is different. Two important differences, when small samples are involved, are that the populations from which the samples are selected must each be normal in distribution and the sampling distribution of the test statistic $\bar{X}_1 - \bar{X}_2$, when expressed in standard units based upon an estimated standard error, is like the t distribution. *Model I*, which follows, is the appropriate sampling model. The same notation will be used as for large samples (presented in Section 12.3).

Model I: Let population 1 and population 2 represent normal populations, with means μ_1 and μ_2, respectively; n_1 and n_2 represent small, independent, random samples selected from population 1 and population 2, respectively. Denote the mean and standard deviation as $\bar{X}_1$ and s_1 for sample n_1, and as $\bar{X}_2$ and s_2 for sample n_2. The sampling distribution of the statistic

$$\frac{(\bar{X}_1 - \bar{X}_2) - \mu_{(\bar{X}_1 - \bar{X}_2)}}{s_{(\bar{X}_1 - \bar{X}_1)}} = \frac{(\bar{X}_1 - \bar{X}_2) - (\mu_1 - \mu_2)}{\sqrt{\dfrac{s_1^2}{n_1} + \dfrac{s_2^2}{n_2}}} \tag{12.4.1}$$

is like the t distribution, with $n_1 - 1$ df for sample n_1 and $n_2 - 1$ df for sample n_2. Let t_1 denote the *critical value* for $n_1 - 1$ df (the t value which determines the region of rejection) and let t_2 denote the *critical value* for $n_2 - 1$ df, then the critical t value to be used in a statistical test is approximated as

$$t = \frac{s_{\bar{X}_1}^2 t_1 + s_{\bar{X}_2}^2 t_2}{s_{\bar{X}_1}^2 + s_{\bar{X}_2}^2}$$

$$= \frac{\dfrac{s_1^2}{n_1} t_1 + \dfrac{s_2^2}{n_2} t_2}{\dfrac{s_1^2}{n_1} + \dfrac{s_2^2}{n_2}} \tag{12.4.2}$$

Model I is applicable to problems where the populations involved are each very large and closely normal in distribution, the sampling ratio n/N is less than .05 for each sample, with sample size less than 30.

Suppose it is desired to determine whether there is or is not a difference in effectiveness between two methods of teaching reading to first graders. The principal of a large elementary school selects a sample of $n_1 = 8$ pupils who were taught by method 1 and a sample of $n_2 = 10$ pupils who were taught by method 2. After a period of time, a reading test is administered to the pupils in each sample. The mean score on the test for each sample is to be used as the basis for comparing the effectiveness of the two teaching methods. The level of significance to be used is specified as .05 by the principal.

A. Formulation of the Problem

1. Test parameter: $\mu_1 - \mu_2$, the difference between the mean test score for population 1 (test scores for all first graders, assuming they were all taught by method 1) and population 2 (test scores for all first graders, assuming they were all taught by method 2).
2. $H_0: \mu_1 - \mu_2 = 0$.
3. $H_1: \mu_1 - \mu_2 \neq 0$.
4. If H_0 is not rejected, it will be accepted.
5. $\alpha = .05$.

B. Construction of the Decison Model

1. Test statistic: $\bar{X}_1 - \bar{X}_2$, the difference between the mean test scores in the two samples.

2. Sampling *Model I* is appropriate. Therefore, the appropriate sampling distribution is the t distribution, with t computed and the critical value determined according to the model (Equations 12.4.1 and 12.4.2).

3. Test variable:

$$t = \frac{(\bar{X}_1 - \bar{X}_2) - (\mu_1 - \mu_2)}{\sqrt{\dfrac{s_1^2}{n_1} + \dfrac{s_2^2}{n_2}}}$$

$$= \frac{\bar{X}_1 - \bar{X}_2}{\sqrt{\dfrac{s_1^2}{n_1} + \dfrac{s_2^2}{n_2}}}$$

The second form is obtained by recognizing that $\mu_1 - \mu_2 = 0$, on the assumption that H_0 is true.

4. If $t < -t_{.05}$ or $t > t_{.05}$, reject H_0 and accept H_1, where $t_{.05}$ (the critical value of t for a two-sided alternative with $\alpha = .05$) is determined according to Equation 12.4.2. Otherwise, accept H_0 (see Figure 12.4.1).

C. Evaluation of the Sample Data

Suppose the findings are that $\bar{X}_1 = 31.6$ and $s_1 = 5.3$ for sample $n_1 = 8$, and $\bar{X}_2 = 38.1$ and $s_2 = 4.9$ for sample $n_2 = 10$.

1. Test statistic: $\bar{X}_1 - \bar{X}_2 = 31.6 - 38.1 = -6.5$

2. Test variable: $t = \dfrac{31.6 - 38.1}{\sqrt{(5.3)^2/8 + (4.9)^2/10}} = -2.77$

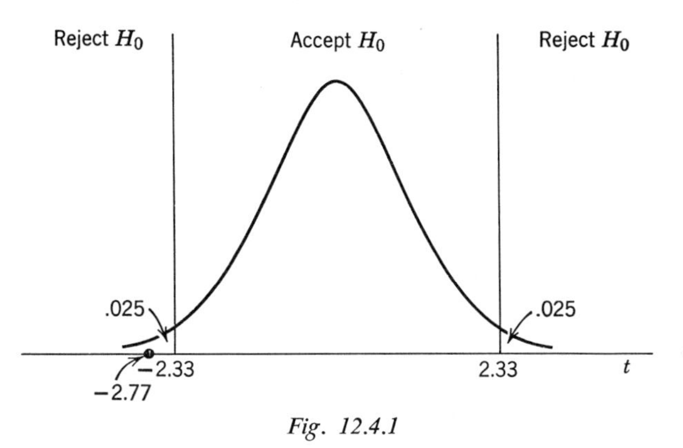

Fig. 12.4.1

Applying Equation 12.4.2, the critical $t_{.05}$ value is determined as follows:

$$t_1 = 2.365 \quad \text{for} \quad 8 - 1 = 7 \text{ df}$$
$$t_2 = 2.262 \quad \text{for} \quad 10 - 1 = 9 \text{ df}$$

$$t_{.05} = \frac{\dfrac{(5.3)^2}{8}(2.365) + \dfrac{(4.9)^2}{10}(2.262)}{(5.3)^2/8 + (4.9)^2/10} = 2.33$$

(Note that, in Figure 12.4.1, $-t_{.05} = -2.33$ and $t_{.05} = 2.33$.)

3. $t = -2.77$ falls in the region of rejection. Therefore, reject H_0 and accept H_1.

4. The principal decides that there is a difference in the effectiveness of the two teaching methods.

12.5 MEANS: EQUAL VARIANCES

In decision-making problems involving the comparison of means, it is often appropriate to assume that the variance σ_1^2 for population 1 is equal to the variance σ_2^2 for population 2. For example, *where populations* 1 *and* 2 *are normally distributed, if* $\sigma_1^2 = \sigma_2^2$, *the null hypothesis that the population means are equal amounts to the hypothesis that populations* 1 *and* 2 *are one and the same population.* Where it is appropriate to state that the population variances (or standard deviations) are equal, the procedures for comparing μ_1 and μ_2 presented in Sections 12.3 and 12.4 are applicable. However, a more efficient testing procedure is available in such situations based upon a *pooling* of the information obtained from both samples to estimate the common population variance. Denote this common population variance as σ^2, so that $\sigma_1^2 = \sigma_2^2 = \sigma^2$.

As presented in Sections 12.3 and 12.4, when carrying out a test of hypothesis involving two means, the test variable z for large samples and t for small samples are both equal to

$$\frac{\bar{X}_1 - \bar{X}_2}{\sqrt{s_1^2/n_1 + s_2^2/n_2}} \tag{12.5.1}$$

We may estimate the common variance σ^2 by pooling the data for the two samples n_1 and n_2 to compute

$$s^2 = \frac{\sum(X_i - \bar{X}_1)^2 + \sum(X_i - \bar{X}_2)^2}{n_1 + n_2 - 2} \tag{12.5.2}$$

Equation 12.5.2 may look a little complicated at first. However, conceptually it is similar to s^2 computed from the data in a *single* sample. It will be recalled that s^2 is computed by dividing the sum of the squared deviations from the mean, $\Sigma(X_i - \bar{X})^2$, by $n - 1$, which represents the number of degrees of freedom involved. (Recall that $n - 1$ represents the degrees of freedom which determined the particular t value to be used in problems discussed earlier.) Similarly, for computing s^2 according to Equation 12.5.2, the numerator represents the *pooled* sum of squared deviations from each sample mean. The first part of this numerator is the sum of squared deviations of the n_1 items in the first sample around *its* mean of $\bar{X}_1$, whereas the second part represents the sum of the squared deviations of the n_2 items in the second sample around *its* mean of $\bar{X}_2$. The denominator is obtained by adding the df for sample n_1, which is $n_1 - 1$, and the df for sample n_2, which is $n_2 - 1$. This gives $(n_1 - 1) + (n_2 - 1) = n_1 + n_2 - 2$. Consequently, where it is appropriate to state that the two populations have a common variance, σ^2 estimated as s^2 (based upon the *pooled* sums of squares with a *greater* number of degrees of freedom) is a better estimate than the individual variances s_1^2 and s_2^2 (which are computed from the individual samples each with a smaller number of degrees of freedom). In some problems, the individual variances computed from each sample are available. Then, a more convenient form of Equation 12.5.2 is

$$s^2 = \frac{(n_1 - 1)s_1^2 + (n_2 - 1)s_2^2}{n_1 + n_2 - 2} \tag{12.5.3}$$

We may modify the test variable as expressed in Equation 12.5.1 by substituting s^2 for both $s_1{}^2$ and $s_2{}^2$ to obtain

$$\frac{\bar{X}_1 - \bar{X}_2}{\sqrt{s^2/n_1 + s^2/n_2}} = \frac{\bar{X}_1 - \bar{X}_2}{\sqrt{s^2(1/n_1 - 1/n_2)}} \tag{12.5.4}$$

For a test of hypothesis involving the comparison of means, where the population variances are equal, the test should be conducted as described in Section 12.3 for large samples and in Section 12.4 for small samples, with the following modification. For large samples, the test variable z is determined according to Equation 12.5.4. For small samples the test variable t is also determined according to Equation 12.5.4 and the critical value of t, which determines the regions of rejection and acceptance, is read out of Table B.3 for $n_1 + n_2 - 2$ df. The estimated variance s^2 in Equation 12.5.4 is computed according to Equation 12.5.2 or Equation 12.5.3, whichever is more convenient.

As an illustration, suppose two samples of guinea pigs were put through the same program of activities after each group of animals had been subjected to a different set of treatments. The number of errors was recorded for each animal. One sample, of size $n_1 = 11$, has $\bar{X}_1 = 90.6$ errors and $s_1 = 9.1$ errors. The other sample, of size $n_2 = 13$, has $\bar{X}_2 = 107.2$ errors and $s_2 = 9.7$ errors. It is desired to test, at the .02 level of significance, whether or not the two sets of treatments have the same effect on the performance of the guinea pigs, as measured by the mean number of errors per sample. Based upon previous experimentation, it is assumed that, for the populations involved, $\sigma_1 = \sigma_2$.

A. Formulation of the Problem

1. Test parameter: $\mu_1 - \mu_2$, the difference between the mean number of errors for population 1 (the number of errors for all guinea pigs of the same strain, assuming they were all subjected to a given set of treatments) and population 2 (the number of errors for all guinea pigs of the same strain, assuming they were all subjected to the other set of treatments).
2. $H_0: \mu_1 - \mu_2 = 0$.
3. $H_1: \mu_1 - \mu_2 \neq 0$.
4. If H_0 is not rejected, it will be accepted.
5. $\alpha = .02$.

B. Construction of the Decision Model

1. Test statistic: $\bar{X}_1 - \bar{X}_2$, the difference between the mean number of errors in the two samples.
2. Sampling *Model I*, modified by the assumption of equal population variances, is appropriate. Therefore, the appropriate sampling distribution

is the t distribution, with t computed according to Equation 12.5.4 (s^2 computed according to Equation 12.5.3) and with $n_1 + n_2 - 2$ df.

3. Test variable: $t = \dfrac{\bar{X}_1 - \bar{X}_2}{\sqrt{s^2(1/n_1 + 1/n_2)}}$

where $$s^2 = \frac{(n_1 - 1)s_1^2 + (n_2 - 1)s_2^2}{n_1 + n_2 - 2}$$

4. If $t < -2.508$ or $t > 2.508$, reject H_0 and accept H_1. Otherwise, accept H_0. ($t_{.02} = 2.508$ for $11 + 13 - 2 = 22$ df, according to Table B.3)

C. Evaluation of the Sample Data

1. Test statistic: $\bar{X}_1 - \bar{X}_2 = 90.6 - 107.2 = -16.6$

2. Test variable: $s^2 = \dfrac{(11 - 1)(9.1)^2 + (13 - 1)(9.7)^2}{11 + 13 - 2} = 88.96$

$$t = \frac{-16.6}{\sqrt{88.96(\frac{1}{11} + \frac{1}{13})}} = -3.86$$

3. $t = -3.86$ falls in the region of rejection. Therefore, reject H_0 and accept H_1.

4. The two sets of treatments do not have the same effect on the performance of the guinea pigs.

12.6 MEANS: DEPENDENT SAMPLES

In our study of two-sample tests we have confined our attention, so far, to *independent samples*. However, tests are often conducted where *dependent samples* are involved. We will now consider the statistical theory and sampling models appropriate for such tests. Different types of test situations involving dependent samples may be encountered. For example, a psychologist may wish to test whether an intensive discussion program has any effect on specified social attitudes. He may decide to conduct this test by selecting a sample of subjects and testing them both before and after they have experienced the discussion program. The before and after scores for these subjects clearly represent dependent samples, since there is a score in each sample for each of the subjects. In this illustration, we are dealing with a single population of subjects. However, the statistical test is concerned with two populations of scores (the before and the after score populations).

An educational research worker may wish to investigate whether junior high school boys or junior high school girls learn mathematics more rapidly. This study may be carried out by selecting a sample of junior high school boys, each of whom has a sister in junior high school. Then, a sister (who attends junior high school) of each of the boys in the sample is selected for the sample of girls. In this way, the boys and girls in the two samples pair off as brothers and sisters. The research worker will then test each of the boys and girls in the samples on achievement, after each has been put through an identical learning experience in mathematics, and the scores obtained by the boys and the girls will be compared. The reason for selecting brother and sister pairs for the samples is to remove some of the extraneous factors which may be expected to affect the score differences between two independent samples. For example, it may be expected that any effect on scores due to family influence will be the same for both samples. In this way, a research worker attempts to insure that, as far as possible, any score differences observed between the samples are caused by the experimental variable (in this case, sex) and not by extraneous factors, such as the educational background of the family, etc.

It may be desired to compare the effects of two drugs on motor activity. Such a study may be accomplished by selecting two *matched samples* and administering one drug to one sample of subjects and the other drug to the other sample of subjects. Samples which are matched on one or more characteristics are called *matched samples*. For example, in the illustration, it may be desired to match the samples on, say, muscular coordination. This is accomplished by selecting the subjects for each sample in such a way that they pair off on some measure of muscular coordination. In other words, the subjects are selected so that, if there is a subject with a given score on muscular coordination in one sample, there is a subject with the same score in the other sample. It may be desired to match the samples on *both* muscular coordination and IQ. This is accomplished by selecting the subjects so that they pair off (one in each sample) on *both* these characteristics. Then, after the appropriate drug is administered to each subject, each one may be required to perform a specified activity. Each subject is scored on his performance and the scores for the two samples compared. When matched samples are used, it is for the purpose of eliminating the effects of extraneous factors from score comparisons between the samples. In this way, it is more likely that observed differences between the two samples are caused by the experimental variable (in this instance, the drug administered).

Let us consider a decision-making problem involving the comparison of means based upon dependent samples. Suppose it is desired to determine whether or not the muscular coordination of male adults aged 21 to 30 are differently affected by drugs A and B. A sample of 14 subjects are selected and each drug administered, one week apart, to each subject. After each drug administration, the subject is required to perform a specified task and the time required to accomplish the task recorded. Table 12.6.1 presents the time scores obtained, two for each subject. These scores make up the two samples, n_1 for drug A and n_2 for drug B, each containing 14 scores. Since these scores represent paired data (14 pairs of scores), the appropriate

Table 12.6.1 DEPENDENT SAMPLES: TIME REQUIRED TO PERFORM A GIVEN TASK AFTER ADMINISTRATION OF TWO DRUGS

	Time required (minutes)			
Subject	Sample n_1, Drug A	Sample n_2, Drug B	Difference, d	d^2
A	32	35	−3	9
B	28	26	2	4
C	37	40	−3	9
D	30	33	−3	9
E	29	24	5	25
F	23	22	1	1
G	31	31	–	–
H	34	30	4	16
I	27	27	–	–
J	30	30	–	–
K	29	28	1	1
L	34	33	1	1
M	33	34	−1	1
N	32	31	1	1
		Sum	5	77

statistical test is conducted on the basis of the *difference* between each pair of scores. These differences (d) are shown in the table.

The test parameter is $\bar{D}$, the mean difference between each pair of scores in the population. That is, imagine that the same procedure of drug administration and testing (performance of the specified task) is carried out for *all* male adults aged 21 to 30 and the score differences between pairs (d) computed. Then $\bar{D}$ is the mean of all these differences. If μ_1 is the mean of the scores obtained (in our imagination) after drug A is administered to the entire population and μ_2 is the mean of the scores obtained after drug B is administered, then $\bar{D} = \mu_1 - \mu_2$. In other words, using $\bar{D}$ as the test parameter amounts to using $\mu_1 - \mu_2$, the test parameter used for testing the difference between means based upon independent samples. The test statistic is $\bar{d}$, the mean of the sample of pair differences. If $\bar{X}_1$ is the mean of the sample of 14 scores obtained after drug A is administered and $\bar{X}_2$ is the mean of the sample of 14 scores obtained after drug B is administered, $\bar{d} = \bar{X}_1 - \bar{X}_2$, the test statistic used for independent samples. Clearly, then, the test parameter and the test statistic to be used for dependent samples are equivalent to those used for independent samples. However, in the case of dependent samples, the statistical test is conducted on the basis of a *single* variable (d) instead of two score variables (the scores obtained after each drug is administered). In other words, the two-sample test, in the case of dependent samples, reduces to a *single-sample* test.

The appropriate sampling model is the same as in the case of single-sample tests relating to means. For large samples, the procedure to follow is the same as described in Chapter 11, Section 11.2, where it is indicated that *Model B* is the appropriate sampling model. The sample size, when dealing with dependent samples, is the *number of pairs*. In our illustration, the sample size n $(= n_1 = n_2) = 14$. A sample of 30 or more *pairs* satisfies our definition of a large sample. The mean of the *sampling distribution of the mean differences between pairs*, $\mu_{\bar{d}}$, is equal to $\bar{D}$. The sample mean difference $\bar{d}$ is computed by the use of Equation 4.2.4, where d replaces X as the variable. We may rewrite this equation as

$$\bar{d} = \frac{\sum d}{n} \tag{12.6.1}$$

The standard deviation of the differences s_d is computed by the use of Equation 5.3.2, where d replaces X as the variable. We may rewrite this equation as

$$s_d = \sqrt{\frac{n \sum d^2 - (\sum d)^2}{n(n-1)}} \tag{12.6.2}$$

Then, the standard error of the mean difference is estimated as

$$s_{\bar{d}} = \frac{s_d}{\sqrt{n}} \tag{12.6.3}$$

The test variable z is computed as

$$z = \frac{\bar{d} - \bar{D}}{s_d/\sqrt{n}} \tag{12.6.4}$$

In the case of small samples, the procedure to follow is the same as described in Chapter 11, Section 11.3, where it is indicated that *Model F* is the appropriate sampling model. The test variable is computed according to Equation 12.6.4. However, it is now labeled t (with $n - 1$ df) instead of

z. Referring to our illustrative problem (Table 12.6.1), we will use this test procedure to test whether the effects of drugs A and B on muscular co-ordination are the same or different. First, using Equation 12.6.1, compute the mean difference

$$\bar{d} = \tfrac{5}{14} = .36$$

Using Equation 12.6.2, compute the standard deviation

$$s_d = \sqrt{\frac{(14)(77) - (5)^2}{(14)(13)}} = 2.40$$

Now, let us apply the three-phase testing procedure, using the .05 level of significance.

A. Formulation of the Problem

1. Test parameter: $\bar{D}$, the mean difference in pairs of scores for adults aged 21 to 30.
2. $H_0: \bar{D} = 0$
3. $H_1: \bar{D} \neq 0$
4. If H_0 is not rejected, it will be accepted.
5. $\alpha = .05$

B. Construction of the Decision Model

1. Test statistic: $\bar{d}$, the mean difference between score pairs for the sample of 14 pairs.
2. Sampling *Model F* is appropriate (assuming that the distribution of d in the population is closely approximated by the normal curve). The sampling distribution pertinent to this problem is like the t distribution, with $14 - 1 = 13$ df.
3. Test variable: $$t = \frac{\bar{d} - \bar{D}}{s_d/\sqrt{n}} = \frac{\bar{d}}{s/\sqrt{14}}$$

The second form is obtained by recognizing that $\bar{D} = 0$, assuming that H_0 is true and $n = 14$.

4. If $t < -2.160$ or $t > 2.160$, reject H_0 and accept H_1. Otherwise, accept H_0. (This t value was determined for 13 df by referring to Table B.3, the column corresponding to the probability .05.)

C. Evaluation of the Sample Data

1. Test statistic: $\bar{d} = .36$
2. Test variable: $$t = \frac{.36}{2.40/\sqrt{14}} = 2.098$$

3. $t = 2.098$ falls in the region of acceptance. Therefore, accept H_0.

4. Conclude that there is no difference between drug A and drug B in the effect on muscular coordination.

PROBLEMS FOR PRACTICE AND REVIEW

1. A sample of 25 subjects required a mean time of 13.6 minutes to assemble a simple toy, after administration of a new muscle relaxer. The standard deviation was 2.4 minutes. A sample of 20 subjects required a mean of 13.2 minutes to perform the same task with a standard deviation of 2.0 minutes, after administration of a well-known muscle relaxer. Would you conclude that the mean time required to perform the task is the same after administration of each of these muscle relaxers? Use the .05 level of significance.

2. A sample of 22 foreign language students made a mean of 131.2 errors, with a standard deviation of 26.3, in translating a technical article from English into French. A sample of 20 foreign language students made a mean of 116.2 errors, with a standard deviation of 18.1, in translating the same article from French into English. Would you conclude, at the .05 level of significance, that the number of errors made in translating from English to French and French to English is the same, on the average?

3. A sample of 15 subjects was asked to estimate the length of an object dangling from a string at a distance of ten feet. The subjects had both eyes open when making the estimate. The mean length estimated was 27.18 inches,with a standard deviation of 7.21 inches. A sample of 22 subjects was asked to make the estimate with one eye closed. The mean length estimated by this sample was 45.33 inches, with a standard deviation of 10.14 inches. Would you conclude at the .02 level of significance that in the population there is no difference between the mean of estimated lengths made with one or both eyes opened?

4. A reading comprehension test was administered to a sample of 35 subjects after they were given a full hour of quiet, restful activity. For this sample, the mean score was 24.7 and the standard deviation, 6.3. A second sample, made up of 47 subjects, took the same test after a full hour of vigorous physical activity. For this sample, the mean test score was 22.4, with a standard deviation of 5.1. Would you conclude, at the .05 level of significance, that the nature of activity preceding test administration has no effect upon the mean test score? Assume equal population variance.

5. In Problem 4, conduct the test without the assumption of equal population variance.

6. In a sample of ten subjects, each was required to perform a task with one eye closed. For this sample, a mean of 110.7 minutes was required to perform the task, with a standard deviation of 23.8 minutes. In a sample of 12 subjects, each was required to perform the same task with both eyes open. For this sample, a mean of 82.8 minutes was required, with a standard deviation of 20.1 minutes. Would you conclude, at the .05 level of significance, that the mean time required is the same with one or both eyes open? Assume equal variance in the populations.

7. Each of 88 subjects (sample A) was asked to estimate the length of a certain line on a chart, where the line was in blue on a red background. The mean of the estimated lengths was 16.47 inches, with a standard deviation of 3.32 inches. Each of 105 subjects (sample B) was asked to estimate the length of a line of the same length as before, but this time the line was red on a blue background. The mean of the estimated lengths was 15.04, with a standard deviation of 4.06. Would you claim, at the .02 level of significance, that the mean length estimated is the same (in the population) for each color situation? Assume equal population variance.

8. Two forms of a spatial perception test were developed for junior high school boys. Form A was administered to a sample of nine junior high school boys. A week later, Form B was administered to this same sample of nine boys. The following scores were obtained:

Subject	Form A	Form B
A	96	93
B	103	99
C	101	105
D	94	103
E	83	96
F	90	85
G	97	92
H	106	108
I	100	91

Would you conclude, at the .05 level of significance, that the same mean score may be expected to be obtained, as a rule, for Form A and Form B?

9. A sample of 12 right-handed adults aged 21 or over was asked to copy a specified text, using the left hand. A second sample of 12 adults aged 21 or over was selected. This second sample was matched on writing speed with the first sample; however, these were all left-handed. They were asked to copy the same text using the right hand. The time required to copy the text (in minutes) for matched pairs of subjects follows:

First Sample	Second Sample
12	9
17	20
10	15
16	18
18	13
18	22
14	10
10	9
13	19
17	16
15	18
18	16

Would you conclude, at the .05 level of significance, that the time required to copy the text is, on the average, the same for right-handed adults aged 21 or over who write with their left hand as it is for left-handed adults aged 21 or over who write with their right hand?

10. A sample of ten high school seniors was required to estimate the length of each of a number of wooden rods. An estimate off by more than a certain specified amount was counted as an error. Then, this sample of ten seniors was given a one-hour period of training in blueprint reading. Afterwards, each senior in the sample was required to estimate the length of a similar group of wooden rods of equal number. The number of errors made by each senior follows:

Subject	Before Training	After Training
A	20	25
B	18	20
C	14	17
D	30	11
E	20	5
F	17	7
G	14	5
H	19	23
I	23	7
J	32	20

Would you conclude, at the .05 level of significance, that the ability of high school seniors to estimate the length of wooden rods is the same with or without the one-hour training in blue-print reading?

Part V
Association and Prediction

13

MEASURES OF ASSOCIATION

13.1 INTRODUCTION

The presentation of statistical methods so far has been concerned with problems involving a *single* variable. However, many statistical problems in the fields of psychology and education, as well as in other fields, involve more than one variable. Such problems often arise in the area of prediction. For example, it may be required to determine whether a certain test battery is suitable for predicting on-the-job success. This may be determined by statistical analysis of the relationship between two variables for each subject in a sample of subjects, a measure of on-the-job performance and test battery scores. Or it may be required to determine whether high school grades may be used as a predictor of success in college. This may be determined by statistical analysis of the relationship between the average grade per student earned in high school and the average grade per student earned in college for a sample of students. Or a university may wish to restrict special student grants to sophomores who may be expected to achieve better than average grades in the junior and senior years. It may be desired to determine whether average grades obtained during both the freshman and sophomore years should be used to predict achievement in the junior and senior years or whether average grades obtained during the sophomore year alone would be a better predictor. This may be determined by comparing the results of two statistical analyses. One would analyze the relationship between average grades earned during the freshman and sophomore years, on the one hand, and average grades earned during the junior and senior years, on the other, for a sample of students. The other would analyze the relationship between average grades obtained during the sophomore year and the average obtained during the junior and senior years for these students.

13.2 BASIC CONCEPTS

Table 13.2.1 presents the number of students enrolled in a course on Theory of Criminal Behavior during the ten semesters it has been offered

Table 13.2.1 ENROLLMENT IN A COURSE ON THEORY OF CRIMINAL BEHAVIOR DURING A PERIOD OF TEN SEMESTERS

Semester	Enrollment
1	6
2	9
3	12
4	10
5	12
6	12
7	16
8	14
9	15
10	20

by a university. These data are plotted in the usual manner for time series data (measurements for a series of time periods, such as semesters) as shown in Figure 13.2.1. Part *A* shows the 10 plotted points, one for each semester. Each dot is placed directly above the semester number (indicated on the horizontal scale) at a height equal to the enrollment for the semester (indicated on the vertical scale). For example, for the first semester, enrollment was equal to 6. This is shown in Part *A* by the dot directly above semester 1 at a height equal to 6 on the enrollment (vertical) scale. For the second semester, enrollment was equal to 9. This is shown in part *A* by the dot directly above semester 2 at a height equal to 9 on the enrollment scale. It is customary, for a time series, to connect the dots as indicated in part *B* of the figure. This is an aid to visualizing the variation in enrollment number from semester to semester. In both parts *A* and *B*, there is a clear indication of an upward trend in enrollment. Very often, the trend in a time series is shown by a *trend line*, as in part *C*. This trend line summarizes the generally upward tendency of class enrollment exhibited during the 10-semester period. There are various ways of constructing a trend line. A rough approach is to draw a free-hand line, as was done in part *C*.

Part *C* in Figure 13.2.1 presents the typical graphic means of displaying

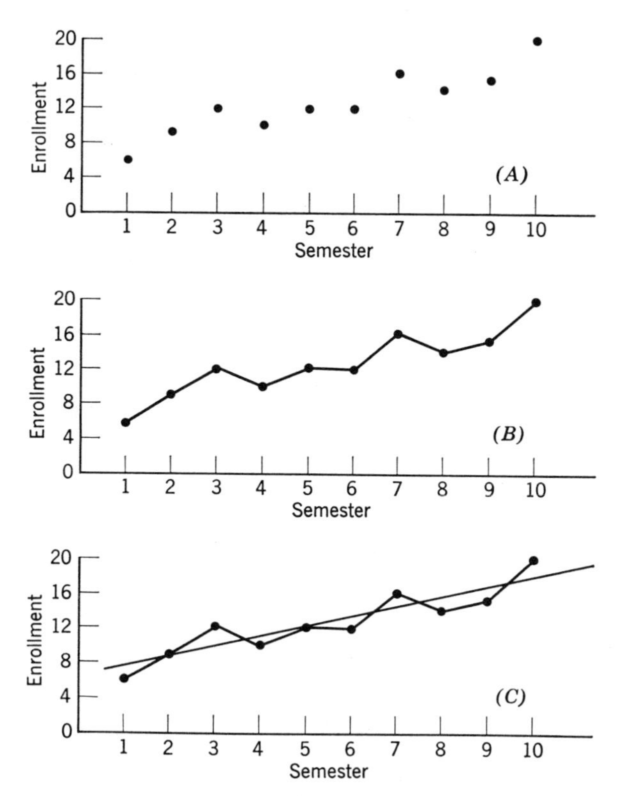

Fig. 13.2.1. Graphs showing variation in enrollment.

the variation of time series data. Generally, data such as in Table 13.2.1 are considered to involve a single variable. In this illustration, the variable is "enrollment." However, there are actually *two variables* involved in Table 13.2.1. The variable of direct interest is "enrollment." The other variable is "semester." The variable "semester" is a *time* variable. Generally, when the variation in two variables is displayed graphically, the dots are connected, as in part *B*, only if one of these variables is a time variable. Otherwise, the dots are presented unconnected, as in part *A*. Such a chart is called a *dot chart* or a *scatter diagram*. The trend line is used to represent the *joint variation*, often called the *covariation*, of the two variables, whether or not one of the two variables is a time variable. Such a trend line is usually called a *regression line*, especially when a time variable is not involved. The regression line is constructed directly upon the scatter

Table 13.2.2 SCORES ON READING COMPREHENSION AND WRITING ABILITY FOR 22 SUBJECTS

Subject	Reading Comprehension Score, X	Writing Ability Score, Y
A	5	20
B	20	23
C	45	45
D	9	7
E	50	65
F	30	30
G	57	65
H	55	50
I	65	60
J	13	13
K	67	72
L	23	32
M	70	80
N	45	55
O	75	73
P	33	45
Q	75	85
R	12	12
S	60	70
T	35	51
U	25	40
V	19	17

diagram, where the dots are not connected. The regression line represents the *relationship between the two variables.*

When studying the relationship between two variables, the chief interest may be in determining whether one variable may be used to *predict* the other variable. In such an analysis, the variable you want to *predict* is called the *dependent variable*. The other variable is called the *independent variable*. The *regression line* is used to predict one variable based upon the other. That is, the dependent variable is predicted on the basis of the independent variable by the use of a regression line. On the other hand the chief interest may be in determining *how closely* two variables are related to each other. In such analyses, the important measure to compute is the *coefficient of correlation*, which is a measure of the *extent* or *degree* to which two variables are related or associated. The various aspects involved in the *relationship between two variables* will now be further considered.

Table 13.2.2 presents scores on reading comprehension and writing ability for 22 subjects. Suppose a psychologist wishes to determine, based

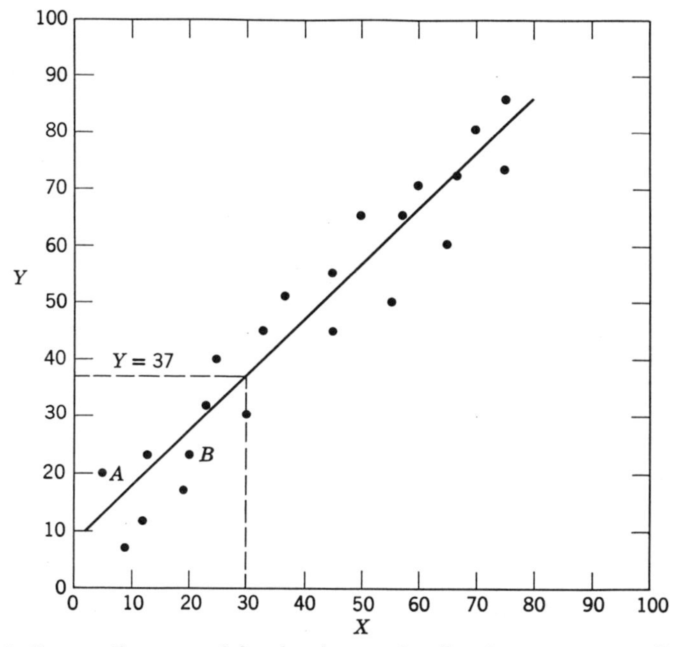

Fig. 13.2.2. Scatter diagram and free-hand regression line for scores on reading comprehension and writing ability for 22 subjects.

upon these data, whether reading comprehension scores are a good predictor of writing ability. Then, writing ability (as measured by the writing ability scores) is the variable to be predicted, or the dependent variable, whereas reading comprehension (as measured by the reading comprehension scores) is the independent variable. It is customary to denote the dependent variable as Y and the independent variable as X, as indicated in the table. The scatter diagram for these two variables is presented in Figure 13.2.2. This figure contains 22 dots, one for each subject. Each dot represents the X and Y scores for a subject. The location of each dot is determined in the same manner as for Figure 13.2.1. For example, for subject A, $X = 5$ and $Y = 20$. Locating $X = 5$ on the horizontal scale in Figure 13.2.2, place a dot directly above $X = 5$ at a height corresponding to $Y = 20$, according to the vertical scale. This dot is identified as dot A in the figure. For subject B, $X = 20$ and $Y = 23$. Locating $X = 20$ on the horizontal scale, place a dot directly above at a height corresponding to $Y = 23$. This dot is identified as dot B in the figure. The other dots are determined in the same way.

Note that the X-variable scale appears as the horizontal scale and the Y-variable scale appears as the vertical scale. It is customary to use the horizontal scale for the independent variable X and the vertical scale for the dependent variable Y. A free-hand regression line has been drawn, as shown in the figure. Suppose it is desired to predict the writing ability score for a subject whose reading comprehension score is 30. This may be done by referring to the regression line in Figure 13.2.2. Find $X = 30$ on the horizontal scale, then move up perpendicularly (as shown by the broken line in the figure) until the regression line is reached. Now, move to the left, parallel to the X-axis (horizontal scale), until the Y-axis (vertical scale) is reached. The predicted writing ability score for this subject is read off the Y-axis at this point. This is shown in the figure as $Y = 37$. In other words, the relationship between the reading comprehension scores X and the writing ability scores Y for the 22 subjects, as expressed by the regression line, indicates that a subject who obtains a score of 30 on reading comprehension may be expected to obtain a score of 37 on writing ability. A free-hand regression line is, of course, rough and subjectively determined. No two analysts would arrive at precisely the same regression line, if drawn independently of each other. A more precise method for constructing a regression line will be presented in Section 13.3.

Suppose it is desired to determine whether aptitude test A is a good predictor for performance on aptitude test B, when used on college freshmen. Say, a sample of 15 college freshmen are selected and both aptitude tests administered to each subject. Table 13.2.3 presents the two test scores obtained by each of the 15 subjects. Figure 13.2.3 presents the scatter diagram of these scores, together with a free-hand regression line. The scatter diagram is a very useful device which permits appraisal of the relationship between two variables. Comparison of the scatter diagrams in Figure 13.2.2 and Figure 13.2.3 reveals important differences in the *type* and *degree* of relationship between two variables.

Observe that, in Figure 13.2.2, low values of X are associated with low values of Y and high values of X are associated with high values of Y. When two variables are so related, they are said to be *directly* or *positively* related. In such scatter diagrams, we can see that the regression line slopes *upward* (from the lower left corner to the upper right corner), as indicated in Figure 13.2.2. Such a regression line is said to be *positively sloped.* On the other hand, observe Figure 13.2.3. In this figure it is apparent that low

Table 13.2.3 SCORES ON TWO APTITUDE TESTS FOR 15 SUBJECTS

Subject	Aptitude Test A Score, X	Aptitude Test B Score, Y
A	50	25
B	15	72
C	20	30
D	50	10
E	60	30
F	40	40
G	30	70
H	20	50
I	5	55
J	75	15
K	40	20
L	45	55
M	60	10
N	55	45
O	30	50

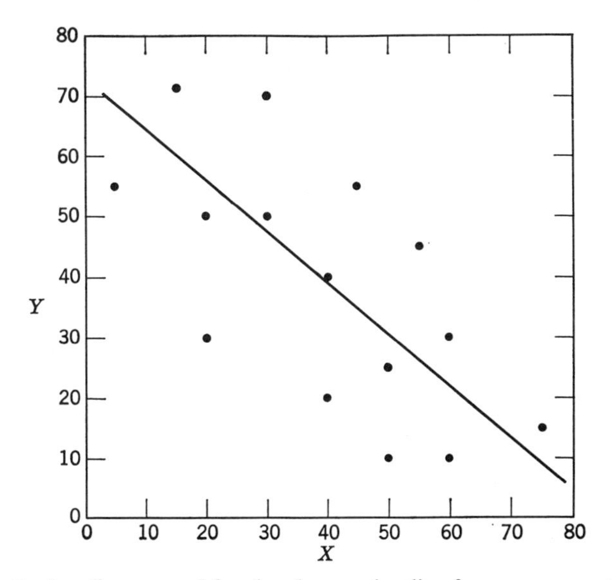

Fig. 13.2.3. Scatter diagram and free-hand regression line for scores on aptitude test A and aptitude test B for 15 subjects.

values of X are associated with high values of Y and high values of X are associated with low values of Y. When two variables are so related, they are said to be *inversely* or *negatively* related. In such scatter diagrams, as we can see from Figure 13.2.3, the regression line slopes *downward* (from the upper left corner to the lower right corner). Such a regression line is said to be *negatively sloped.* In other words, when two variables are positively associated, a high (low) score on one variable will lead to a prediction of a high (low) score on the other variable. On the other hand, when two variables are negatively associated, a high (low) score on one variable will lead to a prediction of a low (high) score on the other variable.

There is a second important difference in the scatter diagrams of Figures 13.2.2 and 13.2.3. In Figure 13.2.2, the dots are very much more closely clustered around the regression line than is the case in Figure 13.2.3.

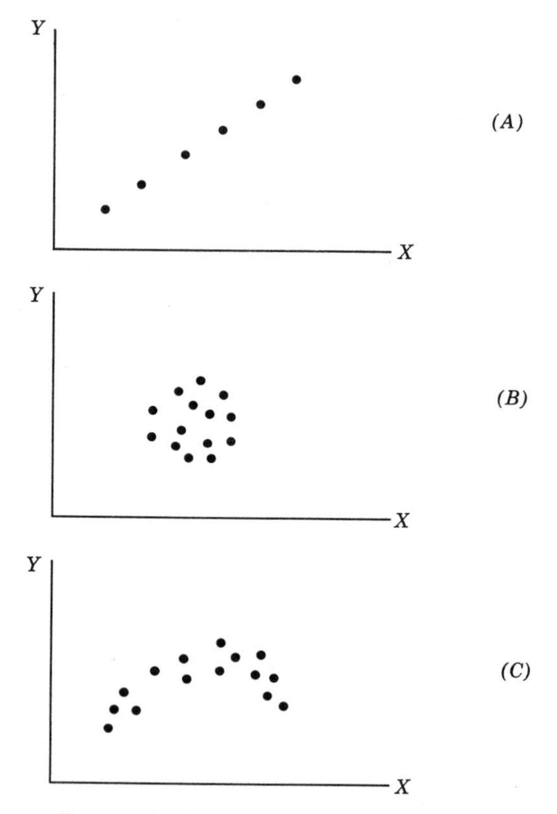

Fig. 13.2.4. Scatter diagrams indicating various types of relationships between two variables.

This indicates that the two variables, X and Y, are *more closely* related or associated in Figure 13.2.2 than in Figure 13.2.3. In the extreme case, where all the dots fall on the regression line, the relationship between X and Y is *perfect*. This is illustrated by the scatter diagram in part *A*, Figure 13.2.4. Clearly, a straight line could be drawn through *all* the points in this scatter diagram. On the other hand, part *B* of this figure illustrates a scatter diagram where the two variables involved have *no* relationship to each other. That is, the pattern of dots in this scatter diagram does not suggest any particular regression line. As noted previously, the *coefficient of correlation* (to be discussed in Section 13.4) is a measure of the *degree* or the *closeness* of the relationship between two variables.

The regression lines which we have considered so far are all *linear* (straight line). This need not always be so. The distribution of dots in a scatter diagram may suggest that the relationship between two variables is *nonlinear* or *curvilinear*. The scatter diagram in part *C*, Figure 13.2.4, indicates a curvilinear relationship between the two variables, so that the regression line would be curvilinear.

13.3 REGRESSION

It has already been noted that free-hand regression lines are not precise and depend upon the judgment of the analyst. Such a line of regression is satisfactory only where a rough estimate of the line of relationship between two variables is needed. Generally, a more precise determination is required. We will examine this problem more closely by referring to Figure 13.3.1, which presents a scatter diagram for two variables X and Y. A free-hand regression line has been fitted to these data. If a "more precise" regression line is required, we need to consider what is meant by "more precise." The first consideration is to find a method which *objectively* determines the line of regression. This would remove the personal judgments involved in a free-hand determination. Then, we must agree upon a method which, in some acceptable manner, produces a "best-fitting" line. Remember that the line of regression is a representation of the way in which two variables are associated or related. How can we best represent this association? The key to this search for a "best" line lies in its use in the prediction of Y for a specified value of X. For example, in Table 13.2.2, we note that the writing ability score Y is 30 for a subject whose reading comprehension score X is 30. However, as indicated in Figure 13.2.2, the predicted Y score for $X = 30$, based upon the free-hand regression line, is 37. Therefore, with respect to this subject, there is a deviation of $30 - 37$ or -7 points between the observed Y score (30) and the predicted Y score (37). In other words, the observed score is 7 points *below* the predicted score. We will use the symbol Y to denote the *observed* value of the Y variable and the symbol Y_e to denote the corresponding *predicted* (or *estimated*) value. In terms of these symbols, we are interested in the *deviation between the observed and predicted values of Y for a specified value of X* or

$$(Y - Y_e) \tag{13.3.1}$$

Clearly, it is desirable for a "best-fitting" line to *minimize* these deviations. Referring to Figure 13.3.1, these deviations are indicated by the vertical

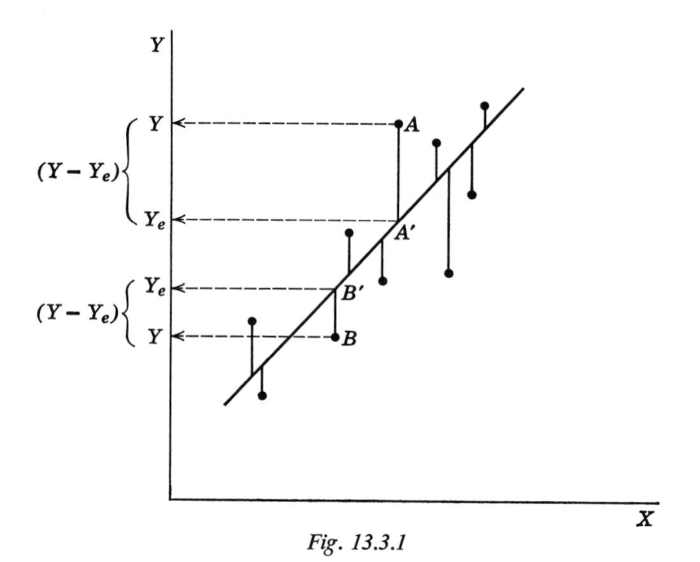

Fig. 13.3.1

lines connecting each dot to the regression line. For example, consider dots A and B. The observed Y value for dot A is indicated by the dashed-line arrow leading from dot A to the Y-axis. The point on the regression line corresponding to A is A' and the corresponding predicted Y_e value is indicated by the dashed-line arrow leading from A' to the Y-axis. The *deviation* between the observed and predicted values of Y is indicated as $(Y - Y_e)$ in the figure. In the same manner, the deviation $(Y - Y_e)$ is determined for dot B, as shown in the figure. It is apparent from this figure that some dots deviate more from the regression line than others. However, if the free-hand line is adjusted so as to reduce the larger deviations, it will result in increasing other deviations. Note that some dots, such as dot A, are *above* the regression line. The deviations for these dots, computed according to Equation 13.3.1, are *positive*, since the observed Y is *greater than* Y_e. The deviations are *negative* for dots which are *below* the line of regression, such as dot B, since, in such instances, the observed Y is *less than* Y_e.

The method generally used to obtain the best-fitting regression line is called the *method of least squares.* It is not appropriate to explain the mathematical development of this method in an introductory text. However, *this method results in a line which reduces the sum of the squared deviations of observed Y values from the regression line to a minimum.* That is, if we determine the deviation of *each* dot from the regression line, according to Equation 13.3.1, and *square each such deviation,* then the *sum of these squared deviations will be a minimum if the regression line is determined by the method of least squares.* This may be stated in symbols as

$$\sum (Y - Y_e)^2 \text{ is a minimum} \qquad (13.3.2)$$

In other words, the best-fitting line of regression has the *least squares property.* We encountered this *least squares property before when we discussed the properties of the mean.* This was discussed in Chapter 4, Section 4.9, where Equation 4.9.6 expresses this property of the mean symbolically. Furthermore, the best-fitting regression line determined by the method of least squares has the additional property that the *sum of the deviations computed according to Equation* 13.3.1 (*not squared*) *is equal to zero.* In other words, the positive and negative deviations just balance out. This property of the best-fitting regression line is expressed symbolically as

$$\sum (Y - Y_e) = 0 \qquad (13.3.3)$$

This property, too, has its counterpart in the case of the mean. In Section 4.9, it was pointed out that the sum of the deviations of a set of scores from its mean is equal to zero. This was expressed in symbols in Equation 4.9.1.

The computations required to determine a *least squares regression line* are not difficult. However, first consider the algebraic equation of a straight line

$$Y = a + bX \qquad (13.3.4)$$

In Equation 13.3.4, Y and X represent the dependent and independent variables, respectively. This follows the use of the symbols Y and X for two variables, where Y represents the variable to be predicted based upon the X variable. The letters a and b represent constants. Equation 13.3.4 represents the *general equation* of a straight line and only when values are assigned to a and b is a *specific line* identified. For example, consider the *specific equation*

$$Y = 10 + 2X \qquad (13.3.5a)$$

Equation 13.3.5a was determined by substituting $a = 10$ and $b = 2$ into

Table 13.3.1 VALUES OF Y FOR SPECIFIED VALUES OF X DETERMINED ACCORDING TO EQUATIONS 13.3.5 a, b, AND c

X	Y	Y'	Y''
0	10	5	10
2	14	9	16
4	18	13	22
6	22	17	28
8	26	21	34
10	30	25	40

Equation 13.3.4. If, arbitrarily, we specify values for X, we may use Equation 13.3.5a to determine the associated or corresponding values of Y. Table 13.3.1 presents such X and Y values in the first two columns. For example, if we assume $X = 0$, then, substituting 0 for X in Equation 13.3.5a we obtain

$$Y = 10 + 2(0) = 10$$

Then, substituting 2 for X, we obtain

$$Y = 10 + 2(2) = 14$$

In this way, each of the associated Y values shown in the second column of Table 13.3.1 are obtained for the X values specified in the first column. These X and Y values are plotted as dots in Figure 13.3.2, with a line

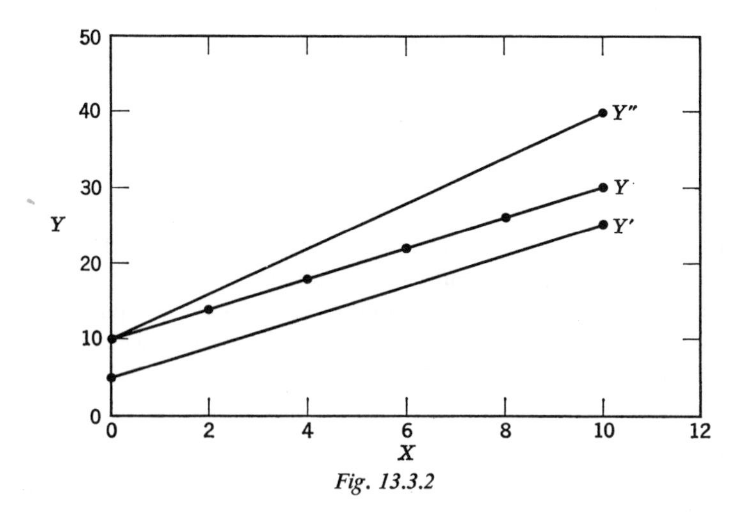

Fig. 13.3.2

drawn through the dots (identified as line Y). This is the line represented by Equation 13.3.5a.

Since two points determine a straight line, we could have constructed this line just as well by plotting only two dots on the scatter diagram in Figure 13.3.2. It is a good idea to plot a point (dot) corresponding to a low value of X (say, $X = 0$, $Y = 10$) and a second point corresponding to a high value of X (say, $X = 10$, $Y = 30$). Then, the required line may be conveniently drawn connecting these two plotted points. It will be observed that this line cuts (intercepts) the Y-axis at the point $Y = 10$. This is the point where $X = 0$. This point ($Y = 10$), called the *Y-intercept*, is where $Y = a$ ($= 10$). Consequently, *a represents the Y-intercept* or the point on the Y-axis where this axis is cut by a line of Equation 13.3.4. The constant a is said to determine the *height* of the line. In other words, if the equation of a line is changed merely by changing the value of a, the height of the line is changed. For example, reducing the value of a from 10 to 5 in Equation 13.3.5a, we obtain

$$Y' = 5 + 2X \tag{13.3.5b}$$

The third column of Table 13.3.1 presents the Y' values, based upon Equation 13.3.5b, corresponding to the X values in the first column of the table. The two points $X = 0$, $Y' = 5$ and $X = 10$, $Y' = 25$ are plotted in Figure 13.3.2 and a line drawn connecting them. This line, identified as Y' in the figure, represents Equation 13.3.5b. Observe that the Y' line is parallel to the Y line *at a lower height* corresponding to the *lower* value of a (5 instead of 10). If we change a to a *higher* value, it will result in a parallel line located at a *greater* height.

The constant b represents the *slope* of the line. For example, let us replace $b = 2$ with $b = 3$ in Equation 13.3.5a, obtaining

$$Y'' = 10 + 3X \tag{13.3.5c}$$

The last column in Table 13.3.1 presents the Y'' values, based upon Equation 13.3.5c, corresponding to the X values in the first column of the table. The two points $X = 0$, $Y'' = 10$ and $X = 10$, $Y'' = 40$ are plotted in Figure 13.3.2 and a line drawn connecting them. This line, identified as Y'' in the figure, represents Equation 13.3.5c. Note that this line intercepts the Y-axis at the point $Y'' = 10$, as in the case of the Y line. Of course, this is to be expected since, for both lines, a is equal to 10. However, the Y'' line has a *steeper slope*, since it has a *higher b* value. A *higher b* value indicates a *steeper slope*, whereas a *smaller b* value indicates a *lesser slope* or a *flatter line*.

The similarity between the lines constructed in Figure 13.3.2 and regression lines is apparent. In order to obtain the regression line for a set of data for two variables X and Y in such a way that it fulfills the requirements of the method of least squares, we must determine the constants a and b as follows:

$$b = \frac{\sum xy}{\sum x^2} \qquad (13.3.6)$$

$$a = \frac{\sum Y - b \sum X}{n} \qquad (13.3.7)$$

where

$$\sum xy = \sum XY - \frac{(\sum X)(\sum Y)}{n} \qquad (13.3.8)$$

$$\sum x^2 = \sum X^2 - \frac{(\sum X)^2}{n} \qquad (13.3.9)$$

n = number of *pairs* of X and Y values

Notice that in Equation 13.3.6, for b, lower-case x and y letters are used whereas, in the other equations, upper-case letters X and Y are used. The lower-case and upper-case letters are related as follows:

$$x_i = X_i - \bar{X} \qquad (13.3.10)$$

$$y_i = Y_i - \bar{Y} \qquad (13.3.11)$$

The symbols $\bar{X}$ and $\bar{Y}$, of course, denote the mean of the X's and Y's, respectively. Although the subscript i is shown in Equations 13.3.10 and 13.3.11, we will generally omit it as a matter of convenience. This abbreviated use of symbolic notation has been encountered frequently throughout the text. In some texts, substitutions are made for Σxy and Σx^2, according to Equations 13.3.8 and 13.3.9, in the equation for b. However, such substitution results in a very complicated looking equation. It is recommended that the following sequence of steps be used to determine the *least squares regression equation* for a set of data involving two variables:

STEP 1: Compute ΣX, ΣY, ΣX^2, and ΣXY.

STEP 2: Compute Σxy according to Equation 13.3.8.

STEP 3: Compute Σx^2 according to Equation 13.3.9.

STEP 4: Compute b according to Equation 13.3.6.

STEP 5: Compute a according to Equation 13.3.7.

Finally, the least squares regression equation becomes

$$Y_e = a + bX \qquad (13.3.12)$$

The constants a and b are called *regression coefficients*. Note that we use Y_e instead of Y in Equation 13.3.12 to indicate that the Y value computed from this equation is the *predicted* Y value. We will apply this procedure to an illustration or two. It will become apparent that it is a simple matter to compute a least squares regression equation, even though the computational labor is fairly considerable. It is very important, however, that the computations are well organized in order to reduce the possibility of error. Table 13.3.2 presents scores on depth perception and mechanical ability

Table 13.3.2 SCORES ON DEPTH PERCEPTION AND MECHANICAL ABILITY FOR TEN SUBJECTS

Subject	Depth Perception Scores, X	Mechanical Ability Scores, Y	X^2	XY
A	63	91	3,969	5,733
B	69	87	4,761	6,003
C	74	99	5,476	7,326
D	81	120	6,561	9,720
E	83	116	6,889	9,628
F	90	131	8,100	11,790
G	95	125	9,025	11,875
H	101	149	10,201	15,049
I	103	145	10,609	14,935
J	104	148	10,816	15,392
Total	863	1211	76,407	107,451

for a sample of $n = 10$ subjects. It is desired to determine the regression equation, by the method of least squares, to be used to predict mechanical ability scores based upon depth perception scores. Therefore, we denote depth perception scores as X (independent variable) and mechanical ability scores as Y (dependent variable), as shown in Table 13.3.2. Set up the columns headed X^2 and XY. The first item in the X^2 column, 3969, is obtained by squaring the first item in the X column, 63. Succeeding items in the X^2 column are obtained in a similar manner. The first item in the XY column, 5733, is obtained by multiplying the first item in the X column, 63, by the first item in the Y column, 91. Succeeding items in the XY column are obtained in a similar manner. The four column totals in the table provide all the information needed for *Step* 1. For *Step* 2, using Equation 13.3.8 and these column totals, compute

$$\sum xy = 107{,}451 - \frac{(863)(1211)}{10} = 2942$$

For *Step* 3, using Equation 13.3.9 and the appropriate column totals from Table 13.3.2, compute

$$\sum x^2 = 76{,}407 - \frac{(863)^2}{10} = 1930$$

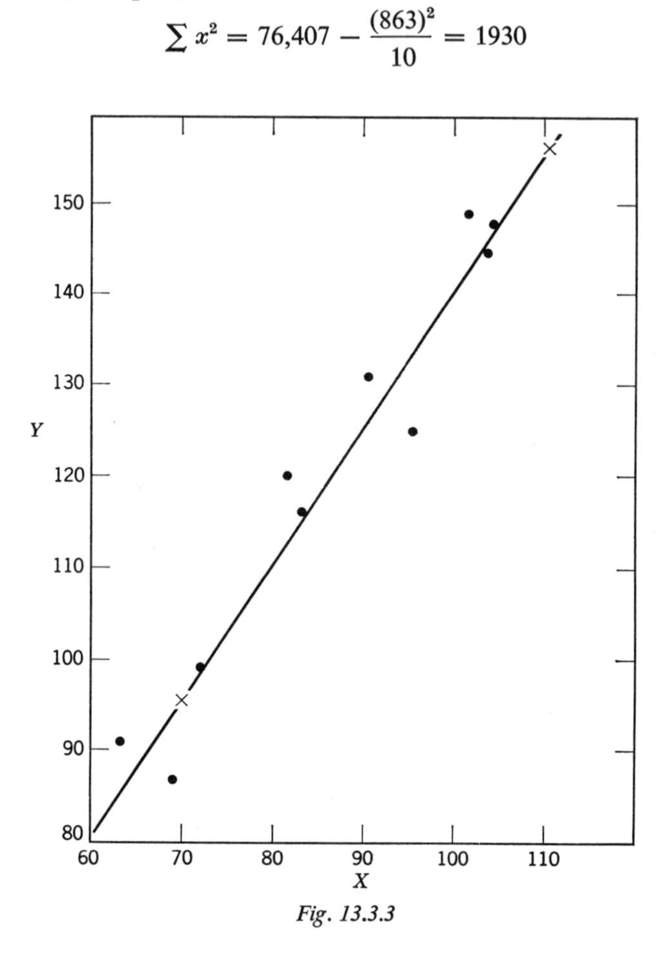

Fig. 13.3.3

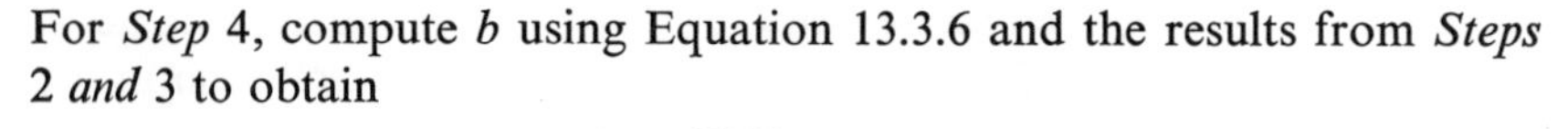

For *Step* 4, compute b using Equation 13.3.6 and the results from *Steps* 2 *and* 3 to obtain

$$b = \frac{2942}{1930} = 1.5244$$

Then, for *Step* 5, compute a using Equation 13.3.7 and the results from previous steps, as appropriate, to obtain

$$a = \frac{1211 - (1.5244)(863)}{10} = -10.4557$$

Finally, we may write the least squares regression equation as

$$Y_e = -10.46 + 1.52X$$

Figure 13.3.3 presents the scatter diagram for the data in Table 13.3.2. The location of the regression line on the chart may be determined by computing the predicted value Y_e for two values of X, using the computed regression equation. Substituting $X = 70$ into the regression equation, we obtain

$$Y_e = -10.46 + 1.52(70) = 95.94$$

Then, substituting $X = 110$ into this equation, we obtain

$$Y_e = -10.46 + 1.52(110) = 156.74$$

The two points $X = 70$, $Y_e = 95.94$ and $X = 110$, $Y_e = 156.74$ are plotted as crosses in Figure 13.3.3 and connected by a straight line. This is the computed least squares regression line.

It is possible to read predicted Y_e values for specified values of X from Figure 13.3.3, as was done from Figure 13.2.2. However, this is no longer necessary. It is more convenient, as well as more precise, to compute the required Y_e values from the regression equation. For example, suppose it is desired to predict the mechanical ability score Y_e for subjects who obtain a score of 82 on depth perception X. Substituting $X = 82$ in the regression equation, we obtain

$$Y_e = -10.46 + 1.52(82) = 114.18$$

Therefore, we may expect that a subject who obtains a score of 82 on depth perception will obtain a score of 114 (to use a rounded figure) on mechanical ability.

Since it has been noted that the constant a indicates the height of the regression line, there may be some question as to the interpretation of a negative a value, such as $a = -10.46$ in the illustration. A negative a value indicates that the regression line intercepts the Y-axis *below* $Y = 0$. This is shown in Figure 13.3.4. The solid-line portions of the X and Y axes in the figure represent the *positive* portions. The dashed-line extensions represent the *negative* portions. For example, the extension of the X-axis to the left represents the scale of *negative X values*, and the extension of the Y-axis downward represents the scale of *negative Y values*. The negative portions of the axes are not shown in scatter diagrams since only positive X and Y scores are of concern. However, it is apparent from Figure 13.3.4 that a regression line which intercepts the Y-axis below

$Y = 0$ will have a negative a value. This is not apparent from a chart as in Figure 13.3.3 because the point $X = 0$, $Y = 0$, called the *origin*, is not shown as it is in Figure 13.3.4. In some scatter diagrams, as in Figures 13.2.2 and 13.2.3, the origin is shown.

Referring to the regression equation, note that when X increases by 1, Y_e increases by b, or, in the illustration, by 1.52. For example, we have

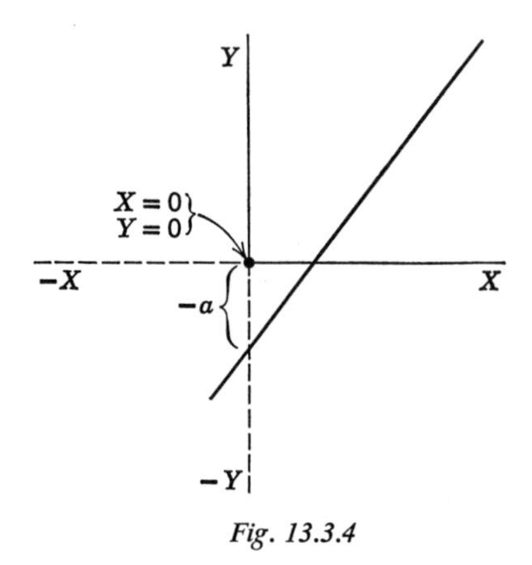

Fig. 13.3.4

shown that when $X = 82$, $Y_e = 114.18$. Now, we will compute Y_e when $X = 83$.

$$Y_e = -10.46 + 1.52(83) = 115.70$$

Clearly, 115.70 is exactly 1.52 ($= b$) greater than 114.18. Consequently, *b indicates the increase in Y_e per unit increase in X.* In the illustration, the predicted mechanical ability score increases 1.52 points for each point increase in the depth perception score.

As a second illustration, suppose it is required to determine a regression equation to predict the scores on Test Battery B based on the scores obtained on Test Battery A. These test batteries are to be used for high school graduates. Consequently, these batteries were administered to a sample of ten high school graduates. The scores obtained are presented in Table 13.3.3. The four column totals in the table provide the information needed for *Step* 1. For *Step* 2, using Equation 13.3.8 and the column totals, we obtain

$$\sum xy = 14{,}436 - \frac{(349)(429)}{10} = -536.1$$

For *Step* 3, using Equation 13.3.9 and the appropriate column totals from

Table 13.3.3, we obtain

$$\sum x^2 = 13{,}233 - \frac{(349)^2}{10} = 1052.9$$

For *Step* 4, compute b using Equation 13.3.6 and the results from *Steps* 2 *and* 3 to obtain

$$b = \frac{-536.1}{1052.9} = -.5092$$

Table 13.3.3 SCORES ON TWO TEST BATTERIES, A AND B, ADMINISTERED TO TEN HIGH SCHOOL GRADUATES

Subject	Battery A Scores, X	Battery B Scores, Y	X^2	XY
A	41	37	1681	1517
B	50	37	2500	1850
C	23	50	529	1150
D	32	43	1024	1376
E	18	52	324	936
F	25	46	625	1150
G	33	47	1089	1551
H	42	42	1764	1764
I	36	41	1296	1476
J	49	34	2401	1666
Total	349	429	13,233	14,436

Now, for *Step* 5, compute a using Equation 13.3.7 and the results from previous steps, as appropriate, to obtain

$$a = \frac{429 - (-.5092)(349)}{10} = 60.6711$$

Then, the least squares regression equation is

$$Y_e = 60.67 - .51X$$

Notice that, in this equation, b is negative, indicating that the scores on the two test batteries are *negatively* associated. It should be observed that Σxy is also negative. That is, *b always has the same sign as Σxy.* Figure 13.3.5 presents the scatter diagram for the data in Table 13.3.3, as well as the line of regression.

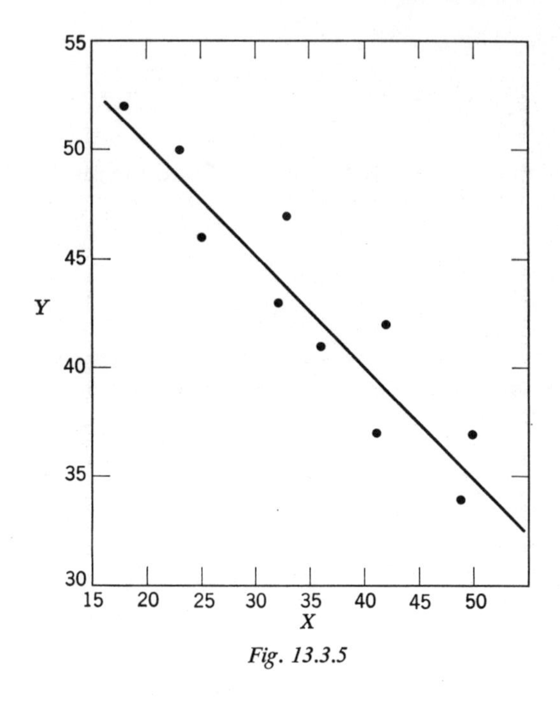

Fig. 13.3.5

PROBLEMS FOR PRACTICE AND REVIEW

1. Construct the scatter diagrams and compute the regression equations by the method of least squares for the following pairs of X and Y scores:

(a)	X	4	7	9	6	10		
	Y	1	3	4	2	5		
(b)	X	7	3	10	9	11	5	
	Y	5	13	1	3	1	10	
(c)	X	11	15	14	17	13	18	22
	Y	19	29	25	34	22	34	41

2. Construct the scatter diagram and compute the least squares regression equation to predict science test scores based upon algebra test scores, using the following data for seven junior high school students:

Student	Algebra Test Scores	Science Test Scores
A	9	23
B	7	15
C	10	18
D	11	25
E	7	12
F	9	24
G	8	16

What would you predict as the science test score for junior high school students who obtain a score of 8 on the algebra test? For those who obtain a score of 10 on the algebra test?

3. In Problem 2, compute the least squares regression equation to predict algebra test scores based upon science test scores.

4. Scores on social attitude and personality ratings for eight high school seniors follow:

High School Seniors	Social Attitude Scores	Personality Ratings
A	11	24
B	9	17
C	10	17
D	12	18
E	8	16
F	10	20
G	7	12
H	9	16

Suppose you are interested in predicting personality ratings based upon social attitude scores. Using the above data:

(a) construct the scatter diagram.

(b) determine the least squares regression equation.

(c) using the regression equation, predict the personality rating for a high school senior who obtains a social attitude score of 9, 13, 11.

5. In Problem 4, determine the least squares regression equation to predict social attitude scores based upon personality ratings.

6. Time-reaction scores (in seconds) for ten subjects, before and after drug administration are as follows:

Before	After
14	10
10	11
13	12
13	11
11	9
9	10
11	11
7	9
12	10
13	12

Suppose you wish to predict the time-reaction scores after drug administration based upon time-reaction scores obtained before drug administration. Using the data previously given:

(a) construct the scatter diagram.

(b) determine the least squares regression equation.

(c) show the regression equation on the scatter diagram.

(d) using the regression equation, predict the "after" time-reaction score for subjects who have a "before" score of 12, 14.

7. The number of months of typing experience and the number of errors made in typing from specified copy are presented below for 12 typists:

Number of Months Experience	Number of Errors
6	19
2	26
1	30
8	12
10	7
8	10
3	25
5	19
3	24
9	10
11	1
7	14

It is desired to develop a basis for predicting the number of typing errors based upon the number of months of typing experience, using the data just given:
(a) construct the scatter diagram.
(b) determine the least squares regression equation.
(c) show the regression line on the scatter diagram.
(d) using the regression equation, predict the number of typing errors you would expect for typists with 4, 10, 11 months of experience.

8. Scores on Form A and Form B of an aptitude test administered to 25 subjects are as follows:

Form A	Form B
18	33
17	28
12	21
11	19
15	26
15	25
10	16
10	17
11	19
11	23
14	21
13	24
12	22
13	19
19	39
18	25
19	29
19	28
23	36
20	32
20	35
18	37
16	26
15	27
15	23

Compute the regression equation by the method of least squares to predict Form B scores based upon Form A scores.

13.4 CORRELATION

The regression equation provides a means for predicting the value of one variable Y based upon its association with another variable X. However,

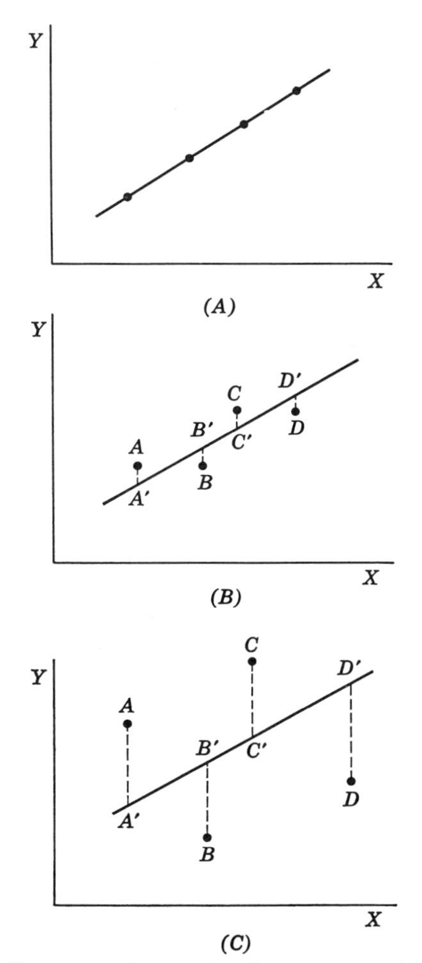

Fig. 13.4.1. Scatter diagrams and regression lines showing different degrees of association between X and Y.

the usefulness of a predicted value depends upon how good a prediction it is. Clearly, if X and Y are closely related, it is to be expected that X will provide a better basis for predicting Y than if X and Y bear little relationship to each other. For example, Figure 13.4.1 presents scatter diagrams and regression lines indicating various degrees of association between the two variables X and Y. Part A indicates that X and Y are perfectly associated, since all the dots fall on the regression line. In such situations, the observed Y values are equal to the corresponding predicted values Y_e. In other words, we are able to make perfectly correct predictions of Y based upon X. In part B, the dots are close to the regression line but not *on* the line. Hence, the observed values of Y deviate from the predicted values Y_e. These deviations, measured according to Equation 13.3.1 $(Y - Y_e)$, are indicated by the dashed line connecting each dot to the regression line. The deviations are considerably greater in part C than in part B. Consequently, in part C, X provides a poorer basis for predicting Y than in part B. The smaller the deviations $(Y - Y_e)$, the closer is the relationship between X and Y and the better predictor is X of Y.

Consider the variable Y. Suppose we have a sample of Y scores for n subjects. Based upon this sample we could compute the mean $\bar{Y}$, using Equation 4.2.4, and the standard deviation s_Y, using Equations 5.2.3 and 5.2.4. Of course, in these equations we substitute Y for X, since we are now speaking about the Y variable. Previously, we used the symbol s to denote the standard deviation of X. However, since we are now concerned with two variables X and Y, we need to distinguish between the standard deviations of each of these variables. We will use s_X to denote the standard deviation of X. We will use s_Y to denote the standard deviation of Y, and rewrite Equations 5.2.3 and 5.2.4 to read

$$s_Y^2 = \frac{\sum (Y - \bar{Y})^2}{n - 1} \tag{13.4.1}$$

$$s_Y = \sqrt{s_Y^2} \tag{13.4.2}$$

While s_Y^2 is called the *variance* of Y, we will refer to the *numerator* of Equation 13.4.1, $\Sigma (Y - \bar{Y})^2$, as the *total variation* in Y. In other words, *the sum of the squared deviations of a set of scores from its mean represents a measure of the total variation in the set*. We may write this as

$$\sum (Y - \bar{Y})^2 = \text{total variation in } Y \tag{13.4.3}$$

Figure 13.4.2 presents one dot, A, from a set of dots in a scatter diagram, as well as the regression line. This dot is at the height Y, as indicated by the dashed-line arrow. The corresponding predicted value Y_e is indicated as point A' on the regression line. A horizontal dashed line is constructed at a height equal to $\bar{Y}$. The deviation $(Y - \bar{Y})$ in the figure represents the difference between the observed value of Y (at dot A) and the mean of Y (at point A''). This deviation (distance), represented by the line connecting

A and A'', may be called the *total deviation* of the observed Y value from the mean $\overline{Y}$. As indicated in the figure, this total deviation may be considered as made up of two parts as follows:

$$(Y - \overline{Y}) = (Y - Y_e) + (Y_e - \overline{Y}) \qquad (13.4.4)$$

The part $(Y_e - \overline{Y})$ represents the deviation of the predicted value Y_e (based upon the regression line) from the mean $\overline{Y}$. This part of the total

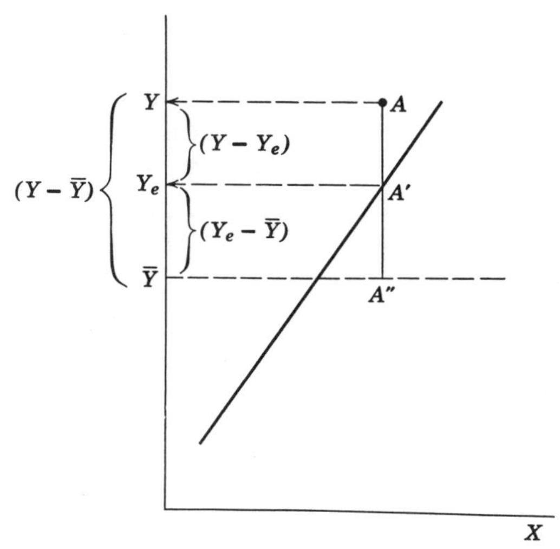

Fig. 13.4.2

deviation of the observed Y from $\overline{Y}$ is *due to regression*. That is, it is *explained* by the association between Y and X. The other part of the total deviation $(Y - Y_e)$ is *unexplained* by the association between the two variables. This is the deviation between the observed and predicted values of Y expressed by Equation 13.3.1.

The meaning of these deviations is more easily grasped through an illustration. Suppose X denotes height and Y denotes weight for six-year-old boys. Then dot A in Figure 13.4.2 represents the height X and weight Y for a particular boy and the regression line represents the regression equation for predicting weight Y based upon height X for six-year-old boys. Suppose it is desired to predict the weight of a six-year-old boy of a specified height (a specified value of X). Generally, weight would be expected to depend upon a variety of factors, such as height, heredity, etc. However, if no information is available concerning the relationship of weight to such factors, the best prediction of such a boy's weight is $\overline{Y}$, the mean for a sample of six-year-old boys. However, if sufficient related information is available, it is possible to produce a better prediction.

Suppose we have information on height as well as weight for the sample of six-year-old boys. We are now able to compute the regression equation (for the regression line shown in Figure 13.4.2) and predict weight based on height. The deviation between this predicted weight Y_e and the sample mean $\bar{Y}$ represents the improvement over the use of $\bar{Y}$ as the predicted weight *due to information concerning the regression relationship*. Or, it represents that part of the deviation from $\bar{Y}$ *explained* by height X. On the other hand, we may observe the weight Y of a six-year-old boy with the specified height and find that it differs from both $\bar{Y}$ and Y_e. The balance of the deviation from $\bar{Y}$, $(Y - Y_e)$, is presumably due to other factors (such as heredity), or it may be due to measurement errors, or it may reflect a combination of factors. In any event, this latter deviation is *unexplained* by regression or by the variable X (height).

If the total deviation $(Y - \bar{Y})$ is determined for *each* dot in a scatter diagram and then squared and summed for all dots, it can be shown mathematically that this *total sum of squares* is related to the *explained* and *unexplained* portions of the total deviations as follows:

$$\sum (Y - \bar{Y})^2 = \sum (Y - Y_e)^2 + \sum (Y_e - \bar{Y})^2 \qquad (13.4.5)$$

We recognize that the *total sum of squares* represents the *total variation* in Y, as expressed by Equation 13.4.3. The first sum of squares to the right of the equality sign in Equation 13.4.5, based upon the *unexplained* portion of the total deviation for each dot, represents *the variation in Y unexplained by, or not associated with, X*. The second sum of squares to the right of the equality sign, based upon the portion of the total variation for each dot which is *explained* by X, represents *the variation in Y explained by, or associated with, X*. Consequently, we may write Equation 13.4.5 in words as

$$\begin{pmatrix}\text{Total variation}\\ \text{in } Y\end{pmatrix} = \begin{pmatrix}\text{Variation in } Y\\ \text{not associated}\\ \text{with } X\end{pmatrix} + \begin{pmatrix}\text{Variation in } Y\\ \text{associated with } X\end{pmatrix} \qquad (13.4.6)$$

Equations 13.4.5 and 13.4.6 represent a fundamental relationship in statistics. Dividing each equation through by the total variation in Y, $\Sigma (Y - \bar{Y})^2$, we obtain

$$1 = \frac{\sum (Y - Y_e)^2}{\sum (Y - \bar{Y})^2} + \frac{\sum (Y_e - \bar{Y})^2}{\sum (Y - \bar{Y})^2} \qquad (13.4.7)$$

and, in words,

$$1 = \begin{pmatrix} \text{Proportion of the total} \\ \text{variation in } Y \text{ not} \\ \text{associated with } X \end{pmatrix} + \begin{pmatrix} \text{Proportion of} \\ \text{the total} \\ \text{variation} \\ \text{in } Y \\ \text{associated} \\ \text{with } X \end{pmatrix} \tag{13.4.8}$$

The foregoing equations provide a convenient basis for measuring *how closely* the two variables X and Y are associated. Clearly, *the more closely the variables are associated, the greater will be the proportion of the total variation in Y which is associated with X.* Let us use r^2 to denote this proportion. Then, we may write

$$r^2 = \frac{\sum (Y_e - \bar{Y})^2}{\sum (Y - \bar{Y})^2} \tag{13.4.9}$$

This proportion r^2 is called the *coefficient of determination.* Thus, the larger r^2, the greater is the proportion of the total variation in Y which is associated with X and the closer are X and Y related. The smaller r^2, the less is the proportion of the total variation in Y which is associated with X and the less closely are X and Y related. Finally, let us write

$$r = \sqrt{\frac{\sum (Y_e - \bar{Y})^2}{\sum (Y - \bar{Y})^2}} \tag{13.4.10}$$

Then, r, which is the square root of the coefficient of determination, is called the *coefficient of correlation.*

Usually r is used to indicate the degree to which X and Y are associated. However, the interpretation of r is easier when we think in terms of r^2. Actually, there is a tendency for research workers to show the value of r^2 as well as r in published results, since r^2 is a more meaningful measure. Clearly, the lowest possible value for r^2 (or any proportion) is 0 and the highest is 1. Similarly, for r, the lowest possible magnitude is 0 and the highest is 1. However, since the relationship between X and Y may be positive or negative, a sign (+ or −) is attached to r to indicate the *direction* of relationship as well as the *degree* of relationship. Generally, when the relationship between X and Y is positive, r is written without the + sign, the sign being understood. The sign determined for b (Equation 13.3.6) is the sign to be used for r. Equation 13.4.10 is a *definitional* equation for r and is inconvenient to use for computational purposes. It can be shown mathematically that the following equation for r is equivalent to

Equation 13.4.10 and convenient for computational use

$$r = \frac{\sum xy}{\sqrt{(\sum x^2)(\sum y^2)}} \tag{13.4.11}$$

where $\Sigma\, xy$ is computed according to Equation 13.3.8

$\sum x^2$ is computed according to Equation 13.3.9

$$\sum y^2 = \sum Y^2 - \frac{(\sum Y)^2}{n} \tag{13.4.12}$$

Let us use Equation 13.4.11 to compute the correlation coefficient for the data in Table 13.3.2. In Section 13.3 we have already determined $\Sigma\, xy = 2942$ and $\Sigma\, x^2 = 1930$. We may determine from Table 13.3.2 that $n = 10$ and $\Sigma\, Y = 1211$. If we square each Y value in the table and sum all these squared values, we obtain $\Sigma\, Y^2 = 151{,}423$. Then, we may compute

$$\sum y^2 = 151{,}423 - \frac{(1211)^2}{10} = 4771$$

Finally, using Equation 13.4.11, we compute

$$r = \frac{2942}{\sqrt{(1930)(4771)}} = .97$$

A correlation coefficient of .97 is, clearly, very high, since the maximum value of r is 1. It should be noted that Equation 13.4.11 results in the *signed* value of r, so that it is not necessary to refer to the sign of b. Actually, the sign attached to the term $\Sigma\, xy$, which is in the numerator of both Equation 13.4.11 for r and Equation 13.3.6 for b, determines the sign for both r and b. Computing the coefficient of determination, we obtain $r^2 = (.97)^2 = .94$. This indicates that .94 or 94% of the variation in mechanical ability scores Y is associated with the variation in depth perception scores X. Conversely, we may also state that 94% of the variation in depth perception scores X is associated with the variation in mechanical ability scores Y. Of course, these are arbitrarily selected scores for illustrative purposes. It is hardly to be expected that score variables such as these will be as closely associated as in this illustration.

We will now determine the correlation between the hypothetical scores for Battery A (X) and Battery B (Y) presented in Table 13.3.3. We have already determined $\Sigma\, xy = -536.1$ and $\Sigma\, x^2 = 1052.9$. We obtain from Table 13.3.3 $n = 10$ and $\Sigma\, Y = 429$. Then, squaring each Y value in the table and summing these squares, we obtain $\Sigma\, Y^2 = 18{,}717$. Computing according to Equation 13.4.12, we obtain

$$\sum y^2 = 18{,}717 - \frac{(429)^2}{10} = 312.9$$

Finally, using Equation 13.4.11, we obtain

$$r = \frac{-536.1}{\sqrt{(1052.9)(312.9)}} = -.93$$

Computing r^2, we obtain .86, indicating that 86% of the variation of either one of the variables (scores on Battery A or Battery B) is associated with the variation in the other.

When computing regression equations, it was stated that Y denotes the variable to be predicted and X denotes the variable upon which the prediction is based. However, if only the correlation coefficient is to be computed, it does not matter to which variable is assigned the symbol Y and to which is assigned the symbol X. No matter how these symbols are assigned, the same value for r will be obtained.

PROBLEMS FOR PRACTICE AND REVIEW

For each of these problems which follow Section 13.3, compute the coefficient of correlation and the coefficient of determination. Explain the meaning of the coefficient of determination.

(1) Problem 1: a, b, c
(2) Problem 2
(3) Problem 3
(4) Problem 4
(5) Problem 5
(6) Problem 6
(7) Problem 7
(8) Problem 8

13.5 FREQUENCY DISTRIBUTIONS

In Chapter 3 we discussed the need for organization of large sets of raw data. If organization and summarization of data are necessary when a single variable is involved, it is considerably more important for data involving two variables. For example, although there are 100 scores on a test administered to 100 subjects, 200 scores are involved when we have two tests per subject. Not only is the volume of data increased, but it is necessary to take into account the *pairing* of the two scores per subject.

Table 13.5.1 presents scores on test X and test Y for 83 subjects. A convenient method for organization and summarization of such data is

Table 13.5.1 SCORES ON TEST *X* AND TEST *Y* FOR 83 SUBJECTS

X	Y	X	Y	X	Y	X	Y	X	Y
101	42	87	77	88	77	108	40	98	66
109	59	81	73	87	73	95	63	90	61
115	44	111	44	97	59	81	73	102	49
106	52	99	53	87	78	85	79	91	63
107	54	104	58	95	63	93	52	87	77
104	49	89	60	102	41	109	59	87	73
95	51	99	52	105	53	85	79	89	70
90	63	88	60	104	48	114	45	110	49
103	47	112	43	108	59	94	64	103	56
98	66	106	53	93	57	90	51	106	40
91	62	91	64	103	49	98	53	118	49
94	50	91	63	91	55	100	46	99	54
95	62	98	66	90	62	108	57	89	62
85	79	92	61	100	54	104	57	90	53
89	70	100	52	90	64	105	52	109	52
98	68	91	62	94	64	90	56		
93	53	93	61	114	45	90	54		

Y \ X	80–89	90–99	100–109	110–119
40–49			𝍸 𝍸	𝍸 ||
50–59		𝍸 𝍸 𝍸	𝍸 𝍸 𝍸	
60–69	|||	𝍸 𝍸 𝍸 𝍸		
70–79	𝍸 𝍸 |||			

Fig. 13.5.1. Bivariate or two-way tally table.

provided by the use of a *bivariate or two-way tally table*, as presented in Figure 13.5.1. The *column headings* indicate class intervals for the X variable, while the *stub* (on the left) indicates class intervals for the Y variable. Equal class intervals are determined for each variable, following the general procedure developed in Chapter 3 for a single variable. (Only a few classes are used in order to keep the illustration simple.) Each *pair* of X and Y scores in Table 13.5.1 represents one tally in the tally table.

	Midpoint	84.5	94.5	104.5	114.5	
Midpoint	X \ Y	80–89	90–99	100–109	110–119	f_Y
44.5	40–49			10	7	17
54.5	50–59		15	15		30
64.5	60–69	3	20			23
74.5	70–79	13				13
	f_X	16	35	25	7	$n = 83$

Fig. 13.5.2. Bivariate or two-way frequency table.

For example, the first pair of scores in Table 13.5.1, $X = 101$ and $Y = 42$, appears as a tally mark in the cell for the X class interval 100–109 and the Y class interval 40–49. Each fifth tally is drawn diagonally across the first four to tie each five tallies into a bundle convenient for counting. This follows the tallying procedure discussed in Chapter 3.

Using the tally table, we set up a *bivariate or two-way frequency table*, as shown in Figure 13.5.2. This is called a *correlation table* or a *scatter plot* in some texts. The class intervals for the X and Y scores are shown, as well as the class midpoints. The frequencies (number of tallies in the tally table) are entered in each cell. Then, column and row totals are obtained, as shown. The *row totals* are the class frequencies for the *Y scores* and are denoted as f_Y. The *column totals* are the class frequencies for the *X scores* and are denoted as f_X. The frequencies *within a cell* represent *pair* frequencies. For example, the cell identified by the X midpoint 104.5 and the Y midpoint 44.5 contains the frequency 10, indicating that 10 out of the 83 subjects have X scores which fall in the interval 100–109 and Y scores which fall in the interval 40–49. Clearly, information as to the *specific* pairings of X and Y scores is lost when data are summarized in a two-way frequency table. This is similar to the loss of *specific* score information when data are organized into a frequency distribution, discussed in Chapter 3. Following the approach used for single-variable frequency tables, we will assume that, for each cell, midpoints for the corresponding X class interval and the corresponding Y class interval represent the X and Y scores for all the subjects included. For example,

Table 13.5.2 GROUPED DATA: SCORES ON TEST X AND TEST Y FOR 83 SUBJECTS

Midpoints							
X	Y	f	Xf	Yf	X^2f	Y^2f	XYf
104.5	44.5	10	1045.0	445.0	109,202.50	19,802.50	46,502.50
114.5	44.5	7	801.5	311.5	91,771.75	13,861.75	35,666.75
94.5	54.5	15	1417.5	817.5	133,953.75	44,553.75	77,253.75
104.5	54.5	15	1567.5	817.5	163,803.75	44,553.75	85,428.75
84.5	64.5	3	253.5	193.5	21,420.75	12,480.75	16,350.75
94.5	64.5	20	1890.0	1290.0	178,605.00	83,205.00	121,905.00
84.5	74.5	13	1098.5	968.5	92,823.25	72,153.25	81,838.25
	Total	83	8073.5	4843.5	791,580.75	290,610.75	464,945.75

for the three subjects in the cell identified by the X midpoint 84.5 and the Y midpoint 64.5, we assume that their X and Y scores are 84.5 and 64.5, respectively.

After the data are grouped and summarized in a frequency table, such as Figure 13.5.2, it is a relatively simple matter to compute the least squares regression equation and the coefficient of correlation. The recommended sequence of computations, which is similar to the procedure presented for raw (ungrouped) data, is as follows:

STEP 1: Set up a table like Table 13.5.2. Note that X and Y represent *class midpoints* and f denotes the *cell frequencies*. The cell frequency column is copied from the two-way frequency table, row by row. That is, referring to Figure 13.5.2, the first row has the cell frequencies 10 and 7. These are the first two cell frequencies shown in Table 13.5.2. The second row has the cell frequencies 15 and 15. These are the next two cell frequencies shown, etc. The first two columns in Table 13.5.2 present the X and Y class midpoints which correspond to each cell frequency. For example, the first cell frequency in the f column is 10 and the corresponding X and Y midpoints (from Figure 13.5.2) are 104.5 and 44.5, respectively. These are shown in the X and Y columns of Table 13.5.2. The totals Σf, ΣXf, ΣYf, ΣX^2f, ΣY^2f, and ΣXYf, shown in the table, are used in subsequent steps.

STEP 2: Compute, using the summations from *Step* 1

$$\sum x^2f = \sum X^2f - \frac{(\sum Xf)^2}{n} \tag{13.5.1}$$

$$\sum y^2f = \sum Y^2f - \frac{(\sum Yf)^2}{n} \tag{13.5.2}$$

$$\sum xyf = \sum XYf - \frac{(\sum Xf)(\sum Yf)}{n} \tag{13.5.3}$$

where, as before

$$x = X - \bar{X}$$
$$y = Y - \bar{Y}$$
$$n = \Sigma f = \text{number of } \textit{pairs} \text{ of } X \text{ and } Y \text{ values}$$

STEP 3: Compute, using results from *Steps* 1 and 2

$$b = \frac{\sum xyf}{\sum x^2f} \tag{13.5.4}$$

$$a = \frac{\sum Yf - b\sum Xf}{n} \tag{13.5.5}$$

Then, the least squares regression equation is $Y_e = a + bX$, as before.

STEP 4: Compute, using results from *Step* 2

$$r = \frac{\sum xyf}{\sqrt{(\sum x^2f)(\sum y^2f)}} \tag{13.5.6}$$

The similarity between the foregoing equations and those presented previously for ungrouped data is apparent. Apply this procedure to the X and Y scores in the illustration. Table 13.5.2 presents the summations required for *Step* 1. Using these summations, we compute according to *Step* 2

$$\sum x^2f = 791{,}580.75 - \frac{(8073.5)^2}{83} = 6262.65$$

$$\sum y^2f = 290{,}610.75 - \frac{(4843.5)^2}{83} = 7966.27$$

$$\sum xyf = 464{,}945.75 - \frac{(8073.5)(4843.5)}{83} = -6186.75$$

Then, for *Step* 3 we obtain

$$b = \frac{-6186.75}{6262.65} = -.9879$$

$$a = \frac{4843.5 - (-.9879)(8073.5)}{83} = 154.4495$$

The least squares regression equation is

$$Y_e = 154.45 - .99X$$

Finally, for *Step* 4 we obtain

$$r = \frac{-6186.75}{\sqrt{(6262.65)(7966.27)}} = -.88$$

PROBLEMS FOR PRACTICE AND REVIEW

1. The following bivariate frequency table was prepared for "hours of training" and "number of errors" for 55 subjects:

Number of Errors	Hours of Training				
	5–9	10–14	15–19	20–24	25–29
6–8				2	8
9–11		1	2	5	2
12–14	3	3	7	4	1
15–17		8	1	2	
18–20	6				

(a) Determine the least squares regression equation to predict "number of errors" based upon "hours of training."

(b) Determine the coefficient of correlation for "number of errors" and "hours of training."

2. The following bivariate frequency table was prepared for scores on aptitude test A and aptitude test B for 105 subjects:

Aptitude Test A	Aptitude Test B				
	3–5	6–8	9–11	12–14	15–17
0–4	20	5			
5–9	2	16	2		
10–14		12	9	2	1
15–19			8	10	
20–24			3	6	3
25–29				1	5

(a) Determine the least squares regression equation to predict aptitude test A scores based upon aptitude test B scores.

(b) Determine the coefficient of correlation for aptitude test A and aptitude test B scores.

13.6 COMPUTATIONAL NOTES

It is apparent that the computations required to determine a least squares regression equation and the coefficient of correlation are quite lengthy and involve considerable labor. Therefore, it is useful to have available various procedures which reduce the computational labor.

Table 13.6.1 SCORES ON TEST X AND TEST Y FOR TWELVE SUBJECTS

Subject	X Scores	Y Scores	$X' = X - 100$	$Y' = Y - 200$
A	131	209	31	9
B	126	200	26	0
C	130	202	30	2
D	132	207	32	7
E	144	216	44	16
F	129	203	29	3
G	140	210	40	10
H	136	211	36	11
I	128	200	28	0
J	138	210	38	10
K	149	221	49	21
L	129	201	29	1

Table 13.6.1 presents X and Y scores for 12 subjects. It is clear that determination of the regression equation and the correlation coefficient would involve laborious computations. However, the work may be made considerably easier if an appropriate constant is *subtracted* from each X score and a second appropriate constant is *subtracted* from each Y score. For example, in the illustration, we will transform the X scores to X' scores by subtracting 100 from each score. Then, we will transform the Y scores to Y' scores by subtracting 200 from each score. The resulting X' and Y' scores, shown in the table, are considerably smaller numbers and easier to use in computations. The following equations are to be used:

$$\sum x^2 = \sum (X')^2 - \frac{(\sum X')^2}{n} \tag{13.6.1}$$

$$\sum y^2 = \sum (Y')^2 - \frac{(\sum Y')^2}{n} \tag{13.6.2}$$

$$\sum xy = \sum X'Y' - \frac{(\sum X')(\sum Y')}{n} \tag{13.6.3}$$

where n = number of pairs of X' and Y' (or X and Y) scores

$$b = \frac{\sum xy}{\sum x^2} \tag{13.6.4}$$

$$a = \frac{\sum Y - b \sum X}{n} \tag{13.6.5}$$

Note that Equation 13.6.4 for b is the same as Equation 13.3.6. Furthermore, Equation 13.6.5 for a uses the *original* X and Y score values, *not* the transformed scores X' and Y'. This is more convenient than computing a

Table 13.6.2 SCORES ON TEST X AND TEST Y FOR TEN SUBJECTS

Subject	X Scores	Y Scores	$X' = X/4$	$Y' = Y/100$
A	88	800	22	8
B	144	1000	36	10
C	72	900	18	9
D	80	900	20	9
E	84	1000	21	10
F	128	1100	32	11
G	120	1000	30	10
H	116	800	29	8
I	76	900	19	9
J	92	1200	23	12

based upon the transformed scores. Equation 13.6.5 is identical with Equation 13.3.7. Finally,

$$r = \frac{\sum xy}{\sqrt{(\sum x^2)(\sum y^2)}} \tag{13.6.6}$$

This is the same as Equation 13.4.11. Sometimes, subtraction of a constant results in negative scores. This causes no problem. However, the sign should be taken into account in the computations. Sometimes it is desirable to transform only one variable, not both. Suppose we transform Y by subtracting a constant k and leave X unchanged. In such case, proceed as before, with $Y' = Y - k$ and $X' = X$. It will be left as an exercise for the reader to compute the regression equation and the correlation coefficient for the data in Table 13.6.1, using the transformed scores.

In some problems, the work of computing correlation and regression coefficients is considerably reduced if one or both variables are *divided* by an appropriate constant. For example, Table 13.6.2 presents scores on test X and test Y for 10 subjects. If we divide each X score by 4 and each Y

score by 100, the resulting transformed scores are easier to use in the computations. We will use c_X to denote the constant by which the X scores are divided and c_Y to denote the constant by which the Y scores are divided. We will denote the transformed scores as $X' = X/c_X$ and $Y' = Y/c_Y$. The following equations are to be used:

$$\sum (x')^2 = \sum (X')^2 - \frac{(\sum X')^2}{n} \tag{13.6.7}$$

$$\sum (y')^2 = \sum (Y')^2 - \frac{(\sum Y')^2}{n} \tag{13.6.8}$$

$$\sum x'y' = \sum X'Y' - \frac{(\sum X')(\sum Y')}{n} \tag{13.6.9}$$

where: n = number of pairs of X' and Y' (or X and Y) scores

$$b = \frac{c_Y \sum x'y'}{c_X \sum (x')^2} \tag{13.6.10}$$

$$a = \frac{c_Y \sum Y' - bc_X \sum X'}{n} \tag{13.6.11}$$

$$r = \frac{\sum x'y'}{\sqrt{[\sum (x')^2][\sum (y')^2]}} \tag{13.6.12}$$

It may be desirable to transform one variable by dividing by a constant and not the other. Suppose we transform X to X/c_X and leave Y unchanged. In this instance, proceed as before, with $Y' = Y$, $X' = X/c_X$, $c_Y = 1$, and c_X = a specified constant. It will be left as an exercise for the reader to compute the regression equation and the correlation coefficient for the scores in Table 13.6.2.

When using a bivariate or two-way frequency table for computation of regression and correlation coefficients, the procedure presented in Section 13.5 is convenient only when the number of cells which contain frequencies of 1 or more are few in number. For example, the illustrative problem in that section involved only seven such cells, as can be seen in Figure 13.5.2. When the cells with a frequency of 1 or more are numerous, the table to be constructed for computational purposes, such as Table 13.5.2, becomes quite long and inconvenient. In such situations, it is desirable to use the two-way frequency table itself for some of the computations. Figure 13.6.1 illustrates such use of a two-way frequency table, using the data of Figure 13.5.2. This table is constructed as follows: Set up columns for the X class intervals and rows for the Y class intervals; post the cell frequencies; then, obtain column frequency totals and post them in the f_X row; obtain row frequency totals and post them in the f_Y column, as shown in Figure 13.6.1. So far, this table is no different than the table in Figure 13.5.2, except that the class midpoints are omitted.

Now, transform the X variable to a U variable by entering 0 in the U row corresponding to the largest value of f_X (35) and entering the other values as shown in Figure 13.6.1. This is the double transformation procedure discussed for the mean in *Situation* 8 and for the standard deviation

Y \ X	80–89	90–99	100–109	110–119	f_Y	V	Vf_Y	V^2f_Y	UVf
40–49			(10) 10	(14) 7	17	−1	−17	17	−24
50–59		(0) 15	(0) 15		30	0	0	0	0
60–69	(−3) 3	(0) 20			23	1	23	23	−3
70–79	(−13) 13				13	2	26	52	−26
f_X	16	35	25	7	$n = 83$		32	92	−53
U	−1	0	1	2					
Uf_X	−16	0	25	14	23				
U^2f_X	16	0	25	28	69				

Fig. 13.6.1. Bivariate or two-way frequency table used for computations.

in *Situation G*. However, now we use the upper-case letter U instead of the lower-case letter u. (It is unnecessary to compute the class midpoints.) In the same way, transform the Y variable to a V variable by entering 0 in the V column corresponding to the largest value of f_Y (30) and entering the other values as shown in the figure. The two remaining rows in the figure, Uf_X and U^2f_X, are easily computed. The first item in the Uf_X row (−16) is obtained as the product of the first item in the U row (−1) and the first item in the f_X row (16). The balance of the Uf_X row is determined in a similar manner. The first item in the U^2f_X row (16) is obtained as the product of the first item in the Uf_X row (−16) and the first item in the U row (−1). The balance of the items in the U^2f_X row are similarly computed. The two columns Vf_Y and V^2f_Y are similarly determined. The first item in the Vf_Y column (−17) is the product of the first item in the V column (−1) and the first item in the f_Y column (17). The balance of the Vf_Y column is computed in the same way. The first item in the V^2f_Y column (17) is computed as the product of the first item in the Vf_Y column (−17) and the first item in the V column (−1). The remaining items in the V^2f_Y column are similarly determined.

The last column in Figure 13.6.1, UVf, contains items which are computed by multiplying three figures: U, V, and f (cell frequency). This is accomplished most easily in two steps. First, multiply each cell frequency by the corresponding U value. For example, in the first row of cell frequencies, multiply the frequency 10 by the corresponding U value 1. This product is shown in the cell as 10, *written in a circle*. The second cell frequency in this row (7) times the corresponding U value (2), or 14, is written in a circle in the cell. This is done for all cells with frequencies of 1 or more, row by row. The second step is to add all circled numbers in a row and multiply this sum by the corresponding V value. This product is entered in the UVf column. For example, in the first row of cell frequencies, the circled numbers ⑩ and ⑭ add to 24. Multiplying this sum by the corresponding V value (-1), we obtain -24. This is the first entry in the UVf column. This two-step computation is carried out for each row in the table.

Notice that some circles contain a *dash* instead of a figure. It is a good idea to place a dash in the circle for any cell where *either* the corresponding U value *or* the corresponding V value or *both* are equal to 0. Then, consider these dashes as equal to 0 when performing the second step noted previously. This approach avoids unnecessary computations. For example, the cells in the column where $U = 0$ will always have a 0 in the circle since, in the first step, each cell frequency in this column is multiplied by $U = 0$. Observe that, in the second step, the sum of the circled numbers in the row where $V = 0$ is multiplied by $V = 0$. Therefore, there is no need to multiply the cell frequencies in this row by the corresponding U values. Just enter a 0 in the corresponding position in the UVf column.

The two-way frequency table, expanded as in Figure 13.6.1, provides the data needed to compute the regression equation and the correlation coefficient. The following computational sequence and equations may be used:

STEP 1: Using *row and column sums* from a two-way frequency table (as in Figure 13.6.1), compute

$$\sum u^2 f_X = \sum U^2 f_X - \frac{(\sum U f_X)^2}{n} \tag{13.6.13}$$

$$\sum v^2 f_Y = \sum V^2 f_Y - \frac{(\sum V f_Y)^2}{n} \tag{13.6.14}$$

$$\sum uvf = \sum UVf - \frac{(\sum U f_X)(\sum V f_Y)}{n} \tag{13.6.15}$$

where $u = U - \overline{U}$
$v = V - \overline{V}$
$n = \Sigma f =$ number of *pairs* of X and Y values

STEP 2: Using the results of *Step* 1 and the computations in the two-way frequency table, compute

$$b = \frac{c_Y \sum uvf}{c_X \sum u^2 f_X} \tag{13.6.16}$$

$$a = \frac{c_Y \sum Vf_Y - bc_X \sum Uf_X}{n} + Y_0 - bX_0 \tag{13.6.17}$$

where c_X = length of X class intervals
c_Y = length of Y class intervals
X_0 = X midpoint corresponding to $U = 0$
Y_0 = Y midpoint corresponding to $V = 0$

Then, as before, the least squares regression equation is $Y_e = a + bX$.

STEP 3: Compute, using the results from *Step* 1

$$r = \frac{\sum uvf}{\sqrt{(\sum u^2 f_X)(\sum v^2 f_Y)}} \tag{13.6.18}$$

We will apply these steps to compute the regression equation and the coefficient of correlation for the data in Figure 13.6.1

STEP 1:

$$\sum u^2 f_X = 69 - \frac{(23)^2}{83} = 62.6265$$

$$\sum v^2 f_Y = 92 - \frac{(32)^2}{83} = 79.6627$$

$$\sum uvf = -53 - \frac{(23)(32)}{83} = -61.8675$$

STEP 2:

$$c_X = 10$$

$$c_Y = 10$$

$$X_0 = \frac{90 + 99}{2} = 94.5$$

$$Y_0 = \frac{50 + 59}{2} = 54.5$$

$$b = \frac{(10)(-61.8675)}{(10)(62.6265)} = -.9879$$

$$a = \frac{(10)(32) - (-.9879)(10)(23)}{83} + 54.5 - (-.9879)(94.5)$$

$$= 154.4495$$

The least squares regression equation is

$$Y_e = 154.45 - .99X$$

This is the same result obtained in Section 13.5 for these data. Then, applying *Step* 3, we obtain

$$r = \frac{-61.8675}{\sqrt{(62.6265)(79.6627)}} = -.88$$

This is the same result obtained previously.

PROBLEMS FOR PRACTICE AND REVIEW

1. Given X and Y scores for 11 subjects:

X	Y
58	139
54	127
57	130
59	146
60	137
53	132
51	112
58	147
62	147
56	139
55	136

(a) Determine the least squares regression equation to predict Y scores based on X scores. (*Hint:* Transform X scores to X' scores by subtracting 50 from each score. Transform Y scores to Y' scores by subtracting 130 from each score.)
(b) Determine the coefficient of correlation for the X and Y scores.

2. Given the following X and Y scores for nine subjects:

X	Y
148	151
152	159
121	167
136	150
141	164
149	152
137	160
135	170
129	160

(a) Determine the least squares regression equation to predict Y scores based upon X scores. (*Hint:* Transform X scores to X' scores by subtracting 120 from each score. Transform Y scores to Y' scores by subtracting 150 from each score.)
(b) Determine the coefficient of correlation for the X and Y scores.

3. Given the following X and Y scores for 12 subjects:

X	Y
90	87
100	84
120	75
150	75
170	72
180	60
200	54
200	45
220	45
220	45
220	39
230	39

(a) Determine the least squares regression equation to predict Y scores based upon X scores. (*Hint:* Transform X scores to X' scores by dividing each score by 10. Transform Y scores to Y' scores by dividing each score by 3.)

(b) Determine r for the X and Y scores.

4. For Problem 1, following Section 13.5, recompute the least squares regression equation and the coefficient of correlation, using the computational procedure of this section.

5. For Problem 2, following Section 13.5, recompute the least squares regression equation and coefficient of correlation, using the computational procedure of this section.

14

PREDICTION

14.1 USES AND ABUSES

In Chapter 13, we introduced the basic concepts and computations involved in correlation and regression analysis. Methods for determining a least squares regression equation to express the association between two variables have been presented, as well as the methods for computing the coefficients of correlation and determination to measure the extent to which two variables are associated. Generally, these methods provide a useful basis for evaluating the relationship between two variables and for predicting the value of one variable based upon another. However, unless properly used, the application of these methods to specific problems may well lead to spurious, even ridiculous, results. For example, suppose it is found that, for a particular period of time, two variables, say, average salary of college professors and the number of juvenile delinquents committing serious crimes, are very closely associated. A high correlation between two such variables notwithstanding, would anyone be willing to announce that an increase in the average salary of college professors may be expected to lead to an increase in the number of juvenile delinquents who commit serious crimes? Or say it is found that, for a certain period, the proportion of all college seniors who major in psychology and education is negatively correlated with the number of inches of rainfall recorded by the U.S. Weather Bureau. As a consequence of such a "finding," would anyone conclude that a decline in the proportion of college seniors who major in psychology and education would be expected to result in an increase in the number of inches of rainfall?

The two ridiculous illustrations just presented are meant to emphasize that the methods presented in Chapter 13 are purely *mechanical procedures* which may be applied to data for *any* pair of variables. The fact that the coefficient of correlation computed for a pair of variables is high does not, *in itself*, denote a cause and effect relationship between the variables. *Purely by chance*, two variables may appear to be closely related based upon the correlation coefficient computed from a given set of data. When there is no logical or sensible relationship between two variables, such computational exercises represent *spurious* correlations, often called *nonsense* correlations.

Generally, correlation and regression analysis is applied to test hypotheses developed by subject-matter specialists. For example, a psychological test battery may have been developed to measure research aptitude. Say, it is hypothesized that this test battery may be a good predictor of on-the-job success in research management type of positions. This hypothesis may be tested by administering the test battery to a sample of recently employed research management personnel. At an appropriate time, each subject is rated on "on-the-job success" by a panel of experts. Then, the correlation coefficient may be computed for the two variables, test battery score and on-the-job rating, for this sample of subjects. A least squares regression equation may also be computed ($Y =$ on-the-job rating, $X =$ test battery score) to predict on-the-job success based upon test battery performance. The correlation and regression analysis may be used to evaluate the hypothesis.

As a second illustration, say it is hypothesized that the average grade obtained in secondary school may be used as a predictor of the average grade obtained as a college undergraduate. This hypothesis may be evaluated by the methods of correlation and regression analysis based upon data collected from an appropriate sample. Sometimes there is less than adequate understanding of a problem, so that an *exploratory* type of correlation and regression analysis is helpful. For example, what is the best single predictor of the time required by a subject to perform a certain mechanical task? Is it his score on a manual dexterity test, his score on an available mechanical aptitude test, or, perhaps, his general IQ score? Such an inquiry would require separate analysis, based upon sample data, of the relationship between the time required to perform the specified task and each of the score predictors under consideration. It goes without saying that only logically related predictor variables should be considered in an exploratory analysis. Of course, exploratory analysis is risky, since it is always possible that a particular predictor looks best only because of the vagaries of sampling. Hence, as a general rule, it is necessary to carefully evaluate a pair of variables to ascertain whether it is logical to expect them to bear a relationship to each other.

14.2 THE NORMAL MODEL

Typically, the methods of correlation and regression analysis are applied to sample data and, as in the case of single-variable problems,

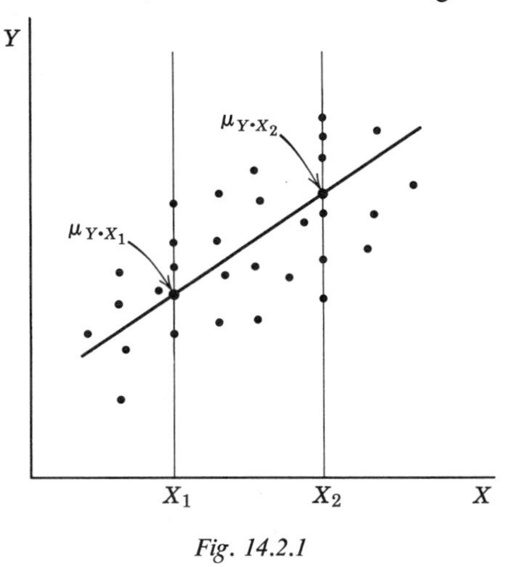

Fig. 14.2.1

inferences are made concerning the population. It will be recalled that, for single-variable problems, *theoretical sampling models* were constructed which provided the basis for formulating statistical inferences. In this section, we will consider a theoretical sampling model appropriate for formulation of statistical inferences in two-variable correlation and regression analyses.

Figure 14.2.1 presents a scatter diagram for variables X and Y. The regression line shown in the figure is based upon the full *population* of X and Y pairs. However, only some of the paired X and Y values (dots) are shown. More than one Y value is paired or associated with a given value of X, as specifically indicated by the two vertical lines constructed at the points $X = X_1$ and $X = X_2$ (a number of dots fall on each of these vertical lines). Assume that we have a very large population of males between the ages of 21 and 65 and $X =$ height and $Y =$ weight. Then, X_1 and X_2 represent specific heights. Suppose $X_1 = 62.53$ inches and $X_2 = 73.11$ inches. Even though height and weight are related variables, it is not to be expected that all males of a given height will have the same weight. Actually, for any specified height, we would expect a *distribution* of weights.

For example, in Figure 14.2.1, we note several different weights (Y values) for males who are X_1 or 62.53 inches tall (also X_2 or 73.11 inches tall). If the full set of dots for the population were shown, we would see a large number of weights associated with a given height. The distribution of weights for males with a given height is called a *conditional distribution.*

Generally, in a two-variable problem, we are concerned with the *conditional distribution of Y for a given value of X.* For example, in Figure 14.2.1, the conditional distribution of Y, given that $X = X_1$, is represented by the dots in the population which fall on the vertical line constructed at the point $X = X_1$. Or we could say that the conditional distribution of weight Y for the height X_1 or 62.53 inches is the distribution of weights for males in the population with the specified height. It may be helpful to distinguish between the distribution of all the weights in the population, without any regard to height, which is the distribution we studied when dealing with a single variable, and the conditional distribution. The former may be called the *unconditional* distribution of weights, representing the distribution of *all* the weights in the population. The latter, the conditional distribution of Y, represents the distribution of weights *only for males with a specified height.* Clearly, *there is a conditional distribution of Y for each possible value of X.*

We will consider the conditional distribution of Y corresponding to X_1 and imagine that small coins are placed on the scatter diagram instead of the dots shown in Figure 14.2.1. If a small coin is placed on the scatter diagram for each Y value which is paired with X_1, the coins would pile up along the vertical line constructed at X_1 in the figure, reflecting the frequency of the various values of Y. A three-dimensional diagram is required to illustrate this. For example, Figure 14.2.2 presents a possible pile-up of coins for Y values which are paired with X_1 in the population. In this figure, the largest pile-up of coins (frequency) occurs in the center of the distribution. The general shape of the pile-up of coins suggests a histogram. In fact, a histogram could be constructed for the Y values in the population which are paired with a specified value of X. Such a histogram would exhibit the conditional distribution of Y. We may, of course, approximate a histogram by a smooth continuous curve. (Figure 14.2.2 also presents a possible pile-up of coins for Y values which are paired with X_2.)

The theoretical sampling model appropriate for formulation of statistical inferences in two-variable correlation and regression analyses, which we will call the Normal Model, specifies that the conditional distribution of Y is a normal distribution, with the mean located on the regression line. Figure 14.2.3 presents the conditional normal distributions of Y corresponding to X_1 and X_2. We have been using μ to denote a population mean. Therefore, to denote the mean for the population of Y values, we will use the

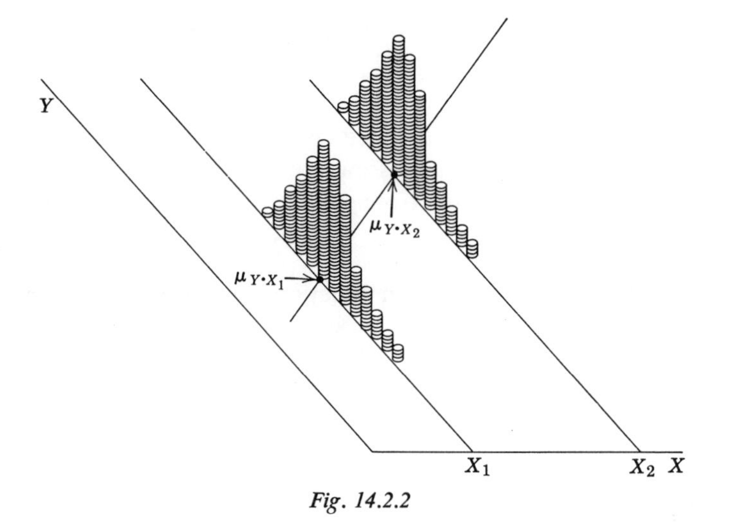

Fig. 14.2.2

symbol μ_Y. However, we must distinguish between the mean of *all* Y values, for which μ_Y is an appropriate symbol, and the *conditional mean*, which is the mean for those values of Y which are paired or associated with a specified value of X. We will denote the *mean of the conditional distribution of* Y as $\mu_{Y.X}$, indicating that this is the mean of the Y values in the population associated with a specified value of X. We will speak of this simply as the *conditional mean of* Y. In Figures 14.2.1, 14.2.2, and 14.2.3, we identify the specific conditional means $\mu_{Y.X_1}$ and $\mu_{Y.X_2}$ by heavy dots.

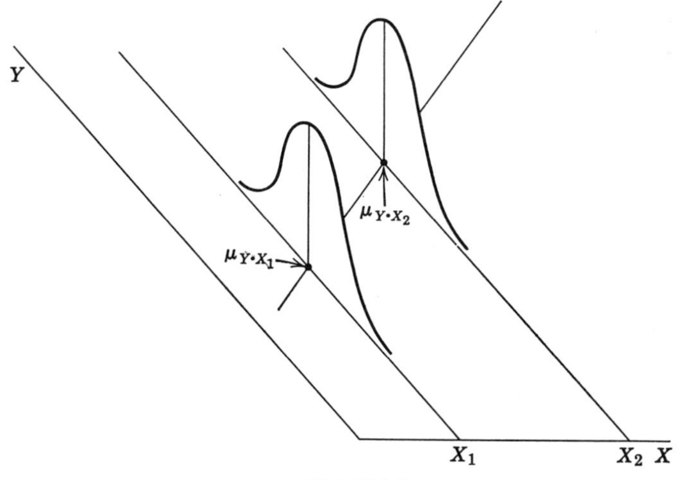

Fig. 14.2.3

Previously, we expressed the equation of a least squares regression line as

$$Y_e = a + bX \tag{14.2.1}$$

This denotes the equation computed from *sample data* and should be referred to as the *estimated* regression equation. We may write the *true* regression equation, computed from *population data*, as

$$\mu_{Y.X} = \alpha + \beta X \tag{14.2.2}$$

Notice that, in the *true* regression equation, we use $\mu_{Y.X}$ to denote the predicted Y value compared with Y_e used in the *estimated* equation. We are assuming that the population satisfies the requirements of the *Normal Model*, where (as illustrated in Figure 14.2.3) the conditional mean of Y, $\mu_{Y.X}$, falls *on the regression line*. Consequently, *the predicted value of Y based upon a specified value of X is the conditional mean of Y, if determined from the true regression equation and assuming that the Normal Model is applicable*. On the other hand, Y_e, computed according to Equation 14.2.1, may be considered to be a *point estimate of the conditional mean* $\mu_{Y.X}$. The coefficients in the true regression equation (Equation 14.2.2), α and β, represent the *true* regression coefficients, whereas a and b (Equation 14.2.1) represent *estimated* regression coefficients. That is, a is a *point estimate of* α and b is a *point estimate of* β. (The symbols α and β in Equation 14.2.2 should not be confused with the probabilities of committing Type I and Type II errors, for which the same α and β symbols have been used. Unfortunately, it is common for α and β to be used for both of these pairs of concepts.)

Referring to Chapter 5, Equations 5.2.1 and 5.2.2 and substituting Y for X, the equations for the population variance of Y (to be denoted ${\sigma_Y}^2$) and the population standard deviation of Y (to be denoted σ_Y) may be written as

$${\sigma_Y}^2 = \frac{\sum (Y - \mu_Y)^2}{N} \tag{14.2.3}$$

$$\sigma_Y = \sqrt{{\sigma_Y}^2} \tag{14.2.4}$$

where N denotes the number of Y values (or X and Y pairs) in the population.

As noted previously, μ_Y denotes the mean of the Y population. Combining the foregoing equations, we may write

$$\sigma_Y = \sqrt{\frac{\sum (Y - \mu_Y)^2}{N}} \tag{14.2.5}$$

Computation of σ_Y, as indicated in Equation 14.2.5, is based upon the sum of the squared deviations from the *population mean* μ_Y *of all Y values in the population*. The equation for the *standard deviation of a conditional distribution of Y*, denoted as $\sigma_{Y.X}$, may be written as

$$\sigma_{Y.X} = \sqrt{\frac{\sum (Y - \mu_{Y.X})^2}{N'}} \tag{14.2.6}$$

The *conditional standard deviation of Y*, $\sigma_{Y.X}$, is computed based upon the sum of the squared deviations *from the conditional mean*, $\mu_{Y.X}$, *of those Y values in the population which are paired with a specified value of X*. The number of Y values in the population which are paired with the specified value of X is denoted as N' in Equation 14.2.6.

Let us assume that the *conditional standard deviation of Y*, $\sigma_{Y.X}$, *is constant for all conditional distributions of Y* in a two-variable analysis. This is usually referred to as the assumption of *homoscedasticity*. We will rewrite Equation 14.2.6 to provide for the computation of the conditional standard deviation of Y *which is assumed to be common to all conditional distributions of Y* as follows:

$$\sigma_{Y.X} = \sqrt{\frac{\sum (Y - \mu_{Y.X})^2}{N}} \tag{14.2.7}$$

Equation 14.2.7 differs from Equation 14.2.6 in that it provides for the computation of $\sigma_{Y.X}$ based upon the sum of squares (in the numerator) relating to *all Y values in the population*, instead of only the Y values which are paired with an X of a specified value. Hence, Equation 14.2.7 has N in the denominator, denoting the number of Y values (or X and Y pairs) in the population. This compares with N' in the denominator of Equation 14.2.6 which denotes the number of Y values which are paired with an X of a specified value. However, in Equation 14.2.7, each Y value is expressed as a deviation from the mean of *its conditional distribution*, just as in Equation 14.2.6. For example, referring to Figure 14.2.3, each Y value which is paired with X_1 is expressed as a deviation from its conditional mean, $\mu_{Y.X_1}$, whereas each Y value which is paired with X_2 is expressed as a deviation from $\mu_{Y.X_2}$. These deviations may be written as $(Y - \mu_{Y.X_1})$ and $(Y - \mu_{Y.X_2})$, respectively.

The interpretation of $\sigma_{Y.X}$ is the same as for any standard deviation. This is true whether $\sigma_{Y.X}$ is computed according to Equation 14.2.6 or Equation 14.2.7. Equation 14.2.6 is to be used if it is desired to compute the standard deviation for a *given* conditional distribution of Y. However, if the assumption of homoscedasticity holds, $\sigma_{Y.X}$ is the same whether computed by one or the other of these two equations. Actually, the only reason for introducing Equation 14.2.7 is to provide a basis for estimating $\sigma_{Y.X}$ from sample data. When sample data are to be used to estimate $\sigma_{Y.X}$, the number of Y values which are paired with a specified value of X is usually very small, providing a poor basis for estimating $\sigma_{Y.X}$ for a given conditional distribution of Y. However, if it is reasonable to make the assumption of homoscedasticity, then, we may use *all* the Y values in the sample to compute an estimate of $\sigma_{Y.X}$. Equation 14.2.7 provides the basis for such a computation. We must modify Equation 14.2.7, for this purpose, by substituting the estimate Y_e for the true conditional mean $\mu_{Y.X}$ and using $n - 2$ in the denominator (n is sample size) instead of N. Then, we may write the equation for $s_{Y.X}$, the *estimated* conditional standard deviation of Y, as

$$s_{Y.X} = \sqrt{\frac{\sum (Y - Y_e)^2}{n - 2}} \tag{14.2.8}$$

The deviation $(Y - Y_e)$ appearing in the numerator of Equation 14.2.8 should be familiar. We have encountered this deviation before. For example, this deviation was presented in Figure 13.4.2 where it is clear that it is a measure of the *error* involved in using Y_e as a prediction (estimate) of the corresponding value Y. Generally, $s_{Y.X}$ is known as the *standard error of estimate. It is a measure of the extent to which, on the average, the observed values of Y are dispersed around the line of regression.* The computation of the *standard error of estimate*, $s_{Y.X}$, is quite laborious when using Equation 14.2.8, since it requires the computation of Y_e (based upon the least squares regression equation) corresponding to each observed Y value in the sample. A more convenient equation, computationally, is

$$s_{Y.X} = \sqrt{\frac{1}{n - 2}\left[\sum y^2 - \frac{(\sum xy)^2}{\sum x^2}\right]} \tag{14.2.9}$$

where Σxy, Σx^2, and Σy^2 are computed according to Equations 13.3.8, 13.3.9, and 13.4.12, respectively. We will compute the standard error of estimate $s_{Y.X}$ for the depth perception scores (X) and mechanical ability scores (Y) in Table 13.3.2. In Chapter 13, Section 13.3 we determined $\Sigma xy = 2942$ and $\Sigma x^2 = 1930$. In Section 13.4, where the correlation coefficient was discussed, we determined $\Sigma y^2 = 4771$. Then, noting that we have a sample of $n = 10$ pairs of X and Y scores, we compute

$$s_{Y.X} = \sqrt{\frac{1}{10 - 2}\left[4771 - \frac{(2942)^2}{1930}\right]} = 5.98$$

This result, $s_{Y.X} = 5.98$, indicates the extent to which the dots in the scatter diagram (Figure 13.3.3), on the average, are dispersed around the regression line. More specifically, we may state that, on the average, the observed scores on mechanical ability (Y) deviate 5.98 points (above or below) the predicted (or estimated) score (Y_e), based upon the least squares line of regression.

We may now specify the *Normal Model* more fully. In the *Normal Model*

1. The conditional distributions of Y for specified values of X are normal, with mean $\mu_{Y.X}$ and standard deviation $\sigma_{Y.X}$.
2. The conditional means $\mu_{Y.X}$ fall on a linear (straight-line) regression line, which is the least squares regression line for the population of X and Y pairs.
3. The conditional standard deviation $\sigma_{Y.X}$ is constant for all conditional distributions of Y which can be formed from the population of X and Y pairs.

14.3 INTERVAL ESTIMATION

In regression analyses based upon sample data, we face the problem of preparing estimates of population parameters and evaluating these estimates. For example, the regression coefficients a and b in a regression equation determined by the method of least squares represent point estimates of the true regression coefficients α and β, as already noted. We may evaluate these point estimates by constructing confidence intervals, following the same general procedure as explained in Chapter 9. However, first something must be said about the sampling distribution of the statistics a and b.

Suppose we select a random sample of n pairs of X and Y values from a population of X and Y pairs which satisfy the conditions of the *Normal Model*, as described in Section 14.2. Based upon this sample, we compute a and b by the method of least squares (Equations 13.3.6 and 13.3.7). Now, suppose we select a second random sample of n pairs of X and Y values from this population and, again, compute a and b. Imagine that we repeat this sample selection and computation procedure an infinite number of times. As a result, we have an infinite number of a and b values. Now, imagine that we construct a table for the a values, similar to Table 7.4.2 (Chapter 7, Section 7.4), presenting the different values obtained for a, the corresponding frequencies, and the corresponding probabilities (relative frequencies). We have now constructed, in our imagination, the *theoretical sampling distribution of the regression coefficient a*. Now, imagine that we construct a similar table for the b values, showing the different values obtained for b, the corresponding frequencies, and the corresponding probabilities (relative frequencies). We have now constructed, again in our imagination, the *theoretical sampling distribution of the regression coefficient b*. These sampling distributions are described by the following *Normal Model A* and *Normal Model B*.

Normal Model A: If samples of n pairs of X and Y values are selected from a population of X and Y pairs which satisfy the conditions of the *Normal Model*, the *sampling distribution of the statistic b* is normal, with mean β (the true coefficient) and estimated standard error

$$s_b = \frac{s_{Y.X}}{\sqrt{\sum x^2}} \tag{14.3.1}$$

Furthermore, the *sampling distribution of the statistic*

$$t = \frac{b - \beta}{s_b} \tag{14.3.2}$$

is like the t distribution, with $n - 2$ degrees of freedom.

Normal Model B: If samples of n pairs of X and Y values are selected from a population of X and Y pairs which satisfy the conditions of the *Normal Model*, the *sampling distribution of the statistic a* is normal, with mean α (the true coefficient) and estimated standard error

$$s_a = s_{Y.X}\sqrt{\frac{1}{n} + \frac{\bar{X}^2}{\sum x^2}} \tag{14.3.3}$$

Furthermore, the *sampling distribution of the statistic*

$$t = \frac{a - \alpha}{s_a} \tag{14.3.4}$$

is like the t distribution, with $n - 2$ degress of freedom.

The symbols used in the foregoing models should be familiar. The summation Σx^2 is computed according to Equation 13.3.9 and $\bar{X}$, of course, denotes the mean of the sample X values. Confidence intervals are computed in the same way as presented in Chapter 9. Following construction of confidence limits in Equation 9.3.7 (lower limit) and Equation 9.3.8 (upper limit), the analogous equations for the confidence limits for β may be written as follows:

$$LL = b - ts_b \tag{14.3.5}$$

$$UL = b + ts_b \tag{14.3.6}$$

We use the symbol t, as previously, to denote a t value for any specified number of degrees of freedom and any desired level of confidence. In order to construct a confidence interval for β in a given problem, we must first compute s_b according to Equation 14.3.1; then, substitute this result into Equations 14.3.5 and 14.3.6. For example, we determined that $b =$ 1.52 for the depth perception scores X and mechanical ability scores Y in Table 13.3.2. In Section 13.3 we computed $\Sigma x^2 = 1930$ and in Section 14.2 we determined $s_{Y.X} = 5.98$. Applying Equation 14.3.1, we obtain

$$s_b = \frac{5.98}{\sqrt{1930}} = .14$$

Suppose it is desired to construct a .95 confidence interval for β. Then, degrees of freedom (df) $= n - 2$ or $10 - 2 = 8$. Referring to Table B.3, column headed .05, we find the required t value, 2.306. We refer to the column headed .05, where .05, computed as $1 - .95$ (confidence coefficient), is the area in both tails of the t distribution. Making the proper substitutions into Equations 14.3.5 and 14.3.6, we obtain

$$LL = 1.52 - (2.306)(.14) = 1.20$$
$$UL = 1.52 + (2.306)(.14) = 1.84$$

We may state, therefore, that we are 95% confident that the interval 1.20 to 1.84 contains the true regression coefficient β.

The confidence limits for α may be written, similarly

$$LL = a - ts_a \qquad (14.3.7)$$
$$UL = a + ts_a \qquad (14.3.8)$$

Referring to the X and Y scores in Table 13.3.2, we note that $a = -10.46$. Also, $\Sigma X = 863$, so that $\bar{X} = 863/10 = 86.3$. Then, substituting the appropriate values, as noted above, we compute according to Equation 14.3.3

$$s_a = 5.98\sqrt{\frac{1}{10} + \frac{(86.3)^2}{1930}} = 11.90$$

We will use Equations 14.3.7 and 14.3.8 to construct a .95 confidence interval for α. The number of df is $n - 2$ or $10 - 2 = 8$ and the required t value is 2.306, as before. Making the proper substitutions, we obtain

$$LL = -10.46 - (2.306)(11.90) = -37.90$$
$$UL = -10.46 + (2.306)(11.90) = 16.96$$

We may state that we are 95% confident that the interval -37.90 to 16.98 contains the true regression coefficient α.

Two important problems encountered in regression analysis relate to the evaluation of a prediction. In each case, the question is "*How good is the predicted value?*" Clearly, this is the kind of question which we have been answering by construction of confidence intervals. As discussed in Chapter 9, such intervals indicate the maximum error which may be made, at a specified level of confidence, when using a statistic as a point estimate of a parameter. An interval constructed around a predicted value is called a *prediction interval*. Predictions may be one of two types. We may wish to predict the *average value* of Y for a given value of X, or we may wish to predict the *particular value* of Y for a subject with a specified value of X. For example, for the depth perception scores X and mechanical ability scores Y in Table 13.3.2, we obtained the least squares regression equation $Y_e = -10.46 + 1.52X$. We may wish to predict the average score on mechanical ability to be expected for subjects who obtain a given score on depth perception. On the other hand, we may wish to predict the mechanical ability score for a particular subject based upon the score he obtained on depth perception. *In each case, the predicted score on mechanical ability* (Y_e) *is the same; however, the maximum error which may be made, at a specific level of confidence, is different*. Below, we present a sampling model which provides the basis for constructing *prediction intervals*.

Normal Model C: If samples of n pairs of X and Y values are selected from a population of X and Y pairs which satisfies the conditions of the *Normal Model*, the *sampling distribution of the statistic* Y_e $(= a + bX)$ has the mean $\mu_{Y.X}$. Then,
1. if Y_e is considered to represent the *average value* of Y when $X = X_0$, the estimated standard error is

$$s_{Y_e} = s_{Y.X}\sqrt{\frac{1}{n} + \frac{(X_0 - \bar{X})^2}{\sum x^2}} \tag{14.3.9}$$

2. if Y_e is considered to represent the *specific value* of Y when $X = X_0$, the estimated standard error is

$$s_{Y_e} = s_{Y.X}\sqrt{1 + \frac{1}{n} + \frac{(X_0 - \bar{X})^2}{\sum x^2}} \tag{14.3.10}$$

Furthermore, the *sampling distribution of the statistic*

$$t = \frac{Y_e - \mu_{Y.X}}{s_{Y_e}} \tag{14.3.11}$$

is like the t distribution, with $n - 2$ degrees of freedom, where s_{Y_e} is determined in either of the two ways shown above, as appropriate.

When Y_e is used as a predicted *average value*, it represents a point estimate of the conditional mean $\mu_{Y.X}$. On the other hand, when Y_e is used as a prediction of a *particular value* of Y, it represents a point estimate of this particular value. *Prediction limits* may be determined as follows:

$$LL = Y_e - ts_{Y_e} \tag{14.3.12}$$

$$UL = Y_e + ts_{Y_e} \tag{14.3.13}$$

The estimated standard error for these equations, s_{Y_e}, is determined in either of the two ways specified in *Normal Model C*, as appropriate. Using the regression equation $Y_e = -10.46 + 1.52X$, we may predict (or estimate) the average score expected on mechanical ability Y for subjects who obtain 100 on depth perception X as

$$Y_e = -10.46 + 1.52(100) = 141.54$$

In order to construct a *prediction interval*, we must first determine the estimated standard error of Y_e, according to Equation 14.3.9. We have already determined $s_{Y.X} = 5.98$, $\bar{X} = 86.3$, and $\Sigma x^2 = 1930$. Substituting these values, as well as $X_0 = 100$ (the X value used for the prediction) and $n = 10$, into Equation 14.3.9, we obtain

$$s_{Y_e} = 5.98\sqrt{\frac{1}{10} + \frac{(100 - 86.3)^2}{1930}} = 2.63$$

Suppose we wish to construct a .95 prediction interval. We determine degrees of freedom as $n - 2$ or $10 - 2 = 8$ and, referring to Table B.3, column headed .05, we find that the t value corresponding to 8 df is 2.306. Then, noting that the predicted mean score Y_e was computed as 141.54, we make the appropriate substitutions in Equations 14.3.12 and 14.3.13 to obtain

$$LL = 141.54 - (2.306)(2.63) = 135.48$$

$$UL = 141.54 + (2.306)(2.63) = 147.60$$

Therefore, we may predict, at the 95% level of confidence, that the interval 135.48 to 147.60 contains the mean score on mechanical ability for subjects who score 100 on depth perception.

Suppose, on the other hand, we wish to predict the mechanical ability score Y for a given subject whose depth perception score X is 100. We compute $Y_e = 141.54$, as before, using the regression equation $Y_e' = -10.46 + 1.52X$. Clearly, the predicted value, $Y_e = 141.54$, is the same whether we wish to predict the *average score* or a *particular score*. However, the *prediction interval* is different. That is, we use Equations 14.3.12 and 14.3.13 to determine prediction limits, as before, but the estimated standard error s_{Y_e} is computed according to Equation 14.3.10, instead of Equation 14.3.9. We will construct a .95 prediction interval. First, making the appropriate substitutions in Equation 14.3.10, we obtain

$$s_{Y_e} = 5.98\sqrt{1 + \frac{1}{10} + \frac{(100 - 86.3)^2}{1930}} = 6.52$$

The number of degrees of freedom is 10 − 2 or 8 and the corresponding t value for the .95 level of confidence is 2.306, as before. Then, noting that the predicted mechanical ability score is 141.54, we make the appropriate substitutions in Equations 14.3.12 and 14.3.13 to obtain

$$LL = 141.54 - (2.306)(6.52) = 126.19$$

$$UL = 141.54 + (2.306)(6.52) = 156.89$$

Hence, we may predict, at the 95% level of confidence, that the interval 126.19 to 156.89 contains the mechanical ability score for a given subject who achieves 100 on depth perception.

Notice that the prediction interval is *wider* when predicting a *particular* score than an *average* score. This is always true, since the estimated standard error of Y_e is larger when computed according to Equation 14.3.10 than according to Equation 14.3.9. This is apparent from a comparison of the two equations. Furthermore, since each of these equations contains the squared deviation $(X_0 - \bar{X})^2$, the estimated standard error s_{Y_e} becomes larger, the further the X value used for prediction (X_0) is from the mean $\bar{X}$. Consequently, the further X_0 is from $\bar{X}$, the wider is the prediction interval. Finally, when the X value used for prediction is 0, so that $X_0 = 0$, the regression equation ($Y_e = a + bX$) becomes $Y_e = a$. That is, the average value of Y predicted when $X = 0$ is the Y-intercept a. Then, when 0 is substituted for X_0 in Equation 14.3.9, s_{Y_e} becomes equal to s_a, as expressed by Equation 14.3.3 in *Normal Model B*. In other words, when $X = 0$, the Y-intercept a represents the point estimate of $\mu_{Y.X}$, and the estimated standard errors s_{Y_e} and s_a are identical.

PROBLEMS FOR PRACTICE AND REVIEW

1. In Problem 2, following Section 13.3, compute:
(a) $s_{Y.X}$
(b) s_b
(c) s_a
(d) confidence intervals, at the .95 level of confidence, for (1) β, (2) α.

Problems 2 through 10 refer to the Problems following Section 13.3.

2. In Problem 4, determine (a), (b), (c), (d), as for Problem 1.

3. In Problem 6, determine (a), (b), (c), (d), as for Problem 1.

4. In Problem 7, determine (a), (b), (c), (d), as for Problem 1.

5. In Problem 8, determine (a), (b), (c), (d), as for Problem 1.

6. In Problem 2, compute:

(a) s_{Y_e} relating to prediction of Y_e as an average value corresponding to $X_0 = 8$.

(b) Prediction interval for the Y_e value noted in (a), at the .95 level of confidence.

(c) s_{Y_e} relating to prediction of Y_e for a subject corresponding to $X_0 = 8$.

(d) Prediction interval for the Y_e value noted in (c), at the .95 level of confidence.

7. In Problem 4, determine (a), (b), (c), (d), as for Problem 6, just presented.

8. In Problem 6, determine (a), (b), (c), (d), as for Problem 6.

9. In Problem 7, determine (a), (b), (c), (d), as for Problem 6.

10. In Problem 8, determine (a), (b), (c), (d), as for Problem 6. (Use $X_0 = 18$.)

14.4 TESTS OF HYPOTHESES

Various tests of hypotheses are of interest in correlation and regression analyses. The three-phase decision-making procedure presented in Chapter 10 and summarized in Section 10.7 is applicable in such situations. A frequently used test relates to the true regression coefficient β. It is usually desired to test the hypothesis that $\beta = 0$ against the alternative hypothesis that $\beta \neq 0$. In certain situations, the hypothesis to be tested is that β has some specified value, and, sometimes, a one-sided alternative is more appropriate than a two-sided alternative. As an illustration, we will refer to the depth perception scores X and the mechanical ability scores Y presented in Table 13.3.2. We will suppose that the computed regression equation is being considered for some particular application (perhaps, to select applicants for mechanical-type positions based upon information available on their depth perception scores). Of course, if the true value of β is 0, then X (depth perception score) is worthless as a predictor of Y (mechanical ability score). Hence, before a decision is made to adopt the regression equation for the desired application, it is necessary to test the null hypothesis that $\beta = 0$. The usual alternative hypothesis is that $\beta \neq 0$. The test will be conducted at, say, the .05 level of significance. We will apply the three-phase decision-making procedure.

A. Formulation of the Problem

1. Test parameter: β, the true regression coefficient.
2. $H_0 : \beta = 0$.
3. $H_1 : \beta \neq 0$.
4. If H_0 is not rejected, it will be accepted.
5. $\alpha = .05$.

B. Construction of the Decision Model

1. Test statistic: b, the estimated regression coefficient.
2. *Normal Model A* is appropriate. The sampling distribution pertinent has the t distribution, with $n - 2$ or $10 - 2 = 8$ df.
3. Test variable: $t = (b - \beta)/s_b = b/s_b$, since, under the null hypothesis H_0, $\beta = 0$.
4. If $t < -2.306$ or $t > 2.306$, reject H_0 and accept H_1. Otherwise, accept H_0. This t value was determined by referring to Table B.3, column headed .05, and finding the t value corresponding to 8 df.

C. Evaluation of the Sample Data

1. Test statistic: $b = 1.52$.
2. Test variable: $t = 1.52/.14 = 10.9$. (It was determined in Section 14.3 that $s_b = .14$.)
3. $t = 10.9$ falls in the region of rejection. Therefore, reject H_0 and accept H_1.
4. The decision is made to adopt the regression equation for the desired application.

A second frequently used test relates to the true coefficient of correlation. We use r to denote the coefficient of correlation computed from sample data. Consequently, r denotes the *estimated* correlation coefficient. The *true* correlation coefficient, computed from population data, is usually denoted by ρ (the Greek letter *rho*). It is usually desired to test the null hypothesis that $\rho = 0$ against the alternative that $\rho \neq 0$. Of course, the hypothesis that $\rho = 0$ is equivalent to the hypothesis that $\beta = 0$, since under either hypothesis X is worthless as a predictor of Y. Strictly speaking, these hypotheses imply that there is no *linear* (straight-line) relationship between X and Y. (In Chapter 15, Section 15.1 we will consider nonlinear relationships between X and Y.) It should be observed that the condition $\rho = 0$, or the equivalent condition $\beta = 0$, may indicate that two variables X and Y are not at all related, or that they are not related *linearly*. That is, X and Y may be very closely related, but the relationship is curvilinear. This will be further considered in section 15.1. A test of the hypothesis $\beta = 0$ is actually a test of the linearity of the relationship between X and Y. We will now consider an equivalent test, the test of the hypothesis that $\rho = 0$ against the alternative hypothesis $\rho \neq 0$. First, we present an additional theoretical sampling model.

Normal Model D: If samples of n pairs of X and Y values are selected from a population of X and Y pairs which satisfies the *Normal Model* and

ρ, the coefficient of correlation in the population, is 0, the *sampling distribution of the statistic*

$$t = \sqrt{\frac{(n-2)r^2}{1-r^2}} \tag{14.4.1}$$

has the t distribution, with $n - 2$ df.

Refer once again to the depth perception X and mechanical ability Y scores in Table 13.3.2 and again suppose that the computed regression equation is being considered for some particular application. However, before a decision on its use is made, it is desired to test the null hypothesis $\rho = 0$ against the alternative $\rho \neq 0$, at the .05 level of significance.

A. Formulation of the Problem

1. Test parameter: ρ, the true correlation coefficient.
2. $H_0 : \rho = 0$.
3. $H_1 : \rho \neq 0$.
4. If H_0 is not rejected, it will be accepted.
5. $\alpha = .05$.

B. Construction of the Decision Model

1. Test statistic: r, the estimated correlation coefficient.

2. *Normal Model D* is appropriate. The sampling distribution pertinent has the t distribution, with $n - 2$ or $10 - 2 = 8$ df.

3. Test variable: $t = \sqrt{\dfrac{(n-2)r^2}{1-r^2}}$

4. If $t < -2.306$ or $t > 2.306$, reject H_0 and accept H_1. Otherwise, accept H_0. (This t value was determined as explained in the previous test.)

C. Evaluation of the Sample Data

1. Test statistic: $r = .97$.

2. Test variable: $t = \sqrt{\dfrac{(10-2)(.97)^2}{1-(.97)^2}} = 11.3$

3. $t = 11.3$ falls in the region of rejection. Therefore, reject H_0 and accept H_1.

4. The decision is made to adopt the regression equation for the desired application.

The two tests, $\beta = 0$ and $\rho = 0$, lead to the same decision. This, of course, is to be expected since, as noted previously, they are equivalent tests. Actually, the test variable, $t = 10.9$ obtained previously and $t = 11.3$

just obtained, should be equal. The difference is due to the accumulated effects of rounding during the various computational steps involved.

PROBLEMS FOR PRACTICE AND REVIEW

Problems 1 through 5 refer to the Problems following Section 13.3.

1. In Problem 2, test the hypothesis that $\beta = 0$ against the alternative that $\beta \neq 0$, using the .05 level of significance.

2. In Problem 4, test the hypothesis that $\beta = 0$ against the alternative that $\beta \neq 0$, using the .05 level of significance.

3. In Problem 6, using the .05 level of significance, test $H_0 : \beta = 0$ against $H_1 : \beta \neq 0$.

4. In Problem 7, using the .05 level of significance, test the hypothesis that $\rho = 0$ against the alternative that $\rho \neq 0$.

5. In Problem 8, using the .05 level of significance, test $H_0 : \rho = 0$ against $H_1 : \rho \neq 0$.

15

FURTHER MEASURES OF ASSOCIATION

15.1 CURVILINEAR RELATIONSHIPS

The two-variable relationships generally encountered in the fields of psychology and education are linear in nature. However, it is useful to explore, to some extent, the methods of correlation and regression to be used when the relationship is nonlinear. Although the general approach for curvilinear relationships is not too much different, the application of these methods and the interpretation of the results require more discussion than is possible in the present text. We will discuss the application of correlation and regression methods to nonlinearly related variables sufficiently to show how such situations are handled.

Table 15.1.1 presents X and Y scores for a sample of ten subjects. The relationship between these two variables may be examined by inspection of the scatter diagram in Figure 15.1.1. The scatter diagram indicates that a straight-line regression line is not appropriate. *In order to fit a least squares regression line to these data, using the methods previously presented, it is necessary to transform one or both variables so that the resulting relationship may be appropriately represented by a straight line.* For example, we will transform X to $\log X$, as shown in Table 15.1.2. (Logarithms are explained in the Appendix, Section A.11.) Figure 15.1.2 presents the scatter diagram for the two variables, $\log X$ and Y. (The X-scale is a logarithmic scale, so that this is actually the $\log X$ scale.) Clearly, the scatter diagram indicates that the relationship between these two variables

Table 15.1.1 *X* AND *Y* SCORES FOR A SAMPLE OF TEN SUBJECTS

X	Y
16	54.5
24	59.5
34	64.5
39	68.5
10	48.5
27	64.5
43	67.5
13	54.0
31	66.0
20	60.0

(log X and Y) may appropriately be represented by a straight line. Hence, we may compute the correlation coefficient and the least squares *linear* regression equation for log X and Y. Applying the equations previously presented (substituting log X for X) and using the data in Table 15.1.2, we obtain

From Equation 13.3.9,

$$\sum (\log x)^2 = \sum (\log X)^2 - \frac{(\sum \log X)^2}{n}$$

$$= 19.101 - \frac{(13.676)^2}{10} = .398$$

Table 15.1.2 *X*, LOG *X*, AND *Y* SCORES FOR THE SAMPLE OF TEN SUBJECTS IN TABLE 15.1.1

X	$\log X$	Y	$(\log X)^2$	Y^2	$(\log X)Y$
16	1.204	54.5	1.450	2970.25	65.618
24	1.380	59.5	1.904	3540.25	82.110
34	1.531	64.5	2.344	4160.25	98.750
39	1.591	68.5	2.531	4692.25	108.984
10	1.000	48.5	1.000	2352.25	48.500
27	1.431	64.5	2.048	4160.25	92.300
43	1.633	67.5	2.667	4556.25	110.228
13	1.114	54.0	1.241	2916.00	60.156
31	1.491	66.0	2.223	4356.00	98.406
20	1.301	60.0	1.693	3600.00	78.060
Total	13.676	607.5	19.101	37,303.75	843.112

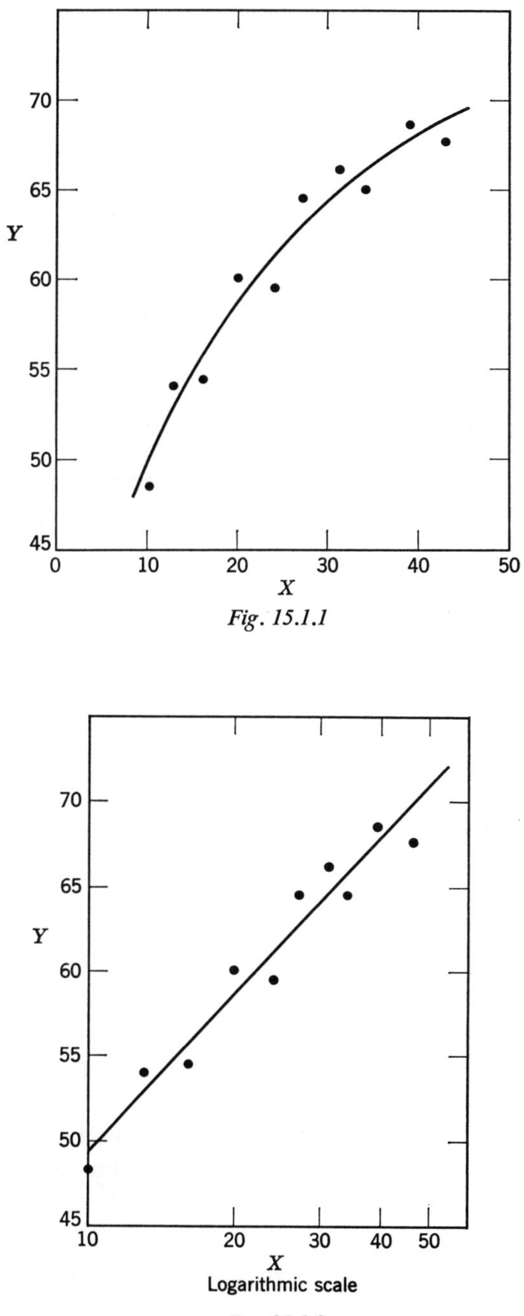

Fig. 15.1.1

Fig. 15.1.2

From Equation 13.4.12,

$$\sum y^2 = \sum Y^2 - \frac{(\sum Y)^2}{n}$$

$$= 37{,}303.75 - \frac{(607.5)^2}{10} = 398.12$$

From Equation 13.3.8,

$$\sum (\log x)y = \sum (\log X)Y - \frac{(\sum \log X)(\sum Y)}{n}$$

$$= 843.112 - \frac{(13.676)(607.5)}{10}$$

$$= 12.295$$

From Equation 13.3.6,

$$b = \frac{\sum (\log x)y}{\sum (\log x)^2} = \frac{12.295}{.398} = 30.892$$

From Equation 13.3.7,

$$a = \frac{\sum Y - b \sum \log X}{n}$$

$$= \frac{607.5 - (30.892)(13.676)}{10} = 18.50$$

From Equation 13.4.11,

$$r = \frac{\sum (\log x)y}{\sqrt{\sum (\log x)^2 \sum y^2}}$$

$$r = \frac{12.295}{\sqrt{(.398)(398.12)}} = .98$$

Therefore, we may write the *linear* regression equation for predicting Y based upon log X, as

$$Y_e = 18.500 + 30.892 \log X$$

In order to plot the regression line, we must compute Y_e corresponding to values selected for X. Using $X = 10$ and $X = 45$, we compute the corresponding Y_e values by, first, finding the logarithm for each of the selected values of X and, then, substituting these logarithms in the regression equation. Referring to Table B.4, we note that log 10 = 1.000 and log 45 = 1.653. Entering these logarithms into the equation, we obtain

$$Y_e = 18.500 + (30.892)(1.000) = 49.39$$

$$Y_e = 18.500 + (30.892)(1.653) = 69.56$$

Table 15.1.3 presents the predicted (or estimated) Y_e values corresponding to selected values of X, including the two we have just computed. Using the data in this table, we may plot the *linear* regression line for Log X and Y shown in Figure 15.1.2 and the *curvilinear* regression line for X and Y shown in Figure 15.1.1.

Clearly, an important problem in determining the curvilinear relationship for a pair of variables is to find the transformation for one or both of the variables which results in a linear relationship after transformation. This could be a difficult problem and requires a knowledge of mathematical relationships. We will not consider this problem further in this text. However, two more illustrations will be presented to indicate other types of transformations which, in certain situations, result in a linear relationship for the transformed variables.

Table 15.1.3 DATA FOR PLOTTING THE REGRESSION EQUATIONS BASED UPON THE SAMPLE DATA IN TABLE 15.1.1

X	log X	Y_e
10	1.000	49.39
15	1.176	54.83
20	1.301	58.69
25	1.398	61.69
30	1.477	64.13
35	1.544	66.20
40	1.602	67.99
45	1.653	69.56

It should be noted that the symbol r denotes the correlation coefficient based upon the *linear* relationship between two variables. However, when a curvilinear regression equation is computed for a pair of variables, we use the symbol r but refer to it as the *index of correlation*. In the illustration, r, the index of correlation, is .98. Furthermore, whenever a curvilinear relationship is the basis for computing r, it is *absolutely necessary* to specify the transformation or transformations used. For example, the index of correlation in the illustration is .98 for Log X and Y. If r has been computed using the original variables X and Y, without transformation, the resulting value of r would have been considerably less than .98. Similarly, if some other type of transformation had been used, a different value of r would have been obtained. Consequently, the computed value of r can be interpreted only if the transformation used is specified.

Table 15.1.4 *X* AND *Y* SCORES FOR A SAMPLE OF 13 SUBJECTS

X	Y	$\log X$	$\log Y$	$(\log X)^2$	$(\log Y)^2$	$\log X \log Y$
20	25	1.301	1.398	1.693	1.954	1.819
30	75	1.477	1.875	2.182	3.516	2.769
50	200	1.699	2.301	2.887	5.295	3.909
17	10	1.230	1.000	1.513	1.000	1.230
25	45	1.398	1.653	1.954	2.732	2.311
35	75	1.544	1.875	2.384	3.516	2.895
40	105	1.602	2.021	2.566	4.084	3.238
45	300	1.653	2.477	2.732	6.136	4.094
17	13	1.230	1.114	1.513	1.241	1.370
30	50	1.477	1.699	2.182	2.887	2.509
36	125	1.556	2.097	2.421	4.397	3.263
41	175	1.613	2.243	2.602	5.031	3.618
20	15	1.301	1.176	1.693	1.383	1.530
	Total	19.081	22.929	28.322	43.172	34.555

As a second illustration, Table 15.1.4 presents the X and Y scores for a sample of 13 subjects. The scatter diagram for these scores, presented in Figure 15.1.3, clearly indicates a curvilinear relationship. However, if *both* X and Y scores are transformed to logarithms, so that we have the two new variables $\log X$ and $\log Y$ (as shown in the table), the relationship becomes linear. This is apparent by inspection of Figure 15.1.4 which presents the scatter diagram for the $\log X$ and $\log Y$ scores. In this scatter diagram both scales are logarithmic scales, so that we have $\log X$ and $\log Y$ pairs plotted. Using the data in Table 15.1.4 and the equations we have learned (substituting $\log X$ for X and $\log Y$ for Y), we obtain

From Equation 13.3.9,

$$\sum (\log x)^2 = \sum (\log X)^2 - \frac{(\sum \log X)^2}{n}$$

$$= 28.322 - \frac{(19.081)^2}{13} = .315$$

From Equation 13.4.12,

$$\sum (\log y)^2 = \sum (\log Y)^2 - \frac{(\sum \log Y)^2}{n}$$

$$= 43.172 - \frac{(22.929)^2}{13} = 2.731$$

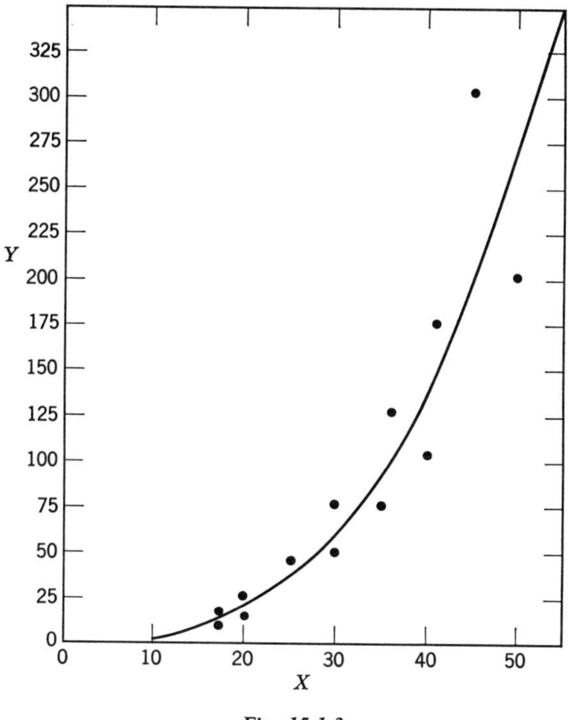

Fig. 15.1.3

From Equation 13.3.8,

$$\sum \log x \log y = \sum \log X \log Y - \frac{(\sum \log X)(\sum \log Y)}{n}$$

$$= 34.555 - \frac{(19.081)(22.929)}{13} = .901$$

From Equation 13.3.6,

$$b = \frac{\sum \log x \log y}{\sum (\log x)^2} = \frac{.901}{.315} = 2.860$$

From Equation 13.3.7,

$$a = \frac{\sum \log Y - b \sum \log X}{n}$$

$$= \frac{22.929 - (2.860)(19.081)}{13} = -2.434$$

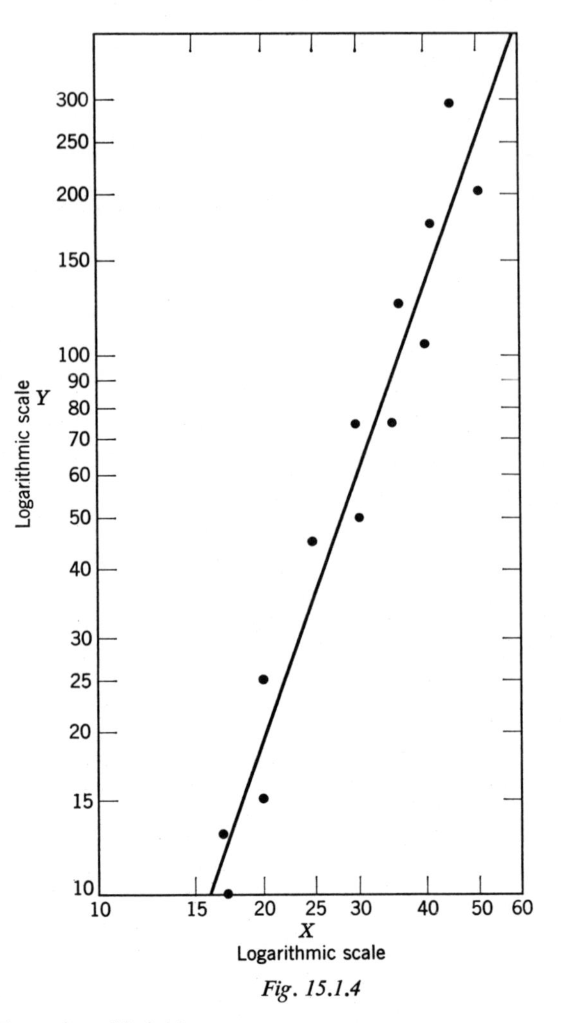

Fig. 15.1.4

From Equation 13.4.11,

$$r = \frac{\sum \log x \log y}{\sqrt{\sum (\log x)^2 \sum (\log y)^2}}$$

$$= \frac{.901}{\sqrt{(.315)(2.731)}} = .97$$

Therefore, we may write the *linear* regression equation for predicting log Y based upon log X, as

$$\log Y_e = -2.434 + 2.860 \log X$$

where log Y_e represents the predicted value of log Y. In order to plot the regression line, we will compute Y_e corresponding to values selected for X. Using $X = 10$ and $X = 55$, we first compute the corresponding log Y_e values by substituting the log X values into the regression equation. Noting from Table B.4 that log 10 = 1.000 and log 55 = 1.740, we enter these logarithms into the regression equation to obtain

$$\log Y_e = -2.434 + (2.860)(1.000) = .426$$
$$\log Y_e = -2.434 + (2.860)(1.740) = 2.542$$

Then, Y_e is the antilog of log Y_e. We obtain 2.7 as the antilog of .426 and 348.3 as the antilog of 2.542. Therefore, the predicted value Y_e is 2.7 based upon $X = 10$ and 348.3 based upon $X = 55$. Table 15.1.5 presents

Table 15.1.5 DATA FOR PLOTTING THE REGRESSION EQUATIONS BASED UPON THE SAMPLE DATA IN TABLE 15.1.4

X	log X	log Y_e	Y_e
10	1.000	.426	2.7
15	1.176	.929	8.5
20	1.301	1.287	19.4
25	1.398	1.564	36.6
30	1.477	1.790	61.7
35	1.544	1.982	95.9
40	1.602	2.148	140.6
45	1.653	2.294	196.8
50	1.699	2.425	266.1
55	1.740	2.542	348.3

the predicted Y_e values corresponding to selected values of X, including the two we have just computed. Using the data in this table, we may plot the *linear* regression line for log X and log Y shown in Figure 15.1.4 and the *curvilinear* regression line for X and Y shown in Figure 15.1.3.

As a final illustration, consider the ten X and Y scores in Table 15.1.6. The scatter diagram for this sample of scores, presented in Figure 15.1.5, clearly indicates a curvilinear relationship between X and Y. However, if the Y scores are transformed to reciprocals ($1/Y$), as shown in the table, the relationship between X and $1/Y$ is linear. This may be observed from the scatter diagram in Figure 15.1.6. We will compute the least squares linear regression equation to predict $1/Y$ based upon X and the index of correlation. First, however, as a matter of convenience, we multiply each reciprocal $1/Y$ by 10,000 in order to get rid of the decimal point. We will

Table 15.1.6 *X* AND *Y* SCORES FOR A SAMPLE OF TEN SUBJECTS

X	Y	$\frac{1}{Y}$	$Z = (10{,}000)\frac{1}{Y}$	X^2	Z^2	XZ
56	24	.0417	417	3136	173,889	23,352
42	28	.0357	357	1764	127,449	14,994
45	31	.0323	323	2025	104,329	14,535
36	34	.0294	294	1296	86,436	10,584
40	37	.0270	270	1600	72,900	10,800
31	43	.0233	233	961	54,289	7223
34	49	.0204	204	1156	41,616	6936
26	53	.0189	189	676	35,721	4914
32	55	.0182	182	1024	33,124	5824
24	59	.0169	169	576	28,561	4056
366		.2638	2638	14,214	758,314	103,218

denote the resulting variable $(10{,}000)(1/Y)$ as Z. Then, using the data in Table 15.1.6 and the appropriate equations (substituting Z for Y), we obtain:

From Equation 13.3.9,

$$\sum x^2 = \sum X^2 - \frac{(\sum X)^2}{n}$$

$$= 14{,}214 - \frac{(366)^2}{10} = 818$$

From Equation 13.4.12,

$$\sum z^2 = \sum Z^2 - \frac{(\sum Z)^2}{n}$$

$$= 758{,}314 - \frac{(2638)^2}{10} = 62{,}410$$

From Equation 13.3.8,

$$\sum xz = \sum XZ - \frac{(\sum X)(\sum Z)}{n}$$

$$= 103{,}218 - \frac{(366)(2638)}{10} = 6667$$

From Equation 13.3.6,

$$b' = \frac{\sum xz}{\sum x^2} = \frac{6667}{818} = 8.150$$

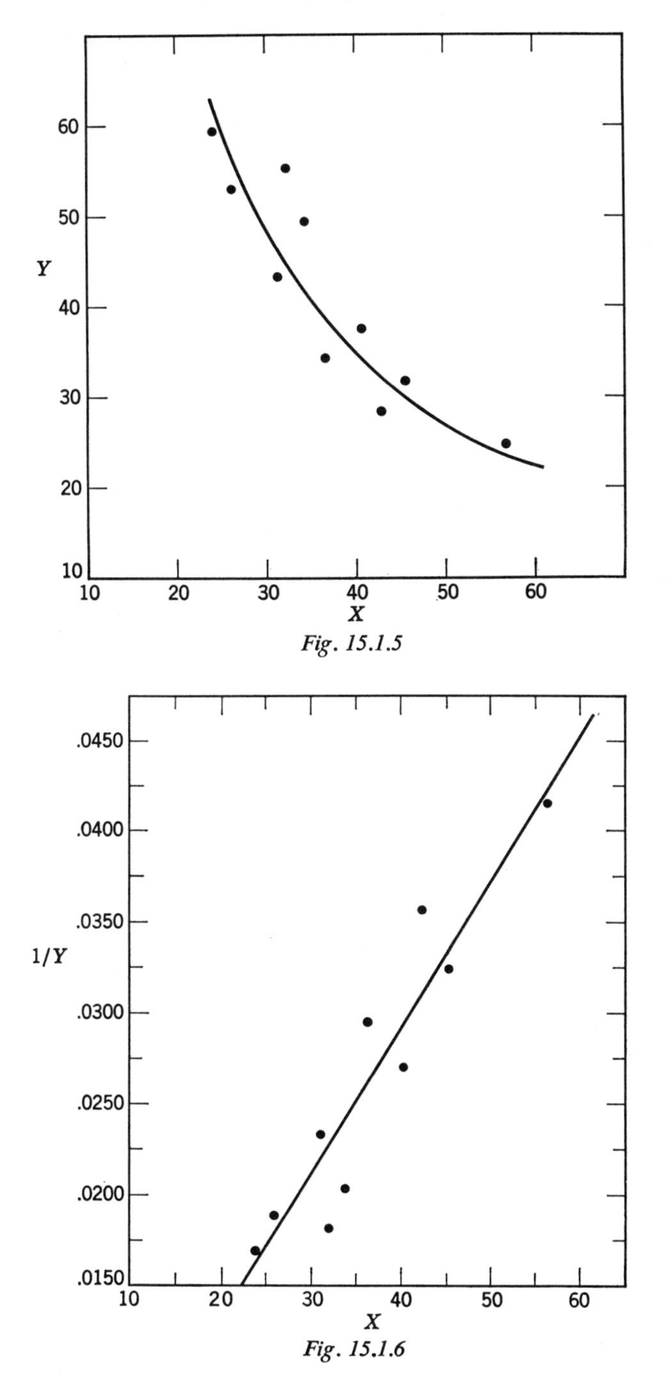

Fig. 15.1.5

Fig. 15.1.6

We use b' to indicate that the variables involved are X and Z. However, since $Z = (10{,}000)(1/Y)$, we may obtain b for X and $1/Y$ as

$$b = \frac{b'}{10{,}000} = \frac{8.150}{10{,}000} = .000815$$

From Equation 13.3.7,

$$a = \frac{\sum\left(\frac{1}{Y}\right) - (b)(\sum X)}{n}$$

$$= \frac{.2638 - (.000815)(366)}{10} = -.00345$$

From Equation 13.4.11.

$$r = \frac{\sum xz}{\sqrt{(\sum x^2)(\sum z^2)}} = \frac{6667}{\sqrt{(818)(62{,}410)}} = .93$$

We may write the *linear* regression equation for predicting $1/Y$ based upon X, as

$$\frac{1}{Y_e} = -.00345 + .000815X$$

where $1/Y_e$ denotes the predicted value of $1/Y$. Table 15.1.7 presents the $1/Y_e$ values for selected values of X. For example, substituting $X = 25$

Table 15.1.7 DATA FOR PLOTTING THE REGRESSION EQUATIONS BASED UPON THE SAMPLE DATA IN TABLE 15.1.6

X	$\frac{1}{Y_e}$	Y_e
25	.0169	59.1
30	.0210	47.6
35	.0251	39.9
40	.0292	34.3
45	.0332	30.1
50	.0373	26.9
55	.0414	24.2
60	.0455	22.0

into the regression equation we obtain

$$\frac{1}{Y_e} = -.00345 + (.000815)(25) = .0169$$

This is the first $1/Y_e$ value shown in the table. Then, Y_e is computed as the reciprocal of $1/Y_e$. For example, $1/.0169 = 59.1$. This is the Y_e value corresponding to $1/Y_e = .0169$, as shown in Table 15.1.7. Using the data from this table, we may plot the *linear* regression line for X and $1/Y$ shown in Figure 15.1.6 and the *curvilinear* regression line for X and Y shown in Figure 15.1.5.

PROBLEMS FOR PRACTICE AND REVIEW

1. The following X and Y scores were obtained for 17 subjects:

X	Y	X	Y
5	93	10	145
4	96	16	154
6	107	14	159
5	105	22	155
9	116	20	164
6	118	24	172
13	132	17	171
9	136	23	178
18	175		

(a) Transform X to log X. Determine the least squares regression equation to predict Y based upon log X.

(b) Construct the scatter diagram for log X and Y and plot the regression line.

(c) Construct the scatter diagram for X and Y and plot the regression line.

(d) Compute the index of correlation.

2. The following X and Y scores were obtained for 15 subjects:

X	Y	X	Y
22	9	71	50
25	18	79	79
32	12	79	126
50	23	100	159
50	40	112	200
45	56	126	159
63	100	126	282
159	250		

(a) Transform X to log X and Y to log Y. Determine the least squares regression equation to predict log Y based upon log X.

(b) Construct the scatter diagram for log X and log Y and plot the regression line.

(c) Construct the scatter diagram for X and Y and plot the regression line.
(d) Compute the index of correlation.

3. The following X and Y scores were obtained for ten subjects:

X	Y	X	Y
34	35	8	103
16	51	10	117
18	67	6	134
10	84	7	158
12	98	4	163

(a) Transform Y to $1/Y$. Determine the least squares regression equation to predict $1/Y$ based upon X.
(b) Construct the scatter diagram for X and $1/Y$ and plot the regression line.
(c) Construct the scatter diagram for X and Y and plot the regression line.
(d) Compute the index of correlation.

15.2 CORRELATION OF RANKS

The need to determine the degree of association between two sets of *ranks* frequently arises in the fields of psychology and education. For example, Table 15.2.1 presents the ranks for ten subjects on anxiety (X)

Table 15.2.1 TEN SUBJECTS RANKED ON ANXIETY (X) AND RESPONSE TO STRESS (Y)

Subject	X	Y	X^2	Y^2	XY	$D = Y - X$	D^2
A	1	10	1	100	10	9	81
B	2	8	4	64	16	6	36
C	3	7	9	49	21	4	16
D	4	9	16	81	36	5	25
E	5	6	25	36	30	1	1
F	6	3	36	9	18	−3	9
G	7	5	49	25	35	−2	4
H	8	1	64	1	8	−7	49
I	9	4	81	16	36	−5	25
J	10	2	100	4	20	−8	64
	55	55	385	385	230		310

and response to stress (Y). The rank of 1 for X denotes the least anxious subject and the rank of 10, the most anxious subject. The rank of 1 for Y denotes the subject with the slowest response to a stress agent, whereas, the rank of 10 denotes the subject with the fastest response. Using the data in Table 15.2.1 and the appropriate equations, we may compute the coefficient of correlation as follows:

From Equation 13.3.9,

$$\sum x^2 = 385 - \frac{(55)^2}{10} = 82.5$$

From Equation 13.4.12,

$$\sum y^2 = 385 - \frac{(55)^2}{10} = 82.5$$

From Equation 13.3.8,

$$\sum xy = 230 - \frac{(55)(55)}{10} = -72.5$$

From Equation 13.4.11,

$$r = \frac{-72.5}{\sqrt{(82.5)(82.5)}} = -.88$$

The coefficient of correlation $-.88$ indicates a high degree of negative association between X and Y. In other words, the fictitious pair of ranks in Table 15.2.1 indicates that a low rank on anxiety is associated with a high rank on response, whereas a high rank on anxiety is associated with a low rank on response. The same result could be obtained more conveniently by the following equation:

$$r' = 1 - \frac{6 \sum D^2}{n(n^2 - 1)} \tag{15.2.1}$$

where D = difference between ranks

n = number of pairs of ranks

We will apply Equation 15.2.1 to compute the correlation coefficient between the X and Y ranks in Table 15.2.1. It does not matter whether D is computed as $X - Y$ or as $Y - X$, since only D^2 appears in the equation. Using the data in Table 15.2.1, we obtain

$$r' = 1 - \frac{(6)(310)}{10(100 - 1)} = -.88$$

The result is identically the same as obtained previously. However, Equation 15.2.1 provides a quicker and more convenient method for determining the degree of association between two sets of ranks. This approach may be used even if actual measures are available. For example, Table 15.2.2 presents the scores for 12 subjects on a social attitudes test (X) and a personality test (Y). Say, it is desired to determine the degree of association between the X and Y scores. This may be accomplished by computing r based upon Equation 13.4.11. However, only a rapid approximation may be required. This may be done by ranking the X and Y scores, as shown in Table 15.2.2 and computing r' by the use of Equation 15.2.1. This yields only an approximation to the value of r which would be obtained by correlating the original X and Y scores according to Equation 13.4.11. It frequently happens that the differences among the scores in a set of psychological test scores are not considered to be meaningful, but

Table 15.2.2 SCORES ON A SOCIAL ATTITUDES TEST (X) AND A PERSONALITY TEST (Y) FOR TWELVE SUBJECTS

Subject	X	Y	Rank X	Rank Y
A	132	56	8	4
B	110	66	4	10
C	100	73	1	12
D	112	63	3	9
E	103	67	2	11
F	120	61	6	7
G	115	60	5	6
H	140	53	11	3
I	135	55	9	5
J	139	52	10	2
K	125	62	7	8
L	147	51	12	1

that the rankings are considered to be meaningful. In such instances, r' provides a more desirable measure of the degree of association than r. The measure r' is known as Spearman's *coefficient of rank correlation;* and r is known as Pearson's *product-moment coefficient of correlation.*

It may happen that a set of scores contains ties. In such cases, ranks may be assigned by assuming that the tied scores can be ranked and then by assigning the mean of the ranks so obtained to each of the tied scores. For example, say, we have the scores 20, 25, 28, 28, 29, 31, 31, 31, 33. We start by assigning the ranks 1, 2, 3, 4, 5, 6, 7, 8, 9. Notice that the rank 3 is assigned to one of the scores of 28 and 4 to the other. Then, computing the mean, $\frac{1}{2}(3 + 4) = 3.5$, we assign the rank 3.5 to *each* score of 28. Similarly, the three scores of 31 are ranked 6, 7, and 8. Computing the mean, $\frac{1}{3}(6 + 7 + 8) = 7$, we assign the rank 7 to *each* of the scores of 31. Then, the ranks for this set of scores may be written as 1, 2, 3.5, 3.5, 5, 7, 7, 7, 9.

PROBLEMS FOR PRACTICE AND REVIEW

1. A group of nine students were ranked on research aptitude and clerical aptitude as follows (1 = highest, etc.):

Student	Research Aptitude	Clerical Aptitude
A	3	8
B	6	4
C	1	9
D	5	6
E	7	1
F	9	3
G	2	7
H	8	2
I	4	5

Compute the correlation coefficient between the research aptitude and clerical aptitude ranks for these students.

2. A class of 12 high school seniors were ranked on proficiency in mathematics and proficiency in physics as follows (1 = highest, etc.):

	Proficiency in	
Senior	Math	Physics
A	12	9
B	4	2
C	6	4
D	9	7
E	11	10
F	5	5
G	7	11
H	1	6
I	2	3
J	8	8
K	10	12
L	3	1

Compute the correlation coefficient between proficiency in mathematics and physics for these high school seniors.

3. The following scores on a memory test and a vocabulary recall test were obtained by ten junior high school students:

Student	Memory Test	Vocabulary Recall Test
A	91.4	42.0
B	101.4	45.0
C	86.3	42.9
D	97.0	40.3
E	89.1	44.9
F	94.6	38.4
G	109.8	48.0
H	107.3	47.2
I	103.7	50.4
J	90.6	39.1

Compute r' after ranking the students on each test.

4. The following scores on two aptitude tests were obtained for 14 subjects:

Subject	Aptitude Test A	Aptitude Test B
A	120	145
B	107	155
C	129	137
D	105	166
E	126	134
F	117	169
G	143	154
H	123	152
I	133	141
J	101	158
K	137	150
L	113	163
M	134	147
N	109	167

Compute r' after ranking the subjects on each test.

5. The following scores were obtained by 15 subjects on typing speed and mechanical speed:

Subject	Typing Speed	Mechanical Speed
A	34	64
B	50	76
C	27	49
D	42	66
E	32	59
F	42	68
G	34	53
H	39	70
I	31	46
J	36	56
K	47	73
L	37	56
M	44	77
N	34	62
O	24	58

Compute r' after ranking the subjects on typing speed and mechanical speed.

Appendix A

REVIEW OF BASIC ALGEBRA

A.1 INTRODUCTION

Many students who take a first course in statistics feel a sense of concern when they realize that some knowledge of mathematics is required. Actually, all the mathematical background required for a course in introductory statistics as presented in this text includes the simple operations of arithmetic and the bare essentials of elementary algebra. It is realized that many students will have become somewhat "rusty" in their elementary algebra, some will have forgotten much of what they learned, and some may feel that they never quite learned it in the first place. It is for such readers, those who have already had a first course in elementary algebra, that this Appendix is intended.

An attempt has been made to cover all of the algebraic symbols and operations required to follow the presentation in the text. Symbols and operations which are introduced and explained throughout the text as needed are not, for the most part, presented in this Appendix. Most of the material will be sketched, rather than discussed.

A.2 GENERAL ALGEBRAIC SYMBOLS

Symbol	*Explanation*
$a \neq b$	a is not equal to b.
$a \sim b$, $a \cong b$	Alternative ways of writing "a is approximately equal to b."

Symbol	*Explanation*
$a > b$	a is greater than b (or, b is less than a).
$a < b$	a is less than b (or, b is greater than a).
$a \geq b$	a is greater than or equal to b (or, b is less than or equal to a).
$a \leq b$	a is less than or equal to b (or, b is greater than or equal to a).
$a \leq x \leq b$	The variable x may be greater than or equal to a and less than or equal to b. In other words, x can have any value in the interval (range) from a (lower limit) to b (upper limit), both inclusive.
$a \pm b$	This has either of two meanings: (1) $a + b$ or $a - b$; (2) the interval from $a - b$ (lower limit) to $a + b$ (upper limit). It will be apparent from the text which meaning is appropriate.
$a \times b$, $a \cdot b$, $(a)(b)$ or ab	Alternative ways of writing the product a times b.
a^2	$a \cdot a$, called a square or a to the second power. The little 2 is called the *exponent*.
a^3	$a \cdot a \cdot a$, called a cube or a to the third power.
a^4	$a \cdot a \cdot a \cdot a$, called a to the fourth power.
a^n	$a \cdot a \cdots a$ (n times), called a to the nth power.
$1/a$, a^{-1}	Alternative ways of writing the reciprocal of a. A negative exponent indicates that the term (a) is a reciprocal.
$1/a^n$, a^{-n}	Alternative ways of writing the reciprocal of a^n.
a/b, $(1/b)(a)$	Alternative ways of writing a divided by b. The second form states this as $1/b$ times a.

$\sqrt{a}$, $a^{1/2}$	Alternative ways of writing the square root of a.
∞	Infinitely or indefinitely large.
$-\infty$	Infinitely or indefinitely less than zero.

A.3 OPERATIONS INVOLVING + AND − SIGNS

Operation	*Illustrations*
To add a negative number to a positive number, *subtract* it.	$a + (-b) = a - b$ $6 + (-3) = 6 - 3 = 3$ $6 + (-8) = 6 - 8 = -2$
To subtract a negative number from a positive number, reverse the negative sign (make it positive) and then *add* it.	$a - (-b) = a + b$ $6 - (-3) = 6 + 3 = 9$
To add two negative numbers, add the quantities and consider the sum negative.	$(-a) + (-b) = -a - b = -(a + b)$ $(-6) + (-3) = -6 - 3 = -(6 + 3)$ $= -9$
To subtract a negative number $-b$ from a negative number $-a$, reverse the negative sign of $-b$ (making it positive b) and then subtract a from b.	$(-a) - (-b) = -a + b = b - a$ $(-7) - (-10) = -7 + 10$ $= 10 - 7 = 3$ $(-12) - (-8) = -12 + 8$ $= 8 - 12 = -4$
To add a positive number to a negative number, *subtract* the negative quantity from the positive quantity.	$(-a) + b = b - a$ $(-8) + 10 = 10 - 8 = 2$ $(-15) + 5 = 5 - 15 = -10$
To subtract a positive number from a negative number, *add* the quantities and consider the sum as negative.	$-a - (b) = -a - b = -(a + b)$ $-11 - (3) = -11 - 3$ $= -(11 + 3) = -14$
The product of two positive numbers is a positive number.	$a \cdot b = ab$ $(2)(3) = 6$
The product of two negative numbers is a positive number.	$(-a)(-b) = ab$ $(-6)(-3) = 18$
The product of two numbers with opposite signs (one positive, one negative) is a negative number.	$(-a)(b) = -ab$ $(a)(-b) = -ab$ $(-3)(4) = -12$ $(3)(-4) = -12$

Operation	*Illustrations*
Division involving only negative numbers results in a positive number.	$-a/-b = a/b$ $-6/-3 = 6/3 = 2$
Division involving numbers of a different sign, one positive and one negative, results in a negative number.	$-a/b = -(a/b)$ $a/-b = -(a/b)$ $-12/4 = -(12/4) = -3$ $12/-4 = -(12/4) = -3$

A.4 OPERATIONS INVOLVING PARENTHESES

A positive sign before parentheses indicates that the parentheses may be removed without changing signs.	$a + (b - c + d)$ $= a + b - c + d$ $6 + (3 - 4 + 2)$ $= 6 + 3 - 4 + 2 = 7$
A negative sign before parentheses indicates that each term inside the parentheses must have its sign reversed, if you wish to remove the parentheses.	$a - (b - c + d) = a - b + c - d$ $6 - (3 - 4 + 2)$ $= 6 - 3 + 4 - 2 = 5$
Algebraic expressions may occur where more than a single pair of parentheses is needed. In such instances, other similar symbols are used jointly with the parentheses, such as brackets [ ] and braces { }. Such symbols may be removed by starting with the *innermost* symbol and *working outward*, taking into consideration the sign before each such symbol, as noted previously.	$a\{b - c[(a + b) - (c - d)]\}$ $= a\{b - c[a + b - c + d]\}$ $= a\{b - ca - cb + c^2 - cd\}$ $= ab - a^2c - acb + ac^2 - acd$

A.5 OPERATIONS INVOLVING FRACTIONS

1.
$$\frac{a + b}{c} = \frac{a}{c} + \frac{b}{c}$$
$$\frac{a - b}{c} = \frac{a}{c} - \frac{b}{c}$$

2. However,

$$\frac{c}{a+b} \neq \frac{c}{a} + \frac{c}{b}$$

$$\frac{c}{a-b} \neq \frac{c}{a} - \frac{c}{b}$$

3. $$\frac{a+b+c}{d} = \frac{1}{d}(a+b+c)$$

4. $$\frac{a}{b/c} = a \div \frac{b}{c} = a \cdot \frac{c}{b} = \frac{ac}{b}$$

5. $$\frac{a/b}{c/d} = \frac{a}{b} \div \frac{c}{d} = \frac{a}{b} \cdot \frac{d}{c} = \frac{ad}{bc}$$

A.6 OPERATIONS INVOLVING EXPONENTS

1. $$a^2a^3 = (a \cdot a)(a \cdot a \cdot a) = a^{2+3} = a^5$$

2. $$a^na^m = a^{n+m}$$

3. $$\frac{a^3}{a^2} = a^3 \cdot a^{-2} = a^{3-2} = a$$

4. $$\frac{a^5}{a^8} = a^5 \cdot a^{-8} = a^{5-8} = a^{-3} = \frac{1}{a^3}$$

5. $$\frac{a^n}{a^m} = a^n \cdot a^{-m} = a^{n-m}$$

6. $$a^0 = 1, (a \neq 0)$$

A.7 OPERATIONS INVOLVING MULTIPLICATION

1. $$(ax)(by) = abxy$$

$$(2a)(3b) = 6ab$$

2. $$(-ax)(by) = -abxy$$

$$(2a)(-3b) = -6ab$$

3. $$(a+b)^2 = (a+b)(a+b) = a^2 + 2ab + b^2$$

The expansion of $(a + b)^2$, as just shown, is obtained as follows:

STEP 1: Write:

Row 1	$a + b$
Row 2	$a + b$

STEP 2: Multiply each term in Row 1 by a, the *first* term in Row 2: $a^2 + ab$

STEP 3: Multiply each term in Row 1 by b, the *second* term in Row 2, and line up corresponding terms: $ab + b^2$

STEP 4: Add: $a^2 + 2ab + b^2$

4. $$(a - b)^2 = (a - b)(a - b) = a^2 - 2ab + b^2$$

The expansion of $(a - b)^2$ is obtained by following *Steps* 1 through 4, as outlined previously. It is a good idea for the reader to work through these steps. (Be careful about the + and − signs.)

A.8 HOW TO COMPUTE A SQUARE ROOT

Compute $\sqrt{117{,}237.76}$

STEP 1: Starting at the decimal point, mark off *pairs of digits*, proceeding to the left, and then mark off *pairs* proceeding to the right. This gives: 11 72 37 . 76. It may happen that the "pair" farthest *left* consists of only one digit. This causes no problem. However, if the "pair" farthest *right* comes out with only one digit, then add a 0 to make it a true pair.

STEP 2: Start the computation by considering the pair farthest *left* (in this instance, it is 11). Find the largest whole number of which the square is 11 or less. This number is 3 ($3^2 = 9$). Write this 3 just above the pair 11. Write 3^2 or 9 just below this pair. Subtract the 9 from 11. The 3 is the first digit in our answer. So far, our work looks as follows:

```
   3      .
 √11 72 37 . 76
   9
  --
   2
```

STEP 3: Note the next pair (72) and write it next to the 2, giving the number 272. Draw a vertical bar to the left of this number. Double the first digit in the answer (3) and write it to the left of the vertical bar. So far, our work looks as follows:

$$\begin{array}{r|l} & \;3\quad\;\; . \\ & \sqrt{11\ 72\ 37\,.\,76} \\ & \;9 \\ 6 & \overline{\;272} \\ & \end{array}$$

STEP 4: Mentally, place a 0 after the 6, giving the number 60. If we divide 60 into 272, we get 4 plus some fraction. Then, place a 4 after the 6, to get 64. Multiply this 64 by the 4, to get 256. Place the 4 above the 72 also, since it is the second digit in the answer. Place the 256 below 272 and subtract, obtaining 16. At this point, our work looks as follows:

$$\begin{array}{r|l} & \;3\ \ 4\quad . \\ & \sqrt{11\ 72\ 37\,.\,76} \\ & \;9 \\ 64 & \overline{\;272} \\ & \;256 \\ & \;\;\overline{16} \end{array}$$

STEP 5: Note the next pair (37) and write it next to the 16, giving the number 1637. Draw a vertical bar to the left of this number. Double the first two digits in the answer (34) and write it to the left of the vertical bar. (This is similar to Step 3.) Our work now looks as follows:

$$\begin{array}{r|l} & \;3\ \ 4\quad . \\ & \sqrt{11\ 72\ 37\,.\,76} \\ & \;9 \\ 64 & \overline{\;272} \\ & \;256 \\ \hline 68 & \;\;1637 \\ & \end{array}$$

STEP 6: Mentally, place a 0 after the 68, giving 680. If we divide 680 into 1637, we get 2 plus some fraction. Then, place a 2 after the 68, to get 682. Multiply this 682 by the 2, to get 1364. Place the 2 also above the 37, since it is the third digit in the answer. Place the 1364 below 1637 and subtract, obtaining 273. (This is similar to Step 4.) At this point, our work looks as follows:

```
          3  4  2 .
       √11 72 37 . 76
          9
   64 |  272
      |  256
  682 |   1637
      |   1364
           273
```

Notice that, starting with *Step* 5, we repeat *Step* 3 and then *Step* 4. This cycle of repetition continues until we obtain the answer to any desired number of decimal places. Referring to *Step* 6, we found that 680 went into 1637 2 times plus a fraction. This led to the number 682 and 682 times 2 gave 1364. Sometimes when this step is performed, the product (which here is 1364) may be greater than the number from which it is to be subtracted (which here is 1637). In such an instance, instead of using 2 to form 682, drop down one unit (to 1) and form 681. Then, continue as before using 1 instead of 2 in the balance of the instructions in *Step* 6. (Sometimes it may be necessary to drop down an additional unit.) Since *Step* 6 is similar to *Step* 4, this comment pertains to *Step* 4, as well.

Since there is only one pair to the right of the decimal, our answer will go out to one decimal. If we wish additional decimal places in our answer, add a pair of zeros (00) after the last pair (76) for each additional decimal place desired. The complete solution is shown below

```
          3  4  2 .  4
       √11 72 37 . 76
          9
   64 |  272
      |  256
  682 |   1637
      |   1364
 6844 |    27376
      |    27376
```

Notice that the decimal point is placed directly above the decimal point in the original number. It is always necessary to check your work. This is easy, since the answer squared should equal the original number (except for possible rounding differences). Checking, we find: $(342.4)^2 =$ 117,237.76.

A.9 OPERATIONS INVOLVING SQUARE ROOTS

$$\sqrt{aXY} = \sqrt{a}\sqrt{X}\sqrt{Y}$$

$$\sqrt{a^2XY^2} = aY\sqrt{X}$$

$$\sqrt{\frac{aX}{n^2}} = \frac{1}{n}\sqrt{aX}$$

A.10 OPERATIONS INVOLVING EQUATIONS

1. The use and understanding of simple equations are important in applications of elementary algebra to statistics. Consider the following algebraic equation:

$$Y_i = 3 + 2X_i$$

This equation expresses Y_i *as a function of* X_i. That is, this equation can be used to compute a value for Y_i corresponding to a selected value of X_i. Y_i is called the *dependent variable* and X_i, the *independent variable*. Suppose we select two values for X_i: 0, 4. We will use this equation to compute the corresponding values for Y_i by substituting each of these X_i values, in turn, into the equation:

when $\quad X_i = 0\colon Y_i = 3 + 2(0) = 3 + 0 = 3$

$\quad X_i = 4\colon Y_i = 3 + 2(4) = 3 + 8 = 11$

Clearly, then, the foregoing equation expresses the relationship between the two variables X_i and Y_i. Often, the subscript i is omitted, so that the equation appears as

$$Y = 3 + 2X$$

2. Equations may sometimes be simplified by factoring out a common constant or variable. Examples are

	Original equation	*After factoring*
(a)	$Y = a + aX$	$Y = a(1 + X)$
(b)	$Y = \frac{a}{b} + \frac{X}{b}$	$Y = \frac{1}{b}(a + X)$
(c)	$Y = kX + X^2$	$Y = X(k + X)$
(d)	$Y = 6 + 4X$	$Y = 2(3 + 2X)$
(e)	$Z = a + kX + kY^2$	$Z = a + k(X + Y^2)$

3. Given an equation involving a single variable (X)

$$15X - 7 = 3X + 29$$

We may solve for X, first, by collecting all terms involving X on the left side of the equal sign and all other terms on the right side. This is accomplished as follows:

(a) To move the *positive* term $3X$ to the left side, *subtract* it from *each* side, obtaining

$$15X - 7 - 3X = 29$$

(b) To move the *negative* term -7 to the right side, *add* it to *each* side, obtaining

$$15X - 3X = 29 + 7$$

(c) Then, combining like terms on each side of the equal sign, we obtain

$$12X = 36$$

(d) To eliminate the 12 from the left side, divide each side by 12, obtaining

$$X = 3$$

This is our answer. We can prove the answer by substituting 3 for X in the original equation. This gives

$$(15)(3) - 7 = 3(3) + 29$$

And so,

$$38 = 38$$

Since substituting $X = 3$ maintains the equality of the two sides of the original equation, we have proven that $X = 3$ is the correct solution.

4. Given an equation which expresses Y as a function of X

$$Y = 25 - 6X$$

It is sometimes desired to solve such an equation for X; in other words, to express X as a function of Y. This may be accomplished, first, by moving the term (or terms) involving X to the left side of the equal sign and all other terms to the right side, in the same manner as just shown in 3. We will apply this procedure, as follows:

(a) Move the negative term $-6X$ to the left side by adding it to both sides, to obtain

$$Y + 6X = 25$$

(b) Move the positive term Y to the right side by subtracting it from both sides to obtain

$$6X = 25 - Y$$

(c) Then, eliminate the 6 from the left side by dividing both sides by 6, to obtain

$$X = \frac{25 - Y}{6}$$

This is the solution desired.

5. Given a pair of simultaneous equations (I and II) in two unknowns, X and Y

$$\text{(I)} \qquad 3X + 8Y = 30$$

$$\text{(II)} \qquad 20X - 12Y = 50$$

It is desired to solve these equations, that is, obtain values for X and Y which will satisfy them. The general approach used in solving such equations simultaneously is to combine them in such a way as to obtain a single equation which contains only one unknown (X or Y). This may be accomplished, first, by changing one or both equations so that either the X terms or the Y terms in the two equations are identical except, perhaps, for sign. We will make the Y terms identical. The coefficient of Y in Equation I is 8 which can be factored into 2×4. The coefficient of Y in Equation II is 12 (ignoring the negative sign for the moment) which can be factored into 3×4. Note that if we multiply 8 ($= 2 \times 4$) by 3, and 12 ($= 3 \times 4$) by 2, the result will be that the coefficient of the Y term in each equation will equal $2 \times 3 \times 4$ or 24. In other words, the Y terms in the two equations will then be identical except for sign. Therefore, multiply Equation I by 3 and Equation II by 2, to obtain Equations I′ and II′ as follows:

$$\begin{array}{lll} & \text{(I}'\text{)} & 9X + 24Y = 90 \\ & \text{(II}'\text{)} & \underline{40X - 24Y = 100} \\ \text{add:} & \text{(III}'\text{)} & 49X \qquad\quad = 190 \end{array}$$

Note that the *entire* Equation I is multiplied by 3 and the *entire* Equation II by 2, not merely the Y terms. This is done to maintain the equality for each equation. Now that we have adjusted Equations I and II in order to make the coefficients of the Y terms identical (except for sign), the next step is to combine the adjusted equations (I′ and II′) so as to obtain a single equation containing only one unknown. Since the coefficients of the Y terms differ *only* in *sign*, we *add* Equations I′ and II′, as shown previously. This results in eliminating the Y terms, so that the resulting Equation III′ contains X as the only unknown. (If the coefficients of Y were identical, *including identical signs*, then the correct procedure would have been to *subtract* Equation II′ from Equation I′, or Equation I′ from Equation II′. This also would have resulted in an equation with a single unknown.)

Solving Equation III′ for X by dividing both sides of the equation by 49, we obtain $X = 3.88$. This is the solution for X. Now, to obtain the solution for Y, substitute $X = 3.88$ into one of the two original equations (I or II). Selecting Equation I, substitute 3.88 for X to obtain

$$3(3.88) + 8Y = 30$$

Solving the foregoing equation for Y, we obtain

$$11.64 + 8Y = 30$$

$$8Y = 30 - 11.64 = 18.36$$

$$Y = \frac{18.36}{8} = 2.29$$

Finally, substitute the solutions obtained ($X = 3.88$, $Y = 2.29$) into the other original equation (Equation II) to check them. Making these substitutions, we obtain

$$20(3.88) - 12(2.29) = 50$$

$$77.60 - 27.48 = 50$$

$$50.12 = 50$$

The small difference between 50.12 and 50 is because of rounding. Therefore, we may accept the obtained solutions for X and Y as correct.

A.11 LOGARITHMS

Logarithms are actually *exponents.* For example

$3^2 = 9$
3 is called the *base*
2, the exponent, is also called the *logarithm of* 9 *to the base* 3. This is written, symbolically, as $\log_3 9 = 2$.

$5^3 = 125$
5 is called the *base*
3, the exponent, is also called the *logarithm of* 125 *to the base* 5. This is written, symbolically, as $\log_5 125 = 3$.

In a large number of applications, the base 10 is used. Logarithms to the base 10 are called *common logarithms.* Illustrations involving common logarithms are

$10^2 = 100$
10 is the *base*
2 is the *logarithm of* 100 *to the base* 10. This is written as $\log_{10} 100 = 2$. When dealing with common logarithms (to the base 10), it is customary not

to show the base and to write log 100 = 2. When the base is not shown, it is understood to be 10.

$10^3 = 1000$
10 is the *base*
3 is the *logarithm of* 1000 *to the base* 10. This may be written as log 1000 = 3.

Sometimes, the exponent (logarithm) is not a whole number. For example

$10^{1.350} = 22.40$. The exponent 1.350 is the logarithm of 22.40 to the base 10. This may be written as log 22.40 = 1.350.
$10^{1.82601} = 66.99$, and log 66.99 = 1.82601
$10^{2.000} = 100$, and log 100 = 2.000
$10^{2.07004} = 117.5$, and log 117.5 = 2.07004

Notice, from the foregoing illustrations, that a logarithm is made up of two parts. The part before the decimal is called the *characteristic;* the decimal part is called the *mantissa*. Logarithms for numbers between 0 and 1 (fractions) are negative. For example

$$\frac{1}{10^2} = 10^{-2} = .01, \text{ and } \log .01 = -2$$

$$\frac{1}{10^3} = 10^{-3} = .001, \text{ and } \log .001 = -3$$

The logarithm of a number is obtained by determining the characteristic by inspection of the number and then looking up the mantissa in a table, such as Table B.4 in Appendix B. The characteristic is determined differently for numbers which are equal to or greater than 1 and those which are between 0 and 1. *If a number is equal to or greater than* 1, *the characteristic is equal to one less than the number of digits before the decimal point.* For example: the characteristic for 23.31 is 1; for 23.062 , it is 1; for 1.802, it is 0; for 206.1, it is 2, etc. On the other hand, *for numbers between* 0 *and* 1, *the characteristic is equal to one more than the number of zeros between the decimal point and the first non-zero number to the right of the decimal point, with a negative sign attached.* For example: the characteristic for .00601 is −3; for .03000, it is −2; for .8000, it is −1, etc. There is no logarithm for 0 nor for negative numbers. *The mantissa depends upon the particular digits contained in a number, without regard to the position of the decimal point.* For example, the mantissa is identical for 372, 3.72, 37.2, .000372, .372. We may determine the mantissa for any of these numbers by referring to Table B.4, finding 37 in the first column (headed "*N*"), moving along that row to the entry in the column headed "2," and reading out .5705. (All mantissas are decimals.) This is the required mantissa.

As an illustration, the logarithm for 372 has the characteristic 2 and the mantissa .5705. Hence, we write: log 372 = 2.5705. The logarithm for 37.2 has the characteristic 1 and the mantissa .5705, so that we write log 37.2 = 1.5705. The logarithm for .00372 has the characteristic −3 and the mantissa .5705. Therefore, we write log .00372 = −3.5705. However, in the case of negative logarithms, it is customary to write the characteristic as a deviation from 10. For example, if the characteristic is −3, we write 7 − 10; if it is −1, we write 9 − 10, etc. Then, we reflect this practice in the way we write the logarithm. For example, in the illustration, instead of writing log .00372 = −3.5705, we write log .00372 = 7.5705 − 10.

We may know the logarithm of a number and wish to determine the number itself. For example, say, we have the logarithm 2.8927. What is the number? We may determine this by looking for the *mantissa* .8927 in Table B.4. After locating this mantissa, read off the two digits which are in the first column of the table (headed N) and in the same row as the mantissa. For the mantissa .8927, these two digits are 78. Then, read off the digit at the head of the column where the mantissa .8927 is located. This digit is 1. Putting these three digits together, we obtain 781. Finally, note that the *characteristic* of the logarithm is 2. Remembering that a positive characteristic is equal to one less than the number of digits before the decimal point in the number itself, we conclude that the number we are seeking has 2 + 1 or 3 digits before the decimal. Consequently, the number we are seeking is 781. This number, 781, is called the *antilogarithm*. Generally, this term is shortened to *antilog*, just as logarithm is usually referred to as *log*.

As a second illustration, what is the antilog of 1.6170? Referring to Table B.4, find the mantissa .6170 and note that in the same row as this mantissa in the N column appear the digits 41. At the head of the column where this mantissa appears we find the digit 4. Putting these three digits together we obtain 414. Noting that the characteristic is 1, we know that there must be 1 + 1 or 2 digits before the decimal. Consequently, the antilog of 1.6170 is 41.4.

Appendix B

TABLES

Table B.1 TABLE OF RANDOM NUMBERS

Line \ Col.	(1)	(2)	(3)	(4)	(5)	(6)	(7)	(8)	(9)	(10)	(11)	(12)	(13)	(14)
1	10480	15011	01536	02011	81647	91646	69179	14194	62590	36207	20969	99570	91291	90700
2	22368	46573	25595	85393	30995	89198	27982	53402	93965	34095	52666	19174	39615	99505
3	24130	48360	22527	97265	76393	64809	15179	24830	49340	32081	30680	19655	63348	58629
4	42167	93093	06243	61680	07856	16376	39440	53537	71341	57004	00849	74917	97758	16379
5	37570	39975	81837	16656	06121	91782	60468	81305	49684	60672	14110	06927	01263	54613
6	77921	06907	11008	42751	27756	53498	18602	70659	90655	15053	21916	81825	44394	42880
7	99562	72905	56420	69994	98872	31016	71194	18738	44013	48840	63213	21069	10634	12952
8	96301	91977	05463	07972	18876	20922	94595	56869	69014	60045	18425	84903	42508	32307
9	89579	14342	63661	10281	17453	18103	57740	84378	25331	12566	58678	44947	05585	56941
10	85475	36857	53342	53988	53060	59533	38867	62300	08158	17983	16439	11458	18593	64952
11	28918	69578	88231	33276	70997	79936	56865	05859	90106	31595	01547	85590	91610	78188
12	63553	40961	48235	03427	49626	69445	18663	72695	52180	20847	12234	90511	33703	90322
13	09429	93969	52636	92737	88974	33488	36320	17617	30015	08272	84115	27156	30613	74952
14	10365	61129	87529	85689	48237	52267	67689	93394	01511	26358	85104	20285	29975	89868
15	07119	97336	71048	08178	77233	13916	47564	81056	97735	85977	29372	74461	28551	90707
16	51085	12765	51821	51259	77452	16308	60756	92144	49442	53900	70960	63990	75601	40719
17	02368	21382	52404	60268	89368	19885	55322	44819	01188	65255	64835	44919	05944	55157
18	01011	54092	33362	94904	31273	04146	18594	29852	71585	85030	51132	01915	92747	64951
19	52162	53916	46369	58586	23216	14513	83149	98736	23495	64350	94738	17752	35156	35749
20	07056	97628	33787	09998	42698	06691	76988	13602	51851	46104	88916	19509	25625	58104
21	48663	91245	85828	14346	09172	30168	90229	04734	59193	22178	30421	61666	99904	32812
22	54164	58492	22421	74103	47070	25306	76468	26384	58151	06646	21524	15227	96909	44592
23	32639	32363	05597	24200	13363	38005	94342	28728	35806	06912	17012	64161	18296	22851
24	29334	27001	87637	87308	58731	00256	45834	15398	46557	41135	10367	07684	36188	18510
25	02488	33062	28834	07351	19731	92420	60952	61280	50001	67658	32586	86679	50720	94953

26	81525	72295	04839	96423	24878	82651	66566	14778	76797	14780	13300	87074	79666	95725
27	29676	20591	68086	26432	46901	20849	89768	81536	86645	12659	92259	57102	80428	25280
28	00742	57392	39064	66432	84673	40027	32832	61362	98947	96067	64760	64584	96096	98253
29	05366	04213	25669	26422	44407	44048	37937	63904	45766	66134	75470	66520	34693	90449
30	91921	26418	64117	94305	26766	25940	39972	22209	71500	64568	91402	42416	07844	69618
31	00582	04711	87917	77341	42206	35126	74087	99547	81817	42607	43808	76655	62028	76630
32	00725	69884	62797	56170	86324	88072	76222	36086	84637	93161	76038	65855	77919	88006
33	69011	65795	95876	55293	18988	27354	26575	08625	40801	59920	29841	80150	12777	48501
34	25976	57948	29888	88604	67917	48708	18912	82271	65424	69774	33611	54262	85963	03547
35	09763	83473	73577	12908	30883	18317	28290	35797	05998	41688	34952	37888	38917	88050
36	91567	42595	27958	30134	04024	86385	29880	99730	55536	84855	29080	09250	79656	73211
37	17955	56349	90999	49127	20044	59931	06115	20542	18059	02008	73708	83517	36103	42791
38	46503	18584	18845	49618	02304	51038	20655	58727	28168	15475	56942	53389	20562	87338
39	92157	89634	94824	78171	84610	82834	09922	25417	44137	48413	25555	21246	35509	20468
40	14577	62765	35605	81263	39667	47358	56873	56307	61607	49518	89686	20103	77490	18062
41	98427	07523	33362	64270	01638	92477	66969	98420	04880	45585	46565	04102	46880	45709
42	34914	63976	88720	82765	34476	17032	87589	40836	32427	70002	70663	88863	77775	69348
43	70060	28277	39475	46473	23219	53416	94970	25832	69975	94884	19661	72828	00102	66794
44	53976	54914	06990	67245	68350	82948	11398	42878	80287	88267	47363	46634	06541	97809
45	76072	29515	40980	07391	58745	25774	22987	80059	39911	96189	41151	14222	60697	59583
46	90725	52210	83974	29992	65831	38857	50490	83765	55657	14361	31720	57375	56228	41546
47	64364	67412	33339	31926	14883	24413	59744	92351	97473	89286	35931	04110	23726	51900
48	08962	00358	31662	25388	61642	34072	81249	35648	56891	69352	48373	45578	78547	81788
49	95012	68379	93526	70765	10592	04542	76463	54328	02349	17247	28865	14777	62730	92277
50	15664	10493	20492	38391	91132	21999	59516	81652	27195	48223	46751	22923	32261	85653

Source: *Table of 105,000 Random Decimal Digits*, Statement No. 4914, File No. 261-A-1, Interstate Commerce Commission, Washington, D.C., May 1949, Page 1.

Table B.2 TABLE OF AREAS UNDER THE NORMAL CURVE: AREAS FROM THE MEAN TO SPECIFIED VALUES OF z.

z	.00	.01	.02	.03	.04	.05	.06	.07	.08	.09
0.0	.0000	.0040	.0080	.0120	.0160	.0199	.0239	.0279	.0319	.0359
0.1	.0398	.0438	.0478	.0517	.0557	.0596	.0636	.0675	.0714	.0753
0.2	.0793	.0832	.0871	.0910	.0948	.0987	.1026	.1064	.1103	.1141
0.3	.1179	.1217	.1255	.1293	.1331	.1368	.1406	.1443	.1480	.1517
0.4	.1554	.1591	.1628	.1664	.1700	.1736	.1772	.1808	.1844	.1879
0.5	.1915	.1950	.1985	.2019	.2054	.2088	.2123	.2157	.2190	.2224
0.6	.2257	.2291	.2324	.2357	.2389	.2422	.2454	.2486	.2518	.2549
0.7	.2580	.2612	.2642	.2673	.2704	.2734	.2764	.2794	.2823	.2852
0.8	.2881	.2910	.2939	.2967	.2995	.3023	.3051	.3078	.3106	.3133
0.9	.3159	.3186	.3212	.3238	.3264	.3289	.3315	.3340	.3365	.3389
1.0	.3413	.3438	.3461	.3485	.3508	.3531	.3554	.3577	.3599	.3621
1.1	.3643	.3665	.3686	.3708	.3729	.3749	.3770	.3790	.3810	.3830
1.2	.3849	.3869	.3888	.3907	.3925	.3944	.3962	.3980	.3997	.4015
1.3	.4032	.4049	.4066	.4082	.4099	.4115	.4131	.4147	.4162	.4177
1.4	.4192	.4207	.4222	.4236	.4251	.4265	.4279	.4292	.4306	.4319
1.5	.4332	.4345	.4357	.4370	.4382	.4394	.4406	.4418	.4429	.4441
1.6	.4452	.4463	.4474	.4484	.4495	.4505	.4515	.4525	.4535	.4545
1.7	.4554	.4564	.4573	.4582	.4591	.4599	.4608	.4616	.4625	.4633
1.8	.4641	.4649	.4656	.4664	.4671	.4678	.4686	.4693	.4699	.4706
1.9	.4713	.4719	.4726	.4732	.4738	.4744	.4750	.4756	.4761	.4767
2.0	.4772	.4778	.4783	.4788	.4793	.4798	.4803	.4808	.4812	.4817
2.1	.4821	.4826	.4830	.4834	.4838	.4842	.4846	.4850	.4854	.4857
2.2	.4861	.4864	.4868	.4871	.4875	.4878	.4881	.4884	.4887	.4890
2.3	.4893	.4896	.4898	.4901	.4904	.4906	.4909	.4911	.4913	.4916
2.4	.4918	.4920	.4922	.4925	.4927	.4929	.4931	.4932	.4934	.4936
2.5	.4938	.4940	.4941	.4943	.4945	.4946	.4948	.4949	.4951	.4952
2.6	.4953	.4955	.4956	.4957	.4959	.4960	.4961	.4962	.4963	.4964
2.7	.4965	.4966	.4967	.4968	.4969	.4970	.4971	.4972	.4973	.4974
2.8	.4974	.4975	.4976	.4977	.4977	.4978	.4979	.4979	.4980	.4981
2.9	.4981	.4982	.4982	.4983	.4984	.4984	.4985	.4985	.4986	.4986
3.0	.49865	.4987	.4987	.4988	.4988	.4989	.4989	.4989	.4990	.4990
4.0	.4999683									

Illustration: For $z = 1.93$, shaded area is .4732 out of total area of 1.
Source: John Neter and William Wasserman, Fundamental Statistics for Business and Economics, Second Edition, Allyn and Bacon, Inc., Boston, 1961, with the permission of the publisher.

Table B.3 *t* DISTRIBUTION: TABLE OF AREAS IN BOTH TAILS OF THE DISTRIBUTION

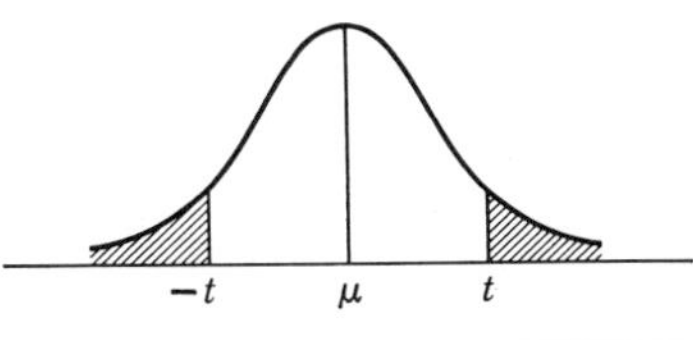

df	Probability (Total area in *both* tails)								
	.5	.4	.3	.2	.1	.05	.02	.01	.001
1	1.000	1.376	1.963	3.078	6.314	12.706	31.821	63.657	636.619
2	.816	1.061	1.386	1.886	2.920	4.303	6.965	9.925	31.598
3	.765	.978	1.250	1.638	2.353	3.182	4.541	5.841	12.941
4	.741	.941	1.190	1.533	2.132	2.776	3.747	4.604	8.610
5	.727	.920	1.156	1.476	2.015	2.571	3.365	4.032	6.859
6	.718	.906	1.134	1.440	1.943	2.447	3.143	3.707	5.959
7	.711	.896	1.119	1.415	1.895	2.365	2.998	3.499	5.405
8	.706	.889	1.108	1.397	1.860	2.306	2.896	3.355	5.041
9	.703	.883	1.100	1.383	1.833	2.262	2.821	3.250	4.781
10	.700	.879	1.093	1.372	1.812	2.228	2.764	3.169	4.587
11	.697	.876	1.088	1.363	1.796	2.201	2.718	3.106	4.437
12	.695	.873	1.083	1.356	1.782	2.179	2.681	3.055	4.318
13	.694	.870	1.079	1.350	1.771	2.160	2.650	3.012	4.221
14	.692	.868	1.076	1.345	1.761	2.145	2.624	2.977	4.140
15	.691	.866	1.074	1.341	1.753	2.131	2.602	2.947	4.073
16	.690	.865	1.071	1.337	1.746	2.120	2.583	2.921	4.015
17	.689	.863	1.069	1.333	1.740	2.110	2.567	2.898	3.965
18	.688	.862	1.067	1.330	1.734	2.101	2.552	2.878	3.922
19	.688	.861	1.066	1.328	1.729	2.093	2.539	2.861	3.883
20	.687	.860	1.064	1.325	1.725	2.086	2.528	2.845	3.850
21	.686	.859	1.063	1.323	1.721	2.080	2.518	2.831	3.819
22	.686	.858	1.061	1.321	1.717	2.074	2.508	2.819	3.792
23	.685	.858	1.060	1.319	1.714	2.069	2.500	2.807	3.767
24	.685	.857	1.059	1.318	1.711	2.064	2.492	2.797	3.745
25	.684	.856	1.058	1.316	1.708	2.060	2.485	2.787	3.725
26	.684	.856	1.058	1.315	1.706	2.056	2.479	2.779	3.707
27	.684	.855	1.057	1.314	1.703	2.052	2.473	2.771	3.690
28	.683	.855	1.056	1.313	1.701	2.048	2.467	2.763	3.674
29	.683	.854	1.055	1.311	1.699	2.045	2.462	2.756	3.659
∞	.674	.842	1.036	1.282	1.645	1.960	2.326	2.576	3.291

Source: Table III of Fisher and Yates, *Statistical Tables for Biological, Agricultural and Medical Research*, Oliver & Boyd Ltd., Edinburgh, and by permission of the authors and publishers.

Table B.4 COMMON LOGARITHMS

N	0	1	2	3	4	5	6	7	8	9
10	0000	0043	0086	0128	0170	0212	0253	0294	0334	0374
11	0414	0453	0492	0531	0569	0607	0645	0682	0719	0755
12	0792	0828	0864	0899	0934	0969	1004	1038	1072	1106
13	1139	1173	1206	1239	1271	1303	1335	1367	1399	1430
14	1461	1492	1523	1553	1584	1614	1644	1673	1703	1732
15	1761	1790	1818	1847	1875	1903	1931	1959	1987	2014
16	2041	2068	2095	2122	2148	2175	2201	2227	2253	2279
17	2304	2330	2355	2380	2405	2430	2455	2480	2504	2529
18	2553	2577	2601	2625	2648	2672	2695	2718	2742	2765
19	2788	2810	2833	2856	2878	2900	2923	2945	2967	2989
20	3010	3032	3054	3075	3096	3118	3139	3160	3181	3201
21	3222	3243	3263	3284	3304	3324	3345	3365	3385	3404
22	3424	3444	3464	3483	3502	3522	3541	3560	3579	3598
23	3617	3636	3655	3674	3692	3711	3729	3747	3766	3784
24	3802	3820	3838	3856	3874	3892	3909	3927	3945	3962
25	3979	3997	4014	4031	4048	4065	4082	4099	4116	4133
26	4150	4166	4183	4200	4216	4232	4249	4265	4281	4298
27	4314	4330	4346	4362	4378	4393	4409	4425	4440	4456
28	4472	4487	4502	4518	4533	4548	4564	4579	4594	4609
29	4624	4639	4654	4669	4683	4698	4713	4728	4742	4757
30	4771	4786	4800	4814	4829	4843	4857	4871	4886	4900
31	4914	4928	4942	4955	4969	4983	4997	5011	5024	5038
32	5051	5065	5079	5092	5105	5119	5132	5145	5159	5172
33	5185	5198	5211	5224	5237	5250	5263	5276	5289	5302
34	5315	5328	5340	5353	5366	5378	5391	5403	5416	5428
35	5441	5453	5465	5478	5490	5502	5514	5527	5539	5551
36	5563	5575	5587	5599	5611	5623	5635	5647	5658	5670
37	5682	5694	5705	5717	5729	5740	5752	5763	5775	5786
38	5798	5809	5821	5832	5843	5855	5866	5877	5888	5899
39	5911	5922	5933	5944	5955	5966	5977	5988	5999	6010
40	6021	6031	6042	6053	6064	6075	6085	6096	6107	6117
41	6128	6138	6149	6160	6170	6180	6191	6201	6212	6222
42	6232	6243	6253	6263	6274	6284	6294	6304	6314	6325
43	6335	6345	6355	6365	6375	6385	6395	6405	6415	6425
44	6435	6444	6454	6464	6474	6484	6493	6503	6513	6522
45	6532	6542	6551	6561	6571	6580	6590	6599	6609	6618
46	6628	6637	6646	6656	6665	6675	6684	6693	6702	6712
47	6721	6730	6739	6749	6758	6767	6776	6785	6794	6803
48	6812	6821	6830	6839	6848	6857	6866	6875	6884	6893
49	6902	6911	6920	6928	6937	6946	6955	6964	6972	6981
50	6990	6998	7007	7016	7024	7033	7042	7050	7059	7067
51	7076	7084	7093	7101	7110	7118	7126	7135	7143	7152
52	7160	7168	7177	7185	7193	7202	7210	7218	7226	7235
53	7243	7251	7259	7267	7275	7284	7292	7300	7308	7316
54	7324	7332	7340	7348	7356	7364	7372	7380	7388	7396

Source: John E. Freund and Frank J. Williams, *Modern Business Statistics*, 1958. Reprinted by permission of Prentice-Hall, Inc., Englewood Cliffs, N.J.

Table B.4 (*Continued*)

N	0	1	2	3	4	5	6	7	8	9
55	7404	7412	7419	7427	7435	7443	7451	7459	7466	7474
56	7482	7490	7497	7505	7513	7520	7528	7536	7543	7551
57	7559	7566	7574	7582	7589	7597	7604	7612	7619	7627
58	7634	7642	7649	7657	7664	7672	7679	7686	7694	7701
59	7709	7716	7723	7731	7738	7745	7752	7760	7767	7774
60	7782	7789	7796	7803	7810	7818	7825	7832	7839	7846
61	7853	7860	7868	7875	7882	7889	7896	7903	7910	7917
62	7924	7931	7938	7945	7952	7959	7966	7973	7980	7987
63	7993	8000	8007	8014	8021	8028	8035	8041	8048	8055
64	8062	8069	8075	8082	8089	8096	8102	8109	8116	8122
65	8129	8136	8142	8149	8156	8162	8169	8176	8182	8189
66	8195	8202	8209	8215	8222	8228	8235	8241	8248	8254
67	8261	8267	8274	8280	8287	8293	8299	8306	8312	8219
68	8325	8331	8338	8344	8351	8357	8363	8370	8376	8382
69	8388	8395	8401	8407	8414	8420	8426	8432	8439	8445
70	8451	8457	8463	8470	8476	8482	8488	8494	8500	8506
71	8513	8519	8525	8531	8537	8543	8549	8555	8561	8567
72	8573	8579	8585	8591	8597	8603	8609	8615	8621	8627
73	8633	8639	8645	8651	8657	8663	8669	8675	8681	8686
74	8692	8698	8704	8710	8716	8722	8727	8733	8739	8745
75	8751	8756	8762	8768	8774	8779	8785	8791	8797	8802
76	8808	8814	8820	8825	8831	8837	8842	8848	8854	8859
77	8865	8871	8876	8882	8887	8893	8899	8904	8910	8915
78	8921	8927	8932	8938	8943	8949	8954	8960	8965	8971
79	8976	8982	8987	8993	8998	9004	9009	9015	9020	9025
80	9031	9036	9042	9047	9053	9058	9063	9069	9074	9079
81	9085	9090	9096	9101	9106	9112	9117	9122	9128	9133
82	9138	9143	9149	9154	9159	9165	9170	9175	9180	9186
83	9191	9196	9201	9206	9212	9217	9222	9227	9232	9238
84	9243	9248	9253	9258	9263	9269	9274	9279	9284	9289
85	9294	9299	9304	9309	9315	9320	9325	9330	9335	9340
86	9345	9350	9355	9360	9365	9370	9375	9380	9385	9390
87	9395	9400	9405	9410	9415	9420	9425	9430	9435	9440
88	9445	9450	9455	9460	9465	9469	9474	9479	9484	9489
89	9494	9499	9504	9509	9513	9518	9523	9528	9533	9538
90	9542	9547	9552	9557	9562	9566	9571	9576	9581	9586
91	9590	9595	9600	9605	9609	9614	9619	9624	9628	9633
92	9638	9643	9647	9652	9657	9661	9666	9671	9675	9680
93	9685	9689	9694	9699	9703	9708	9713	9717	9722	9727
94	9731	9736	9741	9745	9750	9754	9759	9763	9768	9773
95	9777	9782	9786	9791	9795	9800	9805	9809	9814	9818
96	9823	9827	9832	9836	9841	9845	9850	9854	9859	9863
97	9868	9872	9877	9881	9886	9890	9894	9899	9903	9908
98	9912	9917	9921	9926	9930	9934	9939	9943	9948	9952
99	9956	9961	9965	9969	9974	9978	9983	9987	9991	9996

Source: John E. Freund and Frank J. Williams, *Modern Business Statistics*, 1958. Reprinted by permission of Prentice-Hall, Inc., Englewood Cliffs, N.J.

TABLE B.5 TABLE OF SQUARES AND SQUARE ROOTS

Number	Square	Square Root	Number	Square	Square Root
1	1	1.0000	41	16 81	6.4031
2	4	1.4142	42	17 64	6.4807
3	9	1.7321	43	18 49	6.5574
4	16	2.0000	44	19 36	6.6332
5	25	2.2361	45	20 25	6.7082
6	36	2.4495	46	21 16	6.7823
7	49	2.6458	47	22 09	6.8557
8	64	2.8284	48	23 04	6.9282
9	81	3.0000	49	24 01	7.0000
10	1 00	3.1623	50	25 00	7.0711
11	1 21	3.3166	51	26 01	7.1414
12	1 44	3.4641	52	27 04	7.2111
13	1 69	3.6056	53	28 09	7.2801
14	1 96	3.7417	54	29 16	7.3485
15	2 25	3.8730	55	30 25	7.4162
16	2 56	4.0000	56	31 36	7.4833
17	2 89	4.1231	57	32 49	7.5498
18	3 24	4.2426	58	33 64	7.6158
19	3 61	4.3589	59	34 81	7.6811
20	4 00	4.4721	60	36 00	7.7460
21	4 41	4.5826	61	37 21	7.8102
22	4 84	4.6904	62	38 44	7.8740
23	5 29	4.7958	63	39 69	7.9373
24	5 76	4.8990	64	40 96	8.0000
25	6 25	5.0000	65	42 25	8.0623
26	6 76	5.0990	66	43 56	8.1240
27	7 29	5.1962	67	44 89	8.1854
28	7 84	5.2915	68	46 24	8.2462
29	8 41	5.3852	69	47 61	8.3066
30	9 00	5.4772	70	49 00	8.3666
31	9 61	5.5678	71	50 41	8.4261
32	10 24	5.6569	72	51 84	8.4853
33	10 89	5.7446	73	53 29	8.5440
34	11 56	5.8310	74	54 76	8.6023
35	12 25	5.9161	75	56 25	8.6603
36	12 96	6.0000	76	57 76	8.7178
37	13 69	6.0828	77	59 29	8.7750
38	14 44	6.1644	78	60 84	8.8318
39	15 21	6.2450	79	62 41	8.8882
40	16 00	6.3246	80	64 00	8.9443

Source: H. Sorenson, *Statistics for Students of Psychology and Education*, McGraw-Hill Book Company, 1936, used with permission.

TABLE B.5 (*Continued*)

Number	Square	Square Root	Number	Square	Square Root
81	65 61	9.0000	121	1 46 41	11.0000
82	67 24	9.0554	122	1 48 84	11.0454
83	68 89	9.1104	123	1 51 29	11.0905
84	70 56	9.1652	124	1 53 76	11.1355
85	72 25	9.2195	125	1 56 25	11.1803
86	73 96	9.2736	126	1 58 76	11.2250
87	75 69	9.3274	127	1 61 29	11.2694
88	77 44	9.3808	128	1 63 84	11.3137
89	79 21	9.4340	129	1 66 41	11.3578
90	81 00	9.4868	130	1 69 00	11.4018
91	82 81	9.5394	131	1 71 61	11.4455
92	84 64	9.5917	132	1 74 24	11.4891
93	86 49	9.6437	133	1 76 89	11.5326
94	88 36	9.6954	134	1 79 56	11.5758
95	90 25	9.7468	135	1 82 25	11.6190
96	92 16	9.7980	136	1 84 96	11.6619
97	94 09	9.8489	137	1 87 69	11.7047
98	96 04	9.8995	138	1 90 44	11.7473
99	98 01	9.9499	139	1 93 21	11.7898
100	1 00 00	10.0000	140	1 96 00	11.8322
101	1 02 01	10.0499	141	1 98 81	11.8743
102	1 04 04	10.0995	142	2 01 64	11.9164
103	1 06 09	10.1489	143	2 04 49	11.9583
104	1 08 16	10.1980	144	2 07 36	12.0000
105	1 10 25	10.2470	145	2 10 25	12.0416
106	1 12 36	10.2956	146	2 13 16	12.0830
107	1 14 49	10.3441	147	2 16 09	12.1244
108	1 16 64	10.3923	148	2 19 04	12.1655
109	1 18 81	10.4403	149	2 22 01	12.2066
110	1 21 00	10.4881	150	2 25 00	12.2474
111	1 23 21	10.5357	151	2 28 01	12.2882
112	1 25 44	10.5830	152	2 31 04	12.3288
113	1 27 69	10.6301	153	2 34 09	12.3693
114	1 29 96	10.6771	154	2 37 16	12.4097
115	1 32 25	10.7238	155	2 40 25	12.4499
116	1 34 56	10.7703	156	2 43 36	12.4900
117	1 36 89	10.8167	157	2 46 49	12.5300
118	1 39 24	10.8628	158	2 49 64	12.5698
119	1 41 61	10.9087	159	2 52 81	12.6095
120	1 44 00	10.9545	160	2 56 00	12.6491

Source: H. Sorenson, *Statistics for Students of Psychology and Education*, McGraw-Hill Book Company, 1936, used with permission.

TABLE B.5 (*Continued*)

Number	Square	Square Root	Number	Square	Square Root
161	2 59 21	12.6886	201	4 04 01	14.1774
162	2 62 44	12.7279	202	4 08 04	14.2127
163	2 65 69	12.7671	203	4 12 09	14.2478
164	2 68 96	12.8062	204	4 16 16	14.2829
165	2 72 25	12.8452	205	4 20 25	14.3178
166	2 75 56	12.8841	206	4 24 36	14.3527
167	2 78 89	12.9228	207	4 28 49	14.3875
168	2 82 24	12.9615	208	4 32 64	14.4222
169	2 85 61	13.0000	209	4 36 81	14.4568
170	2 89 00	13.0384	210	4 41 00	14.4914
171	2 92 41	13.0767	211	4 45 21	14.5258
172	2 95 84	13.1149	212	4 49 44	14.5602
173	2 99 29	13.1529	213	4 53 69	14.5945
174	3 02 76	13.1909	214	4 57 96	14.6287
175	3 06 25	13.2288	215	4 62 25	14.6629
176	3 09 76	13.2665	216	4 66 56	14.6969
177	3 13 29	13.3041	217	4 70 89	14.7309
178	3 16 84	13.3417	218	4 75 24	14.7648
179	3 20 41	13.3791	219	4 79 61	14.7986
180	3 24 00	13.4164	220	4 84 00	14.8324
181	3 27 61	13.4536	221	4 88 41	14.8661
182	3 31 24	13.4907	222	4 92 84	14.8997
183	3 34 89	13.5277	223	4 97 29	14.9332
184	3 38 56	13.5647	224	5 01 76	14.9666
185	3 42 25	13.6015	225	5 06 25	15.0000
186	3 45 96	13.6382	226	5 10 76	15.0333
187	3 49 69	13.6748	227	5 15 29	15.0665
188	3 53 44	13.7113	228	5 19 84	15.0997
189	3 57 21	13.7477	229	5 24 41	15.1327
190	3 61 00	13.7840	230	5 29 00	15.1658
191	3 64 81	13.8203	231	5 33 61	15.1987
192	3 68 64	13.8564	232	5 38 24	15.2315
193	3 72 49	13.8924	233	5 42 89	15.2643
194	3 76 36	13.9284	234	5 47 56	15.2971
195	3 80 25	13.9642	235	5 52 25	15.3297
196	3 84 16	14.0000	236	5 56 96	15.3623
197	3 88 09	14.0357	237	5 61 69	15.3948
198	3 92 04	14.0712	238	5 66 44	15.4272
199	3 96 01	14.1067	239	5 71 21	15.4596
200	4 00 00	14.1421	240	5 76 00	15.4919

Source: H. Sorenson, *Statistics for Students of Psychology and Education*, McGraw-Hill Book Company, 1936, used with permission.

TABLE B.5 (*Continued*)

Number	Square	Square Root	Number	Square	Square Root
241	5 80 81	15.5242	281	7 89 61	16.7631
242	5 85 64	15.5563	282	7 95 24	16.7929
243	5 90 49	15.5885	283	8 00 89	16.8226
244	5 95 36	15.6205	284	8 06 56	16.8523
245	6 00 25	15.6525	285	8 12 25	16.8819
246	6 05 16	15.6844	286	8 17 96	16.9115
247	6 10 09	15.7162	287	8 23 69	16.9411
248	6 15 04	15.7480	288	8 29 44	16.9706
249	6 20 01	15.7797	289	8 35 21	17.0000
250	6 25 00	15.8114	290	8 41 00	17.0294
251	6 30 01	15.8430	291	8 46 81	17.0587
252	6 35 04	15.8745	292	8 52 64	17.0880
253	6 40 09	15.9060	293	8 58 49	17.1172
254	6 45 16	15.9374	294	8 64 36	17.1464
255	6 50 25	15.9687	295	8 70 25	17.1756
256	6 55 36	16.0000	296	8 76 16	17.2047
257	6 60 49	16.0312	297	8 82 09	17.2337
258	6 65 64	16.0624	298	8 88 04	17.2627
259	6 70 81	16.0935	299	8 94 01	17.2916
260	6 76 00	16.1245	300	9 00 00	17.3205
261	6 81 21	16.1555	301	9 06 01	17.3494
262	6 86 44	16.1864	302	9 12 04	17.3781
263	6 91 69	16.2173	303	9 18 09	17.4069
264	6 96 96	16.2481	304	9 24 16	17.4356
265	7 02 25	16.2788	305	9 30 25	17.4642
266	7 07 56	16.3095	306	9 36 36	17.4929
267	7 12 89	16.3401	307	9 42 49	17.5214
268	7 18 24	16.3707	308	9 48 64	17.5499
269	7 23 61	16.4012	309	9 54 81	17.5784
270	7 29 00	16.4317	310	9 61 00	17.6068
271	7 34 41	16.4621	311	9 67 21	17.6352
272	7 39 84	16.4924	312	9 73 44	17.6635
273	7 45 29	16.5227	313	9 79 69	17.6918
274	7 50 76	16.5529	314	9 85 96	17.7200
275	7 56 25	16.5831	315	9 92 25	17.7482
276	7 61 76	16.6132	316	9 98 56	17.7764
277	7 67 29	16.6433	317	10 04 89	17.8045
278	7 72 84	16.6733	318	10 11 24	17.8326
279	7 78 41	16.7033	319	10 17 61	17.8606
280	7 84 00	16.7332	320	10 24 00	17.8885

Source: H. Sorenson, *Statistics for Students of Psychology and Education*, McGraw-Hill Book Company, 1936, used with permission.

TABLE B.5 (*Continued*)

Number	Square	Square Root	Number	Square	Square Root
321	10 30 41	17.9165	361	13 03 21	19.0000
322	10 36 84	17.9444	362	13 10 44	19.0263
233	10 43 29	17.9722	363	13 17 69	19.0526
324	10 49 76	18.0000	364	13 24 96	19.0788
325	10 56 25	18.0278	365	13 32 25	19.1050
326	10 62 76	18.0555	366	13 39 56	19.1311
327	10 69 29	18.0831	367	13 46 89	19.1572
328	10 75 84	18.1108	368	13 54 24	19.1833
329	10 82 41	18.1384	369	13 61 61	19.2094
330	10 89 00	18.1659	370	13 69 00	19.2354
331	10 95 61	18.1934	371	13 76 41	19.2614
332	11 02 24	18.2209	372	13 83 84	19.2873
333	11 08 89	18.2483	373	13 91 29	19.3132
334	11 15 56	18.2757	374	13 98 76	19.3391
335	11 22 25	18.3030	375	14 06 25	19.3649
336	11 28 96	18.3303	376	14 13 76	19.3907
337	11 35 69	18.3576	377	14 21 29	19.4165
338	11 42 44	18.3848	378	14 28 84	19.4422
339	11 49 21	18.4120	379	14 36 41	19.4679
340	11 56 00	18.4391	380	14 44 00	19.4936
341	11 62 81	18.4662	381	14 51 61	19.5192
342	11 69 64	18.4932	382	14 59 24	19.5448
343	11 76 49	18.5203	383	14 66 89	19.5704
344	11 83 36	18.5472	384	14 74 56	19.5959
345	11 90 25	18.5742	385	14 82 25	19.6214
346	11 97 16	18.6011	386	14 89 96	19.6469
347	12 04 09	18.6279	387	14 97 69	19.6723
348	12 11 04	18.6548	388	15 05 44	19.6977
349	12 18 01	18.6815	389	15 13 21	19.7231
350	12 25 00	18.7083	390	15 21 00	19.7484
351	12 32 01	18.7350	391	15 28 81	19.7737
352	12 39 04	18.7617	392	15 36 64	19.7990
353	12 46 09	18.7883	393	15 44 49	19.8242
354	12 53 16	18.8149	394	15 52 36	19.8494
355	12 60 25	18.8414	395	15 60 25	19.8746
356	12 67 36	18.8680	396	15 68 16	19.8997
357	12 74 49	18.8944	397	15 76 09	19.9249
358	12 81 64	18.9209	398	15 84 04	19.9499
359	12 88 81	18.9473	399	15 92 01	19.9750
360	12 96 00	18.9737	400	16 00 00	20.0000

Source: H. Sorenson, *Statistics for Students of Psychology and Education*, McGraw-Hill Book Company, 1936, used with permission.

TABLE B.5 (*Continued*)

Number	Square	Square Root	Number	Square	Square Root
401	16 08 01	20.0250	441	19 44 81	21.0000
402	16 16 04	20.0499	442	19 53 64	21.0238
403	16 24 09	20.0749	443	19 62 49	21.0476
404	16 32 16	20.0998	444	19 71 36	21.0713
405	16 40 25	20.1246	445	19 80 25	21.0950
406	16 48 36	20.1494	446	19 89 16	21.1187
407	16 56 49	20.1742	447	19 98 09	21.1424
408	16 64 64	20.1990	448	20 07 04	21.1660
409	16 72 81	20.2237	449	20 16 01	21.1896
410	16 81 00	20.2485	450	20 25 00	21.2132
411	16 89 21	20.2731	451	20 34 01	21.2368
412	16 97 44	20.2978	452	20 43 04	21.2603
413	17 05 69	20.3224	453	20 52 09	21.2838
414	17 13 96	20.3470	454	20 61 16	21.3073
415	17 22 25	20.3715	455	20 70 25	21.3307
416	17 30 56	20.3961	456	20 79 36	21.3542
417	17 38 89	20.4206	457	20 88 49	21.3776
418	17 47 24	20.4450	458	20 97 64	21.4009
419	17 55 61	20.4695	459	21 06 81	21.4243
420	17 64 00	20.4939	460	21 16 00	21.4476
421	17 72 41	20.5183	461	21 25 21	21.4709
422	17 80 84	20.5426	462	21 34 44	21.4942
423	17 89 29	20.5670	463	21 43 69	21.5174
424	17 97 76	20.5913	464	21 52 96	21.5407
425	18 06 25	20.6155	465	21 62 25	21.5639
426	18 14 76	20.6398	466	21 71 56	21.5870
427	18 23 29	20.6640	467	21 80 89	21.6102
428	18 31 84	20.6882	468	21 90 24	21.6333
429	18 40 41	20.7123	469	21 99 61	21.6564
430	18 49 00	20.7364	470	22 09 00	21.6795
431	18 57 61	20.7605	471	22 18 41	21.7025
432	18 66 24	20.7846	472	22 27 84	21.7256
433	18 74 89	20.8087	473	22 37 29	21.7486
434	18 83 56	22.8327	474	22 46 76	21.7715
435	18 92 25	20.8567	475	22 56 25	21.7945
436	19 00 96	20.8806	476	22 65 76	21.8174
437	19 09 69	20.9045	477	22 75 29	21.8403
438	19 18 44	20.9284	478	22 84 84	21.8632
439	19 27 21	20.9523	479	22 94 41	21.8861
440	19 36 00	20.9762	480	23.04 00	21.9089

Source: H. Sorenson, *Statistics for Students of Psychology and Education*, McGraw-Hill Book Company, 1936, used with permission.

TABLE B.5 (*Continued*)

Number	Square	Square Root	Number	Square	Square Root
481	23 13 61	21.9317	521	27 14 41	22.8254
482	23 23 24	21.9545	522	27 24 84	22.8473
483	23 32 89	21.9773	523	27 35 29	22.8692
484	23 42 56	22.0000	524	27 45 76	22.8910
485	23 52 25	22.0227	525	27 56 25	22.9129
486	23 61 96	22.0454	526	27 66 76	22.9347
487	23 71 69	22.0681	527	27 77 29	22.9565
488	23 81 44	22.0907	528	27 87 84	22.9783
489	23 91 21	22.1133	529	27 98 41	23.0000
490	24 01 00	22.1359	530	28 09 00	23.0217
491	24 10 81	22.1585	531	28 19 61	23.0434
492	24 20 64	22.1811	532	28 30 24	23.0651
493	24 30 49	22.2036	533	28 40 89	23.0868
494	24 40 36	22.2261	534	28 51 56	23.1084
495	24 50 25	22.2486	535	28 62 25	23.1301
496	24 60 16	22.2711	536	28 72 96	23.1517
497	24 70 09	22.2935	537	28 83 69	23.1733
498	24 80 04	22.3159	538	28 94 44	23.1948
499	24 90 01	22.3383	539	29 05 21	23.2164
500	25 00 00	22.3607	540	29 16 00	23.2379
501	25 10 01	22.3830	541	29 26 81	23.2594
502	25 20 04	22.4054	542	29 37 64	23.2809
503	25 30 09	22.4277	543	29 48 49	23.3024
504	25 40 16	22.4499	544	29 59 36	23.3238
505	25 50 25	22.4722	545	29 70 25	23.3452
506	25 60 36	22.4944	546	29 81 16	23.3666
507	25 70 49	22.5167	547	29 92 09	23.3880
508	25 80 64	22.5389	548	30 03 04	23.4094
509	25 90 81	22.5610	549	30 14 01	23.4307
510	26 01 00	22.5832	550	30 25 00	23.4521
511	26 11 21	22.6053	551	30 36 01	23.4734
512	26 21 44	22.6274	552	30 47 04	23.4947
513	26 31 69	22.6495	553	30 58 09	23.5160
514	26 41 96	22.6716	554	30 69 16	23.5372
515	26 52 25	22.6936	555	30 80 25	23.5584
516	26 62 56	22.7156	456	30 91 36	23.5797
517	26 72 89	22.7376	557	31 02 49	23.6008
518	26 83 24	22.7596	558	31 13 64	23.6220
519	26 93 61	22.7816	559	31 24 81	23.6432
520	27 04 00	22.8035	560	31 36 00	23.6643

Source: H. Sorenson, *Statistics for Students of Psychology and Education*, McGraw-Hill Book Company, 1936, used with permission.

TABLE B.5 (*Continued*)

Number	Square	Square Root	Number	Square	Square Root
561	31 47 21	23.6854	601	36 12 01	24.5153
562	31 58 44	23.7065	602	36 24 04	24.5357
563	31 69 69	23.7276	603	36 36 09	24.5561
564	31 80 96	23.7487	604	36 48 16	24.5764
565	31 92 25	23.7697	605	36 60 25	24.5967
566	32 03 56	23.7908	606	36 72 36	24.6171
567	32 14 89	23.8118	607	36 84 49	24.6374
568	32 26 24	23.8328	608	36 96 64	24.6577
569	32 37 61	23.8537	609	37 08 81	24.6779
570	32 49 00	23.8747	610	37 21 00	24.6982
571	32 60 41	23.8956	611	37 33 21	24.7184
572	32 71 84	23.9165	612	37 45 44	24.7385
573	32 83 29	23.9374	613	37 57 69	24.7588
574	32 94 76	23.9583	614	37 69 96	24.7790
575	33 06 25	23.9792	615	37 82 25	24.7992
576	33 17 76	24.0000	616	37 94 56	24.8193
577	33 29 29	24.0208	617	38 06 89	24.8395
578	33 40 84	24.0416	618	38 19 24	24.8596
579	33 52 41	24.0624	619	38 31 61	24.8797
580	33 64 00	24.0832	620	38 44 00	24.8998
581	33 75 61	24.1039	621	38 56 41	24.9199
582	33 87 24	24.1247	622	38 68 84	24.9399
583	33 98 89	24.1454	623	38 81 29	24.9600
584	34 10 56	24.1661	624	38 93 76	24.9800
585	34 22 25	24.1868	625	39 06 25	25.0000
586	34 33 96	24.2074	626	39 18 76	25.0200
587	34 45 69	24.2281	627	39 31 29	25.0400
588	34 57 44	24.2487	628	39 43 84	25.0599
589	34 69 21	24.2693	629	39 56 41	25.0799
590	34 81 00	24.2899	630	39 69 00	25.0998
591	34 92 81	24.3105	631	39 81 61	25.1197
592	35 04 64	24.3311	632	39 94 24	25.1396
593	35 16 49	24.3516	633	40 06 89	25.1595
594	35 28 36	24.3721	634	40 19 56	25.1794
595	35 40 25	24.3926	635	40 32 25	25.1992
596	35 52 16	24.4131	636	40 44 96	25.2190
597	35 64 09	24.4336	637	40 57 69	25.2389
598	35 76 04	24.4540	638	40 70 44	25.2587
599	35 88 01	24.4745	639	40 83 21	25.2784
600	36 00 00	24.4949	640	40 96 00	25.2982

Source: H. Sorenson, *Statistics for Students of Psychology and Education*, McGraw-Hill Book Company, 1936, used with permission.

TABLE B.5 (*Continued*)

Number	Square	Square Root	Number	Square	Square Root
641	41 08 81	25.3180	681	46 37 61	26.0960
642	41 21 64	25.3377	682	46 51 24	26.1151
643	41 34 49	25.3574	683	46 64 89	26.1343
644	41 47 36	25.3772	684	46 78 56	26.1534
645	41 60 25	25.3969	685	46 92 25	26.1725
646	41 73 16	25.4165	686	47 05 96	26.1916
647	41 86 09	25.4362	687	47 19 69	26.2107
648	41 99 04	25.4558	688	47 33 44	26.2298
649	42 12 01	25.4755	689	47 47 21	26.2488
650	42 25 00	25.4951	690	47 61 00	26.2679
651	42 38 01	25.5147	691	47 74 81	26.2869
652	42 51 04	25.5343	692	47 88 64	26.3059
653	42 64 09	25.5539	693	48 02 49	26.3249
654	42 77 16	25.5734	694	48 16 36	26.3439
655	42 90 25	25.5930	695	48 30 25	26.3629
656	43 03 36	25.6125	696	48 44 16	26.3818
657	43 16 49	25.6320	697	48 58 09	26.4008
658	43 29 64	25.6515	698	48 72 04	26.4197
659	43 42 81	25.6710	699	48 86 01	26.4386
660	43 56 00	25.6905	700	49 00 00	26.4575
661	43 69 21	25.7099	701	49 14 01	26.4764
662	43 82 44	25.7294	702	49 28 04	26.4953
663	43 95 69	25.7488	703	49 42 09	26.5141
664	44 08 96	25.7682	704	49 56 16	26.5330
665	44 22 25	25.7876	705	49 70 25	26.5518
666	44 35 56	25.8070	706	49 84 36	26.5707
667	44 48 89	25.8263	707	49 98 49	26.5895
668	44 62 24	25.8457	708	50 12 64	26.6083
669	44 75 61	25.8650	709	50 26 81	26.6271
670	44 89 00	25.8844	710	50 41 00	26.6458
671	45 02 41	25.9037	711	50 55 21	26.6646
672	45 15 84	25.9230	712	50 69 44	26.6833
673	45 29 29	25.9422	713	50 83 69	26.7021
674	45 42 76	25.9615	714	50 97 96	26.7208
675	45 56 25	25.9808	715	51 12 25	26.7395
676	45 69 76	26.0000	716	51 26 56	26.7582
677	45 83 29	26.0192	717	51 40 89	26.7769
678	45 96 84	26.0384	718	51 55 24	26.7955
679	46 10 41	26.0576	719	51 69 61	26.8142
680	46 24 00	26.0768	720	51 84 00	26.8328

Source: H. Sorenson, *Statistics for Students of Psychology and Education*, McGraw-Hill Book Company, 1936, used with permission.

TABLE B.5 (*Continued*)

Number	Square	Square Root	Number	Square	Square Root
721	51 98 41	26.8514	761	57 91 21	27.5862
722	52 12 84	26.8701	762	58 06 44	27.6043
723	52 27 29	26.8887	763	58 21 69	27.6225
724	52 41 76	26.9072	764	58 36 96	27.6405
725	52 56 25	26.9258	765	58 52 25	27.6586
726	52 70 76	26.9444	766	58 67 56	27.6767
727	52 85 29	26.9629	767	58 82 89	27.6948
728	52 99 84	26.9815	768	58 98 24	27.7128
729	53 14 41	27.0000	769	59 13 61	27.7308
730	53 29 00	27.0185	770	59 29 00	27.7489
731	53 43 61	27.0370	771	59 44 41	27.7669
732	53 58 24	27.0555	772	59 59 84	27.7849
733	53 72 89	27.0740	773	59 75 29	27.8029
734	53 87 56	27.0924	774	59 90 76	27.8209
735	54 02 25	27.1109	775	60 06 25	27.8388
736	54 16 96	27.1293	776	60 21 76	27.8568
737	54 31 69	27.1477	777	60 37 29	27.8747
738	54 46 44	27.1662	778	60 52 84	27.8927
739	54 61 27	27.1846	779	60 68 41	27.9106
740	54 76 00	27.2029	780	60 84 00	27.9285
741	54 90 81	27.2213	781	60 99 61	27.9464
742	55 05 64	27.2397	782	61 15 24	27.9643
743	55 20 49	27.2580	783	61 30 89	27.9821
744	55 35 36	27.2764	784	61 46 56	28.0000
745	55 50 25	27.2947	785	61 62 25	28.0179
746	55 65 16	27.3130	786	61 77 96	28.0357
747	55 80 09	27.3313	787	61 93 69	28.0535
748	55 95 04	27.3496	788	62 09 44	28.0713
749	56 10 01	27.3679	789	62 25 21	28.0891
750	56 25 00	27.3861	790	62 41 00	28.1069
751	56 40 01	27.4044	791	62 56 81	28.1247
752	56 55 04	27.4226	792	62 72 64	28.1425
753	56 70 09	27.4408	793	62 88 49	28.1603
754	56 85 16	27.4591	794	63 04 36	28.1780
755	57 00 25	27.4773	795	63 20 25	28.1957
756	57 15 36	27.4955	796	63 36 16	28.2135
757	57 30 49	27.5136	797	63 52 09	28.2312
758	57 45 64	27.5318	798	63 68 04	28.2489
759	57 60 81	27.5500	799	63 84 01	28.2666
760	57 76 00	27.5681	800	64 00 00	28.2843

Source: H. Sorenson, *Statistics for Students of Psychology and Education*, McGraw-Hill Book Company, 1936, used with permission.

TABLE B.5 (*Continued*)

Number	Square	Square Root	Number	Square	Square Root
801	64 16 01	28.3019	841	70 72 81	29.0000
802	64 32 04	28.3196	842	70 89 64	29.0172
803	64 48 09	28.3373	843	71 06 49	29.0345
804	64 64 16	28.3049	844	71 23 36	29.0517
805	64 80 25	28.3725	845	71 40 25	29.0689
806	64 96 36	28.3901	846	71 57 16	29.0861
807	65 12 49	28.4077	847	71 74 09	29.1033
808	65 28 64	28.4253	848	71 91 04	29.1204
809	65 44 81	28.4429	849	72 08 01	29.1376
810	65 61 00	28.4605	850	72 25 00	29.1548
811	65 77 21	28.4781	851	72 42 01	29.1719
812	65 93 44	28.4956	852	72 59 04	29.1890
813	66 09 69	28.5132	853	72 76 09	29.2062
814	66 25 96	28.5307	854	72 93 16	29.2233
815	66 42 25	28.5482	855	73 10 25	29.2404
816	66 58 56	28.5657	856	73 27 36	29.2575
817	66 74 89	28.5832	857	73 44 49	29.2746
818	66 91 24	28.6007	858	73 61 64	29.2916
819	67 07 61	28.6082	859	73 78 81	29.3087
820	67 24 00	28.6356	860	73 96 00	29.3258
821	67 40 41	28.6531	861	74 13 21	29.3428
822	67 56 84	28.6705	862	74 30 44	29.3598
823	67 73 29	28.6880	863	74 47 69	29.3769
824	67 89 76	28.7054	864	74 64 96	29.3939
825	68 06 25	28.7228	865	74 82 25	29.4109
826	68 22 76	28.7402	866	74 99 56	29.4279
827	68 39 29	28.7576	867	75 16 89	29.4449
828	68 55 84	28.7750	868	75 34 24	29.4618
829	68 72 41	28.7924	869	75 51 61	29.4788
830	68 89 00	28.8097	870	75 69 00	29.4958
831	69 05 61	28.8271	871	75 86 41	29.5127
832	69 22 24	28.8444	872	76 03 84	29.5296
833	69 38 89	28.8617	873	76 21 29	29.5466
834	69 55 56	28.8791	874	76 38 76	29.5635
835	69 72 25	28.8964	875	76 56 25	29.5804
836	69 88 96	28.9137	876	76 73 76	29.5973
837	70 05 69	28.9310	877	76 91 29	29.6142
838	70 22 44	28.9482	878	77 08 84	29.6311
839	70 39 21	28.9655	879	77 26 41	29.6479
840	70 56 00	28.9828	880	77 44 00	29.6648

Source: H. Sorenson, *Statistics for Students of Psychology and Education*, McGraw-Hill Book Company, 1936, used with permission.

TABLE B.5 (*Continued*)

Number	Square	Square Root	Number	Square	Square Root
881	77 61 61	29.6816	921	84 82 41	30.3480
882	77 79 24	29.6985	922	85 00 84	30.3645
883	77 96 89	29.7153	923	85 19 29	30.3809
884	78 14 56	29.7321	924	85 37 76	30.3974
885	78 32 25	29.7489	925	85 56 25	30.4138
886	78 49 96	29.7658	926	85 74 76	30.4302
887	78 67 69	29.7825	927	85 93 29	30.4467
888	78 85 44	29.7993	928	86 11 84	30.4631
889	79 03 21	29.8161	929	86 30 41	30.4795
890	79 21 00	29.8329	930	86 49 00	30.4959
891	79 38 81	29.8496	931	86 67 61	30.5123
892	79 56 64	29.8664	932	86 86 24	30.5287
893	79 74 49	29.8831	933	87 04 89	30.5450
894	79 92 36	29.8998	934	87 23 56	30.5614
895	80 10 25	29.9166	935	87 42 25	30.5778
896	80 28 16	29.9333	936	87 60 96	30.5941
897	80 46 09	29.9500	937	87 79 69	30.6105
898	80 64 04	29.9666	938	87 98 44	30.6268
899	80 82 01	29.9833	939	88 17 21	30.6431
900	81 00 00	30.0000	940	88 36 00	30.6594
901	81 18 01	30.0167	941	88 54 81	30.6757
902	81 36 04	30.0333	942	88 73 64	30.6920
903	81 54 09	30.0500	943	88 92 49	30.7083
904	81 72 16	30.0666	944	89 11 36	30.7246
905	81 90 25	30.0832	945	89 30 25	30.7409
906	82 08 36	30.0998	946	89 49 16	30.7571
907	82 26 49	30.1164	947	89 68 09	30.7734
908	82 44 64	30.1330	948	89 87 04	30.7896
909	82 62 81	30.1496	949	90 06 01	30.8058
910	82 81 00	30.1662	950	90 25 00	30.8221
911	82 99 21	30.1828	951	90 44 01	30.8383
912	83 17 44	30.1993	952	90 63 04	30.8545
913	83 35 69	30.2159	953	90 82 09	30.8707
914	83 53 96	30.2324	954	91 01 16	30.8869
915	83 72 25	30.2490	955	91 20 25	30.9031
916	83 90 56	30.2655	956	91 39 36	30.9192
917	84 08 89	30.2820	957	91 58 49	30.9354
918	84 27 24	30.2985	958	91 77 64	30.9516
919	84 45 61	30.3150	959	91 96 81	30.9677
920	84 64 00	30.3315	960	92 16 00	30.9839

Source: H. Sorenson, *Statistics for Students of Psychology and Education*, McGraw-Hill Book Company, 1936, used with permission.

TABLE B.5 (*Continued*)

Number	Square	Square Root	Number	Square	Square Root
961	92 35 21	31.0000	981	96 23 61	31.3209
962	92 54 44	31.0161	982	96 43 24	31.3369
963	92 73 69	31.0322	983	96 62 89	31.3528
964	92 92 96	31.0483	984	96 82 56	31.3688
965	93 12 25	31.0644	985	97 02 25	31.3847
966	93 31 56	31.0805	986	97 21 96	31.4006
967	93 50 89	31.0966	987	97 41 69	31.4166
968	93 70 24	31.1127	988	97 61 44	31.4325
969	93 89 61	31.1288	989	97 81 21	31.4484
970	94 09 00	31.1448	990	98 01 00	31.4643
971	94 28 41	31.1609	991	98 20 81	31.4802
972	94 47 84	31.1769	992	98 40 64	31.4960
973	94 67 29	31.1929	993	98 60 49	31.5119
974	94 86 76	31.2090	994	98 80 36	31.5278
975	95 06 25	31.2250	995	99 00 25	31.5436
976	95 25 76	31.2410	996	99 20 16	31.5595
977	95 45 29	31.2570	997	99 40 09	31.5753
978	95 64 84	31.2730	998	99 60 04	31.5911
979	95 84 41	31.2890	999	99 80 01	31.6070
980	96 04 00	31.3050	1000	100 00 00	31.6228

Source: H. Sorenson, *Statistics for Students of Psychology and Education*, McGraw-Hill Book Company, 1936, used with permission.

ANSWERS TO EVEN-NUMBERED PROBLEMS

(Your answer may differ from the answer shown due to rounding.)

SECTION 2.6 (*Page 21*)

6. (a) $\sum_{i=1}^{7} Y_i$ (b) $\sum_{i=1}^{M} R_i$ (c) $\sum_{i=3}^{6} (a_i - X_i)$

(d) $\sum_{i=1}^{4} X_i Y_i$ (e) $\sum_{i=1}^{4} \frac{X_i + Y_i}{k}$ (f) $\sum_{i=3}^{5} (Y_i - Z_i - X_i)$

(g) $\sum_{i=1}^{N} \frac{1}{2} X_i Y_i$ (h) $\sum_{i=4}^{12} X_i(Y_i - Z_i)$

(i) $\sum_{i=1}^{100} [Z_i(4 - Y_i) - X_i]$ (j) $\sum_{i=1}^{8} a$

8. (a) $\sum_{i=1}^{N} X_i - \sum_{i=1}^{N} Z_i + \sum_{i=1}^{N} Y_i$ (b) $\frac{a}{2}\left(\sum_{i=1}^{N} X_i - Nk\right)$

(c) $\sum_{i=2}^{20} \frac{Z_i}{M_i} + \sum_{i=2}^{20} \frac{Y_i}{X_i}$ (d) $\sum_{i=1}^{T} X_i Y_i + 4 \sum_{i=1}^{T} X_i + T(k - 3)$

(e) Gk (f) $\frac{1}{8}\left(\sum_{i=10}^{30} X_i Y_i - \sum_{i=10}^{30} Z_i\right)$

(g) $(11)(10) = 110$

SECTION 3.3 (*Page 50*)

4. Class midpoints: 107, 112, 117, 122, 127, 132. Continuous class limits: 104.5, 109.5, 114.5, 119.5, 124.5, 129.5, 134.5. Length of class interval: 5.

6. Class midpoints: .007, .012, .017, .022, .027. Continuous class limits: .0045, .0095, .0145, .0195, .0245, .0295. Class interval: .005.

8. (a) 23.95, 26.95, 29.95, 32.95, 35.95, 38.95, 41.95, 44.95. (b) 25.45, 28.45, 31.45, 34.45, 37.45, 40.45, 43.45. (c) 100, 97, 80, 60, 30, 15, 4, 0. (d) 0, 3, 20, 40, 70, 85, 96, 100. (e) .03, .17, .20, .30, .15, .11, .04. (f) 1.00, .97, .80, .60, .30, .15, .04, 0. (g) 0, .03, .20, .40, .70, .85, .96, 1.00.

10. (a) 1.245, 1.495, 1.745, 1.995, 2.245, 2.495. (b) 1.37, 1.62, 1.87, 2.12, 2.37. (c) 50, ,36 25, 21, 13, 0. (d) 0, 14, 25, 29, 37, 50. (e) .28, .22, .08, .16, .26. (f) 1.00, .72, .50, .42, .26, 0. (g) 0, .28, .50, .58, .74, 1.00.

SECTION 3.4 (*Page 61*)

2.

Discrete Class Limits	f_i	Continuous Class Limits	Class Midpoints	More than cum f_i
		15.245		49
15.25–15.49	10		15.37	
		15.495		39
15.50–15.74	7		15.62	
		15.745		32
15.75–15.99	5		15.87	
		15.995		27
16.00–16.24	7		16.12	
		16.245		20
16.25–16.49	8		16.37	
		16.495		12
16.50–16.74	12		16.62	
		16.745		0

4.

Discrete Class Limits	f_i	Continuous Class Limits	Class Midpoints	More than cum f_i	Less than cum f_i
		19.5		113	0
20–39	4		29.5		
		39.5		109	4
40–59	4		49.5		
		59.5		105	8
60–79	5		69.5		
		79.5		100	13
80–99	8		89.5		
		99.5		92	21
100–119	11		109.5		
		119.5		81	32
120–139	21		129.5		
		139.5		60	53
140–159	28		149.5		
		159.5		32	81
160–179	32		169.5		
		179.5		0	113

6.

Discrete Class Limits	f_i	Continuous Class Limits	Class Midpoints	More than cum f_i	Less than cum f_i
		79.5		325	0
80–81	15		80.5		
		81.5		310	15
82–83	23		82.5		
		83.5		287	38
84–85	31		84.5		
		85.5		256	69
86–87	36		86.5		
		87.5		220	105
88–89	55		88.5		
		89.5		165	160
90–91	62		90.5		
		91.5		103	222
92–93	51		92.5		
		93.5		52	273
94–95	30		94.5		
		95.5		22	303
96–97	22		96.5		
		97.5		0	325

SECTION 4.3 (*Page 97*)

2. (a) 5.3 (b) 25.3 (c) 3.3

4. .0229

6. 253.3

8. 136.9

10. 29.7

12. 109.51

14. 26.5

16. 53

SECTION 4.4 (*Page 105*)

2. 19.28

4. 44.8

6. .280

8. 126.92

10. 12.0777

SECTION 4.6 (*Page 116*)

2. 102

4. 18.95

6. 45.8

8. 127.08

10. 12.0584

SECTION 4.7 (*Page 120*)

2. $Q_1 = 38.7$; $Q_3 = 52.3$; $D_1 = 31.7$; $P_{35} = 41.7$; $P_{69} = 50.6$

4. $Q_1 = 2.612$; $Q_3 = 3.298$; $D_4 = 2.920$; $D_7 = 3.627$; $P_{22} = 2.562$

SECTION 4.8 (*Page 124*)

2. Crude = 17.95
Refined = 18.12

4. Crude = 47
Refined = 47.1

SECTION 4.9 (*Page 130*)

6. Median and mode = very good

SECTION 5.3 (*Page 156*)

2. (a) $\sigma = 1.98$ (b) $\sigma = 1.98$

4. $\sigma = .0031$

6. $\sigma = 122.8$

8. $s = 38.5$

10. $\sigma = 1.9$

SECTION 5.4 (*Page 161*)

2. 3.93 **4.** 9.1 **6.** .153

8. .75 **10.** .035

SECTION 5.7 (*Page 169*)

2. (a) Quiz 1, $V = 30.3\%$
Quiz 2, $V = 41.2\%$
(b) Quiz 1, $z_4 = -1.6$, $z_9 = .6$
Quiz 2, $z_4 = -1.0$, $z_9 = .8$

4. (a) 6.79 (b) 4.5%

SECTION 6.2 (*Page 196*)

2. (a) $\frac{4}{7}$ (b) $\frac{3}{7}$ (c) 0 (d) 1

4. (a) $\frac{3}{7}$ (b) $\frac{1}{7}$ (c) $\frac{3}{14}$ (d) $\frac{5}{14}$ (e) $\frac{2}{7}$ (f) $\frac{6}{7}$ (g) $\frac{9}{14}$

6. (a) $\frac{2}{5}$ (b) $\frac{1}{10}$ (c) $\frac{1}{2}$ (d) $\frac{7}{15}$

SECTION 6.3 (*Page 202*)

2. 24 **4.** 120 **6.** 720

8. (a) 56 (b) 56 (c) 36 (d) 36

10. 35 **12.** 924 **14.** 455

SECTION 6.4 (*Page 215*)

2. (a) $\frac{1}{2}$ (b) $\frac{5}{6}$ (c) $\frac{1}{6}$
4. $\frac{2}{3}$ **6.** .24 **8.** .57 **10.** $\frac{1}{10}$
12. (a) .04 (b) .60
14. .17
16. (a) $\frac{1}{9}$ (b) $\frac{1}{15}$ (c) $\frac{1}{3}$ (d) $\frac{7}{30}$ (e) $\frac{7}{18}$
18. (a) $\frac{1}{729}$ (b) $\frac{1}{10,710}$ (c) $\frac{1}{729}$ (d) $\frac{1}{1785}$ (e) $\frac{8}{5355}$ (f) 0
20. (a) .018 (b) .004
22. (a) .14 (b) .12
24. .53 **26.** (a) .77 (b) .68

SECTION 6.5 (*Page 223*)

2. $P(X = 0) = .25$, $P(X = 1) = .50$, $P(X = 2) = .25$
4. $P(X = 0) = .237$, $P(X = 1) = .396$, $P(X = 2) = .264$
$P(X = 3) = .088$, $P(X = 4) = .015$, $P(X = 5) = .001$

SECTION 8.3 (*Page 263*)

2. (a) .97 (b) .24 (c) .84 (d) .52 (e) .001
4. $Q_1 = 22.72$, $Q_3 = 30.80$, $D_7 = 29.90$, $P_{28} = 23.26$
6. (a) .002 (b) .045

SECTION 8.4 (*Page 271*)

2. (a) (1) .76 (a) (2) .98 (b) .66 (c) *Model A*
4. .996 **6.** (a) .59 (b) .09 (c) *Model B*
8. .83 **10.** (a) .90 (b) .038 (c) .015

SECTION 8.7 (*Page 299*)

2. (a) .33 (b) .09
4. (a) .25 (b) .05 (c) .30 (d) .30 (e) .14
6. (a) .09 (b) .002 (c) .25 (d) .08
8. $P\left(\frac{X}{n} = 0\right) = .0102$ $P\left(\frac{X}{n} = .6\right) = .3456$
$P\left(\frac{X}{n} = .2\right) = .0768$ $P\left(\frac{X}{n} = .8\right) = .2592$
$P\left(\frac{X}{n} = .4\right) = .2304$ $P\left(\frac{X}{n} = 1.0\right) = .0778$

10. (a) .06 (b) .19 (c) .04

12. (a) .03 (b) .90

14. (a) .08 (b) .02

SECTION 9.2 (*Page 316*)

2. 90.43 to 98.79

4. 21.3 to 24.9 months

6. 22.3 to 23.9 months

8. 101.8 to 116.0

SECTION 9.3 (*Page 322*)

2. 118.2 to 131.0

4. 20.6 to 33.6

6. 14.5 to 18.3 minutes

8. 1.9 minutes

10. 2.50 years

SECTION 9.4 (*Page 325*)

2. .118 to .242

4. .327 to .373

6. .028

8. .729 to .831

SECTION 9.5 (*Page 329*)

2. (a) .17
(b) .91
(c) .027
(d) .327 to .433

SECTION 9.6 (*Page 333*)

2. 384 college seniors

4. At most 9604 married men

6. 1132 high school seniors

CHAPTER 11 (*Page 372*)

2. $z = 2.00$ falls in the region of rejection. School program and teaching methods should be reviewed and appropriate adjustments made.

4. $z = -2.70$ falls in the region of rejection. The decision is made not to purchase the new readers.

6. $z = -1.02$ falls in the region of acceptance. The director should accept the claim.

8. $z = -1.02$ falls in the region of acceptance. The manufacturer decides to use .60 in his literature.

10. $z = 2.31$ falls in the region of rejection. Conclude that higher-quality freshmen have been enrolling in the college.

12. $z = 1.80$ falls in the region of rejection. The decision is made not to use the proposed new method of psychotherapy.

14. $z = 2.41$ falls in the region of acceptance. You would not reject the claim that $\mu = 150$.

16. $z = -2.69$ falls in the region of rejection. Therefore, conclude that the teacher's claim represents an overstatement of the mean time required.

18. $t = -3.10$ falls in the region of rejection. Therefore, conclude that the psychologist's claim cannot be accepted.

20. $t = -1.81$ falls in the region of rejection. Therefore, conclude that it is easier for a rat to locate the food box than claimed.

SECTION 12.2 (*Page 382*)

2. $z = 3.43$ (or -3.43) falls in the region of rejection. Do not conclude that men and women exhibit an equal amount of prejudice.

4. $z = 2.00$ (or -2.00) falls in the region of rejection. Conclude that psychotherapy is the more effective form of treatment.

6. $z = .53$ (or $-.53$) falls in the region of rejection. Conclude that the proportion of scores over 130 is the same for Forms A and B.

SECTION 12.3 (*Page 386*)

2. $z = 2.15$ (or -2.15) falls in the region of acceptance. Conclude that the mean number of letters processed by clerks A and B is the same.

4. $z = 2.04$ (or -2.04) falls in the region of acceptance. Conclude that the mean time required is the same for both methods.

6. $z = 1.20$ (or -1.20) falls in the region of acceptance. Conclude that the mean number of errors is the same when using either brand of typewriter.

SECTION 12.6 (*Page 397*)

2. Critical value $t_{.05} = 2.08$; $t = 2.08$ falls in the region of rejection. Conclude that the mean number of errors is not the same in translating from English to French and French to English.

4. $z = 1.83$ (or -1.83) falls in the region of acceptance. Conclude that the nature of activity preceding test administration has no effect on the mean test score.

6. $t = 2.99$ (or -2.99) falls in the region of rejection. Do not conclude that the mean time required is the same for one or both eyes open.

8. $t = .09$ (or $-.09$) falls in the region of acceptance. Conclude that Form A and Form B may be expected to produce the same mean score.

10. $t = -22.87$ (or 22.87) falls in the region of rejection. Conclude that the one-hour period of training in blueprint reading does make a difference.

SECTION 13.3 (*Page 422*)

2. X = algebra test scores, Y = science test scores
$Y_e = -4.36 + 2.68X$
When: $X = 8$, $Y_e = 17.08$ (or 17)
$X = 10$, $Y_e = 22.44$ (or 22)

4. X = social attitude score
Y = personality rating
$Y_e = 2.19 + 1.61X$
When: $X = 9$, $Y_e = 16.68$ (or 17)
$X = 13$, $Y_e = 23.12$ (or 23)
$X = 11$, $Y_e = 19.90$ (or 20)

6. X = Time-reaction scores "before"
Y = Time-reaction scores "after"
$Y_e = 7.41 + .27X$
When: $X = 12$, $Y_e = 10.65$
$X = 14$, $Y_e = 11.19$

8. X = Form A scores
Y = Form B scores
$Y_e = 1.92 + 1.57X$

SECTION 13.4 (*Page 431*)

2. $r = .80$, $r^2 = .64$

4. $r = .75$, $r^2 = .56$

6. $r = .58$, $r^2 = .34$

8. $r = .89$, $r^2 = .79$

SECTION 13.5 (*Page 436*)

2. X = Aptitude test B scores
Y = Aptitude test A scores
$Y_e = -4.38 + 1.80X$
$r = .88$

SECTION 13.6 (*Page 443*)

2. $Y_e = 117.39 - .30X$
$r = -.45$

SECTION 14.3 (*Page 458*)

2. (a) $s_{Y.X} = 2.49$
(b) $s_b = .587$
(c) $s_a = 5.652$
(d) Confidence interval
(1) For β: .17 to 3.05
(2) For α: -11.38 to 16.28

4. (a) $s_{Y.X} = 1.35$
(b) $s_b = .124$
(c) $s_a = .850$
(d) Confidence interval
(1) For β: -2.93 to -2.37
(2) For α: 30.66 to 34.44

6. (a) $s_{Y_e} = 1.399$
(b) 13.48 to 20.68
(c) $s_{Y_e} = 3.630$
(d) 7.74 to 26.41

8. (a) $s_{Y_e} = .303$
(b) 9.95 to 11.35
(c) $s_{Y_e} = .935$
(d) 8.49 to 12.81

10. (a) $s_{Y_e} = 1.155$
(b) 32.50 to 37.28
(c) $s_{Y_e} = 3.253$
(d) 28.16 to 41.62

SECTION 14.4 (*Page 462*)

2. $t = 2.73$ falls in the region of rejection. Reject the hypothesis that $\beta = 0$ and accept the hypothesis that $\beta \neq 0$.

4. $t = 22.14$ falls in the region of rejection. Reject the hypothesis that $\rho = 0$ and accept the hypothesis that $\rho \neq 0$.

SECTION 15.1 (*Page 475*)

2. $\log Y_e = -1.3506 + 1.7471 \log X$
$r = .95$

SECTION 15.2 (*Page 479*)

2. $r' = .75$

4. $r' = -.61$

INDEX

α (Probability of committing a Type I error), 348
α (Regression coefficient, true), 450
a (Regression coefficient), 415, 417, 419–420
A priori probability, 190–191
Abscissa, 64
Absolute deviations, 127, 162
Absolute frequencies, 49
Absolute zero point, 27
Acceptable error, 330
Acceptable numbers, 239
Acceptance region, 348–349, 354–355
Addition, algebraic, 126, 485–486
  probabilities, *see* Addition rule
  sets, 226
Addition rule, any two events, 203–205
    set notation, 227
  mutually exclusive events, 205
    set notation, 228
  two mutually exclusive events, 205
    set notation, 228
Algebra, addition, 485–486
  division, 486–487
  equations, 413–415, 491–494
  exponents, 487
  factoring, 491
Algebra, fractions, 486–487
  multiplication, 485, 487–488
  notation, 483–485
  parentheses, 486
  review, 5, 483
  subtraction, 485–486
  symbols, 483–485
Algebraic notes, purpose and usefulness, 86, 171
Algebraic proofs, 131–135, 171–183
Algebraic sum, 126
All possible outcomes, 188–189, 193, 223, 224, 226
Alternative hypothesis, 340, 358, 375
  one-sided, 356
  specific, 352–353, 354
  two-sided, 357
Amount of summarization of raw (ungrouped) data, 37–40
Analytical columns, frequency distribution, 43–50
Antilog, *see* Antilogarithms
Antilogarithms, 496
Area under a continuous curve, 77–78, 250
Area under the histogram, 67, 75, 110, 250

Area under the normal curve, application, 252, 255
  computation, 252, 258
  distribution, 250–252, 253
  interpretation, 250
  probability, 255
  relative frequency, 250
Arithmetic mean, 83, 138
  adding a constant, 87–88
  algebraic notes, 86, 131–135
  binomial population, 273–274
  conditional, 449
  confidence interval, 309–322
  definition, 84
  difference between two variables, 96–97
  dividing by a constant, 89–90
  double transformation, 90–92, 101–105
  equilibrium point, 125
  estimated, 85–86, 244
  frequency distribution, 99–105, 126
  general, 95–96
  grouped data, *see* Frequency distribution
  interpretation, 85–86
  least squares property, 126
  multiplying by a constant, 89–90
  normal distribution, 248
  point estimate, 307
  point of reference, 137–138
  population, 84–85, 267
  properties, 125–130
  relative frequencies, 95, 100–101
  sample, 84–86, 267
  sample size, 330–332
  sampling distribution, 242–243, 265–267, 268, 269
  sampling variability, 128–129, 244, 267, 270–271
  scales of measurement, 129
  short-cut methods, 87–88, 89, 91, 101, 104
  simple grouping table, 94–95
  single-sample tests, 364–372
  special situations, 86–97, 99–105
  standard error, 245
  subsets, 95–96
  subtracting a constant, 87–88
  sum of two variables, 96–97
Arithmetic mean, two-sample tests, 383–397
  ungrouped data, 84
  weighted, 92–93, 94
Association, measures of, 403–404
Average, 83–84, 137
  see also Arithmetic mean, Median, Mode
Average predicted value, 456

β (Probability of committing a Type II error), 352
β (Regression coefficient, true), 450
b (Regression coefficient), 417, 420, 421
Bar chart, discrete variable, 74–75
  nominal scale data, 80
  ordinal scale data, 81
Base, logarithms, 494–495
Battery average, *see* Weighted mean
Best-fitting regression line, 411, 412, 413
Bias, downward, 143
Bimodal distribution, 120–121
Binomial distribution, *see* Binomial population, Binomial probability distribution
Binomial population, 76, 247, 272–274
  frequency, 273–274
  mean, 273–274
  proportion, 273–274
  standard deviation, 273–274
Binomial probability distribution, 275–285
  frequency, 275–276, 283
  general term, 282–283
  mean, 283–285
  normal approximation, 285–299
  number of successes, 275, 297–298
  parameters, 286
  probability of success in a single trial, 275
  proportion, 275–276, 283
  proportion of successes, 275
  skewness, 286–287
  standard error, 283–285
  symmetric, 286, 287
  table, National Bureau of Standards, 286
Bivariate frequency table, 433–434
Bivariate tally table, 432–433

Braces, 486
Brackets, 486

Category information, 25
Cell frequency, bivariate frequency table, 440–441
  bivariate tally table, 433–434
  simple grouping, 53
Central limit theorem, 268
Central tendency, *see* Measures of central tendency
Chance, 188, 244, 341
Characteristic, logarithms, 495
Class boundaries, 45
Class frequency, 35, 42–43
  how to determine, 56
  pattern, 73–74, 76
  theoretical, 259, 260, 262–263
Class interval, 36–37
  continuous, 43–47, 111, 122–124
  discrete, 41–42
  length, 42, 47, 55–59, 60, 64, 101
  open-end, 59
Class length, 42, 47, 55–59, 60, 64, 101
Class limits, continuous, 43–47
  discrete, 41–42
Class mark, 43
Class midpoint, 43, 47, 100
Class values, 42
Classes, determination, 52–61
  equal length, 57, 104, 116
  number, 37–40, 55–56
  open-end, 59
  overlapping, 56–57
  unequal length, 57–59, 104, 116
Classificatory scale, 24
Cluster, 240
Cluster sample, 240
Coding, 88
  see also Transformation
Coefficient, confidence, 312
Coefficient of correlation, 407, 411, 429, 467
  computation after dividing by a constant, 438–439
  computation after subtracting a constant, 437–438
  computation from a bivariate frequency distribution, 434–435, 439–443
Coefficient of correlation, computation from ungrouped data, 430
  definitional equation, 429
  interpretation, 407, 429–430
  Pearson's, 478
  product-moment, 478
  rank, 477
  Spearman's, 478
  symbols (use of X and Y), 431
  tests of hypotheses, 460–462
  true, 460
  see also Correlation, Index of Correlation
Coefficient of determination, 429
Coefficient of quartile deviation, 165
Coefficient of variation, 164
Coefficient, regression, *see* Regression coefficient
Combinations, 200–202, 277
  N different objects taken $N - X$ at a time, 201–202
  N different objects taken X at a time, 201
Combining probabilities, 196, 203
  examples with solutions, 213–214
  set notation, 227–230
Common logarithms, 494
  table of, 502–503
Comparison, 375
  among the averages (mean, median, mode), 127–130
  theoretical sampling models, 301–302
Complement, 224
Complementary set, 224–225, 226
Compound events, definition, 206
  probability, 208
  sets, 228
Conditional distribution, 448
  mean, 449
  standard deviation, 451
Conditional mean, 449
  point estimate, 450
Conditional probability, 206–208, 210, 281
  sets, 228, 229
Conditional standard deviation, 451
  estimated, 452
Confidence coefficient, 312

Confidence interval, 308, 312
construction, 308–309
finite population, 326–329
interpretation, 312, 315–316
mean, 309
large sample, 309–316
small sample, 316–322
proportion, 322–325
regression coefficient α, 455
regression coefficient β, 454–455
sample size, 330
summary, 316, 322, 325
theoretical basis, 308–309
width, 314–316
Confidence level, 313, 315, 330, 332
Confidence limits, 312
Constant, 14
adding a, 87–88, 146–147
dividing by a, 89–90, 149, 438–439
multiplying by a, 89–90, 149
probability, 281, 301, 309
subtracting a, 87–88, 146–147, 437–438
Continuous class interval, 43–47, 111, 122–124
Continuous class limits, 43–47, 66
computation, 44
lower, 44
unreal character, 47
upper, 44
Continuous curve, *see* Continuous distribution
Continuous distribution, 75–76, 248, 448
area under the curve, 77–78, 250
theoretical development, 76–78
see also Normal distribution
Continuous interval, 45–47, 256–257
Continuous score interval, 45–47, 256–257
Continuous scale, *see* Continuous variable
Continuous variable, 41, 45–46, 248, 256
Control sample, 384
Converting discrete class limits to continuous class limits, 44
Correction factor, finite population, 327
Correction for continuity, 295–296
Correlation, 425–431
Correlation, coefficient, *see* Coefficient of correlation
computational aids, 437–443, 477
curvilinear, 463–475
exploratory, 446
index, 467
mechanical procedure, 446
nonsense, 446
spurious, 446
Correlation of ranks, 476–478
Correlation table, 433
Covariation, 406
Critical region, 348
Critical value, 387, 391
Crude mode, 121
Cumulative frequency, 49
less than, 67
more than, 67–68
theoretical, 262
Cumulative relative frequency, less than, 50, 68
more than, 50, 68
theoretical, 190
Curve, continuous, *see* Continuous distribution
freehand, 75
mathematical, 75, 250
Curvilinear correlation, 463–475
Curvilinear regression, 463–475
Curvilinear relationships, 411, 463–475

Data, organization of, 33–40, 78–81
Deciles, 119, 257–258
Decision errors, 342, 352
Decision model, 344, 355
Decision risks, 352–355
Decision rule, 344, 345, 348
Decision-making, *see* Statistical decision-making
Decision-routes, 342
Definition 1, 190, 194–195
Definition 2, 193–195, 226
Degree of assurance, 188–189
Degree of confidence, 308, 312
Degree of relationship, 406–407, 425–426, 429
Degrees of freedom, 318, 368–369, 387, 390, 391, 395, 454, 456
Dependent events, definition of, 206

Dependent events, probability, 206
  probability distribution, 218–221, 281
  sets, 228
Dependent samples, definition of, 376
  tests of hypotheses, 392–397
Dependent variable, 406, 407, 491
Descriptive statistics, 9–10, 33
Determination, coefficient of, 429
Determining the number of classes, 39, 55–56, 60
Deviation, absolute, 127, 162
  between observed and predicted values of *Y*, 412, 413, 426–427
  between observed value of *Y* and the mean of *Y*, 426
  between the predicted value of *Y* and the mean of *Y*, 427
  due to regression, 427–428
  explained, 427–428
  from the mean, 125–126, 138–140
  from the median, 127
  from a point of reference, 137–138
  quartile, 138, 162–163
  standard, *see* Standard deviation
  total, 427–428
  unexplained, 427–428
df, *see* Degrees of freedom
Dichotomous population, 272
Difference, algebraic, 485–486
Difference, arithmetic mean of a, 96–97
Difference between means, sampling distribution, 383–384
    dependent samples, 395–396
    equal variance, 391–392
    large samples, 383–384
    small samples, 387
  tests of hypotheses, dependent samples, 392–397
    equal variance, 389–392
    large samples, 383–386
    small samples, 387–389
Difference between pairs, 394–395
  mean, 395
  sampling distribution, 395
  standard error, 395
  tests of hypotheses, 395–396
Difference between proportions, mean, 379, 380
  sampling distribution, 378–379
  standard error, 379, 380
Difference between proportions, tests of hypotheses, 377–382
  tests of significance, 382
Difference between two variables, mean, 96–97
Direct relationship, 408
Discontinuities in a discrete scale, 43–44
Discontinuous variable, 41
Discrete class interval, 41–42
Discrete class limits, 41–42, 45
  computation, 47, 55–56
  conversion to continuous class limits, 45
  lower, 41, 55
  upper, 41, 55–56
Discrete population, 272
Discrete scale, *see* Discrete variable
Discrete variable, 13, 272
  and the normal distribution, 256–257
  discontinuities, 43–44
  gaps, 45–46
Distribution, bimodal, 120–121
  binomial population, 272–274
  binomial probability, 275–285
  conditional, 448
  continuous, 75–76, 248
  frequency, 68–72
  Gaussian, 250
  J, 71
  J, mirror-image, 71
  left-skewed, 69–71
  multimodal, 120–121
  negatively skewed, 69–71, 128
  normal, *see* Normal distribution
  1's and 0's, 272
  positively skewed, 71, 127
  probability, *see* Probability distribution
  rectangular, 68–69
  relative frequency, 41, 42, 64–68, 75, 78, 250
  right-skewed, 71
  S-shape, 69, 71
  sampling, *see* Sampling distribution
  skewed, 69–71
  stretched out, 35, 58, 71, 75
  symmetrical, 69, 71, 127, 248
  t, *see t* distribution
  U, 71

Distribution, unconditional, 448
underlying, 73–78
uniform, 68–69
unimodal, 121, 127
Distribution measures, 73, 83, 117, 136
Division, 486–487
Dot chart, 406
Double transformation, 90–92, 101–105, 151–153, 159–161

Element of a sample space, 224
Empirical probability, 190–191
Empty set, 224
Endpoints, 42
Equations, algebraic, 413–415, 491–494
curvilinear, 463–475
linear, 413, 425, 450
nonlinear, 463
regression, 416
simultaneous, 493–494
straight line, 313–315
Equilibrium point, 125
Equi-probability, 235–237
Equi-probable events, 192
Equivalence, 255
Error, acceptable, 330
decision, 342
maximum possible, 313, 314
of the first kind, 352
of the second kind, 352
relation to sample size, 330
sampling, 128–129, 244
Type I, 342, 352
Type II, 342, 352
Errors of decision-making, *see* Decision errors
Estimate, interval, 307–309
point, 307–309
standard error of, 452
see also Confidence interval, Point estimate
Estimated conditional standard deviation, 452
Estimated correlation coefficient, 460
Estimated mean, 85–86, 244
Estimated probability, 257
Estimated regression coefficient, 450
Estimated regression equation, 450
Estimated standard deviation, 143
Estimated standard error, difference between means, 385
dependent samples, 395
difference between pairs, 395
difference between proportions, 381
frequency, 327
mean, 311, 327
predicted average value, 456
predicted specific value, 456
proportion, 323, 327
regression coefficient *a*, 454
regression coefficient *b*, 454
Estimating means, sample size, 330–332
Estimating proportions, sample size, 332–333
Estimation, *see* Confidence interval, Point estimate
Evaluating a prediction, 455–456
Evaluating the sample data, 350–352
Events, compound, *see* Compound events
definition, 189
dependent, *see* Dependent events
equi-probable, 192
independent, *see* Independent events
joint, 206
see also Compound events
mutually exclusive, *see* Mutually exclusive events
probability, 190, 193
sets, 224
Exact binomial probabilities, 285, 286, 297
compared with normal approximations, 285–299
general terms, 282–283
Exact limits, 45
Exhaustive set of possible outcomes, 191–192
Experimental sample, 384
Experimental variable, 393
Exploratory analysis, 446
Exponent, 487

Factorial, 199
Factoring, 491
Finite population, confidence interval, 326–329
correction factor (fpc), 327
definition, 8–9

Finite population, random sampling, 235, 236, 281
  standard errors, 327
Fitting a normal curve, 258–263
Formulating the problem, 338–343
fpc, 327
Fractions, 486–487
Free-hand curve, 75
Free-hand regression line, 408
Free-hand trend line, 405
Frequency, absolute, 49
  binomial population, 273–274
  binomial probability distribution, 275–276, 283
  cell, 53, 433–434
  class, 35, 42–43, 64, 66–67, 68, 75
  cumulative, *see* Cumulative frequency
  relative, *see* Relative frequency
  relative, cumulative, *see* Cumulative relative frequency
  sampling distribution, 275–276, 283, 297–298
  standard error, 298, 327
Frequency distribution, 35–40, 73, 250
  arithmetic mean, 99–105, 126
  best, 40, 59–60
  construction, 52–61, 73
  correlation, 434–435
  correlation coefficient, 434–435, 441–443
  double transformation, 101–105, 159–161
  equal classes, 57, 104, 116
  graphic representation, 64–68
  interval scale, 78
  median, 109–116, 127
  mode, 121–124
  nominal scale, 78–79
  number of classes, 55
  ordinal scale, 79–80
  ratio scale, 78
  regression equation, 434–435, 441–443
  standard deviation, 157–161
  two variables, 431–434
  unequal classes, 57–59, 104, 116
  see also Frequency table
Frequency polygon, 64–66, 72, 75
Frequency of successes, 275–276
Frequency table, 35–40
  analytical columns, 43–50
  assumptions for computations, 50, 66, 67
  basic information, 43, 56, 60
  bivariate, 433–434
  construction, 52–61
  model, 40–42, 50, 56
  purposes, 50, 52, 59–60
  statistical heading, 59
  subject-matter heading, 59
  two-way, 433–434
  see also Frequency distribution
Functional notation, 491

Gambling problems, 188–189
Gaps, discrete scale, 43–44
Gauss, Karl Friedrich, 250
Gaussian distribution, 250
General mean, 95–96
General term of the binomial probability distribution, 282–283
Generalizing from a sample, 11
Geometric mean, 83–84
Gosset, W. S., 317
Graphic representation, bar chart, 66, 74–75, 80–81
  discrete data, 74–75
  dot chart, 406
  frequency distribution, 64–68
  frequency polygon, 64–66, 72, 75
  histogram, 66–67, 68–72, 73–74, 75
  nominal scale data, 80
  ogive, 67–72
  ordinal scale data, 81
  population data, 74–76, 78–81
  sample data, 76–81
  scatter diagram, 404, 405, 407–408, 410–411
Grouped data, *see* Frequency distribution, Frequency table
Grouping, simple, *see* Simple grouping

H_0 (Null hypothesis), 340
H_1 (Alternative hypothesis), 340
Harmonic mean, 83–84
Heading, statistical, 59
  subject-matter, 59
Height, regression line, 415, 419–420
Histogram, 66–67, 68–72, 73–74, 75, 448

Histogram, area, 67, 75, 110, 250
Homoscedasticity, 451
Hypothesis, alternative, 340, 358, 375
  null, 340
  one-sided, 356
  specific, 340, 342, 352–353, 354, 355, 380
  to be tested, 340, 375–377, 380
  two-sided, 357

Independent events, definition of, 210
  probability, 211, 229, 276, 281
  probability distribution, 221–223, 280–281
  sampling, 276, 280–281
Independent in the probability sense, 211
Independent probabilities, 297, 298
Independent samples, definition of, 376
  tests of hypotheses, 377–392
Independent trials, 298, 301
  probability, 276
  probability distribution, 281
  sampling, 235–237, 309
Independent variable, 406, 407, 491
Index of correlation, 467
Index of summation, 17
Inductive inference, 234
  definition of, 10–11
  see also Statistical inference
Inductive statistics, 234, 250, 302
  definition of, 10–11
  see also Statistical inference
Inequalities (greater than and less than), 484
Inference, probability, 11
  statistical, 11, 67, 78, 187
  see also Statistical inference
Infinite population, 76, 248, 257, 297, 301
  definition of, 9
  random sampling, 265, 268, 276, 281, 309, 317, 323
Interpolation, 111–112
Interquartile range, 163
Intersection of sets, 227, 229
Interval, between scale values, 27
  class, 36–37
  confidence, *see* Confidence interval
  continuous, 45–47, 256–257
Interval, estimate, 307–309
  prediction, 456–458
  range, 137
Interval scale, frequency distribution, 78
  properties, 26–27
Inverse relationship, 410

J-distribution, 71
  mirror image of a, 71
Joint events, 206
  see also Compound events
Joint probability, 207–209
  definition of, 206
  set notation, 228
Joint variation, 406
Judgment sample, 233–234

Large sample, 269–270
Least square method, 413, 416–417, 434, 463
Least squares property, arithmetic mean, 126
  regression equation, 413
  standard deviation, 142
Left-skewed distribution, 69–71
Length of class interval, 42, 47, 55–59, 60, 64, 101
Less than cumulative frequency, 48, 49
Less than cumulative frequency ogive, 67, 68–72
Less than cumulative relative frequency, 50, 68
Level of confidence, 313, 315, 330, 332
Level of significance, 343, 349, 358
Level of measurement, *see* Measurement scales
Limits, class, 41–42, 43–47
  confidence, *see* Confidence interval
  exact, 45
  prediction, 457
  real, 45
Linear equations, 413–415
Linear interpolation, 111–112
Linear regression equation, 464, 466–467, 470–471, 474–475
Linear relationship, 411, 460, 463, 467
Logarithmic transformation, 463–471
Logarithms, base of, 494–495
  characteristic, 495
  how to determine, 495–496

Logarithms, mantissa of, 495
table of, 502–503
Lower continuous class limit, 44
Lower discrete class limit, 41, 55–57, 60

μ (Arithmetic mean, population), 84
M (Median), 107
Mantissa, logarithms, 495
Matched samples, 393
Mathematical curve, 77, 250
Mathematical probability, 11, 188–189, 191
see also Probability
Maximum acceptable error, 330
Maximum expected error, 313, 314, 330, 332, 456
Mean, *see* Arithmetic mean
Measurable characteristics, 338
Measurement scales, 24–29
interval, *see* Interval scale
nominal, *see* Nominal scale
ordinal, *see* Ordinal scale
ratio, *see* Ratio scale
Measures of association, 403–404
basic concepts, 404–411
see also Correlation, Regression
Measures of central tendency, interval scale, 129
nominal scale, 129–130
ordinal scale, 129–130
properties and comparisons, 125–130
ratio scale, 29
sampling models, 265
scales of measurement, 129
see also Arithmetic mean, Median, Mode
Measures of position, 117
deciles, 119, 257–258
median, *see* Median
percentiles, 117–118
quartiles, 119, 162
Measures of variation, 136–138
quartile deviation, 138, 162–163
relative variation, 163
standard deviation, *see* Standard deviation
Median, 83, 162
absolute deviations, 127
class, 111
Median, computation based on less than cumulative frequencies, 111–113
computation based on less than cumulative relative frequencies, 113–114
computation based on more than cumulative frequencies, 114–115
computation based on more than cumulative relative frequencies, 115
computation by the method of linear interpolation, 111
definition of, 107, 110
even number of items, 108–109
frequency distribution, 109–116, 127
midrank value, 126–127
normal distribution, 248
odd number of items, 107–108
point of reference, 162
properties, 126–130
relative frequency, 113, 115
sampling distribution, 269
sampling variability, 270–271
scales of measurement, 129
standard error, 269–271
ties, 108, 109
ungrouped data, 107–109
Method of least squares, 413, 416–417, 434
Midpoint, class interval, 43, 47, 64, 66, 100, 101, 103–104, 122–123, 158
Midrank value, median, 126–127
Minus sign, 485–486
Mirror image of a J-distribution, 71
Modal class, 122
Mode, 83
crude, 121
definition, 120, 127
frequency distribution, 121–124
nominal scale, 129–130
normal distribution, 248
ordinal scale, 129–130
properties, 127–130
refined, 121–124
ungrouped data, 120–121
Model, *see* Decision model, Sampling models
Model A, 265
Model B, 268
Model C, 269

Model D, 283
Model E, 297–298
Model F, 368–369
Model frequency table, 40–42, 50, 64
Model G, 379
Model H, 384
Model I, 387–388
Model, normal, 448, 450, 453
More than cumulative frequency, 48–49
More than cumulative frequency ogive, 67–68, 72
More than cumulative relative frequency, 50, 68
Multimodal distribution, 120–121
Multiplication, probabilities, *see* Multiplication rule
Multiplication rule, any events, 208
    set notation, 229
  any two events, 206
    set notation, 228
  independent events, 211
    set notation, 230
  two independent events, 211
    set notation, 229–230
Mutually exclusive events, definition of, 192
  probability, 208
  sets, 226, 227

N (Population size), 85
n (Sample size), 85
National Bureau of Standards, 286
Negative relationship, 410, 421
Negatively skewed distribution, 69–71, 128
Negatively-sloped regression line, 410
No decision region, 349
Nominal scale, bar chart, 80
  binomial population, 272
  frequency distribution, 78–79
  measures of central tendency, 130
  properties, 24–25
Nonexistent population, 276
Nonlinear relationship, 411
Nonsense correlation, 446
Normal approximation to the binomial, 285–299
  correction for continuity, 295–296
  sample size, 286–292
Normal curve, *see* Normal distribution
Normal curve of errors, 250
Normal distribution, 76, 247, 248, 265, 269
  application to discrete scales, 256–257
  area under the curve, 250–258
  changes in the mean, 249–250, 251
  changes in the standard deviation, 249–250
  computation of measures of position, 257–258
  equation, 248
  family of curves, 248
  fitting the curve, 258–263
  parameters, 248
  probability, 255
  properties, 248
  standard, 251
  standard units, 251, 252, 254
  statistical inference, 252
  table of the, 252–253, 500
Normal model, 448, 450, 453
Normal Model A, 454
Normal Model B, 454
Normal Model C, 456
Normal Model D, 460–461
Notation, *see* Symbols
Null hypothesis, 340, 342, 351
Null set, 224
Number of classes, how to determine, 55–56, 60
  rule of thumb for, 39
Number of classes to use, Table of, 40
Number of successes, 275–276
  sampling distribution, 275–276, 283, 297–298

Observed *Y* value, 412
Ogive, less than cumulative frequency, 67, 68–72
  more than cumulative frequency, 67–68, 72
Ones and zeros, distribution of, 272
One-sided alternative, 356
One-tail test, 356
Open-end classes, 59
Ordinal scale, bar chart, 81
  binomial population, 272
  frequency distribution, 79–80

Ordinal scale, measures of central tendency, 129–130
properties, 26
Ordinate, 64
Organization of data, 9, 33–40, 78–81, 431–434
Origin, 420
Outcomes, all possible, 188–189, 193, 223, 224, 226
Outcomes, possible, 188–189
Overlapping, 56–57

Parameter, 308, 340
as a reference value, 375
as a standard, 375
binomial probability distribution, 286
definition, 240–241
normal distribution, 248
test, 343, 377–378
Parentheses, 486
Particular predicted value, 456
Pattern of class frequencies, 73–74, 76
Pearson's product-moment coefficient of correlation, 478
Percentiles, 117–118
Permutations, 198–200
N different objects taken *N* at a time, 199
N different objects taken *X* at a time 199–200
probability, 207–213
Plus and minus signs, 485–486
Point estimate, 307–309
conditional mean, 450
mean, 307, 330
predicted average value, 456
predicted specific value, 456–457
proportion, 308, 332
regression coefficient α, 450
regression coefficient β, 450
Point of reference, 137–138, 162
Population, arithmetic mean, 84–85, 267
binomial, *see* Binomial population
continuous, *see* Continuous distribution
definition, 8–9
dichotomous, 272
discrete, 272
distributions, 73–76
finite, 8–9, 326
Population, generalizing from a sample, 10–11, 73
infinite, 9, 76, 248, 257
nonexistent, 276
normal, *see* Normal distribution
of 1's and 0's, 272
parameter, 240–241
standard deviation, 138–142, 267
theoretical distributions, 247, 301
variance, 139
Position measures, *see* Measures of position
Positive relationship, 408, 410
Positively skewed distribution, 71, 127
Positively-sloped regression line, 408
Possible outcomes, 188–189
exhaustive set, 191–192
Predicted variable, 406, 407
Predicted *Y* value, 412, 417, 419
Predicting the average value of a variable, 456
Predicting a specific value of a variable, 456
Prediction, 406, 408, 410, 425–426
evaluation, 455–456
interval, 456–458
limits, 457
uses and abuses, 445–447
Probabilities, combining, 196, 203
Probability, *a priori*, 190–191
addition rule for any two events, 203–205
set notation, 227
addition rule for mutually exclusive events, 205
set notation, 228
addition rule for two mutually exclusive events, 205
set notation, 228
alternative possible outcomes, 188–189, 193, 223, 224, 226
committing a Type I error, 347, 354
committing a Type II error, 352, 354
compound events, 208
conditional, 206–208, 210, 281
constant, 281, 309
definition, 187–196
Definition 1, 190, 194–195
Definition 2 193–195, 226
degree of assurance, 188

Probability, dependent events, 206
set notation, 228
empirical, 190–191
equi-probable events, 192
estimated, 257
event, 190, 193
gambling problems, 188–189
in the long run, 190
independent events, 211, 229, 276, 281
set notation, 229
independent trials, 276
joint, 207–209
mathematical, 11, 188–189, 191
multiplication rule for any events, 208
set notation, 229
multiplication rule for any two events, 206
set notation, 228
multiplication rule for independent events, 211
set notation, 230
multiplication rule for two independent events, 211
set notation, 229–230
mutually exclusive events, 208
set notation, 226–227
of X successes in n trials, 276–280, 282
permissible values, 191
permutation considered, 207–213
proportion, 190
random sampling, 234
relative frequency, 190
repeated trials, 190
risk, 11, 335, 354–355
sampling distribution, 242–243, 265
sampling models, 265
sets, 223
statistical inference, 11, 187
success in a single trial, 275, 281
trial, 189
unconditional, 206–208, 210
Probability distribution, 73, 218–223
binomial, 222, 279–281
definition, 220–221
dependent events, 218–221, 281
independent events, 221–223, 280–281
Probability distribution, independent trials, 281
normal distribution, 255
relation to sampling distribution, 242
uses, 221
Probability inference, 11
see also Statistical inference
Probability theory, 187
Product-moment coefficient of correlation, 478
Proportion, 49
binomial population, 273–274
binomial probability distribution, 275–276, 283
computed from pooled data, 381
confidence interval, 322–325
point estimate, 308
probability, 190
sample size, 332–333
sampling distribution, 298
single-sample tests, 345, 360–368
standard error, 298, 327
two-sample tests, 377–382
Proportion of successes, 275

Quartile, 119, 162
Quartile deviation, 138, 162–163
coefficient of, 165

ρ (Coefficient of correlation, population), 460
r (Coefficient of correlation, sample), 429
r' (Coefficient of rank correlation), 477
Random numbers, acceptable numbers, 239
construction, 237–239
table of, *see* Table of random numbers
Random sample, cluster, 240
definition, 234
selection, 235–236, 237–239
simple, 237, 239
stratified, 239
stratified systematic, 240
systematic, 240
Random sampling, constant probability of selection, 236–237, 309
equi-probability, 235–237
finite population, 235, 236, 281, 309

Random sampling, independent trials, 235–236
infinite population, 236, 283
probability, 234
statistical inference, 247
with replacement, 235–236
without replacement, 235–236
Random selection procedure, 234–236, 237–239
Randomizing procedure, 237–238
Range, distance, 55, 60, 137
interquartile, 163
interval, 137
semi-interquartile, 163
Ranking, 35, 53
Ranks, correlation, 476–478
ordinal scale, 26
ties, 108, 109, 478
Ratio scale, frequency distribution, 78
properties, 27–28
Ratio of scale intervals, 27, 28
Ratio of scale values, 28
Raw data, 33
see also Ungrouped data
Raw score, 165
Real limits, 45
Reciprocal, 484
transformation, 471–475
Recorded variable, 257
Rectangular distribution, 68–69
Reference value, 375
Refined mode, 121–124
Region, critical, 348
Region of acceptance, 348–349, 354–355
Region of no decision, 349
Region of rejection, 348, 354–355, 358
Regression, 411–422
coefficient of, *see* Regression coefficient
computational aids, 437–443
deviation due to, 427–428
exploratory, 446
Regression coefficient, 417
confidence interval, 454–455
interpretation, 415, 419–420, 421
point estimate, 450
tests of hypotheses, 459–460
theoretical sampling distribution, 453–454
true, 450
Regression coefficient, *see also* Regression, Regression equation
Regression equation, 425
computation after dividing by a constant, 438–439
computation after subtracting a constant, 437–438
computation from a bivariate frequency distribution, 434–435, 439–443
constant (coefficient a), 415, 417, 419–420
curvilinear, 463–475
estimated, 450
least squares, 413, 416–417, 434, 463
linear, 464, 466–467, 470–471, 474–475
mechanical procedure, 446
nonlinear, 463
slope, 415, 417, 420, 421
true, 450
ungrouped data, 416
see also Regression line, Relationship between two variables
Regression line, 406
best fitting, 411, 412, 413
free-hand, 408, 411
height, 415, 419–420
least squares, 413, 415–416
least squares property, 413
negatively-sloped, 410
positively-sloped, 408
slope, 415
see also Regression equation, Relationship between two variables
Rejection region, 348, 354–355, 358
Relationship between two variables, 406–407
curvilinear, 411, 460, 463–475
degree, 408, 410–411
direct, 408
inverse, 410
linear, 411, 460, 463, 467
negative, 410, 421
nonlinear, 411, 460, 463
positive, 408, 410
trend line, 406
type, 408
see also Correlation, Regression

Relative frequency, 49, 67, 68
  arithmetic mean, 95, 100–101
  cumulative, 50, 68, 190
  distribution, 41, 42, 64–66, 67, 68, 75, 78, 250
  median, 113, 115
  probability, 190–191, 242
  sampling distribution, 242
  standard deviation, 155, 158
Relative importance, 26
Relative variation, 163
  coefficient of quartile deviation, 164–165
  coefficient of variation, 163–164
Repeated sampling, 129, 245, 312, 315
Repeated trials, probability, 190
  sampling, 129, 245
Representative sample, 233–234
Research problems, 3–4
Right-skewed distribution, 71
Risk, 11
  decision, 336, 338, 352–355
  probability, 11, 335, 347
Rule 1, 19
Rule 2, 20
Rule 3, 21
Rule A, 203
Rule A′, 227
Rule B, 205
Rule B extended, 205
Rule B′, 228
Rule B′ extended, 228
Rule C, 206
Rule C extended, 208
Rule C′, 228
Rule C′ extended, 229
Rule D, 210
Rule E, 211
Rule E extended, 211
Rule E′, 230
Rule E′ extended, 230

σ (Standard deviation, population), 138, 140
Σ (Summation), 17
s (standard deviation, sample), 138, 143, 426
Sample, arithmetic mean, 84–86, 267
  cluster, 240
  control, 384
Sample, definition, 9
  dependent, 376
  design, 237
  distributions, 73, 76
  evaluation, 350–352
  experimental, 384
  frequency of successes, 275
  generalizing to the population, 11
  independent, 376
  judgment, 233–234
  large, 269–270
  matched, 393
  number of successes, 275
  proportion of successes, 275
  random, *see* Random sample, Random sampling
  representative, 233–234
  selection procedures, 235–236, 237–239
  simple random, *see* Random sample, Random sampling
  small, 268
  standard deviation, 142–143
  stratified, 239
  stratified systematic, 240
  systematic, 240
  variance, 143
Sample point, 224
Sample size, 329–333
  central limit theorem, 268
  confidence interval, 311, 317, 324, 330
  estimating a mean, 330–332
  estimating a proportion, 332–333
  large sample, 268, 302
  maximum acceptable error, 330
  normal approximation to the binomial, 286–290, 292
  sampling distribution, 265, 267, 268, 269–270
  sampling models, 301–302
  small sample, 268
Sample space, 223–224
Sampling distribution, 73
  definition of, 241
  of the difference between means, 383–384
    dependent samples, 395–396
    equal variance, 391–392
    large samples, 383–384

Sampling distribution, of the difference between means, small samples, 387
of the difference between pairs, 395
between proportions, 378–379
of a frequency, 297–298
inductive statistics, 302
infinite population, 245, 265
of the mean, 242–243, 245, 265, 268, 308
large samples, 265, 268
small samples, 265
of the median, 269
of the number of successes, 297–298
as a population distribution, 243
of a predicted average value, 456
of a predicted specific value, 456
probability statements, 242–243, 265
of a proportion, 298
of the regression coefficient *a*, 453–454
of the regression coefficient *b*, 453–454
relation to probability distribution, 242
relation to sampling models, 302
relative frequencies, 242
repeated sampling, 129, 245
sample size, 243, 265, 267, 268
of the standard deviation, 243
statistic, 241, 243, 338
statistical inference, 241, 302, 335
test statistic, 344, 345, 378
test variable, 345, 390, 391, 395
tests of hypotheses, 335, 337–338
theoretical, 245
Sampling error, 128–129, 244
Sampling models, 247, 265, 344
comparisons, 301–302
relation to statistical inference, 301–303
see also Model A, Model B, etc.; *Normal model, Normal Model A, Normal Model B,* etc., Sampling distribution
Sampling ratio, 309, 326, 328–329
Sampling, repeated, 129, 245, 312, 315
Sampling with replacement, 235–237
Sampling without replacement, 235–237, 309, 326
Sampling variation, arithmetic mean, 128–129, 267
comparison between mean and median, 270–271
median, 270–271
Scale, continuous, *see* Continuous variable
discrete, *see* Discrete variable
interval, 26–27
measurement, *see* Measurement scales
nominal, 24–25
ordinal, 26
properties, 24–28
ratio, 27–28
Scale intervals, ratio of, 27, 28
Scale values, ratio of, 28
Scatter diagram, 405, 408, 410–411
how to plot a, 404, 407–408
Scatter plot, 433
Score, interval, *see* Class interval
limits, *see* Class limits
range, *see* Range
raw, 165
standard, 165–169
Semi-interquartile range, 163
Sets, 223–230
addition, 226
complimentary, 224–225, 226
compound events, 228
conditional probability, 228, 229
definition of, 223
element, 224
empty, 224
events, 224
independent events, 229
intersection, 227, 229
mutually exclusive events, 226, 227
null, 224
probability, 223, 226, 227
see also Probability
sample point, 224
sample space, 223
subsets, 224
union, 226–227
universe, 223
Venn diagrams, 225–226
Sets of points, *see* Sets
S-shape distribution, 69, 71

Short-cut computations, arithmetic mean, 87–88, 89, 91, 101, 104
correlation, *see* Coefficient of correlation
regression, *see* Regression equation
standard deviation, 147, 149, 152
Significance, level of, 343, 349, 358
statistical, 382
tests of, 336, 382
Simple grouping, arithmetic mean, 94–95
binomial population, 273
construction, 53–54
standard deviation, 153
table, 35–36, 53, 74–75
tally table, 53–54
Simple random sample, *see* Random sample, Random sampling
Simultaneous equations, 493–494
Single-sample tests, mean, large sample, 364–368
small sample, 368–372
proportion, 345, 360, 368
Situation 1, 87
Situation 2, 89
Situation 3, 90
Situation 4, 92
Situation 5, 95
Situation 6, 96
Situation 7, 99
Situation 8, 101
Situation A, 144
Situation B, 146
Situation C, 149
Situation D, 151
Situation E, 153
Situation F, 157
Situation G, 159
Skewed distributions, 69–71, 127–128, 286–287
Skewness, binomial probability distribution, 286–287
Slope, regression equation, 415, 417, 420, 421
Small sample, 268
Smooth curve, 75–78
Solving an algebraic equation, 492–494
Spearman's coefficient of rank correlation, 478
Special situations, arithmetic mean, 86–97, 99–105
standard deviation, 144–156, 157–161
Specific alternative, 352–353, 354
Specific hypothesis, 340, 342, 352–353, 354, 355, 380
Specific predicted value, 456
Spurious correlation, 446
Square of a binomial, 487–488
Square root, 488–491
Square roots, table of, 504–516
Squares, table of, 504–516
Standard, 375
Standard deviation, adding a constant, 146–147
algebraic notes, 171–183
bias, 143
binomial population, 273–274
computational equations, 144–145
conditional, 451
definition, 138–143
dividing by a constant, 149
double transformation, 151–153, 159–161
estimated, 143
frequency distribution, 157–161
grouped data, *see* Frequency distribution
interpretation, 140–143
least squares property, 142
multiplying by a constant, 149
normal distribution, 251–252
optimum in the least squares sense, 142
population, 138–142, 267, 450
relative frequencies, 155–158
sample, 142–143
sampling distribution, 244
short-cut computation methods, 147, 149, 152
simple grouping table, 153
special situations, 144–156, 157–161
subtracting a constant, 146–147
ungrouped data, 144–146
see also Standard error
Standard error, 245, 326
of the difference between means, 384
dependent samples, 395
of the difference between pairs, 395

Standard error, of the difference between proportions, 379, 380
of estimate, 452
of a frequency, 298, 327
of the mean, 244–245, 265–267, 268, 327
relation to population standard deviation, 267
relation to sample size, 267
of the median, 269–271
of a proportion, 298, 327
see also Estimated standard error
Standard normal distribution, 251
Standard scores, 165–169
Standard units, 165–169
expressed in words, 266
normal distribution, 251, 252, 254
Statistic, definition, 6, 241
sampling distribution, 242–243
test, 344, 345, 378
Statistical decision-making, 335, 359
constructing the decision model, 343–350
decision errors, 342, 352
decision model, 344, 355
decision-routes, 342
decision rule, 344, 345, 348
evaluating the sample data, 350–352
formulating the alternative hypothesis, 358
formulating the problem, 338–343
risks, 352–355
three phase procedure, 343, 350, 358–359, 376, 377
Statistical heading, frequency distribution, 59
Statistical inference, 11, 67, 78
inductive statistics, 187
normal distribution, 252–253
probability, 187, 265
random sampling, 247
sampling distributions, 244, 265, 335
theoretical sampling models, 247, 265, 301–303, 448
variation, 136
Statistical methods, 3–4, 73, 136
applicability, 6–7
definition, 5–6
descriptive, 9–10, 33
frame of reference, 11
Statistical methods, inductive, 10–11, 234, 250
Statistical sampling models, *see* Sampling models
Statistically independent, 211
Statistically significant, 382
Statistics, definition, 5–6
Straight line, 69
equation, 413–415
interpolation, 111–112
regression, 411
Strata, 239
Stratified random sample, 239
Stratified systematic random sample, 240
Stratum, 239
"Stretched out" distribution, 38, 58, 71, 75
"Student," 317
Student's t distribution, *see* t distribution
Subject-matter heading, frequency distribution, 59
Subpopulation, 8
Subsets, arithmetic mean, 95–96
events, 224
of a set, 224
Subtraction, algebraic, 485–486
Success in a single trial, probability of, 275, 281
Successes, frequency, 275
number, 275
proportion, 275
Sum, algebraic, 126
Sum, arithmetic mean of a, 96–97
Sum of squares, 428
Summarization, amount, 37–40
of data, 9, 35–40
Summation, 16–21
index, 17
notation, 17, 18
rules, 19–21
Symbols, algebraic, 483–485
conventions, 15
sets, 224, 226–227
subscripts, 15, 146–147
use, 14–16, 86
Symmetrical distribution, 69, 71, 127, 248, 287
Systematic random sample, 240

t distribution, 317–320, 368, 387
  comparison with the normal distribution, 317–319
  degrees of freedom, 318–320
  table of the, 501
Table of areas under the normal curve, 500
  how to use, 252–253
Table of areas under the t distribution, 501
  how to use, 319–320
Tables of the binomial probability distribution, U.S. National Bureau of Standards, 286
Table of common logarithms, 502–503
Table of random numbers, 237, 498–499
  acceptable numbers, 239
  construction, 237–238
  forming random numbers for sampling, 238–239
  how to use, 238–239
  point of entry, 238
Table of squares and square roots, 504–516
Table of suggested number of classes, 40
Tail of a distribution, 71
Tally table, bivariate, 432–433
  frequency distribution, 55–56, 60–61
  nominal scale data, 78
  ordinal scale data, 79
  simple grouping, 53–54
  two-way, 432–433
Test parameter, 343, 377–378
Test statistic, 344, 345, 378
  sampling distribution, 344, 345
Test variable, 345, 390, 391, 395
  sampling distribution, 345
Tests of hypotheses, 335–338, 459–462
  coefficient of correlation ρ, 460–462
  constructing the decision model, 343–350
  decision model, 344, 355
  decision risks, 352–355
  decision-routes, 342
  decision rule, 344, 345, 348
  dependent samples, 392–397
  difference between means, dependent samples, 392–397
Tests of hypotheses, difference between means, equal variance, 389–392
    large samples, 383–386
    small samples, 387–389
  difference between pairs, 395–396
  difference between proportions, 377–382
  evaluating the sample data, 350–352
  formulating the problem, 338–343
  independent samples, 377–392
  involving a comparison, 375–377
  involving a standard or reference value, 375–377
  mean, large sample, 364–368
    small sample, 368–372
  measurable characteristics, 338
  one-tail test, 356
  proportion, 345, 360–368
  regression coefficient β, 459–460
  sampling distribution, 338
  single-sample tests, 360–372
  three phase decision-making procedure, 358–359
  two-sample tests, 375–377
  two-tail test, 357
Tests of significance, 336, 382
  difference between proportions, 382
Theoretical class frequencies, 259, 260, 262–263
Theoretical cumulative frequencies, 262
Theoretical distributions, 76, 247, 265
  binomial population, *see* Binomial population
  binomial probability distribution, *see* Binomial probability distribution
  continuous distribution, 76
  discrete distribution, 76
  normal distribution, *see* Normal distribution
Theoretical models, 247, 265
  decision model, 344, 355
  see also Sampling models
Theoretical relative cumulative frequencies, 190
Theoretical sampling distribution, 247
  of a statistic, 242–243
  see also Sampling distribution
Theoretical sampling models, 247, 265, 301, 344, 447

Theoretical sampling models, *see also* *Model A, Model B,* etc., *Normal model, Normal Model A, Normal Model B,* etc., Sampling models
Three phase decision-making procedure, 343, 350, 358–359, 376, 377
Ties, 108, 109, 478
Time series, 404
  scatter diagram, 405
  trend line, 405–406
  variation, 405
Time variable, 405
Total deviation, 427–428
Total sum of squares, 428
Total variation, 426, 428–429
Transformation, adding a constant, 88, 146–149
  arithmetic mean, 88, 90–92, 101–105
  changing the unit of measurement, 90, 149
  correlation coefficient, 437–439
  curvilinear regression, 463
  dividing by a constant, 89–90, 149, 438–439
  double, 90–92, 101–105, 151–153, 159–161, 440
  index of correlation, 467
  logarithmic, 463–471
  multiplying by a constant, 89–90, 149
  reciprocal, 471–475
  regression equation, 437–439
  shifting the zero point, 88, 90, 147
  standard deviation, 146–153
  standard scores, 165–166, 168
  standard units, 165–166, 266
  subtracting a constant, 88, 90, 146–149, 437–438
Trend line, 405–406
Trial, 189
  binomial probability distribution, 275
  independent, 235–236, 276, 281, 283, 298, 301, 309
  probability, 189
  repeated, 190
  sets, 223
True correlation coefficient, 460
True regression coefficient, 450
True regression equation, 450
True zero point, 27
Two-sample tests, 375–377
  means, dependent samples, 392–397
    equal variance, 389–392
    large samples, 383–386
    small samples, 387–389
  pairs, 395–396
  proportions, 377–382
Two-sided alternative, 357
Two-tail test, 357
Two-way frequency table, 433–434
Two-way tally table, 432–433
Type I error, 342, 352
Type II error, 342, 352
Typical values of a set of data, 83–84, 125

U-distribution, 71
Unconditional distribution, 448
Unconditional probability, 206–208, 210
Underlying distribution, 73–78
Unexplained, deviation, 427–428
  variation, 428–429
Unequal classes, 57–59, 104, 116
Ungrouped data, 33
  arithmetic mean, 84
  correlation coefficient, 430
  median, 107–109
  mode, 120–121
  regression equation, 416
  standard deviation, 144–146
Uniform distribution, 68—69
Unimodal distribution, 121, 127
Union of sets, 226–227
Unit of measurement, 26–27, 29, 90, 103
U.S. National Bureau of Standards, 286
Universe, 9
Universe set, 223
Unorganized data, *see* Ungrouped data
Unreal continuous class limits, 47
Upper continuous class limit, 44
Upper discrete class limit, 41, 55–57, 60

V (Coefficient of variation), 164
V_Q (Coefficient of quartile deviation), 165
Variable, 13–14
  continuous, 14

Variable, dependent, 406, 407
discontinuous, 13
discrete, 13
experimental, 393
independent, 406, 407
predicted, 406, 407
recorded, 14
test, 345, 390, 391, 395
time, 405
Variance, computed from pooled data, 390–391
population, 139, 450
sample, 143, 426
Variation, 136
coefficient of, 164
explained, 428–429
joint, 406
point of reference, 137–138, 162
relative, 163
sampling, *see* Sampling variation
statistical inference, 136
time series, 405
total, 426, 428–429
Variation, unexplained, 428–429
Venn diagram, 225–226

Weighted mean, 92–93, 94
Weights, 92
With replacement, 210, 235, 281
Without replacement, 235, 281, 309, 326

$\bar{X}$ (Arithmetic mean, sample), 84

$\bar{Y}$ (Arithmetic mean, sample), 426
$\bar{Y}$-intercept, 415
Y (Observed value), 412
Y_e (Predicted or estimated value), 412

z (Relation expressed in words), 266
z (Standard scores), 165–166
z (Standard units), 165–166
z' (Standard scores), 168
Zero point, absolute, 27
shifting, 88, 90, 103, 147
true, 27, 29